Instructor's Guide
with Solutions

for

Moore and McCabe's

Introduction to the Practice of Statistics

Fifth Edition

Darryl K. Nester
Bluffton University

W. H. Freeman and Company
New York

© 2006 by W. H. Freeman and Company

All rights reserved.

Printed in the United States of America

ISBN: 0-7167-6356-7
EAN: 97807167-6356-7

First printing

W. H. Freeman and Company
41 Madison Avenue
New York, NY 10010
Houndmills, Basingstoke RG21 6XS, England
www.whfreeman.com

CONTENTS

Preface

This Instructor's Guide tries to make it easier to teach from the fifth edition of *Introduction to the Practice of Statistics* (*IPS*). The most helpful material is without doubt the full solutions of all exercises, which make up the second part of the Guide. The first part of the Guide contains additional examples, sample examinations, and suggestions for using the *Against All Odds* and *Decisions Through Data* videos in class. It also contains brief discussions of the approach we have taken in *IPS* for presenting statistics to beginning students. Reasonable people can (and do) differ about the nature of basic instruction in statistics. Our comments in this Guide are one side of a many-sided conversation. Your position in this conversation will no doubt differ at some points. We hope we have at least made clear the reasons for our choices.

We welcome comments, suggestions for improvement of *IPS*, and reports of errors that escaped detection and can be fixed in future printings. You can reach us as follows:

David S. Moore
Department of Statistics
Purdue University
West Lafayette, IN 47907-1399
Telephone: (765) 494-6050
Fax: (765) 494-0558
e-mail: dsm@stat.purdue.edu

George P. McCabe
Department of Statistics
Purdue University
West Lafayette, IN 47907-1399
(765) 494-6047
(765) 494-0558
mccabe@stat.purdue.edu

Notes, comments, and corrections about this Instructor's Guide—especially the solutions—should be sent to

Darryl K. Nester
Department of Mathematics
Bluffton University
Bluffton, OH 45817-2104
Telephone: (419) 358-3483
Fax: (419) 358-3074
e-mail: nesterd@bluffton.edu

1 TO THE INSTRUCTOR

Philosophy and Goals

The text is intended to be used in a first course in statistics for students with limited mathematical background. It covers the basic material presented in many courses at this level—data analysis, a little probability, and standard statistical methods. The emphasis is on understanding how to use statistics to address real problems. In this regard it differs from most introductions.

Many students view statistics (indeed, all of the mathematical sciences) as a collection of formulas that give correct results if the computations are performed accurately. The competence of the student is measured by the complexity of the formula that can be computed correctly. Unfortunately, this view is often reinforced by the way statistics is traditionally taught.

In contemporary practice, computations in statistics and other technical fields are always automated. Students, like users, should ideally employ statistical software, graphing calculators, or spreadsheets for computations and graphics. Even if the available technology is limited, students must prepare for reading and using statistical arguments with understanding. Our focus as teachers should be to help students use statistical tools and reasoning effectively by providing conceptual understanding and practical strategies. We are also free to move closer to the practice of statistics as a tool for learning about the real world.

Consider, for example, a pre-election poll taken for a major news organization. The results are reported as percentages with a margin of error. Typically stratification is used, and perhaps even cluster sampling. The formulas for the standard error are complex. The most important issues for understanding and using the results, however, do not require knowing the details: How was the question phrased? How was the sample designed? What about undercoverage and nonresponse? What does the margin of error tell us in straightforward language? If students are able to analyze and interpret data produced by a simple random sample, then the transfer of the basic ideas to the more complex situation is easy. The meaning of a confidence interval, for example, does not depend upon the formula used to calculate the standard error.

We describe in the Preface an emerging consensus on the nature of a first course among statisticians concerned with teaching, and we try to express that consensus in our writing. As a reminder, here are important ways in which *IPS* differs from more traditional texts:

- There is more attention to data analysis. Chapters 1 and 2 give quite full coverage. It is now becoming common to emphasize data in a first course, but many texts still begin with a brief treatment of "descriptive statistics." Note that we introduce distributions, specifically the normal distributions, in Chapter 1 as models for the overall pattern of data long before probability appears. This is legitimate in itself, and it helps break up the indigestible lump of formal probability that is a traditional stumbling block in learning statistics. Note also that the descriptive aspects of several-variable data (scatterplots, correlation, least-squares lines) are presented as part of data analysis rather than late in the book in conjunction with inference in these settings. We think that this order has important advantages. It emphasizes the centrality of data analysis in statistics and gives students a chance to build fluency in the strategies of data analysis in both one- and several-variable settings. It allows examples and exercises on relationships among variables that don't meet the narrower requirements of inference.

- There is more attention to designing data production. It is surprising to a practicing statistician how little attention these ideas, among the most influential aspects of statistics, receive in most first courses. Chapter 3 discusses sampling and experimental design, with attention to some of the practical issues involved. The importance of deliberate use of randomness and informal discussion of the distribution of results in repeated sampling motivate the introduction of probability and the very important idea of a sampling distribution.

- The introduction to probability in Chapter 4 begins with experience with randomness and is designed to allow instructors to cover only the essentials or to present the full traditional material by omitting or including the optional Section 4.5. For many groups of students, more statistics is a worthy exchange for less probability. Some of the most important probability facts (law of large numbers, central limit theorem) appear in the discussion of sampling distributions in Chapter 5. Some traditional details about binomial distributions are marked as optional. The criterion for optional material in Chapters 4 and 5 is simple: it is not required for the statistical inference presented later in the text.

- There is more emphasis on the reasoning of inference. Chapter 6 discusses this reasoning in some depth, with an optional section 6.4 comparing the "P-value" and "two types of error" approaches to testing. We emphasize P-values. This reflects common practice and helps students understand the output of statistical software.

- There is more attention to statistics in practice. Realism may be too much to claim in a beginning text. Nonetheless, we often give longer-than-usual discussions of examples in order to connect textbook procedures with real-world practice.

Upon completion of a course based on *IPS*, students should be able to think critically about data, to select and use graphical and numerical summaries, to apply standard statistical inference procedures, and to draw conclusions from such analyses. They are ready for more specialized statistics courses (such as applied regression or quality control); for "research methods" courses in many fields of study; and for projects, reports, or employment that require basic data analysis.

Calculators and Computers

The practice of statistics requires a good deal of graphing and numerical calculation. Doing some graphing and calculating "by hand" may build understanding of methods. On the other hand, graphics and calculations are always automated in statistical practice. Moreover, struggling with computational aspects of a procedure often interferes with a full understanding of the concepts. Students are easily frustrated by their inability to complete problems correctly. Automating the arithmetic greatly improves their ability to complete problems. We therefore favor automating calculations and graphics as much as your resources and setting allow.

All students should have a calculator that does "two-variable statistics," that is, that calculates not only $\bar{x}$ and s but the correlation r and the least-squares regression line from keyed-in data. Even if you use computer software, students should have a calculator for use at home and on exams. Two-variable statistics calculators sell for less than \$20. We don't discuss anachronistic "computing formulas" (e.g., for standard deviation and correlation) that presuppose a four-function calculator.

IPS is designed to be used in courses where students have access to computing facilities, and also where they do not have such access. Many of the examples used in the text involve computations that can readily be performed with a two-variable statistics calculator rather than a computer. Each chapter contains exercises with small amounts of data or with the results of some computations given that are suitable for students without a computer. Although the use of a computer for a course based on *IPS* is not required, most people who *do* statistics today use a computer. Any serious attempt to introduce the practice of statistics must recognize this fact. You will find examples of output from a variety of technological tools (statistical software, spreadsheets, graphing calculators) throughout the text. The output appears because any statistics student should become accustomed to looking at output and using the fruits of the study of statistics to recognize terms and results in output from any source.

As computing continues to become cheaper and more readily available, and as statistics software becomes more "user-friendly," use of computers in courses at this level will increase. Typical students have some prior acquaintance with personal computers. For students with this background, modern statistical software speeds work and allows more elaborate work without the added burden that learning software once presented. We encourage use of software, and some exercises are not realistic without it.

As a practical encouragement to software use, the CD-ROM packaged with the text includes most of the data (all of the larger sets of data) used in exercises in *IPS*. The data appear as plain text (ASCII) files and also formatted for Excel, JMP, Minitab, SPSS, S-PLUS, and TI-83 calculators. The files are named by their location in the book:

> `eg01_004.txt` = Example 1.4 (plain text)
> `ex01_030.xls` = Exercise 1.30 (Excel format)
> `ta01_002.mtp` = Table 1.2 (Minitab format)

Course Design

Think of the content of *IPS* this way: The nonoptional parts of Chapters 1–8 form a core. Chapters 9 (Inference for Two-Way Tables), 10 (Inference for Regression), 12 (One-Way ANOVA), 14 (Bootstrap Methods), and 15 (Nonparametric Tests) offer a selection of further topics that are independent of each other. Depending on the length of your course and the quantitative background of your students, you will probably elect one or more of these. Chapters 11 (Multiple Regression), 13 (Two-Way ANOVA), 16 (Logistic Regression), and 17 (Process Control and Capability) are brief introductions to more advanced topics. Each of these chapters requires at least one of the elective chapters as a prerequisite, and all go better with software.

IPS is an elementary but serious introduction to modern statistics for general college audiences. This means that the material is presented in a way that it can be learned by students who are not particularly skillful in mathematics. *IPS* does require more attentive reading (words, not equations) than some other texts. The amount of time required for learning—and hence, the amount of material that can be covered—depends upon the skill level and (more important) the maturity of the students in a particular course.

We have personally used *IPS* for general undergraduates in nontechnical disciplines (agriculture, health sciences, consumer studies, etc.); for graduate students in nonquantitative disciplines (education, social sciences, retailing, etc.) who will be analyzing data for their research; and as a first course for majors in actuarial science, mathematics, and statistics. These are quite varied groups. Because general undergraduates are taking a required course they would not otherwise elect to take, motivation is the big problem in teaching them. More data and less formal probability are helpful. Graduate students often have a weak quantitative background but are mature and hard-working. Many of them will take another course in statistics, but some will not. They need some exposure to analysis of count data, regression, and analysis of variance. Accomplishing this for students with moderate mathematics skills requires skipping or treating lightly many of the optional sections, and encouraging a great deal of work on the part of the students. The practical relevance of the examples and exercises is an important factor for sustaining the motivation and drive that these students bring with them to the first lecture. Our course for potential undergraduate majors is software- and data-intensive. We end with multiple regression, including some material not in *IPS*.

The sample outlines for courses using *IPS* are aids for instructors, not strict rules. You should adapt the pace and extent of your course to your students.

Outline 1. This is a semester course for students with low or moderate skills and motivation. We suggest this outline for general, less quantitative undergraduates. For students with moderate mathematics skills, you can add a little more depth for some topics and assign or discuss some of the more challenging Exercises. We are always tempted to go faster than this outline suggests, and when we do we find that the students don't come with us. In particular, each exam, viewed as an opportunity to solidify learning, uses a week. We suggest the following: Spend one class on active review. Consider distributing a sample exam in class and asking the students to work on the first problem for about 5 minutes—long enough to determine whether they know how to approach it. Then discuss that problem together. Continue through the sample exam in this manner. Working under conditions similar to an exam concentrates the mind. The exam itself occupies a second class period, and returning and discussing it fills most of a third. This isn't lost time: exams are learning tools. We recommend omitting all starred subsections for this audience, but use your judgment.

Week	Material to be Covered
1	Chapter 1, Section 1, Section 2 – measures of center
2	Chapter 1, Sections 2 and 3
3	Chapter 2, Sections 1, 2, and 3
4	Chapter 2, Sections 4 and 5
5	Review Chapters 1 and 2; Exam I on Chapters 1 and 2
6	Chapter 3, Sections 1, 2, and 3
7	Chapter 3, Section 4; Chapter 4, Sections 1, 2, and 3
8	Chapter 4, Section 4; Chapter 5, Section 1
9	Chapter 5, Section 2
10	Review Chapters 3, 4, and 5; Exam II on Chapters 3, 4, and 5
11	Chapter 6, Section 1; start Section 2
12	Chapter 6, Sections 2 and 3
13	Chapter 7, Sections 1 and 2
14	Chapter 8, Sections 1 and 2
15	Review and extended examples
	Comprehensive Final Exam

Outline 2. A semester course for students with either higher skills or stronger motivation. We follow this outline for nonquantitative graduate students. Omit optional material except where noted.

Week	Material to be Covered
1	Chapter 1, Sections 1, 2, and 3
2	Chapter 2, Sections 1, 2, and 3
3	Chapter 2, Sections 4 and 5
4	Chapter 3, Sections 1, 2, 3, and 4
5	Review Chapters 1 to 3; Exam I on Chapters 1 to 3
6	Chapter 4, Sections 1, 2, and 3
7	Chapter 4, Section 4; Chapter 5, Section 1
8	Chapter 5, Section 2
9	Review Chapters 4 and 5; Exam II on Chapters 4 and 5
10	Chapter 6, Sections 1 and 2
11	Chapter 6, Sections 2 and 3, power from Section 4
12	Chapter 7, Sections 1, 2, and 3
13	Chapters 8 and 9
14	Chapter 12
15	Review and extended examples
Comprehensive Final Exam	

Outline 3. A semester course for students with adequate quantitative skills who may need more probability than the previous outlines offer. As outlined, ending with multiple regression, the course is quite ambitious. Use software to accelerate the later chapters.

Week	Material to be Covered
1	Chapter 1, Sections 1, 2, and 3
2	Chapter 2, Sections 1, 2, and 3
3	Chapter 2, Sections 4 and 5
4	Chapter 3, Sections 1, 2, 3, and 4
5	Exam I on Chapters 1 to 3; Chapter 4, Sections 1 and 2
6	Chapter 4, Sections 3 and 4
7	Chapter 4, Section 5
8	Chapter 5, Sections 1 (including optional parts) and 2
9	Chapter 6, Sections 1 and 2
10	Chapter 6, Sections 2 and 3; start Chapter 7
11	Chapter 7, Sections 1, 2, and 3
12	Exam on Chapters 4 to 7; start Chapter 8
13	Chapters 8 and 9
14	Chapter 10
15	Chapter 11
Comprehensive Final Exam	

Outline 4. A one-quarter course for students with low to moderate skills. It covers the essentials, ending with the *t* procedures (and the introduction to inference in practice) in Chapter 7 of *IPS*. This provides a good foundation for any of a number of more specialized courses in statistics or related areas. This outline is quite tentative; the number of class meetings per week varies in institutions using the quarter system. You may be able to assign more than is shown. The main point of this outline is the goal of completing Chapter 7 in even the briefest introduction. *IPS* contains sufficient material for a sequence of two-quarter courses, particularly taking into account the supplementary chapters. You have considerable flexibility in choosing from Chapters 8–17 for the second quarter.

Week	Material to be Covered
1	Chapter 1, Sections 1 and 2
2	Chapter 1, Section 3; Chapter 2, Section 1
3	Chapter 2, Sections 2, 3, 4, and 5
4	Chapter 3, Sections 1, 2, and 3; Review Chapters 1 to 3
5	Exam on Chapters 1 to 3; Chapter 4, Sections 1 and 2
6	Chapter 4, Sections 3 and 4
7	Chapter 5, Sections 1 and 2
8	Chapter 6, Sections 1 and 2
9	Chapter 6, Section 3; Chapter 7, Section 1
10	Chapter 7, Sections 2 and 3
Comprehensive Final Exam	

General Comments

When students complete a course based on *IPS* they should be able to analyze real data and draw conclusions. Since the emphasis is on *doing* statistics rather than talking about statistics, much of the class time should be spent discussing how statistical analysis tells us something about data. The methodologies presented are all based upon sound statistical theory. Details of how the theory leads to particular formulas are neither interesting to the students nor are they essential to the central purpose of learning to do statistics. A minimum amount of time should be spent on examining formulas and procedures in the abstract. Theoretical ideas need to be understood in the context of how they *apply* to the analysis of data.

Consider, for example, the problem of outliers. They are a fact of life for anyone applying statistics to real problems. It is not sufficient to take a strictly mathematical view and assume that they do not exist. A procedure based on normal theory may give very misleading conclusions if applied to data contaminated by outliers. In the practice of statistics it is important to identify outliers and, with an understanding of the area of application, to do something about them. On the other hand, it is not important at this level to know that a *t* distribution can be represented at the ratio of a standard normal to the square root of a chi-square.

To teach students how to use statistical methods with understanding, you will spend most of your class time doing statistics. This means discussing data, not just numbers devoid of any real meaning. It means saying something about the context in which the data were collected and the field of application. Instructors in statistics courses typically are comfortable with the rather elementary mathematical and statistical ideas needed to discuss the methods presented in the text. On the other hand, few of us are experts in the various substantive fields from which the examples and exercises are drawn. Most of these, however, require only a basic understanding, most of which is presented in stating the example or exercise.

Using data from real problems provides many opportunities for the students to become actively involved in the class. Incomplete knowledge of all of the fields covered by the examples and exercises can be turned into a very effective teaching tool. Students have diverse backgrounds and often know a great deal more than we think. It is a very pleasant experience to leave a class session having learned something from the students. Once, when discussing corn yield data, George was unable to remember whether or not the fields were irrigated, but he did remember that they were in Nebraska. He mentioned this, and one woman in the class immediately raised her hand and explained that if it was corn in Nebraska, then it certainly was irrigated. This sort of participation occurs naturally in a teaching environment where the students are encouraged to think about data rather than numbers.

If we could offer just one piece of advice to teachers using *IPS*, it would be this: **A number or a graph, or a formula such as "Reject H_0," is not an adequate answer to a statistical problem.** Insist that students state a brief conclusion in the context of the specific problem setting. We are dealing with data, not just with numbers.

There is a tendency today to try to design statistics courses specifically for students in one particular major or general field. This is particularly true for students in business and the social and behavioral sciences. Even in general courses some students express the opinion that they would prefer examples and homework based on problems coming exclusively from their own field of interest. If we are attempting to educate rather than to simply train students, this view is short-sighted. It overlooks, for example, the fact that most students will change careers several times during their working lives. Ideas learned well in one context are easily translated to others. Barry Bonds' 73 home runs do have something in common with the agricultural production in a drought year. One of the interesting things about statistics as a field is that the same fundamental ideas occur in many diverse settings. Different settings facilitate learning of the big ideas. Furthermore, many fields are not as homogeneous as they might appear at a first glance. Often, interesting problems require the assimilation of material from diverse areas. This is particularly true of business. In summary, do not apologize to your students because all of the examples are not from their field. Explain to them that breadth is part of education.

There are enough examples in the text for some to be used in class lectures. Sometimes it is useful to build a lecture around one or a sequence of exercises. If computers are used, it is a good idea to run some of the examples or exercises on the system you are using. You can distribute copies of output, enlarge the output on a transparency, or ask students to do specific computer work in advance and bring the results to class. Many classrooms now allow you to do the work in real time with projection for the class to follow. If you teach in a computer lab, we recommend doing examples along with the class so that students follow on their machines and can see your projected screen if they get lost.

Teaching Suggestions

Statistics has a well-earned reputation as the dullest of subjects. Tell someone that you teach statistics, and a typical reaction is something like, "I took a course in statistics once. . . . I just barely made it through." We teachers have the responsibility of overcoming that preconception by demonstrating to students that our subject is both intellectually stimulating and useful. We believe that almost any statistics course can be improved by including more data and more emphasis on reasoning, at the expense of fewer recipes and less theory. "Data" means not just numbers, but problems set in a context that require a conclusion or discussion rather than just a calculation or graph. In *IPS* we have tried to emphasize data and reasoning, limited of course by our own ability and by the need to present an exposition accessible to beginning students. We hope the text will at least not stand in the way of teachers who want their students to come away with more than a list of recipes. Here are some suggestions from our experience.

Involve the class Mixing blackboard work with direct address (get out from behind the lectern) helps keep students awake. Even better is discussion with the class. Use some exercises as bases for discussion, assigning them "for discussion" in the next class rather than requiring written answers. Ask a student to present an analysis and then give a nontechnical conclusion, as if reporting to a boss. Then ask the other students to respond with questions or comments.

Leading discussions is interesting but difficult. You must resist the temptation to leap in with the "correct" view. Try rather to guide the class by questions and to get other students to offer alternatives to weak answers. Be patient when asking questions on the spot. An educational psychologist of our acquaintance notes that teachers rarely wait long enough for students to assimilate a question and produce a response. He suggests 30 seconds, which seems an eternity while passing in silence but does produce more response in the end. Above all, don't put down a student who is incorrect or confused. Students notice even the silent disappointment that contrasts so clearly with your response to an intelligent answer. Try to give a positive response to every student who is brave enough to speak up—they are helping you. When you know the class better, you can direct easier questions at the weaker students, thus preventing monopoly by the bright and aggressive. Remember that you are building confidence, not simply conveying information. Discussion isn't easy for teachers oriented toward problem-solution or theorem-proof presentation. But the attempt is essential if your students are afraid of statistics and perceive it as remote from their experience.

Problem assignments   The practice of statistics is learned by doing statistics rather than by reading about it. To master the material in *IPS*, students need to work exercises—many of them. Note that brief answers for the odd-numbered exercises appear in the back of the text. These allow students to check their work, but they are often not complete as responses to the problems because they lack graphics or detailed conclusions.

Ask during the session previous to the session in which homework is due if students are having difficulty with any problems. Most students will not have started the homework yet—you are trying to encourage them to start early. Always ask about special difficulties when the assignment is turned in and spend time clarifying them. If necessary, comment on any additional difficulties when you return the assignments. Don't be overly concerned about "giving away" homework answers. Homework is to help learning; the exams will detect those who didn't do their own work.

Remember that your students don't think like mathematicians   Good teaching requires an awareness of who your students are. Statistics courses are not mathematics classes, so don't emphasize mathematical fine points or mathematical explanations and derivations. You think mathematically, but your students don't. Instead, teach by examples and add comments on statistics in practice when appropriate. Try sometimes to begin with a motivating example rather than always presenting a technique, then illustrate it by an example. Don't just repeat the text. Outline the material (students like an outline style), explain how each point fits into the overall course, then interpret the text. Point out the tough parts, use different examples, say things a different way, try to explain the intuition behind the formal material. Mathematical understanding is not the only kind of conceptual understanding. Don't always do the same thing: vary your style over the class period and from day to day.

Using Video

One of the most effective ways to convince your students that statistics is useful is to show them real people (not professors) using statistics in a variety of settings. Video allows you to do this in the classroom. Two related video series that contain many short documentaries of statistics in use on location are

- *Against All Odds: Inside Statistics* (*AAO*). This telecourse, consisting of 26 half-hour programs, was prepared by COMAP for the Annenberg/CPB Project. You can view *AAO* episodes online at `http://www.learner.org/`, or purchase the series (at a subsidized price, in the United States); visit the Web site or call 1-800-LEARNER for more information.

- *Statistics: Decisions Through Data* (*DTD*). This set of 21 shorter modules (5 hours total) is intended for use as a classroom supplement in secondary schools. It was prepared by COMAP for the National Science Foundation and draws on the location segments of *AAO*. It is available from COMAP. Visit `http://www.comap.com/` or call 1-800-77-COMAP for information.

If you are outside the United States, you can obtain information about both video series by contacting

COMAP Inc.
Suite 210
57 Bedford Street
Lexington, MA 02173 USA
Fax 1-617-863-1202

Because David Moore was the content developer for these video series, they fit the style and sequence of *IPS* well. In several cases, data from the videos appear in the text. We do not recommend showing complete programs from *AAO* in the classroom. The shorter modules from *DTD* are more suitable for classroom use. Video is a poor medium for exposition, and it leaves viewers passive. It is therefore generally not a good substitute for a live teacher. We suggest regular showing of selected on-location stories from *AAO* or *DTD* in most classrooms, rather than full programs. If you have a large lecture (several hundred students), however, full *DTD* video modules along with computer demonstrations will help hold an audience too large for personal interaction.

Video has several strengths that make short segments an ideal supplement to your own teaching. Television can bring real users of statistics and their settings into the classroom. And psychologists find that television communicates emotionally rather than rationally, so it is a vehicle for changing attitudes. One of our goals in teaching basic statistics is to change students' attitudes about the subject. Because video helps do this, consider showing video segments regularly even if you do not think they help students learn the specific topic of that class period.

Here are some specific suggestions for excerpts from *AAO* and *DTD* that work effectively in class.

- The 14-minute video *What Is Statistics?* is a good way to start a course. This collage of examples from *AAO* forms part of the first unit of *AAO* and is the first module of *DTD*. It is available separately (and inexpensively) from

  The American Statistical Association
  1429 Duke Street
  Alexandria, VA 22314 USA
  (703) 684-1221 or www.amstat.org

- *Lightning research* from Program 2 of *AAO*, Module 3 of *DTD*. A study of lightning in Colorado discovers interesting facts from a histogram.

- *Calories in hot dogs* from Program 3 of *AAO*, Module 5 of *DTD*. The five-number summary and box plots compare beef, meat, and poultry hot dogs.

- *The Boston Beanstalk Club* from Program 4 of *AAO*, Module 7 of *DTD*. This social club for tall people leads to discussion of the 68□95□99.7 rule for normal distributions.

- *Saving the manatees* from Program 8 of *AAO*, Module 11 of *DTD*. There is a strong linear relation between the number of power boats registered in Florida and the number of manatees killed by boats.

- *Obesity and metabolism* from Program 8 of *AAO*, Module 12 of *DTD*, looks at the linear relationship between lean body mass and metabolic rate in the context of a study of obesity.

- *Sampling at Frito-Lay* from Program 13 of *AAO*, Module 17 of *DTD*, illustrates the many uses of sampling in the context of making and selling potato chips. A student favorite.

- *The Physicians' Health Study* from Program 12 of *AAO*, Module 15 in *DTD*, is a major clinical trial (aspirin and heart attacks) that introduces design of experiments.

- *Sampling distributions* are perhaps the single most important idea for student understanding of inference. Module 19 of *DTD* presents the general idea, the basic facts about the sampling distribution of the sample mean $\bar{x}$, and the application of these ideas to an $\bar{x}$ control chart. The setting is a highly automated AT&T electronics factory.

- *Battery lifetimes* from Program 19 of *AAO* lead to an animated graphic that illustrates the behavior of confidence intervals in repeated sampling. Module 20 in *DTD* is a presentation of the reasoning of confidence intervals using the same setting that can be shown in its entirety.

- *Taste testing of colas* is the setting for an exposition of the reasoning of significance tests in Module 21 of *DTD*. This treatment is preferable to that in *AAO*.

- *Welfare reform* in Baltimore, from Program 22 of *AAO*, is a comparative study of new and existing welfare systems that leads to a two-sample comparison of means.

- *The Salem witchcraft trials,* revisited in Program 23 of *AAO*, show social and economic differences between accused and accusers via comparison of proportions.

- *Medical practice:* Does the treatment women receive from doctors vary with age? This story in Program 24 of *AAO* produces a two-way table of counts.

- *The Hubble constant* relates velocity to distance among extragalactic objects and is a key to assessing the age of the expanding universe. A story in Program 25 of *AAO* uses the attempt to estimate the Hubble constant to introduce inference about the slope of a regression line.

Here is a complete list of the documentary segments in *AAO*, with timings for use if your VCR measures real time, along with ratings from one to four stars (for some segments, no rating is available). This handy guide was prepared by Professor Edward R. Mansfield of the University of Alabama. We are grateful to him for permission to reproduce it here. Start your VCR timer when the first signal on the tape appears. Remember that *AAO* programs are packaged two to a tape; the timings for the even-numbered programs may need some adjustment because the gap between programs seems to vary a bit.

Program 1: What Is Statistics?

4:48	★ ★ ★	Domino's Pizza
13:15		The "What is statistics?" collage of later examples

Program 2: Picturing Distributions

31:30		When does lightning strike?
43:00		TV programming and demographics
51:45		Diagnostic-related groups

Program 3: Describing Distributions

5:55	★	Comparable worth in Colorado Springs
16:07	★ ★	Calories in hot dogs
21:00	★ ★	Musical analysis of urine data

Program 4: Normal Distributions

33:50	★	Age distributions and Social Security
46:07	★	Boston Beanstalk social club for tall people
50:38	★ ★ ★	Why don't baseball players hit .400 anymore?

Program 5: Normal Calculations

7:07	★	Auto emissions at GM Proving Ground
14:10	★ ★	Cholesterol values
19:50	★ ★	Sizes of military uniforms

Program 6: Time Series

34:50	★	The body's internal clock
43:48	★	Psychology: reaction time study

Program 7: Models for Growth

3:00	★ ★ ★	Children's growth rates and hormone treatment
14:00	★ ★	Gypsy moth infestations

Program 8: Describing Relationships

32:25	★ ★ ★	Manatees versus motorboats in Florida
37:55		Cavities versus fluoride levels
39:31	★ ★ ★	1970 draft lottery
44:04	★	Obesity: metabolic rate versus lean body mass

Program 9: Correlation

5:42	★★★	Identical twins raised apart
16:22	★★	Baseball players' salaries
20:53	★	The Coleman Report (education in the 1960s)

Program 10: Multidimensional Data Analysis

| 32:28 | ★★ | Chesapeake Bay pollution |
| 47:42 | ★★ | Bellcore graphics |

Program 11: The Question of Causation

| 5:42 | ★★★★ | Simpson's paradox |
| 12:47 | ★★★ | Smoking and cancer (historical survey) |

Program 12: Experimental Design

32:46	★	Observational study of lobster behavior
36:14	★★★★	Physicians' Health Study: aspirin and heart attacks
43:39	★★★	Is Ribavirin too good to be true?
47:22	★	Police response to domestic violence

Program 13: Blocking and Sampling

4:45	★	Strawberry field research
13:28	★★★	Undercounting in the Census
20:48	★★★★	Sampling potato chips at Frito-Lay

Program 14: Samples and Surveys

| 41:21 | ★★★★ | National Opinion Research Center |

Program 15: What Is Probability?

| 10:50 | ★ | Persi Diaconis on randomness |
| 17:49 | ★★ | Traffic control in New York (simulation model) |

Program 16: Random Variables

33:36	★	Cheating on AP calculus
34:33	★★★★	Space shuttle *Challenger* disaster
43:02		Points in a professional basketball game
49:10	★	Earthquakes in California

Program 17: Binomial Distributions

3:46	★★★	The "hot hand": free throws in basketball
9:45	★★	A finance class experiment
17:22	★	Sickle-cell anemia
24:25	★★	Quincunx: falling balls

Program 18: The Sample Mean and Control Charts

33:45		Roulette
35:04	★★	Interviews with gamblers
40:44	★★★★	The casino always wins
47:03	★★★	Control charts at Frito-Lay
53:41	★★★★	W. Edwards Deming

Program 19: Confidence Intervals

11:35	★★	Duracell batteries
18.25	★	Rhesus monkeys in medical studies
21:21		Feeding behavior of marmosets

Program 20: Significance Tests

34:18	★★	Is this poem by Shakespeare?
49:06	★★★	Discrimination within the FBI

Program 21: Inference for One Mean

5:55	★★	National Institute of Standards and Technology
13:30	★★★	Taste testing of cola
21:08	★	Autism

Program 22: Comparing Two Means

33:32	★★	Welfare programs in Baltimore
45:05	★★★	Product development at Union Carbide
51:00		SAT exams: Can coaching help?

Program 23: Inference for Proportions

3:03	★	Measuring unemployment (Bureau of Labor Statistics)
11:58	★★★	Safety of drinking water
20:15		The Salem witch trials

Program 24: Inference for Two-Way Tables

34:11	★★	Ancient humans (markings on teeth)
43:30	★★	Does breast cancer treatment vary by age?
52:02	★★	Mendel's peas

Program 25: Inference for Relationships

3:32	★★★★	How fast is the universe expanding (Edwin Hubble)?

Program 26: Case Study

35:49	★★★	How AZT for treatment of AIDS was tested

2 CHAPTER COMMENTS

Along with the text, some instructors might wish to incorporate some of the supplement material, available for download at `http://www.whfreeman.com/ips5e`. These topics—transforming relationships, decision analysis, and data ethics—were removed from the main text for reasons of length. They would most naturally fit (respectively) at the end of Chapter 2, following page 321 in Chapter 4, and following Section 3.3.

Chapter 1: Looking at Data — Distributions

Students taking a first course in statistics often do not know what to expect. Some may view statistics as a field where the major task is to tabulate large collections of numbers accurately. Others have heard that statistics is more like mathematics, with a lot of complicated formulas that are difficult to use. Few are expecting a course where they need to use their common sense and to *think*.

The presentation of the material in Chapter 1 sets the tone for the entire course. Statistics is a subject where intelligent judgments are needed and common sense plays a large role. To the extent that you can get the students to think deeply about the material at this stage, you will have succeeded in setting the proper tone. Most of the examples presented in the text can serve as the basis for extensive class discussions. Depending upon the interests of the students, some of these may be more suitable than others. You can also try to find or collect data that the particular students you are teaching can relate to.

In one class based on this text, students were asked to take their pulse on the first day of class. No particular instructions concerning how to take one's pulse were given. The data that resulted were used in discussions that illustrated several major themes of the course. A stemplot was immediately constructed. There was one very large outlier—180 beats per minute. We discussed whether or not this value was reasonable. Several of the physical education students commented that someone who was very out of shape might elevate their pulse to such a high level by running up to the third floor where the course was held. Someone from psychology mentioned that a person who was very anxious about the course might have an elevated pulse. One conclusion drawn was that if you want to measure anything on people, you must pay attention to the circumstances present when the measurement is taken.

Further examination of the data revealed an exceptionally large number of readings that ended with the digit zero. Students in aerobics classes typically take their pulse for 6 seconds and multiple by 10. This led to a discussion of the possibility that different methods were used to obtain the reported pulse rates. Since it was impractical to ask all 50 or so students what method each used, a random sample was taken using the class list and the table of random numbers given in the back of the text (Table B). Students had no trouble following the method. Successive pairs of digits were used and numbers outside the range 1 to 50 were discarded. It was not surprising to find a number corresponding to a student who was not present in the class on that day. A short discussion about missing data and the problems associated with statistics in the *real* world followed.

The methods reported by the sampled students were very revealing. Most were what you would expect. Measure for 60 seconds, measure for 30 seconds and multiply by 2, measure for 15 seconds and multiply by 4, and of course, the method of those who had taken an aerobics course. One said that he did not have a watch so the value given was a guess. Another (a very polite foreign student whose command of spoken English was not very good) explained that she had no idea about what was asked and simply reported the value given by another student.

The lesson was quite clear. It is not easy to gather good data. What is measured and how it is measured are the two most important questions to ask when undertaking any statistical analysis. Understanding the issues related to these questions does not require mathematical sophistication or the ability to calculate $\sqrt{1/n_1 + 1/n_2}$ by hand. If the students can be sufficiently motivated at the beginning of the course and understand that many interesting things can be learned by looking at data, they will be willing to put in the effort required to master the skills needed for the computations required later.

Look for sets of data that will be interesting to your students. They are not very difficult to find. If the students are concentrated in a few majors, ask faculty from those departments for reprints of articles using elementary statistical methods. Ask questions about how things are measured and whom or what is measured. Do the items or people measured represent any larger group or do they simply represent themselves? Usually we think of statistics as being used only for inference to some larger known or imagined population. However, many interesting sets of data do not fall into this category, and much about data analysis can be learned by studying them. Government statistics often come from a census or samples so large that the sampling variability is negligible. A good job of describing such data is often not a trivial exercise.

The key concepts in this chapter concern ways of looking at and describing one set of data. We start with graphical displays and then move to numerical summaries. The point of the numerical summary is that it quantifies and expresses compactly something that can be seen roughly in a graphical display. The effectiveness of a numerical summary is based on how well it calls to mind what appears in the graphical display. Thus viewed, the mean is not a very good numerical summary for a set of data with two distinct clusters of observations.

From numerical summaries we proceed to models for data, illustrated by the important case of the normal distributions. The progression from graphical display to numerical measures to a compact mathematical model is one of the strategies that unifies data analysis and makes it more than a collection of clever methods.

1.1 Displaying Distributions with Graphs

The introductory material on measurement is short but important. What is measured and how it is measured are two fundamental issues that lie at the foundation of any statistical analysis. Many of the judgments made at this level are subjective and require common sense. Make the point that statistics is about data, not just numbers.

Variation is another key concept. Why are all of the observations in a set of data not the same? Good class discussions can be based on sources of variation in particular sets of data.

The first real statistical analysis presented is the stemplot. Stress the idea that we start with a graphical display before proceeding to numerical summaries. We have presented stemplots with the values increasing as you proceed down the stems. Some computer packages put the larger numbers at the top. Similarly, in the text truncation is recommended (this is clearly the easiest method to use if constructing the plot by hand), whereas some programs will round. Keep in mind that the purpose of the plot is to get a quick look at the data and to help in deciding what sorts of numerical summaries are appropriate. Be flexible. Splitting leaves and other sorts of judgments should be based on common sense rather than on adherence to a set of inflexible rules.

Similar comments regarding flexibility apply to histograms. The histogram is presented as a method for displaying a set of data when a stemplot is unsuitable. It also serves an important role pedagogically. In the last section of this chapter, the density curve is introduced as a model that describes the shape of a histogram when the sample size increases and the widths of the intervals decrease.

The major theme of this section is that we should always carefully look at data. In graphical displays we look for an overall pattern and deviations from that pattern. Simon Newcomb was a famous scientist who was measuring well-defined physical quantities. If he had outliers in his data, we should not be surprised to find them in other sets of data that we may encounter. This section introduces the basic strategy for looking at data: seek first an overall pattern, then deviations from the pattern. This strategy will be used in other settings in Chapters 2 and 3.

1.2 Describing Distributions with Numbers

The mean should be familiar to almost all students. Therefore, the introduction of the summation notation is facilitated by noting that it is a compact way to express something that they already know. Although the idea behind the median is quite intuitive, some students get confused by the manipulations required to find it. Emphasize that it is a numerical measure for something that can be seen in a stemplot or histogram.

Quartiles and the five-number summary build on the idea of the median. Again emphasize that they are numerical summaries for something that can be seen graphically. With the boxplot we complete a circle of sorts. Starting with a graphical summary, we calculate numerical summaries and then present these graphically. Note that there are many variations on boxplots. If you use statistical software, the rules for constructing them may differ slightly from those presented in the text. This should not pose any serious problems. In fact, it can be used to illustrate the point that caution is needed in using statistical packages. We need to know how things are computed if we are to interpret the output meaningfully.

Another thing to emphasize is that no single numerical summary is appropriate for all sets of data. We should examine a stemplot, histogram, or other display to make a decision about which summary is appropriate.

The standard deviation is a fundamental quantity, the meaning of which will be made clear in Section 1.3 on normal distributions. Here, the variance is a necessary intermediate step required for the calculation of the standard deviation. For students who have a great deal of trouble with computations, the calculations can be organized in a table with columns corresponding to x, x^2, $x - \bar{x}$, and $(x - \bar{x})^2$. We recommend that students have a calculator that computes $\bar{x}$ and s from keyed-in data. This inexpensive tool greatly reduces the arithmetical burden for many standard statistical procedures.

Linear functions are used in several places later in the text. Thus, the material on changing the unit of measurement has two purposes. One idea is that when data are transformed in this way, nothing fundamental is changed. The summary statistics in the new scale are easily computed from the original ones. We are simply choosing a different way to express the same thing. The second idea is that we can use an equation of the form $x^* = a + bx$ (or later $y = a + bx$) to express a relationship between two variables.

1.3 The Normal Distributions

Note that normal distributions are introduced here as a common model for the overall pattern of many sets of data, and not in the context of probability theory. Although this ordering of material is unusual, it has several advantages. The normal distributions appear naturally in the description of large amounts of data, so that the later assumption for inference that *the population has a normal distribution* becomes clearer. Moreover, mastering normal calculations at this point makes it easier to teach the material on probability (Chapters 5 and 6). If the students already know how to compute normal probabilities and have a fair understanding of the relative frequency interpretation from this section, the transition to general ideas about probability is facilitated. Of course, later chapters present additional facts about normal distributions in the context of probability.

The key idea is that we can use a mathematical model as an approximation to real phenomena. The 68–95–99.7 rule is a useful device for interpreting μ and σ for normal distributions.

From the viewpoint of statistics, in contrast to that of probability, we always think of our models as approximations rather than the truth. This point can be illustrated by considering Example 1.30. The $N(505, 110)$ distribution is very useful for describing SAT scores of high school seniors. It can give reasonably accurate answers to interesting questions as illustrated in this example. However, it does not work very well in the extreme tails. For example, since the highest score possible is 800, the proportion of students scoring 835 or better is not appropriately calculated by using $Z \geq (835 - 505)/110 = 3$

and normal calculations. In a population of 100,000 students, the calculation would give $100,000(0.00135) = 135$ students scoring above 835!

Normal quantile plots are used frequently in the text. Students should learn to interpret them. If computer software is not available for constructing these plots, we do not recommend that they be drawn by hand. In this case, stemplots should be used to assess normality on a routine basis for the exercises.

Note that software packages that create quantile plots may differ in what variable is put on each axis. Most of the plots in the book place the variable being studied on the vertical axis, and the z score on the horizontal axis. One benefit of this arrangement is that we can interpret the plot in a natural way: if (for example) the upper right part of the plot bends down (below the line), we can interpret it by saying, "The high values of the variable are lower than they 'should' be [to be from a normal distribution]." (This is natural, since the *high* part of the plot is *below* the line.) Likewise, if the lower left part of the plot bends up, we can say, "The low values of the variable are too high [to be from a normal distribution]."

Chapter 2: Looking at Data — Relationships

This chapter concludes the part of the text dealing with methods for looking at data. In the first chapter, techniques for studying a single variable were explored. Here the focus is on general methods for describing relationships between pairs of variables.

Scatterplots are used to examine pairs where both variables are quantitative. Details of least-squares regression are presented. Correlation is introduced and its connection with regression is examined. Relations between categorical variables are described using proportions or percentages calculated from two-way tables. Issues related to the question of causation are illustrated by consideration of smoking and lung cancer.

The descriptive methods in this chapter, like those Chapter 1, correspond to the formal inference procedures presented later in the text. By carefully describing data first, we avoid using inference procedures where they clearly do not apply. Fitting a least-squares line is a general procedure, while using such a line to give a 95% prediction interval requires additional assumptions that are not always valid. In addition, students become accustomed to examining data *before* proceeding to formal inference, an important principle of good statistical practice. The data for a regression (Chapter 10) are displayed in a scatterplot. Side-by-side boxplots are useful with two-sample t tests (Chapter 7) and analysis of variance (Chapter 12). The percentages obtained from two-way tables are the basis for the formal inferences on count data (Chapter 9).

2.1 Scatterplots

From the previous chapter the students will be familiar with the idea that graphical displays of data are useful. The extension to a scatterplot should reinforce this idea. The distinction between explanatory and response variables is a relatively simple distinction that is essential to the least-squares method.

Constructing scatterplots is an easy task, particularly with a computer. Interpreting them, on the other hand, is an art that takes practice. For classroom discussion, you can use the examples given in the text or those presented in the exercises. Stress the idea that common sense and some understanding of the data are necessary to do a good job of description. Computers can make the plots, but people are needed to describe them. Again, the general rule is to look for overall patterns and deviations from them. Dichotomies such as positive and negative association are useful in many cases but can lead to distorted descriptions when imposed in situations where they do not apply.

Scatterplot smoothing is a useful data analytic tool for looking at some kinds of scatterplots. Try to avoid the type of thinking that says: if I have situation *a*, then use method *b*. A method is useful if it helps you to learn something about the data. Sometimes you do not know if it is useful until you try it.

Side-by-side boxplots can give a very informative data summary when one variable (usually the response variable) is quantitative and the other is categorical or concentrated on a small number of possible values. Since the students have already encountered boxplots, the idea of putting several of them alongside each other should follow quite easily.

2.2 Correlation

A key point is that a correlation (or the square of a correlation) is a numerical summary of a relationship between two variables that are linearly related. Thus, as an aid to interpreting a scatterplot, it is a potentially useful descriptor. With outliers, influential observations or nonlinear relationships, however, it may give a very distorted impression. Correlations are somewhat complicated for hand computation, and most of the time they should be found with a calculator or software. However, there may be some benefit to having students compute correlations for some small data sets by hand, to get a "feel" for how correlations work.

2.3 Least-Squares Regression

The principle of least squares is introduced and a method of computation (using r, $\bar{x}$, s_x, $\bar{y}$, and s_y) is presented. Try not to burden the students with excessive computation; most least-squares lines should be found using a computer or calculator. Note that the output may contain many pieces of information related to inference that are not relevant at this time. If computing facilities are not available, assign exercises where most of the computations are given and the amount of arithmetic required is minimal.

2.4 Cautions about Correlation and Regression

A crucial part of using regression and correlation procedures is knowing what can go wrong and when they may not be appropriate tools. Plotting the residuals versus x is very important. Again, construction of the plot is easy and can be done effectively by a computer, but interpreting the results is an art.

Outliers and influential observations can provide interesting class discussion. When a cause can be found or a lurking variable discovered, the value of carefully looking at data is reinforced. Formal rules for dealing with these situations are not advised. The point is that outliers and influential observations are present in many real data sets. A good analysis finds them and assesses their effects on the results.

2.5 The Question of Causation

The final section of this chapter contains no formulas, but there are a lot of important ideas. It brings out the fact that drawing conclusions about relationships may require judgment and expertise beyond the realm of formal statistical inference.

Chapter 3: Producing Data

This is a relatively short chapter with a lot of ideas and little numerical work. The message is that production of good data requires careful planning. Random digits (Table B) are used to assign units to treatments and to select simple random samples. There are several good examples that can serve as the basis for classroom discussion.

3.1 First Steps

This introductory section gives an overview of why careful planning of data collection is needed and makes the point that anecdotal evidence is not a good basis for drawing conclusions. Sampling and experimentation are described in general terms.

3.2 Design of Experiments

Terminology used in experimental design is introduced and is illustrated with examples. The advantages of comparative experiments are shown pointedly with the gastric freezing experiment. Students seem to particularly enjoy this example and they often express outrage at the blatant misuse of the data described.

Once the need for comparison and randomization is established, methods for randomization of experimental units to treatments is presented. Note that there are many correct ways to do these randomizations. Many exercises using Table B are given. If you use statistical software, some particular randomization routines may be available. In very general terms, most randomizations can be accomplished by a random sort of the data. In any package that has a random number generator and a sort, this can be done by assigning a random uniform to each case and then sorting the resulting file. For example, to assign 10 people to each of two treatments, set up a file with cases corresponding to the integers 1 to 20. Then assign a random number to each case and sort the file on the basis of the random numbers. The first 10 cases receive treatment one and the others receive treatment two. Note that this is not a particularly efficient algorithm, but it is very clear and it helps the students understand the principle of randomization.

3.3 Sampling Design

The simple random sample (SRS) is described. Note that in later chapters the assumption that data or errors are normally distributed is expressed by saying that they are an SRS from a normal population.

Other sampling designs are mentioned, including stratified samples, multistage designs, and systematic random samples. The problems of nonresponse and bias are also discussed.

3.4 Toward Statistical Inference

This section introduces some key ideas that will be further explained and used in later chapters. The idea of a parameter in a population contrasted with a statistic in a sample is fundamental. Through an opinion poll example, this distinction is made clear. The sampling distribution of the sample proportion is shown by simulation for samples of size 100 and 2500, thus illustrating the central limit theorem and the fact that the variability decreases as the sample size increases.

Because students often find probability hard and fail to see its relevance, we have tried to motivate probability by first discussing randomization in data collection and its consequences. In teaching this section, try to get the students to think about and discuss the general ideas. This will facilitate their learning of the details to follow in later chapters.

Chapter 4: Probability: The Study of Randomness

In Chapter 3 it is explained that randomization is needed for the proper design of experiments and sampling plans. Therefore, the study of probability as a model for randomness naturally fits here.

An overview of the entire course is given in the following paradigm. In the first three chapters we studied how to look at and describe data. Thus, in a sense, we concentrated on the *sample*. Chapter 3 discussed how data are produced and introduced the idea of the *population* for which inference in desired. Now, we study the population in detail, with emphasis on the mechanisms by which samples are generated. In later chapters, we reverse the orientation and study the methods by which samples lead to inferences about populations.

This chapter and the one that follows will be difficult for many of the students. We have tried to emphasize a conceptual approach to the topics presented. Nonetheless, there are several rules and manipulations that must be mastered.

You should carefully consider how much depth and breadth you want to include for this material. By omitting the optional sections and treating some subjects (such as sample spaces) lightly, you can teach the minimum probability required for a proper understanding of statistical inference. On the other hand, the text provides sufficient material for more comprehensive coverage.

4.1 Randomness

Certainly everyone has some concept of what is meant by the word "random"—but many may have the wrong idea, especially in not understanding the underlying order of "random" events. (Many people might list "chaotic" or "unpredictable" as synonyms for "random.") This section gives some background to understanding randomness and probability in terms of "long-run frequency" by repeated actual or simulated experimentation.

4.2 Probability Models

Sample spaces, assignment of probabilities, and basic probability rules are introduced in this section. Try to emphasize that all of these ideas follow from common sense and are not an arbitrary mathematical system devoid of a intuitive foundation. Many of the students will have had unpleasant experiences with some of this material previously.

Many of the topics can be introduced through an example with the formalization coming later. Give a set of probabilities that have a sum greater than one and ask why this does not make sense. Then explain that their conclusion that the sum must be one is a basic rule of probability theory. Similarly, most of the students can apply the addition rule and the complement rule to real problems without ever having encountered these rules formally. Let them figure out the rule first and then present it formally.

4.3 Random Variables

Random variables are the raw material for statistical inference. We therefore introduce them early in the presentation of probability. If an experiment or sample survey is repeated, different results will be obtained. The probability theory for random variables tells us that there is a certain type of regularity or predictability in these results.

4.4 Means and Variances of Random Variables

The mean, variance, and standard deviation are familiar quantities from Chapter 1. Emphasize that they are a little different here because we are dealing with a population. If the students have a lot of difficulty with this transition, you can ask them to think about some very large samples. For example, in Example 4.21, think of an experiment with 1000 trials in which the results are exactly as expected by Benford's Law: 301 ones, 176 twos, 125 threes, and so on. The calculations can then be performed on this hypothetical large sample (in which the difference between n and $n - 1$ is negligible) and the connection between probability and relative frequency can be reinforced.

In a similar way the rules for means and variances build on the parallel rules for sample statistics. This material can be treated briefly and reinforced with homework exercises.

The law of large numbers is the key concept in this section. It expresses a fundamental idea that is part of the foundation for much of statistical inference. Most of the students will have some intuitive idea about this law. Through class discussion these ideas can be explored and clarified.

4.5 General Probability Rules

This optional section presents some of the traditional material on probability. The addition rules, multiplication rules, and conditional probability are all discussed. The section is optional because these ideas are not essential to an understanding of the statistical ideas that follow in later chapters. Ample exercises are provided for the instructor who wants to cover this material.

Although the basic ideas contained in these probability laws are very intuitive, many students have a great deal of difficulty with the symbolic manipulations involved. By a detailed presentation of examples or exercises you can emphasize that these calculations are based on common sense and are not simply a collection of abstract rules.

Chapter 5: From Probability to Inference

There are two key ideas in this chapter. First, a statistic is a random variable, the value of which varies from experiment to experiment or sample to sample. Second, as a random variable, it has a sampling distribution with a mean and a standard deviation that can be calculated from the distribution of the basic random variables that are combined to calculate the statistic.

The binomial distribution is treated in detail. The normal approximation to the binomial is given as an important special case that sets the stage for the central limit theorem presented in the second section. The chapter concludes with an optional section on control charts where probability ideas are shown to be both useful and important.

5.1 Sampling Distributions for Counts and Proportions

The amount of time you choose to spend on this section is quite flexible. The inference for proportions presented in Chapter 8 is all based on the large sample normal approximation to the binomial. Therefore, the minimum coverage needed consists of the fact that (when n is sufficiently large) the distribution of $\hat{p}$ is approximately normal with mean p and standard deviation $\sqrt{p(1-p)/n}$.

On the other hand, there is sufficient material for a full treatment of the binomial distribution. Table C gives individual probabilities for a variety of values of n and p and the formula for calculating binomial probabilities is explained in detail. Many computer routines are also available for calculating individual or cumulative binomial probabilities.

Try not to let the computational details interfere with the important pedagogical role played by this section. The students should understand that $\hat{p}$ is a random variable with a sampling distribution that is approximately normal for large n. In a given experiment or sample, only *one* realization or value of this statistic is obtained. Our inference will be based on this single observation, and probability calculations will be based on an assumed (testing) or estimated (confidence intervals) sampling distribution for this statistic.

5.2 The Sampling Distribution of a Sample Mean

This is a rather short but important section where the mean and standard deviation for the sample mean are explained and the central limit theorem is presented. In terms of statistical applications, there are two key ideas. First, the central limit theorem is widely applicable and is the basis for normal-based inference. Second, the standard deviation of the mean decreases as $\sqrt{n}$. This section completes the discussion of normal distributions begun in Chapter 1 by showing the normal distributions as sampling distributions.

Chapter 6: Introduction to Inference

This is a chapter with a lot of fundamental ideas. Confidence intervals and tests are presented with some cautions concerning the use and abuse of tests. Throughout, the setting is inference about the mean μ of a normal population with known standard deviation. As a consequence, the z procedures presented are not applicable to most real sets of data, but rather serve to ease the transition to the more useful procedures presented in Chapter 7.

Experience has shown that many students will not master all this material upon seeing it for the first time. Fortunately, they will see all the key ideas again in Chapter 7. By the time they have completed both chapters and worked many exercises, they should be able to grasp the fundamentals. Remember that mastery of the reasoning of inference is far more important than the number of procedures learned.

6.1 Estimating with Confidence

Confidence intervals are straightforward but easily misinterpreted. Try to emphasize the meaning rather than the details of computation. For most students this is accomplished more effectively by a discussion of Figure 6.3 or similar results than by an algebraic deviation of a formula for the coverage probability.

At this stage the students should be comfortable with the sample mean, population parameters versus sample statistics, the fact that $\bar{x}$ is approximately normal with mean μ and standard deviation $\sigma/\sqrt{n}$, and the table of normal probabilities (Table A). Stress the fact that we are simply putting these ideas together in this section to produce a useful statistical procedure. Similar comments hold for Section 6.2.

The subsection on choosing the sample size reinforces the idea that the width of the interval depends upon n. This material is particularly important for students who will design studies in the future.

6.2 Tests of Significance

Although this section is not much longer than the previous one, it contains a few things that students generally find more difficult. The choice of one-sided versus two-sided tests and *P*-values versus fixed significance level testing are in this category. Try not to let these complications interfere with the presentation of the basic ideas.

Students seem to have the most difficulty when they become sufficiently frustrated that they put their common sense aside and start seeking formulas or rules that cover every possible case. Graphs illustrating the calculation of *P*-values are very useful here. Note that statistical software universally gives *P*-values. Therefore, an understanding of this approach to testing is essential for students who will either read or perform statistical studies.

6.3 Use and Abuse of Tests

This section gives some important ideas about significance testing that can serve as the basis for classroom discussion. Students are often reluctant to make judgments about the *importance* of an effect in contrast to its statistical significance. Emphasize that this judgment is an important part of using statistics with real data. Computers are easily programmed to perform calculations and produce *P*-values. Informed judgments (by humans) are needed to translate and interpret these results.

6.4 Power and Inference as a Decision

The optional material on power is similar to the material on selecting the sample size for confidence intervals. It reinforces what has already been said about the dependence of the behavior of the procedure on the sample size and is very important for students who will be planning studies. The use of software—for example, G•Power (available on the Internet for many platforms) or online power calculators—can make this more approachable.

The last subsection on inference as a decision is also optional. It uses the traditional dichotomy between Type I and Type II errors and serves as a brief introduction to more general applications of decision theory.

Chapter 7: Inference for Distributions

The principles underlying confidence intervals and significance tests were presented in Chapter 6. We now apply these principles to inference problems for one and two samples. Throughout the chapter, we work under the realistic assumption that the population standard deviation is unknown.

The first section deals with inference for one sample. The problem of paired comparisons is treated as a special case. Optional sections on power and a nonparametric alternative to the normal based procedure are also given.

Two sample procedures are presented in the second section. The chapter concludes with an optional section on inference for the standard deviation.

From earlier chapters, the students should be familiar with looking at data from one or two samples carefully and with computing sample means and standard deviations. The additional arithmetic required for the construction of confidence intervals and significance tests is not particularly difficult. Many of the exercises provide means and standard deviations so that the students can concentrate on the new ideas presented here.

The transition from the normal to the t table requires some careful explanation. Because we are dealing with a family of distributions indexed by the degrees of freedom, only selected values can be given in a table. Since most of the exercises are based on real data, no attempt has been made to assure that an entry for the exact degrees of freedom for a particular problem are given in the table. Therefore, approximate values of t^* are to be used for confidence intervals. Similarly, bounds on the P-value can be obtained rather than exact P-values, using Table E. (Nonetheless, since software may be used to give more "exact" answers, the solutions in the latter part of this guide contain these more exact answers, as well as those that come easily from Table E.)

A conservative approach for confidence intervals is to use a value for the degrees of freedom that is less than or equal to the required value. This results in intervals that are at least as wide as the exact interval, thereby ensuring that the coverage probability is at least as large as that specified. (In effect, by taking smaller degrees of freedom than we are "entitled" to, we are pretending that we have less information [a smaller sample] than was actually available to us.) The same approach for tests ensures that the probability of a false rejection of H_0 is less than or equal to the value given. Table E provides sufficient detail so that for all practical purposes, inaccuracies resulting from these difficulties are very small. Students checking their solutions for odd-numbered exercises in the back of the text should be aware of these considerations.

Of course, if a probability function for the t distribution is available in computer software, exact values are easily obtained. Note that it is common practice for many computer packages (and in reporting the results of a statistical analysis) to give P-values in the form $P <$ some number. Using Table E, when an extreme value of the t statistic is found, the P-value will be reported as $P < 0.0005$ for a one sided-test and $P < 0.001$ for a two-sided test.

7.1 Inference for the Mean of a Population

The term *standard error* is introduced for the estimated standard deviation of a statistic. Thus, t statistics are normalized by dividing by a standard error, and confidence intervals are constructed by taking the value of a statistic plus or minus a constant times the standard error.

The usual one-sample confidence intervals and significance tests (which assume normal distributions) are presented in this section. By first taking differences between pairs of observations, paired comparisons problems are treated in the same way. The idea of robustness is introduced, and practical guidelines for using the *t* procedures are given.

7.2 Comparing Two Means

Procedures based on normal assumptions for comparing two means are presented in this chapter. To place the problems in a proper perspective, the situation where the standard deviations are known is discussed first.

When replacing the known standard deviations by sample estimates, difficulties regarding the appropriate degrees of freedom for the *t* distribution arise. Most computer software packages use an approximation similar to that given just before Example 7.18 (page 498). This formula is given for information only. From an educational point of view, very little is accomplished by having students do a large amount of computation with this formula. In most practical situations use of the minimum of $n_1 - 1$ and $n_2 - 1$ as the degrees of freedom for the *t* gives essentially the same results. Rather than having students spend a lot of time with computation, it is better to have them concentrate on the appropriate use of the procedures and the interpretation of the results.

The pooled two-sample *t* procedures are presented in the optional last part of this section. Occasionally, students will question the usefulness of these procedures. Why assume that the standard deviations are equal when we have already learned procedures that are valid under less restrictive assumptions? From a theoretical point of view there are answers. We have exact rather than approximate distributions, confidence intervals will be shorter in some stochastic sense, and significance tests have more power. On the other hand, from a practical point of view, there will be very little difference in the results (unless, of course, there are large differences in the standard deviations so that the pooled procedures are invalid). The primary reason for including this material is that it facilitates the introduction of similar ideas in Chapter 12, where analysis of variance is introduced. If you do not plan to cover analysis of variance and time is tight, you could easily omit this material.

7.3 Optional Topics in Comparing Distributions

The usual *F* test for comparing two variances is presented in this section. It is pointed out that this procedure is not robust with respect to the assumption of normality and a general discussion of robustness follows. This section can easily be omitted. The very poor performance of *F* in the two-sample variance setting should not be overlooked merely to teach a procedure for this case.

Note that this is the first place in the text that *F* distributions are used. They appear later in the chapters on regression and analysis of variance (Chapters 10–13). If you do not cover this section, you will need to spend a little more time explaining the tables when they are needed later in the text.

The power of the *t* test is treated in a subsection. This material is very similar to that presented in the fourth section of Chapter 6 and makes use of the noncentral *t* distributions. As was mentioned before, this material reinforces the fundamental idea that the performance characteristics of statistical procedures depend upon the sample size. It is important for students who will be planning statistical studies to be familiar with these ideas.

The final optional subsection discusses what can be done in some situations when the data are not normal. Transformations are mentioned and an explanation of the sign test for paired comparisons is given. The intention here is to point to the two major strategies available, not to discuss them in detail.

Chapter 8: Inference for Proportions

The two sections of this chapter present the standard z procedures for one-sample and two-sample binomial problems. By now the students should be comfortable with the general framework for confidence intervals and significance tests. For those who have not yet completely mastered these concepts, this material affords an additional opportunity to learn these important ideas.

8.1 Inference for a Single Proportion

Confidence intervals and significance tests for a single proportion are presented. A new complication that arises with these problems concerns the standard deviation of $\hat{p}$. For confidence intervals we use the standard error $\sqrt{\hat{p}(1-\hat{p})/n}$, whereas for tests we use $\sqrt{p_0(1-p_0)/n}$. Although this may seem confusing to the students at first, the basic idea is quite reasonable.

The construction of confidence intervals using plus four (Wilson) estimates is introduced here, but is an optional topic that can be omitted without significant repercussions. (This is a change from the more prominent treatment of this topic in the fourth edition.)

We use all of the information available in a problem for our calculations. For the confidence interval, p is assumed to be unknown and the standard error must therefore be estimated using the value of $\hat{p}$ obtained from the data. On the other hand, when testing H_0: $p = p_0$, our calculations are based on the assumption that H_0 is true, and therefore we use the value p_0 in the calculations. Note that these choices destroy the exact correspondence between confidence intervals and tests (reject if the hypothesized parameter value is outside of the confidence interval).

The section concludes with a description of the procedure for choosing a sample size to guarantee a given bound on the width of a confidence interval. From a practical point of view, the table given in Example 8.8 is very informative. The widths of intervals vary relatively little for values of $\hat{p}$ between 0.3 and 0.7.

8.2 Comparing Two Proportions

Confidence intervals and significance tests for comparing two proportions are presented in this section. From Chapter 7, students should be familiar with the basics of two-sample problems. As in Section 8.1, we use different standard errors for confidence intervals and tests. The idea of pooling information from two samples to estimate a standard error was first presented in the optional part of the second section of Chapter 7. This principle will be used again in Chapter 11 when we treat analysis of variance.

Once again, plus four confidence intervals are discussed, but are not vital to the material.

Chapter 9: Analysis of Two-Way Tables

If desired, this material can be omitted without loss of continuity. The notation here is more complex than in earlier chapters. (There is no easy way to describe the general form of a two-dimensional array of data without two subscripts.)

9.1 Data Analysis for Two-Way Tables

The computation required in this section in minimal. Percents and proportions are the numerical summaries. On the other hand, some very important ideas are presented. Judgment is required to select what percents to calculate.

Simpson's paradox is not easily understood when first encountered. Careful class discussion of the examples in the text is needed if students are to grasp this idea.

9.2 Inference for Two-Way Tables

You have some choice regarding depth of coverage for this section. As mentioned, this section can be eliminated entirely if desired. The computations for the X^2 statistic are rather straightforward although a fair amount of arithmetic is required and care must be taken to ensure accurate results. Computers can be a big help here.

9.3 Formulas and Models for Two-Way Tables

The vague idea of testing for a relationship between two categorical variables is also fairly straightforward. Therefore, it is possible to teach this section spending a minimum amount of time on the two models described.

On the other hand, discussion of the models in detail gives the students a good background for learning about model-based inference for more complex situations. The statistical model gives a clear statement of the assumptions needed for a given procedure and specifies the parameters about which inference is desired. A major part of statistical inference concerns the translation of a vague notion, such as dependence between two categorical variables, into a testable hypothesis stated in terms of the parameters of a statistical model. To draw meaningful conclusions, the results of the analysis, stated in terms of the model, must then be translated back into the context of the real problem.

Chapter 10: Inference for Regression

Having completed Chapter 2, students should be familiar with the data analytic issues that arise with simple linear regression. We now focus on applying the statistical inference principles of Chapter 7 to this problem. Note that nothing from Chapters 8 and 9 is needed for an understanding of this chapter.

10.1 Simple Linear Regression

There are many interesting problems for which the relationship between two variables can be summarized graphically and numerically with a least-squares line. Not all of these can be analyzed using the methods of this chapter. Inference for linear regression is based on a statistical model that expresses the assumptions underlying the inference procedures.

10.2 More Detail About Simple Linear Regression

Confidence intervals and significance tests should be familiar concepts for the students at this point. Although the computational details are more difficult in this section, the underlying principles are not new. Use of statistical software is very effective here. It allows the students to concentrate on learning the concepts without being unduly concerned with a long sequence of computations leading to a numerically correct answer. Stress that the number is not the *answer;* the interpretation of the number in the context of a real problem is the proper end result of a statistical analysis.

Prediction intervals are a new idea. By contrasting them with confidence intervals, the students can avoid common misinterpretations of confidence intervals.

Most computer packages provide an analysis of variance table as part of the output for a regression. For simple linear regression the table is not particularly useful. Often it generates more confusion than useful information for students at this point. On the other hand, the ANOVA table is very important for multiple regression, and it is essential for performing analysis of variance. If you plan to cover these topics, discussion of the ANOVA table for linear regression provides an excellent introduction to this topic. Explain that it is a different way to present some of the information already discussed and that it will be important for topics to be covered later.

The section concludes with optional material on inference for correlation. We see that the test for zero correlation is equivalent to the test for zero slope in the regression. The square of the correlation is expressed in a form that generalizes easily to multiple regression.

Chapter 11: Multiple Regression

The model for multiple regression and a brief overview of the inference procedures are presented. This chapter can be omitted without loss of continuity. For students who will take another statistics course in which this material will be covered in great detail, a discussion of the case study can be very valuable. Many important ideas are presented in the context of the problem of predicting grade point average from high school grades and SAT scores.

Chapter 12: One-Way Analysis of Variance

The idea of using a statistical test to compare population means is familiar from Chapter 7. New issues arise because we may have more than two means to compare. The DATA = FIT + RESIDUAL idea is used in presenting the statistical model underlying the analysis. The model is treated first, thereby emphasizing the principle that inference is based upon assumptions and definitions of parameters given by a model.

The analysis of variance table is constructed using some familiar ideas. Pooling of variances was treated in Chapter 8 and again the idea of DATA = FIT + RESIDUAL is used. The ANOVA tables from the regression chapters (Chapter 10 and 11) anticipated many of the ideas presented here.

Some new ideas arise with contrasts and multiple comparisons. Without some discussion of at least one of these topics, one is left with a statistical procedure giving very little in terms of useful interpretable results. Most statistical software packages will perform these computations.

The issue of what multiple comparison procedure to use is rather difficult. We have chosen to present only one procedure—the Bonferroni. However, it is presented in such a way that any other procedure could easily be substituted.

The optional section on power reminds us again that the performance of a statistical procedure depends upon the sample sizes and the true values of the parameters. It is interesting to note that these kinds of calculations are rather easy to perform with any statistical software that has a function for the noncentral F distribution. Tables of power and even graphs of power functions are relatively easy to generate. The use of G•Power (mentioned earlier) also eases these computations.

Note that this edition no longer uses the term "minimum significant difference (MSD)" in the section on multiple comparisons.

Chapter 13: Two-Way Analysis of Variance

Two-way analysis of variance is treated conceptually. A major goal is for the students to understand the meaning of interaction. No computational formulas are given; computation is left for the computer. The emphasis is on understanding the assumptions and interpreting the output.

This chapter is really an introduction to more complex analysis of variance designs. In this context, the initial discussion of advantages of two-way ANOVA is particularly important. Again the description of the model plays a key role.

Interaction is the important new idea. It is illustrated with a variety of examples chosen to demonstrate the different types of interpretations that arise in practice. Stress that the statement that there is interaction between two factors is essentially meaningless in itself. Interpretation requires a careful examination of the means in the context of a given problem.

As in Chapter 12, note that the term "minimum significant difference (MSD)" is no longer used for multiple comparisons procedures.

Chapter 14: Bootstrap Methods and Permutation Tests

This chapter uses computationally demanding resampling procedures, for which the use of a computer is critical. The solutions (prepared by Tim Hesterberg) were written using S-PLUS. More information about the S-PLUS procedures are given in the solutions to Chapter 14 exercises (page 334 of this guide). Note that a free student version of S-PLUS is available, so your students may use it for this chapter, even if they normally work with other software.

Chapter 15: Nonparametric Tests

This chapter presents techniques for use with nonnormal data. It can be used as supplementary material for interested and capable students, building on the sign test introduced in Chapter 7. (In fact, many of the ideas in this chapter are no more difficult than those of earlier chapters; they are arguably much easier than the regression and analysis-of-variance material, even though the Kruskal-Wallis test is an alternative to ANOVA!)

There are only 38 exercises in Chapter 15, but note that one can use these methods on exercises on comparing means (Chapter 7) and analysis of variance (Chapter 12), although in many cases, there may be no reason to question underlying normality.

Chapter 16: Logistic Regression

This chapter might provide useful supplementary material for students who have covered regression, but be aware that even fairly sophisticated statistical software packages may not have the capability to do *multiple* logistic regression. With the right software, and sufficiently prepared students, this short chapter (only 34 exercises) can be covered in a week or two.

Chapter 17: Statistics for Quality: Control and Capability

This chapter may be particularly useful for business students, as it illustrates applications of statistical ideas to a number of common situations in manufacturing and management. For a light introduction to the topic, the first two sections could stand on their own.

3 SAMPLE EXAMINATIONS

In writing exams, here are several points to keep in mind:

- Use current events and local references.

- Decide how much computation to require, and let the students know in advance. Having students compute standard deviations or correlations on exams may not be the best way to measure their comprehension.

- As an alternative to computation, consider placing computer or calculator output on the test and asking students to interpret it.

- Decide what mix of multiple-choice, problem-solving, and discussion questions to use. If class size makes it necessary, use some multiple-choice questions, but by and large, the subject matter of this course is best tested with questions that require writing ("Give reasons to support your answer."). No multiple-choice questions are given in these samples.

The exams given here can be used as examination items or as class examples. As mentioned earlier, a sample exam distributed in class is useful as review before a scheduled exam.

These questions are taken from the Instructor's Guide to the third edition. Of course, the Test Bank CD-ROM (available separately) and the online quizzes accessible from the text Web site (http://www.whfreeman.com/ips5e) are also excellent resources.

Sample examination I

These questions cover Chapters 1 and 2.

1. A study examined how long aircraft air conditioning units operated after being repaired. Here are the operating times (in hours) for one unit:

97	51	11	4	141	18	142	68	77
80	1	16	106	206	82	54	31	216
46	111	39	63	18	191	18	163	24

    (a) Make a histogram, using classes that are 40 hours wide, beginning with

    $$0 \leq \text{time} < 40$$

    $$40 \leq \text{time} < 80$$

    (b) Describe the overall shape of the distribution: Is it roughly symmetric, skewed to the right, or skewed to the left? Are there any outliers?

(c) Is the five-number summary or the mean and standard deviation a better brief summary for this distribution? Explain your choice. Calculate the one of these summaries that you choose.

2. Biologists and ecologists record the distributions of measurements made on animal species to help study the distribution and evolution of the animals. The African finch *Pyrenestes ostrinus* is interesting because the distribution of its bill size has two peaks even though other body measurements follow normal distributions. For example, a study in Cameroon found that the wing length of male finches varies according to a normal distribution with mean 61.2 mm and standard deviation 1.8 mm.

   (a) What proportion of male finches have wings longer than 65 mm?

   (b) What is the wing length that only 2% of male finches exceed?

3. The drug AZT was the first effective treatment for AIDS. An important medical experiment demonstrated that regular doses of AZT delay the onset of symptoms in people in whom the AIDS virus is present. The researchers who carried out this experiment wanted to know

   - Does taking either 500 mg of AZT or 1500 mg of AZT per day delay the development of AIDS?

   - Is there any difference between the effects of these two doses?

   The subjects were 1200 volunteers already infected with the AIDS virus but with no symptoms of AIDS when the study started.

   (a) Outline the design of the experiment.

   (b) Describe briefly how you would use a table of random digits to do the randomization required by your design. Then use Table B beginning at line 110 to choose *the first five* subjects for one of your groups.

4. A long-term study of changing environmental conditions in Chesapeake Bay found the following annual average salinity readings in one location in the bay:

Year	1971	1972	1973	1974	1975	1976	1977
Salinity (%)	13.2	9.3	14.9	13.9	14.8	13.3	15.0

Year	1978	1979	1980	1981	1982	1983	1984
Salinity (%)	15.3	15.1	13.1	17.0	19.3	15.6	15.3

   (a) Make a plot of salinity against time. Was salinity generally increasing or decreasing over these years? Is there an overall straight-line trend over time?

   (b) What is the correlation between salinity and year? What percent of the observed variation in salinity is accounted for by straight line change over time?

(c) Find the least-squares regression line for predicting salinity from year. Explain in simple language what the slope of this line tells you about Chesapeake Bay.

(d) If the trend in these past data had continued, what would be the average salinity at this point in the bay in 1988?

Sample examination I solutions

1. (a) At right.

   (b) The distribution of operating times is strongly skewed to the right. There are no outliers.

   (c) The five-number summary is preferable for this strongly skewed distribution. First arrange the observations in increasing order:

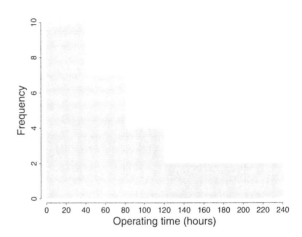

1	4	11	16	18	18	18	24	31	39	46	51	54	63
68	77	80	82	97	106	111	141	142	163	191	206	216	

   The five-number summary of these $n = 27$ observations is

   $$1 \quad 18 \quad 63 \quad 111 \quad 216$$

2. (a) Wing length x has the $N(61.2, 1.8)$ distribution. So we want the area under a normal curve such that

   $$x > 65$$

   $$\frac{x - 61.2}{1.8} > \frac{65 - 61.2}{1.8}$$

   $$z > 2.11$$

   Table A gives this area as $1 - 0.9826 = 0.0174$. About 17.4% of male finches have wing lengths exceeding 64.9 mm.

   (b) We want the x with area 0.02 to its right, or area 0.98 to its left. In the body of Table A, find $z = 2.06$ as the entry with left tail area closest to 0.98. So

   $$x = 61.2 + (1.8)(2.06) = 64.9 \text{ mm}$$

3. (a) The goals of the experiment require *three* treatment groups, one of which
         receives a placebo. (Because AZT was the first AIDS drug, it was considered
         ethical to give a placebo to test its effectiveness. Later drugs were tested
         against AZT.) Here is the design:

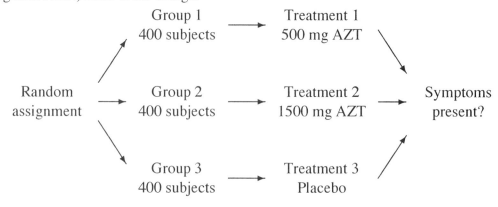

    (b) First assign labels. We use labels 0001 to 1200. Then read four-digit groups
         from line 110, continuing to the following lines. The first five subjects chosen
         are

         0676 0041 0404 1197 0640

4. (a) There is an increasing linear trend over time.

    (b) The correlation (use a calculator) is $r = 0.6386$. Because $r^2 = 0.4079$, linear
         change over time explains about 41% of the observed variation in salinity over
         this period.

    (c) The least-squares line (use a calculator) is

         $$\hat{y} = -659.4385 + 0.340879x$$

         That is, salinity is increasing by 0.34% per year on the average.

    (d) The prediction for $x = 1988$ is

         $$\hat{y} = -659.4385 + (0.3409)(1988) = 18.23\%$$

Sample examination II

These questions cover Chapters 3 through 5.

1. About 22% of the residents of California were born outside the United States. You
    choose an SRS of 1000 California residents for a sample survey on immigration
    issues. You want to find the probability that 250 or more of the people in your
    sample were born outside the United States.

    (a) You would like to use the normal approximation for the sampling distribution
         of a sample proportion to answer this question. Explain carefully why you can
         use the approximation in this setting.

(b) What is the probability that 250 or more of the people in your sample were born outside the United States?

2. The weights of newborn children in the United States vary according to the normal distribution with mean 7.5 pounds and standard deviation 1.25 pounds. The government classifies a newborn as having low birth weight if the weight is less than 5.5 pounds.

    (a) What is the probability that a baby chosen at random weighs less than 5.5 pounds at birth?

    (b) You choose three babies at random. What is the probability that their average birthweight is less than 5.5 pounds?

3. Answer each of the following short questions.

    (a) Give the upper 0.025 critical value for the standard normal distribution.

    (b) An animal scientist is studying factors that affect the level of milk production in dairy cows. He wonders:

    > Is the mean production different for cows who are given forage spread on the ground than for cows whose forage is in bunks?

    State the null and alternative hypotheses that you would use in a statistical test of this question. (We can't test these hypotheses yet.)

    (c) An opinion poll asks 1500 randomly chosen U.S. residents their opinion about relations with Russia. The announced margin of error for 95% confidence is ±3 points. But some people were not on the list from which respondents were chosen, some could not be contacted, and some refused to answer. Does the announced margin of error include errors from these causes?

    (d) A student organization plans to ask 100 randomly selected students whether they favor a change in the grading system. You argue for a sample of 900 students instead of 100. You know that the standard deviation of the proportion $\hat{p}$ of the sample who say "Yes" will be __ times as large with the larger sample. Should this blank be filled in with nine, one-ninth, three, or one-third? Explain your answer.

    (e) You read in a journal a report of a study that found a statistically significant result at the 5% significance level. What can you say about the significance of this result at the 1% level: Is it certainly significant at the 1% level, certainly not significant at the 1% level, or maybe significant and maybe not significant?

4. A friend who hears that you are taking a statistics course asks for help with a chemistry lab report. She has made four independent measurements of the specific gravity of a compound. The results are

   3.82, 3.93, 3.67, 3.78

   The lab manual says that repeated measurements will vary according to a normal distribution with standard deviation $\sigma = 0.15$. (This standard deviation shows how precise the measurement process is.) The mean μ of the distribution of measurements is the true specific gravity.

   (a) The lab manual asks for a 95% confidence interval for the true specific gravity. Your friend doesn't know how to do this. Do it for her.

   (b) Now explain to your friend in simple language what "95% confidence" means.

   (c) What critical value from the normal table would you use if you wanted 80% confidence instead of 95% confidence? Would the 80% confidence interval be wider or narrower than your 95% confidence from (a)? [Do *not* actually compute the 80% confidence interval.]

   (d) The lab manual also asks whether the data show convincingly that the true specific gravity is less than 3.9. State the null and alternative hypotheses used to answer this question. Then calculate the test statistic, and find its P-value.

   (e) Explain to your friend in one or two sentences what the specific P-value you found in (c) means.

5. Here are several statistical statements. In each case, explain to someone who knows no statistics what the boldface term means. Use just a sentence or two, and avoid technical jargon.

   (a) A spinning penny has **probability 0.6** of coming up tails.

   (b) With **90% confidence** we can say that the national unemployment rate for June was between 5.3% and 5.5%.

   (c) The **expected winnings** on a $1 lottery ticket are $0.53.

6. If you pay me $1, I will let you play the following gambling game. You drop your pencil point into the middle of a table of random digits and then look at the digit on which it lands.

   If it is a 7, you win $5.
   If it is a 1, you win $2.
   Otherwise you win nothing.

   Find the expected value of the amount you win in one play of this game. Explain in simple language what the expected value tells you about your winnings if you play the game many times. Is it to your advantage to pay $1 to play?

Sample examination II solutions

1. (a) First (rule of thumb 1), the population of California is much larger than 10 times the sample size $n = 1000$. So we can use the usual formula for the standard deviation of $\hat{p}$.

   Second (rule of thumb 2), for $n = 1000$ and $p = 0.22$ we have $np = 220$ and $n(1 - p) = 780$. Both are much larger than 10, so the normal approximation will be quite accurate.

   (b) The question concerns the *count* of 1000 California residents born outside the United States. Translate into a question about the *proportion:*

   $$\text{count} \geq 250 \quad \text{is} \quad \hat{p} = \frac{\text{count}}{1000} \geq \frac{250}{1000} = 0.25$$

   The mean of $\hat{p}$ is $p = 0.22$. The standard deviation is

   $$\sqrt{\frac{p(1-p)}{n}} = \sqrt{\frac{(0.22)(0.78)}{1000}} = 0.0131$$

   Now use the normal approximation to find the probability:

   $$
   \begin{aligned}
   P(\hat{p} \geq 0.25) &= P\left(\frac{\hat{p} - 0.22}{0.0131} \geq \frac{0.25 - 0.22}{0.0131}\right) \\
   &= P(Z \geq 2.29) \\
   &= 1 - 0.9890 = 0.0110
   \end{aligned}
   $$

2. (a) The weight x of a single child has the $N(7.5, 1.25)$ distribution. So

   $$P(x < 5.5) = P\left(\frac{x - 7.5}{1.25} < \frac{5.5 - 7.5}{1.25}\right) = P(Z < -1.60) = 0.0548$$

   (b) The mean birth weight $\bar{x}$ of a sample of three children still has mean 7.5 pounds, but its standard deviation is

   $$\frac{\sigma}{\sqrt{3}} = \frac{1.25}{\sqrt{3}} = 0.7217 \text{ pound}$$

   The probability we want is therefore

   $$P(\bar{x} < 5.5) = P\left(\frac{\bar{x} - 7.5}{0.7217} < \frac{5.5 - 7.5}{0.7217}\right) = P(Z < -2.77) = 0.0028$$

3. (a) Use Table C to see that the upper 0.025 critical value is $z^* = 1.960$. *Or,* use the 68–95–99.7 rule to approximate it by 2.

(b) The key words are "is different," indicating that the alternative hypothesis is two-sided:

$$H_0 : \mu_G = \mu_B \qquad \text{vs.} \qquad H_a : \mu_G \neq \mu_B$$

Here μ_G and μ_B are the mean milk production for all cows of this breed with forage spread on the ground and in bunks, respectively.

(c) No. The margin of error in a confidence interval covers only the random sampling error due to chance variation in random sampling.

(d) The standard deviation goes down as the sample size n goes up, at the rate $\sqrt{n}$. (The standard deviation of a sample proportion $\hat{p}$ is $\sqrt{p(1-p)/n}$.) So a sample nine times larger has a standard deviation *one-third* as large.

(e) A result significant at the 5% level is in the extreme 5% of the sampling distribution; so it *may or may not* also be in the extreme 1%.

4. (a) First, $\bar{x} = 3.80$. The 95% confidence interval is

$$\bar{x} \pm z^* \frac{\sigma}{\sqrt{n}} = 3.80 \pm 1.960 \frac{0.15}{\sqrt{4}} = 3.80 \pm 0.147$$

(b) "95% confidence" means that we got this interval by using a method that in 95% of all samples will produce an interval that covers the true specific gravity.

(c) $z^* = 1.282$, the upper 0.10 critical value. The 80% confidence interval is narrower than the 95% confidence interval because the critical value required is smaller.

(d) The hypotheses are

$$H_0 : \mu = 3.9 \qquad \text{vs.} \qquad H_a : \mu < 3.9$$

The test statistic is

$$z = \frac{\bar{x} - \mu_0}{\sigma/\sqrt{n}} = \frac{3.8 - 3.9}{0.15/\sqrt{4}} = -1.33$$

and its P-value (one-sided on the low side) is

$$P(Z \leq -1.33) = 0.0918$$

(e) There is probability 0.0918 that the mean of four readings would be as small as 3.8 if the true specific gravity were 3.9. That is, we observed a value in the smallest 9.2% of all results we could get if 3.9 were correct. This is only weak evidence that the specific gravity is less than 3.9, because a value this small would come up more than 9% of the time just by chance.

5. (a) In the long run, the coin comes up tails about 60% of the time.

(b) The interval was derived from a method that gives an interval that includes the true unemployment rate 90% of the time.

(c) If we buy many lottery tickets, the average winnings will be close to $0.53.

6. The expected winnings are $(0.1)(\$5) + (0.1)(\$2) = \$0.70$. This represents average winnings for many plays of the game; it is not a good idea to spend $1 on this game.

Sample final examination

This is comprehensive, covering material from (roughly) Chapters 1–12.

1. An historian examining British colonial records for the Gold Coast in Africa suspects that the death rate was higher among African miners than among European miners. In the year 1936, there were 223 deaths among 33,809 African miners and 7 deaths among 1541 European miners in the Gold Coast. (Data courtesy of Raymond Dumett, Department of History, Purdue University.)

    Consider this year as a sample from the prewar era in Africa. Is there good evidence that the proportion of African miners who died during a year was higher than the proportion of European miners who died? [State hypotheses, calculate a test statistic, give a P-value as exact as the tables in the text allow, and state your conclusion in words.]

2. An agricultural researcher reasons as follows: A heavy application of potassium fertilizer to grasslands in the spring seems to cause lush early growth but depletes the potassium before the growing season ends. So spreading the same amount of potassium over the growing season might increase yields. The researcher therefore compares two treatments: 100 pounds per acre of potassium in the spring (Treatment 1) and 50, 25, and 25 pounds per acre applied in the spring, early summer, and late summer (Treatment 2). The experiment is continued over several years because growing conditions may vary from year to year.

    The table below gives the yields, in pounds of dry matter per acre. It is known from long experience that yields vary roughly normally. (Data from R. R. Robinson, C. L. Rhykerd, and C. F. Gross, "Potassium uptake by orchardgrass as affected by time, frequency and rate of potassium fertilization," *Agronomy Journal*, 54(1962) 351–353.)

Treatment	Year 1	Year 2	Year 3	Year 4	Year 5
1	3902	4281	5135	5350	5746
2	3970	4271	5440	5490	6028

    (a) Do the data give good evidence that Treatment 2 leads to higher average yields? [State hypotheses, carry out a test, give a P-value as exact as the tables in the text allow, and state your conclusions in words.]

    (b) Give a 98% confidence interval for the mean increase in yield due to spreading potassium applications over the growing season.

3. Prior to an intensive TV advertising campaign, the producers of Nike athletic shoes find that 29 of a random sample of 200 upper-income adults are aware of their new leisure shoe line. A second random sample of 300 such adults is taken after the campaign. Now 96 of the persons sampled can identify the new line.

   Give a 99% confidence interval for the increase in the proportion of upper income adults showing brand awareness.

4. Here are data on the years of schooling completed, x, and annual income, y (in thousands of dollars), for a sample of 18 40-year-old men.

Years	10	16	12	6	12	12	16	16	18
Income	28	38	16	13	25	30	35	27	28

Years	12	10	12	16	14	11	12	19	16
Income	28	26	21	34	30	21	27	29	24

   A scatterplot (don't do it) shows a generally linear relation, but with considerable scatter about the line of best fit. A computer least-squares regression program gives the output shown. (The "Coef" column gives the intercept a and slope b; the "Std Err" column gives the standard errors of these statistics. The "Residual Standard Error" is the observed standard deviation s about the regression line.)

   ```
                  Coef      Std Err    t Value
   Intercept   10.84249    5.103363   2.124577
   x2           1.186813   0.372311   3.187693

   Residual Standard Error = 5.02275    R-Square = 0.3884116
   N = 18          F Value = 10.16139 on 1, 16 df
   ```

   (a) What percent of the observed variation in income is explained by the straight-line relation between income and education?

   (b) Is there strong evidence that there is a straight-line relation between education and income? (State hypotheses, carry out a test, use a table to find values between which the P-value falls, and state your conclusion.)

   (c) Consider 40-year-old men who have 16 years of education. (These are men with four years of college but no further education.) Give a 95% confidence interval for their average income.

5. Answer each of the following questions. (No explanation is needed — just a short answer.)

   (a) You are reading an article in your field that reports several statistical analyses. The article says that the P-value for a significance test is 0.045. Is this result significant at the 5% significance level?

   (b) Is the result with P-value 0.045 significant at the 1% significance level?

(c) For another significance test, the article says only that the result was significant at the 1% level. Are such results always, sometimes, or never significant at the 5% level?

(d) Reaction times of a subject to a stimulus are often strongly skewed to the right because of a few slow reaction times. You wish to test

$$H_0 : \mu_1 = \mu_2$$

where μ_1 is the mean reaction time for Stimulus 1, μ_2 for Stimulus 2. You have two independent samples, eight observations for Stimulus 1 and 10 for Stimulus 2. Which, if any, of the tests you have studied can be used to test this?

(e) The article contains a 95% confidence interval. Would the margin of error in a 99% confidence interval computed from the same data be less, the same, or greater?

6. A friend in a political science course asks for your help. She just read that the correlation between the percent of eligible citizens in a city who register to vote and the percent of registered voters in the city who really do vote is 0.88. She read further that the correlation is significant ($P < 0.01$).

(a) Explain to your friend in plain language what $r = 0.88$ means.

(b) Then explain what it means to say that this correlation is statistically significant ($P < 0.01$). Use plain language—no technical terms.

(c) Now explain to you friend what the fact that $r^2 = 0.77$ says about predicting voter turnout from registration data.

7. Here are data on the percent of sugar in some popular breakfast cereals.

Product	% Sugar
All Bran	19
Alpha Bits	38
Cap'n Crunch	40
Cheerios	3
Corn Flakes	5
Golden Grahams	30
Grape Nuts Flakes	13
Post Toasties	5
Product 19	10
Raisin Bran (General Foods)	48
Raisin Bran (Kellogg)	29
Rice Krispies	8
Special K	5
Sugar Smacks	56
Wheaties	8

(a) Make a stemplot of these data. Describe the overall shape of the distribution. Are there any clear outliers?

(b) Based on your findings in part (a), choose a numerical summary for this distribution. Calculate your summary.

Sample final examination solutions

1. This is a two-sample setting with

   Population 1 = African miners
   Population 2 = European miners

   We want to test
   $$H_0 : p_1 = p_2 \qquad \text{vs.} \qquad H_a : p_1 > p_2$$

   The two sample proportions are

   $$\hat{p}_1 = \frac{223}{33,809} = 0.006596 \quad \text{and} \quad \hat{p}_2 = \frac{7}{1541} = 0.004543$$

   The pooled sample proportion is therefore

   $$\begin{aligned}
   \hat{p} &= \frac{\text{count of deaths in both samples combined}}{\text{count of miners in both samples combined}} \\
   &= \frac{223 + 7}{33,809 + 1541} \\
   &= \frac{230}{35,350} = 0.006506
   \end{aligned}$$

   and the test statistic is

   $$\begin{aligned}
   z &= \frac{\hat{p}_1 - \hat{p}_2}{\sqrt{\hat{p}(1-\hat{p})\left(\frac{1}{n_1} + \frac{1}{n_2}\right)}} \\
   &= \frac{0.006596 - 0.004543}{\sqrt{(0.006506)(0.993494)\left(\frac{1}{33,809} + \frac{1}{1541}\right)}} \\
   &= \frac{0.002053}{0.0020943} = 0.980
   \end{aligned}$$

   Table A gives the P-value as $1 - 0.8365 = 0.1635$. There is, surprisingly, no significant evidence that the African death rate is higher.

2. This is a *matched pairs* setting because the observations are paired by years.

   (a) The hypotheses, expressed in terms of the mean differences, Treatment 2 − Treatment 1, are

   $$H_0 : \mu = 0 \qquad \text{vs.} \qquad H_a : \mu > 0$$

   The differences are

   $$68 \quad -10 \quad 305 \quad 140 \quad 282$$

   with

   $$\bar{x} = 157 \quad \text{and} \quad s = 135.672$$

   Apply the one-sample t test to these differences. The test statistic is

   $$t = \frac{\bar{x} - 0}{s/\sqrt{n}} = \frac{157}{135.672/\sqrt{5}} = 2.588$$

   The P-value based on the t distribution with $n - 1 = 4$ degrees of freedom falls between 0.025 and 0.05 (using Table C). This is moderately strong evidence that Treatment 2 produces a higher mean yield.

   (b) For 98% confidence and 4 degrees of freedom, use $t^* = 3.747$. The confidence interval is

   $$\begin{aligned}
   \bar{x} \pm t^* \frac{s}{\sqrt{n}} &= 157 \pm 3.747 \frac{135.672}{\sqrt{5}} \\
   &= 157 \pm 227.3 \\
   &= (-70.3, \ 384.3)
   \end{aligned}$$

3. There are two independent samples. We want a confidence interval for a difference between two population proportions. The sample proportions are

   $$\hat{p}_1 = \frac{29}{200} = 0.145 \quad \text{and} \quad \hat{p}_2 = \frac{96}{300} = 0.320$$

   We can use procedures based on the normal approximation because the population is large and

   $$n\hat{p}_1 = 29 \quad n(1 - \hat{p}_1) = 191 \quad n\hat{p}_2 = 96 \quad n(1 - \hat{p}_2) = 204$$

   are all more than 5.

   The standard error for $\hat{p}_2 - \hat{p}_1$ is

   $$\begin{aligned}
   \text{SE} &= \sqrt{\frac{\hat{p}_1(1 - \hat{p}_1)}{n_1} + \frac{\hat{p}_2(1 - \hat{p}_2)}{n_2}} \\
   &= \sqrt{\frac{(0.145)(0.855)}{200} + \frac{(0.320)(0.680)}{300}} \\
   &= \sqrt{0.0013452} = 0.03668
   \end{aligned}$$

The 99% confidence interval for $p_2 - p_1$ is

$$
\begin{aligned}
(\hat{p}_2 - \hat{p}_1) \pm z^* \text{SE} \quad &= \quad (0.320 - 0.145) \pm (2.576)(0.03668) \\
&= \quad 0.175 \pm 0.0945 \\
&= \quad (0.0805, \ 0.2695)
\end{aligned}
$$

We are 99% confident that between 8% and 27% of upper-income adults are aware of the new shoe line.

4. (a) The output says R-Square = 0.3884116, so the linear relationship explains 38.8% of the observed variation in income.

    (b) The null hypothesis of "no relation" says that the slope of the true regression line is 0. The hypotheses are

$$
H_0 : \beta = 0 \qquad \text{vs.} \qquad H_a : \beta \neq 0
$$

The computer output shows that the t statistic for the test is $t = 3.187693$. The degrees of freedom are $n - 2 = 16$. From Table C we see that t falls between the 0.0025 and 0.005 upper critical values of $t(16)$. Doubling these values because H_a is two-sided, $0.005 < P < 0.01$. There is strong evidence that a linear relationship exists.

    (c) The predicted mean income for $x = 16$ is

$$
\hat{y} = 10.84249 + (1.186813)(16) = 29.831
$$

or \$29,831. The rest of this is a bit tedious by hand, so consider your options. (Not all students may be capable of handling this on a test.) Here goes. Using a calculator for $\bar{x}$ and s_x gives that $\bar{x} = 13.33$ and

$$
\sum(x - \bar{x})^2 = (n - 1)s_x^2 = (17)(3.27198)^2 = 182
$$

The proper standard error for estimating the mean income is

$$
\begin{aligned}
\text{SE}_{\hat{\mu}} \quad &= \quad s \sqrt{\frac{1}{n} + \frac{(x^* - \bar{x})^2}{\sum(x - \bar{x})^2}} \\
&= \quad 5.02275 \sqrt{\frac{1}{18} + \frac{(16 - 13.33)^2}{182}} \\
&= \quad 5.02275 \sqrt{0.0946275} = 1.5451
\end{aligned}
$$

The 90% confidence interval is therefore

$$
\begin{aligned}
\hat{y} \pm t^* \text{SE}_{\hat{\mu}} \quad &= \quad 29.831 \pm (2.120)(1.5451) \\
&= \quad 29.831 \pm 3.276 \\
&= \quad (26.555, \ 33.107)
\end{aligned}
$$

or \$26,555 to \$33,107.

5. (a) Yes. The *P*-value is less than 0.05.

   (b) No. The *P*-value is greater than 0.01.

   (c) A result significant at the 1% level lies in the extreme 1% of a sampling distribution. This is certainly in the extreme 5%, so the result is always significant at the 5% level.

   (d) The samples are small and the distributions are strongly skewed. It would be unwise to use the *t* test in this setting. A nonparametric test (if these have been studied) might be appropriate.

   (e) The margin of error would be greater. Higher confidence is paid for with a greater margin of error.

6. (a) There is a strong tendency for both quantities—percent registered, and the percent who turn out—to both be high, or both be low. That is, when one is high, the other is usually also high, and when one is low, the other is usually low.

   (b) If there was no relationship between the two quantities, a correlation this high would be observed less than 1% of the time.

   (c) There will be variation in voter turnout from one city to the next. If we know the percent registered, we can account for (explain) about 77% of that variation.

7. (a) The distribution is right-skewed, with no particular outliers.

   ```
   0 | 355588
   1 | 039
   2 | 9
   3 | 08
   4 | 08
   5 | 6
   ```

   (b) Because of the skewness, use the five-number summary: 3   5   13   38   56.

4 SOLUTIONS TO EXERCISES

About these solutions

The solutions that follow were prepared by Darryl Nester, with the exception of Chapter 14 (prepared by Tim Hesterberg). In some cases, solutions were based on those prepared for earlier editions of *IPS;* I hope that I did not miss any subtle changes in an exercise that should have resulted in a change in the solution. Should you discover any errors or have any comments about these solutions (or the odd answers, in the back of the text), please report them to me:

> Darryl Nester
> Bluffton University
> Bluffton, Ohio 45817
> e-mail: `nesterd@bluffton.edu`
> WWW: `http://www.bluffton.edu/~nesterd`

Acknowledgments

I should mention the software I used in putting these solutions together:

- For typesetting: TEX — specifically, Textures, from Blue Sky Software.

- For the graphs: DeltaGraph (SPSS) and Adobe Illustrator.

- For statistical analysis: primarily Minitab and Excel, along with S-PLUS (for Chapter 14), SAS (for Chapter 16), and some freeware and shareware software (G•Power and GLMStat). Additionally, I used the TI-83 calculator from Texas Instruments.

Note: The solutions given to the applet exercises, and the sample output screens, were based on the current versions of the applets at the time the solutions were written. As revisions are made to these applets, the appearance of the output screens (and in some cases, the answers) may change. Additionally, output screens look somewhat different on different computers. (Some of these screenshots were taken under Windows 98, some under Windows XP, and others under Mac OS X.)

Using the table of random digits

Grading SRSs chosen from Table B is complicated by the fact that students can find some creative ways to (mis)use the table. Some approaches are not mistakes, but may lead to different students having different "right" answers. Correct answers will vary based on

- The line in the table on which they begin (you may want to specify one if the text does not).

- Whether they start with, e.g., 00 or 01.

- Whether they assign multiple labels to each unit.

- Whether they assign labels across the rows or down the columns (nearly all lists in the text are alphabetized down the columns).

Some approaches can potentially lead to wrong answers. Mistakes to watch out for include the following:

- They may forget that all labels must be the same length (e.g., assigning labels such as $0, 1, 2, \ldots, 9, 10, \ldots$ rather than $00, 01, 02, \ldots$).

- In assigning multiple labels, they may not give the same number of labels to all units. For example, if there are 30 units, they may try to use up all the two-digit numbers, thus assigning four labels to the first 10 units and only three to the remaining 20.

As an alternative to using the random digits in Table B, students can pick a random sample by generating (pseudo)-random numbers, using software (like Excel) or a calculator. With many, if not all, calculators, the sequence of random numbers produced is determined by a "seed value" (which can be specified by the user). Rather than pointing students to a particular line of Table B, you could specify a seed value for generating random numbers, so that all students would obtain the same results (if all are using the same model of calculator).

On a TI-83, for example, after executing the command $0 \rightarrow$ rand, the rand command will produce the sequence (rounded to four decimals) 0.9436, 0.9083, 0.1467, . . ., while $1 \rightarrow$ rand initiates the sequence 0.7456, 0.8559, 0.2254, . . . So to choose, say, an SRS of size 10 from 30 subjects, use the command $0 \rightarrow$ rand to set the seed, and then type 1+30*rand, and press ENTER repeatedly. Ignoring the decimal portion of the resulting numbers, this produces the sample
$$29, \ 28, \ 5, \ 15, \ 13, \ 23, \ 2, \ 11, \ 30, \ 7$$
(Generally, to generate random numbers from 1 to n, use the command 1+n*rand and ignore the decimal portion of the result.)

Using statistical software

The use of computer software or a calculator is a must for all but the most cursory treatment of the material in this text. Be aware of the following considerations:

- *Standard deviations:* Students may be confused by software that gives both the so-called "sample standard deviation" (the one used in the text) and the "population standard deviation" (dividing by n rather than $n - 1$). Symbolically, the former is usually given as s and the latter as σ (sigma), but the distinction is not always clear. For example, many computer spreadsheets have a command such as "STDEV(...)" to compute standard deviations, but you may need to check the manual to find out which kind it is.

As a quick check: For the numbers $1, 2, 3$, $s = 1$ while $\sigma \doteq 0.8165$. In general, if two values are given, the larger one is s and the smaller is σ. If only one value is given, and it is the wrong one, use the relationship $s = \sigma \sqrt{\dfrac{n}{n-1}}$.

- *Stemplots:* The various choices one can make in creating a stemplot (e.g., rounding or truncating the data) have already been mentioned. Minitab opts for truncation over rounding, so all of the solutions in this guide show truncated-data stemplots (except for exercises that instructed students to round). This usually makes little difference in the overall appearance of the stemplot.

- *Significant digits in these solutions:* Most numerical answers in these solutions (and in the odd-numbered answers in the back of the text) are reported to four significant figures. In many cases, that is an absurd overrepresentation of the accuracy of those numbers, but those digits are provided to give students a better "check" on their answers.

  This extra accuracy is a double-edged sword, however, as a student might have a correct answer that does not agree with all the digits in the printed answer. This might occur (rarely, I hope) because my answer is wrong, but it may be due to rounding, differences in software accuracy, or use of an approximation. For example, in reporting binomial probabilities for exercises in Chapter 5, I have listed four or five answers for some problems: exact answers and normal approximations (with or without the continuity correction, and computed with software or using Table A). In the back-of-the-text answers, only one answer is given, so that students may have to be satisfied with being "close."

- *Quartiles and five-number summaries:* Methods of computing quartiles vary between different packages. Some use the approach given in the text (that is, Q_1 is the median of all the numbers below the location of the overall median, etc.), while others use a more complicated approach. For the numbers $1, 2, 3, 4$, for example, we would have $Q_1 = 1.5$ and $Q_3 = 2.5$, but Minitab reports these as 1.25 and 2.75, respectively.

  In these solutions (and the odd-numbered answers in the back of the text), I opted to report five-number summaries are they would be found using the text's method. Because I used Minitab for most of the analysis in these solutions, I wrote a Minitab macro to compute quartiles the *IPS* way. This and other macros are available on my Web site.

- *Boxplots:* Some programs that draw boxplots use the convention that the "whiskers" extend to the lower and upper deciles (the 10th and 90th percentiles) rather than to the minimum and maximum. While the decile method is merely *different* from that given in the text, some methods are (in my opinion) just plain *wrong*. Some early graphing calculators drew "box charts," which have a center line at the mean (not the median), and a box extending from $\bar{x} - \sigma$ to $\bar{x} + \sigma$! I know of no statistics text that uses that method, and I hope that such graphing calculators are no longer manufactured (or used).

Chapter 1 Solutions

1.1. **(a)** The individuals are vehicles (or "cars"). **(b)** The variables are make/model (categorical), vehicle type (categorical), transmission type (categorical), number of cylinders (quantitative), city MPG (quantitative), and highway MPG (quantitative).

1.2. The individuals are students. The variables are name (categorical), major (categorical), points (quantitative), and grade (categorical).

 Note: *One might observe that "name" is more a* label *than a* variable*: For most categorical variables, there is no problem with two individuals having the same value, but for student names, we would like each individual to have a unique name. (Of course, that might not always be the case.)*

1.3. **(a)** Type of wood is categorical. **(b)** Water repellent is categorical. **(c)** Paint thickness is quantitative. **(d)** Paint color is categorical. **(e)** Weathering time is quantitative.

1.4. Possible categorical variables include gender, year in school, race, and perhaps some classification of what the student watched (PBS? MTV? Sitcom? Documentary?). Quantitative variables might include hours watched (per day or week), hours spent studying (per day or week), hours spent sleeping, age (years), GPA.

1.5. Possible answers include time to run a race (instrument: stopwatch), heart rate after exercising (instrument: watch). Answers will depend on how broadly one defines fitness; most instruments will likely be watches or measuring tapes.

1.6. Student answers may vary; for comparison, recent *U.S. News* rankings have used measures such as academic reputation (measured by surveying college and university administrators), retention rate, graduation rate, class sizes, faculty salaries, student-faculty ratio, percentage of faculty with highest degree in their fields, quality of entering students (ACT/SAT scores, high school class rank, enrollment-to-admission ratio), financial resources, and the percentage of alumni who give to the school.

1.7. The rates (in deaths per 100 million miles) are

$$\frac{39,250 \text{ deaths}}{22,470 \text{ hundred million miles}} \doteq 1.75 \quad \text{and} \quad \frac{42,815 \text{ deaths}}{28,300 \text{ hundred million miles}} \doteq 1.51.$$

These numbers suggest that driving was safer in 2002 than in 1992.

 Note: *Most students will have difficulty with one (or both) of two things: expressing distance traveled in units of 100 million miles, and the order of the division (deaths in the numerator, distance in the denominator).*

1.8. (a) The weights add to 231.8 million tons. **(b) & (c)** The bar and pie graphs are shown below.

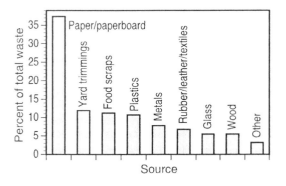 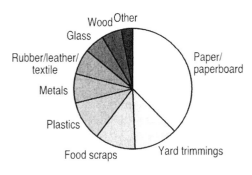

1.9. The given percents add to 85.8%, so the rest (14.2%) are "other colors." Because the numbers represent pieces of a single whole ("all cars"), a pie chart could be used.

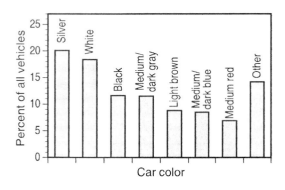 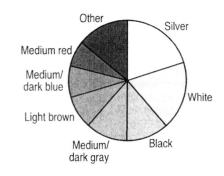

1.10. Shown is one way to create this bar graph, with side-by-side bars, sorted by decreasing luxury-car percentages.

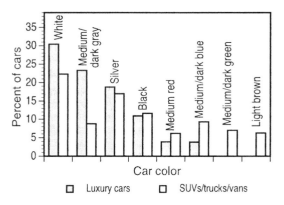

1.11. Unmet need is greatest at private institutions, especially for-profit ones. A pie chart would not be incorrect because these numbers do not represent parts of a single whole. (If the numbers given had been *total* unmet need, rather than *average* unmet need, and if we had information about *all* types of institutions, we would have been able to make a pie chart.)

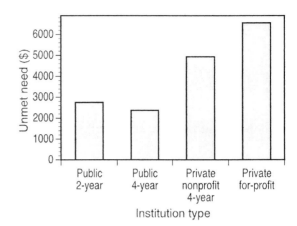

1.12. The time plots show that both manufacturers have generally improved over this period, with one slight jump in problems in 2003. Toyota vehicles typically have fewer problems, but GM has managed to close the gap slightly.

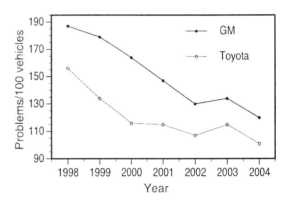

1.13. The two bar graphs are shown below.

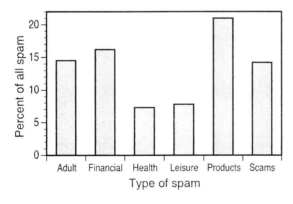

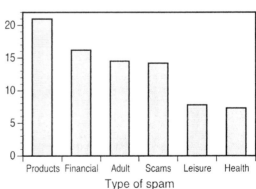

1.14. (a) The given percentages refer to nine distinct groups (all M.B.A. degrees, all M.Ed. degrees, and so on) rather than one single group. **(b)** Bar graph shown on the right.

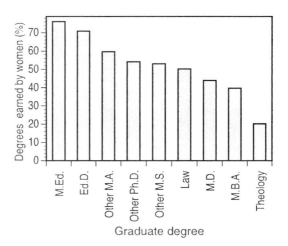

1.15. (a) Alaska is 5.7% (the leaf 7 on the stem 5), and Florida 17.6% (leaf 6 on stem 17). **(b)** The distribution is roughly symmetric (perhaps slightly skewed to the left), centered near 13% (the median [see section 1.2] is 12.85%). Ignoring the outliers, the percentages are spread from 8.5% to 15.6%.

1.16. Shown on the right are the original stemplot (as given in the text for Exercise 1.15, minus Alaska and Florida) and the split-stems version students were asked to construct for this exercise. Preferences may vary between the two.

8	5
9	679
10	6
11	02233677
12	0011113445789
13	00012233345568
14	034579
15	36

8	5
9	
9	679
10	
10	6
11	02233
11	677
12	001111344
12	5789
13	0001223334
13	5568
14	034
14	579
15	3
15	6

1.17. Shown is the stemplot; as the text suggests, we have trimmed numbers (dropped the last digit) and split stems. 359 mg/dl appears to be an outlier. Overall, glucose levels are not under control: Only 4 of the 18 had levels in the desired range.

0	799
1	0134444
1	5577
2	0
2	57
3	
3	5

1.18. The back-to-back stemplot on the right suggests that the individual-instruction group was more consistent (their numbers have less spread), but not more successful (only two had numbers in the desired range).

Individual		Class
	0	799
22	1	0134444
99866655	1	5577
22222	2	0
8	2	57
	3	
	3	5

1.19. The distribution is roughly symmetric, centered near 7 (or "between 6 and 7"), and spread from 2 to 13.

1.20. This distribution is skewed to the right, meaning that Shakespeare's plays contain many short words (up to six letters) and fewer very long words. We would probably expect most authors to have skewed distributions, although the exact shape and spread will vary.

1.21. There are three peaks in the histogram: One at $4–$6 thousand, one at $18–20 thousand, and one at $28–$30 thousand. There is a clear break between the least expensive schools and the rest; the line between the middle and most expensive schools is not so clear. Presumably, the lowest group (up to $10,000) includes public institutions, the highest group (starting around $25,000) exclusive private schools like Harvard, and the middle group other private schools. Of course, these are generalizations; there may be a few exceptions (low-priced private schools, or selective public schools).

1.22. (a) The top five states are Texas, Minnesota, Oklahoma, Missouri, and Illinois. The bottom five are Alaska, Puerto Rico, Rhode Island, Nevada and Vermont. **(b)** The histogram (right) shows a sharp right skew, with a large peak (25 of the 51 numbers) in the "less than 10" category; arguably, that category is the "center" of the distribution. The distribution is spread from $0 to about $90; the top three states (Texas, Minnesota, Oklahoma) might be considered outliers, as that bar is separated from the rest (no states fell in the $70–$80 category). **(c)** The default histogram will vary with the software used.

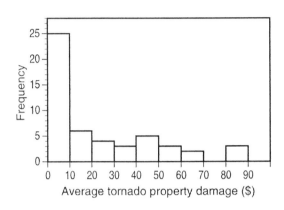

1.23. (a) The applet defaulted (for me) to 25 intervals. This histogram is shown below, along with the nine-class histogram. Note that the latter does not *exactly* match the histogram of the previous problem, because the applet's classes are about 9.85 units wide, rather than 10 units wide. **(b)** The one-class and 51-class histograms are shown below. **(c)** Student opinions about which number of classes is best will vary, but something between 6 to 12 seems like a good range.

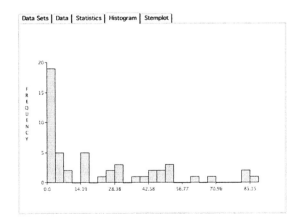
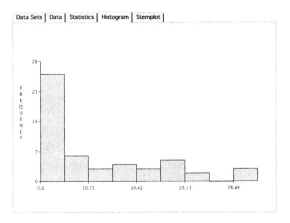

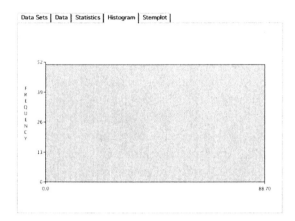

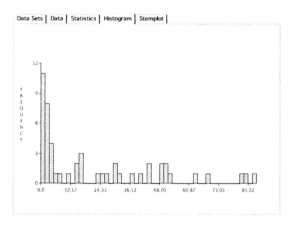

1.24. **(a)** Totals emissions would almost certainly be higher for very large countries; for example, we would expect that even with great attempts to control emissions, China (with over 1 billion people) would have higher total emissions than the smallest countries in the data set. **(b)** A stemplot is shown; a histogram would also be appropriate. We see a strong right skew with a peak from 0 to 0.2 metric tons per person, and a smaller peak from 0.8 to 1. The three highest countries (the U.S., Canada, and Australia) appear to be outliers; apart from those countries, the distribution is spread from 0 to 11 metric tons per person.

0	0000000000000011111
0	222233333
0	445
0	6677
0	888999
1	001
1	
1	
1	67
1	9

1.25. Shown below are two separate graphs (Pasadena on the left, Redding on the right); students may choose to plot both time series on a single set of axes. If two graphs are created, they should have the same vertical scale for easy comparison. Both plots show random fluctuation. Pasadena temperatures show an upward trend. Redding temperatures are initially similar to Pasadena's, but dropped in the mid-1980s.

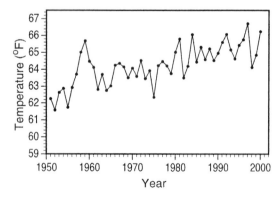

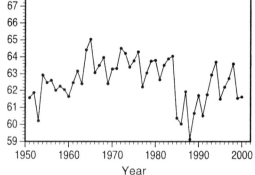

1.26. The distribution is symmetrical and mound-shaped, spread from 61°F to 67°F, with center 64–65°F. The histogram does not show what we see in the time plot from the previous exercise: That mean annual temperature has been rising over time.

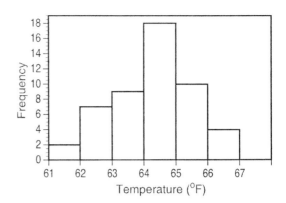

1.27. Shown below are two possible graphs.

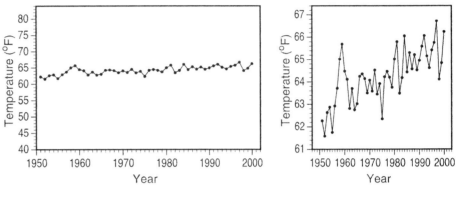

1.28. **(a)** A stemplot is shown; a histogram would also be appropriate. The distribution is right-skewed, with a high outlier (4700 million). Other than the outlier, the numbers range from about 100 million to 2800 million sole. **(b)** The time plot shows that the number

0	12233344
0	55556679
1	01244
1	777
2	24
2	8
3	
3	
4	
4	7

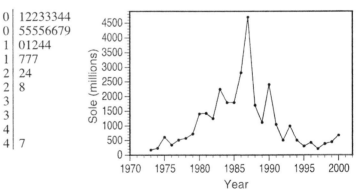

of recruits peaked in the mid-1980s, and in recent years has fallen back to levels similar to those in the 1970s.

1.29. A stemplot or a histogram is appropriate for displaying the distribution. We see that the DT scores are skewed to the right, centered near 5 or 6, spread from

```
0 | 000000000000000000000000000000000000011111111111111111111
0 | 222222222222222223333333333333333333333
0 | 4444444444444444444445555555555555555555
0 | 66666666666666666666677777777777777
0 | 888888888888889999999999999999999
1 | 000000000000111111111
1 | 22222222222233333333333
1 | 444444455
1 | 66666777
1 | 8
```

0 to 18. There are no outliers. We might also note that only 11 of these 264 women (about 4%) scored 15 or higher.

1.30. **(a)** The first histogram shows two modes: 5–5.2 and 5.6–5.8. **(b)** The second histogram has peaks in locations close to those of the first, but these peaks are much less pronounced, so would usually be viewed as distinct modes. **(c)** The results will vary with the software used.

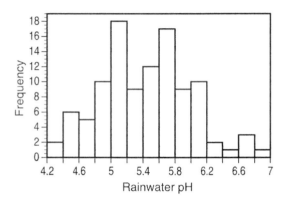
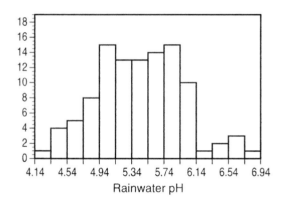

1.31. From the top left histogram: 4, 2, 1, 3. The upper-left hand graph is studying time; it is reasonable to expect this to be right-skewed (many students study little or not at all; a few study longer).

The graph in the lower right is the histogram of student heights: One would expect a fair amount of variation, but no particular skewness to such a distribution.

The other two graphs are handedness (upper right) and gender (lower left)—unless this was a particularly unusual class! We would expect that right-handed students should outnumber lefties substantially. (Roughly 10% to 15% of the population as a whole is left-handed.)

1.32. Sketches will vary. The distribution of coin years would be left-skewed because newer coins are more common than older coins.

1.33. A stemplot or a histogram is appropriate for displaying the distribution. We see that the data are skewed to the right with center near 30 or 40 thousand barrels. At least the top two, and arguably the top three, observations are outliers; apart from these, the numbers are spread from 0 to 110 thousand barrels.

```
0 | 00001111111111
0 | 22222223333333333333
0 | 44444445555555
0 | 6666667
0 | 8899
1 | 01
1 |
1 | 5
1 |
1 | 9
2 | 0
```

1.34. The stemplot gives more information than a histogram (since all the original numbers can be read off the stemplot), but both give the same impression. The distribution is roughly symmetric with one value (4.88) that is somewhat low. The center of the distribution is between 5.4 and 5.5 (the median is 5.46, the mean is 5.448).

```
48 | 8
49 |
50 | 7
51 | 0
52 | 6799
53 | 04469
54 | 2467
55 | 03578
56 | 12358
57 | 59
58 | 5
```

1.35. (a) Not only are most responses multiples of 10; many are multiples of 30 and 60. Most people will "round" their answers when asked to give an estimate like this; in fact, the most striking answers are ones such as 115, 170, or 230. The students who claimed 360 minutes (6 hours) and 300 minutes (5 hours) may have been exaggerating. (Some students might also "consider

Women		Men
	0	033334
96	0	66679999
22222221	1	2222222
888888888875555	1	558
4440	2	00344
	2	
	3	0
6	3	

suspicious" the student who claimed to study 0 minutes per night. As a teacher, I can easily believe that such students exist.) **(b)** The stemplots suggest that women (claim to) study more than men. The approximate centers are 175 minutes for women and 120 minutes for men.

1.36. A stemplot is shown; a histogram would also be appropriate. The distribution is clearly right-skewed, centered near 100 days, and spread from 43 to 598 days. The split stems emphasize the skewness by showing the gaps. Some students might consider some of the highest numbers to be outliers.

```
0 | 44
0 | 555555667778888888888889999999
1 | 00000000000111222223333444
1 | 56777899
2 | 1144
2 |
3 | 2
3 | 8
4 | 0
4 |
5 | 12
5 | 9
```

1.37. (a) There are four variables: GPA, IQ, and self-concept are quantitative, while gender is categorical. (OBS is not a variable, since it is not really a "characteristic" of a student.) **(b)** Below. **(c)** The distribution is skewed to the left, with center (median) around 7.8. GPAs are spread from 0.5 to 10.8, with only 15 below 6. **(d)** There is more variability among the boys; in fact, there seems to be a subset of boys with GPAs from 0.5 to 4.9. Ignoring that group, the two distributions have similar shapes.

	Female		Male
0	5	0	5
1	8	1	8
2	4	2	4
3	4689	4 / 3	689
4	0679	7 / 4	069
5	1259	952 / 5	1
6	0112249	4210 / 6	129
7	22333556666666788899	98866533 / 7	223566666789
8	0000222223347899	997320 / 8	0002222348
9	002223344556668	65300 / 9	2223445668
10	01678	710 / 10	68

1.38. Stemplot at right, with split stems. The distribution is fairly symmetric—perhaps slightly left-skewed—with center around 110 (clearly above 100). IQs range from the low 70s to the high 130s, with a "gap" in the low 80s.

7	24
7	79
8	
8	69
9	0133
9	6778
10	0022333344
10	555666777789
11	00001111222233334444
11	55688999
12	003344
12	677888
13	02
13	6

1.39. Stemplot at right, with split stems. The distribution is skewed to the left, with center around 59.5. Most self-concept scores are between 35 and 73, with a few below that, and one high score of 80 (but not really high enough to be an outlier).

2	01
2	8
3	0
3	5679
4	02344
4	6799
5	1111223344444
5	556668899
6	00001233344444
6	55666677777899
7	0000111223
7	
8	0

1.40. The time plot on the right shows that women's times decreased quite rapidly from 1972 until the mid-1980s. Since that time, they have been fairly consistent: All times since 1986 are between 141 and 147 minutes.

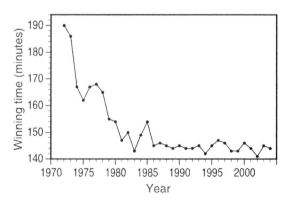

1.41. The five-number summary is

$4123 $15,717 $20,072 $27,957.5 $29,875.

This and the boxplot on the right do not reveal the three groups of schools that are visible in histogram. See also the solution to Exercise 1.21.

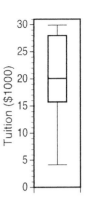

1.42. (a) The five-number summary is

$\text{Min} = 5.7\%$, $Q_1 = 11.7\%$, $M = 12.75\%$, $Q_3 = 13.5\%$, $\text{Max} = 17.6\%$.

(b) The *IQR* is $13.5\% - 11.7\% = 1.8\%$, so outliers are those numbers below $Q_1 - 2.7\% = 9\%$ and above $Q_3 + 2.7\% = 16.2\%$. Alaska and Florida are outliers, along with whichever state has 8.5%.

1.43. (a) The five-number summary (in 1999 dollars) is

$\text{Min} = 0$, $Q_1 = 2.14$, $M = 10.64$, $Q_3 = 40.96$, $\text{Max} = 88.6$.

The evidence for the skew is in the large gaps between the higher numbers; that is, the differences $Q_3 - M$ and $\text{Max} - Q_3$ are large compared to $Q_1 - \text{Min}$ and $M - Q_1$. **(b)** The *IQR* is $Q_3 - Q_1 = 38.82$, so outliers would be less than -56.09 or greater than 99.19. **(c)** The mean is 21.95 (1999 dollars), much greater than the median 10.64. The mean is pulled in the direction of the skew—in this case, to the right, making it larger.

1.44. See also the solution to Exercise 1.24. **(a)** The five-number summary (in units of metric tons per person) is

$\text{Min} = 0$, $Q_1 = 0.75$, $M = 3.2$, $Q_3 = 7.8$, $\text{Max} = 19.9$.

The evidence for the skew is in the large gaps between the higher numbers; that is, the differences $Q_3 - M$ and $\text{Max} - Q_3$ are large compared to $Q_1 - \text{Min}$ and $M - Q_1$. **(b)** The *IQR* is $Q_3 - Q_1 = 7.05$, so outliers would be less than -9.825 or greater than 18.375. According to this rule, only the U.S. qualifies as an outlier, but Canada and Australia seem high enough to also include them.

```
0 | 0000000000000011111
0 | 222233333
0 | 445
0 | 6677
0 | 888999
1 | 001
1 |
1 |
1 | 67
1 | 9
```

1.45. The distribution of household net worth would almost surely be strongly skewed to the right, perhaps more so for young households: A few would have earned (or inherited) substantial assets, but most have not had time to accumulate very much wealth. This strong skew pulls the mean to be higher than the median.

1.46. (a) $\bar{x} = 48.25$ and $M = 37.8$ thousand barrels of oil. The mean is made larger by the right skew. **(b)** The five-number summary (all measured in thousands of barrels) is:

$\text{Min} = 2$, $Q_1 = 21.505$, $M = 37.8$, $Q_3 = 60.1$, $\text{Max} = 204.9$.

The evidence for the skew is in the large gaps between the higher numbers; that is, the differences $Q_3 - M$ and $\text{Max} - Q_3$ are large compared to $Q_1 - \text{Min}$ and $M - Q_1$.

1.47. The total salary is $500,000, so the mean is $\bar{x} = \frac{\$500,000}{8} = \$62,500$. Seven of the eight employees (everyone but the owner) earned less than the mean. The median is $M = \$25,000$.

1.48. If three individuals earn $0, $0, and $20,000, the reported median is $20,000. If the two individuals with no income take jobs at $14,000 each, the median decreases to $14,000. The same thing can happen to the mean: In this example, the mean drops from $20,000 to $16,000.

1.49. The total salary is now $700,000, so the new mean is $\bar{x} = \frac{\$700,000}{8} = \$87,500$. The median is unchanged.

1.50. Details at right.

$$\bar{x} = \frac{11,200}{7} = 1600,$$

$$s^2 = \frac{214,872}{6} = 35,812, \text{ and}$$

$$s = \sqrt{35,812} \doteq 189.24.$$

x_i	$x_i - \bar{x}$	$(x_i - \bar{x})^2$
1792	192	36864
1666	66	4356
1362	−238	56644
1614	14	196
1460	−140	19600
1867	267	71289
1439	−161	25921
11200	0	214872

1.51. The quote describes a distribution with a strong right skew: Lots of years with no losses to hurricane ($0), but very high numbers when they do occur. For example, if there is one hurricane in a ten-year period, the "average annual loss" for that period would be $100,000, but that does not adequately represent the cost for the year of the hurricane. Means are not the appropriate measure of center for skewed distributions.

1.52. **(a)** $\bar{x}$ and s are appropriate for symmetric distributions with no outliers. **(b)** Both high numbers are flagged as outliers. For women, $IQR = 60$, so the upper $1.5 \times IQR$ limit is 300 minutes. For men, $IQR = 90$, so the upper $1.5 \times IQR$ limit is 285 minutes. The table on the right shows the effect of removing these outliers.

	Women		Men	
	$\bar{x}$	s	$\bar{x}$	s
Before	165.2	56.5	117.2	74.2
After	158.4	43.7	110.9	66.9

1.53. **(a)** & **(b)** See the table on the right. In both cases, the mean and median are quite similar.

	$\bar{x}$	s	M
pH	5.4256	0.5379	5.44
Density	5.4479	0.2209	5.46

1.54. See also the solution to Exercise 1.37. **(a)** The mean of
this distribution appears to be higher than 100. (There is
no substantial difference between the standard deviations.)

	$\bar{x}$	s	M
IQ	108.9	13.17	110
GPA	7.447	(2.1)	7.829

(b) The mean and median are quite similar; the mean is slightly smaller due to the slight left
skew of the data. **(c)** In addition to the mean and median, the standard deviation is shown for
reference (the exercise did not ask for it).

   Note: *Students may be somewhat puzzled by the statement in (b) that the median is
"close to the mean" (when they differ by 1.1), followed by (c) where they "differ a bit"
(when $M - \bar{x} = 0.382$). It may be useful to emphasize that we judge the size of such
differences relative to the spread of the distribution. For example, we can note that $\frac{1.1}{13.17} \doteq$
0.08 for (b), and $\frac{0.382}{2.1} \doteq 0.18$ for (c).*

1.55. With only two observations, the mean and median are always equal because the median
is halfway between the middle two (in this case, the only two) numbers.

1.56. (a) The mean (green arrow) moves along with the moving point (in fact, it moves in the
same direction as the moving point, at one-third the speed). At the same time, as long as
the moving point remains to the right of the other two, the median (red arrow) points to the
middle point (the right-most nonmoving point). **(b)** The mean follows the moving point as
before. When the moving point passes the right-most fixed point, the median slides along
with it until the moving point passes the leftmost fixed point, then the median stays there.

1.57. (a) There are several different answers, depending on the configuration of the first five
points. *Most students* will likely assume that the first five points should be distinct (no
repeats), in which case the sixth point *must* be placed at the median. This is because the
median of 5 (sorted) points is the third, while the median of 6 points is the average of the
third and fourth. If these are to be the same, the third and fourth points of the set of 6 must
both equal the third point of the set of 5.

   The diagram below illustrates all of the possibilities; in each case, the arrow shows the
location of the median of the initial five points, and the shaded region (or dot) on the line
indicates where the sixth point can be placed without changing the median. Notice that
there are four cases where the median does not change regardless of the location of the
sixth point. (The points need not be equally spaced; these diagrams were drawn that way for
convenience.)

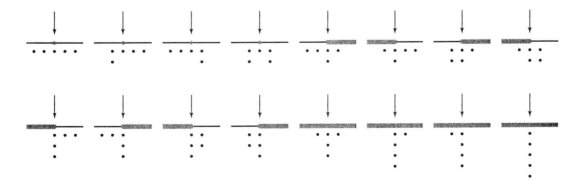

(b) Regardless of the configuration of the first 5 points, if the sixth point is added so as to leave the median unchanged, then in that (sorted) set of 6, the third and fourth points must be equal. One of these 2 points will be the middle (fourth) point of the (sorted) set of 7, no matter where the seventh point is placed.

Note: *If you have a student who illustrates all possible cases above, then it is likely that the student either (1) obtained a copy of this solutions manual, (2) should consider a career in writing solutions manuals, (3) has too much time on his or her hands, or (4) both 2 and 3 (and perhaps 1) are true.*

1.58. The five-number summaries (all in millimeters) are

	Min	Q_1	M	Q_3	Max
bihai	46.34	46.71	47.12	48.245	50.26
red	37.40	38.07	39.16	41.69	43.09
yellow	34.57	35.45	36.11	36.82	38.13

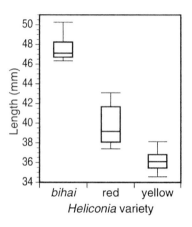

H. bihai is clearly the tallest variety—the shortest *bihai* was over 3 mm taller than the tallest red. Red is generally taller than yellow, with a few exceptions. Another noteworthy fact: The red variety is more variable than either of the other varieties.

1.59. (a) The means and standard deviations (all in millimeters) are

Variety	$\bar{x}$	s
bihai	47.5975	1.2129
red	39.7113	1.7988
yellow	36.1800	0.9753

```
bihai              red               yellow
46 | 3466789       37 | 4789         34 | 56
47 | 114           38 | 0012278      35 | 146
48 | 0133          39 | 167          36 | 0015678
49 |               40 | 56           37 | 01
50 | 12            41 | 4699         38 | 1
                   42 | 01
                   43 | 0
```

(b) Bihai and red appear to be right-skewed (although it is difficult to tell with such small samples). Skewness would make these distributions unsuitable for $\bar{x}$ and s.

1.60. The means and standard deviations (in units of trees) are:

Group	$\bar{x}$	s
1	23.7500	5.06548
2	14.0833	4.98102
3	15.7778	5.76146

```
Never logged       1 year ago        8 years ago
0 |                0 | 2             0 | 4
0 |                0 | 9             0 |
1 |                1 | 2244          1 | 22
1 | 699            1 | 57789         1 | 5889
2 | 0124           2 | 0             2 | 22
2 | 7789           2 |               2 |
3 | 3              3 |               3 |
```

The means, along with the stemplots on the right, appear to suggest that logging reduces the number of trees per plot and that recovery is slow (the 1-year-after and 8-years-after means and stemplots are similar). Use of $\bar{x}$ and s should be acceptable, as the distributions show no extreme outliers or strong skewness (given the small sample sizes).

1.61. Either stemplots or histograms could be used to display the distributions, although with four sets of 200 subjects each, histograms are simpler. All four distributions are symmetric with no outliers, so means and standard deviations are appropriate; they are in

Group	$\bar{x}$	s
Sedentary females	148.00	16.27
Sedentary males	130.00	17.10
Female runners	115.99	15.97
Male runners	103.97	12.50

the table on the right (in units of bpm). The average heart rate for runners is about 30 bpm less than the average sedentary rate.

Note: *Students might also observe that women generally have higher heart rates than men in the same activity-level group, but that is not an effect of running.*

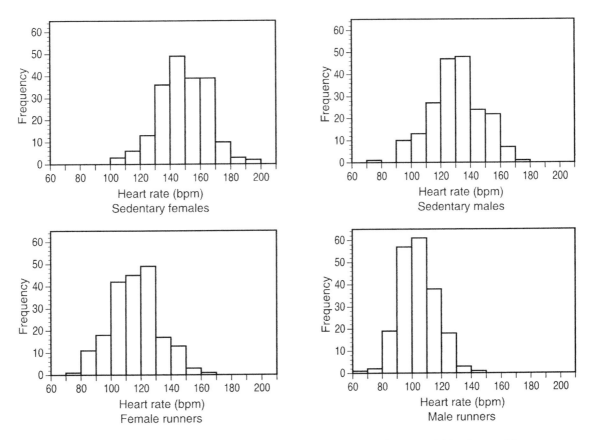

1.62. Note that estimates for (a) and (b) will vary. **(a)** The median would be in position $\frac{14,959+1}{2} = 7480$ in the list; from the boxplot, we estimate it to be about $45,000. **(b)** The quartiles would be in positions 3740 and 11,220, and we estimate their values to be about $32,000 and $65,000. **(c)** Omitting these observations should have *no* effect on the median and quartiles. (The quartiles are computed from the entire set of data; the extreme 5% are omitted only in locating the ends of the lines for the boxplot.)

Note: *The positions of the quartiles were found according to the text's method; that is, these are the locations of the medians of the first and second halves of the list. Students might instead compute $0.25 \times 14,959$ and $0.75 \times 14,959$ to obtain the answers 3739.75 and 11,219.25.*

1.63. The 5th and 95th percentiles would be approximately in positions 748 and 14,211. The "whiskers" on the box extend to approximately $13,000 and $137,000. (Estimates may vary.)

1.64. All five income distributions are skewed to the right. As highest education level rises, the median, quartiles, and extremes rise—that is, all five points on the boxplot increase. Additionally, the width of the box (the *IQR*) and the distance from one extreme to the other (the difference between the 5th and 95th percentiles) also increase, meaning that the distributions become more and more spread out.

1.65. The minimum and maximum are easily determined to be 1 and 12 letters, and the quartiles and median can be found by adding up the bar heights. For example, the first two bars have total height about 22% or 23% (less than 25%); adding the third bar brings the total to about 45%, so Q_1 must equal 3 letters. Continuing this way, we find that the five-number summary, in units of letters, is

$$\text{Min} = 1, \quad Q_1 = 3, \quad M = 4, \quad Q_3 = 5, \quad \text{Max} = 12.$$

1.66. Because the mean is to be 7, the five numbers must add to 35. Also, the third number (in order from smallest to largest) must be 10 because that is the median. Beyond that, there is some freedom in how the numbers are chosen.

   Note: *It is likely that many students will interpret "positive numbers" as meaning positive integers only, which leads to eight possible solutions, shown below.*

1 1 10 10 13	1 1 10 11 12	1 2 10 10 12	1 2 10 11 11
1 3 10 10 11	1 4 10 10 10	2 2 10 10 11	2 3 10 10 10

1.67. The simplest approach is to take (at least) six numbers—say, a, b, c, d, e, f in increasing order. For this set, $Q_3 = e$; we can cause the mean to be larger than e by simply choosing f to be *much* larger than e. For example, if all numbers are nonnegative, $f > 5e$ would accomplish the goal because then $\bar{x} = (a+b+c+d+e+f)/6 > (e+f)/6 > (e+5e)/6 = e$.

1.68. The algebra might be a bit of a stretch for some students:

$$
\begin{array}{ll}
 & (x_1 - \bar{x}) + \quad (x_2 - \bar{x}) + \quad (x_3 - \bar{x}) + \cdots + (x_{n-1} - \bar{x}) + \quad (x_n - \bar{x}) \\
= & x_1 - \bar{x} + \quad x_2 - \bar{x} + \quad x_3 - \bar{x} + \cdots + x_{n-1} - \bar{x} + \quad x_n - \bar{x} \\
 & \hspace{8cm} \textit{(drop all the parentheses)} \\
= & x_1 + x_2 + x_3 + \cdots + x_{n-1} + x_n \qquad -\bar{x} - \bar{x} - \bar{x} - \cdots - \bar{x} - \bar{x} \\
 & \hspace{8cm} \textit{(rearrange the terms)} \\
= & x_1 + x_2 + x_3 + \cdots + x_{n-1} + x_n \qquad -n \cdot \bar{x}
\end{array}
$$

Next simply observe that $n \cdot \bar{x} = x_1 + x_2 + x_3 + \cdots + x_{n-1} + x_n$.

1.69. (a) One possible answer is 1, 1, 1, 1. **(b)** 0, 0, 10, 10. **(c)** For (a), any set of four identical numbers will have $s = 0$. For (b), the answer is unique; here is a rough description of why. We want to maximize the "spread-out"-ness of the numbers (which is what standard deviation measures), so 0 and 10 seem to be reasonable choices based on that idea. We also want to make each individual squared deviation—$(x_1 - \bar{x})^2$, $(x_2 - \bar{x})^2$, $(x_3 - \bar{x})^2$, and

$(x_4 - \bar{x})^2$—as large as possible. If we choose 0, 10, 10, 10—or 10, 0, 0, 0—we make the first squared deviation 7.5^2, but the other three are only 2.5^2. Our best choice is two at each extreme, which makes all four squared deviations equal to 5^2.

1.70. Answers will vary. Typical calculators will carry only about 12 to 15 digits; for example, a TI-83 fails (gives $s = 0$) for 13-digit numbers. *Excel* (at least the version I checked) gives $s = 0$ for nine-digit numbers. The version of Minitab used to prepare these answers fails at 100,000,001 (nine digits).

1.71. See Exercise 1.36 for the stemplot, which shows the expected right skew. The five-number summary is a good choice: Min $= 43$, $Q_1 = 82.5$, $M = 102.5$, $Q_3 = 151.5$, Max $= 598$ days. Half the guinea pigs lived less than 102.5 days; typical lifetimes were 82.5 to 151.5 days. The longest-lived guinea pig died just short of 600 days, while one guinea pig lived only 43 days.

1.72. Convert from kilograms to pounds by multiplying by 2.2: $\bar{x} = (2.39 \text{ kg})(2.2 \text{ lb/kg}) = 5.26$ lb and $s = (1.14 \text{ kg})(2.2 \text{ lb/kg}) = 2.51$ lb.

1.73. The table on the right reproduces the means and standard deviations from the solution to Exercise 1.59, and shows those values expressed in inches. For each conversion, multiply by $39.37/1000 = 0.03937$ (or divide by 25.4—an inch is defined as 25.4 millimeters). For example, for the *bihai* variety,

	(in mm)		(in inches)	
Variety	$\bar{x}$	s	$\bar{x}$	s
bihai	47.5975	1.2129	1.874	0.04775
red	39.7113	1.7988	1.563	0.07082
yellow	36.1800	0.9753	1.424	0.03840

$\bar{x} = (47.5975 \text{ mm})(0.03937 \text{ in/mm}) = (47.5975 \text{ mm}) \div (25.4 \text{ mm/in}) = 1.874$ in.

1.74. (a) $\bar{x} = 5.4479$ and $s = 0.2209$. **(b)** The first measurement corresponds to $5.50 \times 62.43 = 343.365$ pounds per cubic foot. To find $\bar{x}_{\text{new}}$ and s_{new}, we similarly multiply by 62.43: $\bar{x}_{\text{new}} \doteq 340.11$ and $s_{\text{new}} \doteq 13.79$.

  Note: *The conversion from cm to feet is included in the multiplication by 62.43; the step-by-step process of this conversion looks like this:*

$$(1 \text{ g/cm}^3)(0.001 \text{ kg/g})(2.2046 \text{ lb/kg})(30.48^3 \text{ cm}^3/\text{ft}^3) = 62.43 \text{ lb/ft}^3$$

1.75. Multiplying 72 by 0.2, 0.4, 0.6, and 0.8, we find that the quintiles are located at positions 14.4, 28.8, 43.2, and 57.6. The 14th, 29th, 43rd, and 58th numbers in the list are 80, 99, 114, and 178 days.

1.76. Variance is changed by a factor of $2.54^2 = 6.4516$; generally, for a transformation $x_{\text{new}} = a + bx$, the new variance is b^2 times the old variance.

1.77. There are 72 survival times, so to find the 10% trimmed mean, remove the highest and lowest 7 values (leaving 58). Remove the highest and lowest 14 values (leaving 44) for the 20% trimmed mean.

  The mean and median for the full data set are $\bar{x} = 141.8$ and $M = 102.5$. The 10% trimmed mean is $\bar{x}^* = 118.16$, and the 20% trimmed mean is $\bar{x}^{**} = 111.68$. Since the distribution is right-skewed, removing the extremes lowers the mean.

1.78. Sketches will vary.

1.79. Sketches will vary, but should be some variation on the one shown here: The peak at 0 should be "tall and skinny," while near 1, the curve should be "short and fat."

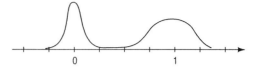

1.80. (a) The curve forms a 1 × 1 square, which has area 1.
(b) $P(X > 0.75) = 0.25$.
(c) $P(0.25 < X < 0.75) = 0.5$.

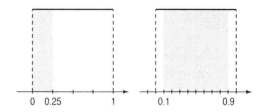

1.81. (a) The height should be $\frac{1}{2}$, since the area under the curve must be 1. The density curve is at right. **(b)** $P(X \le 1) = \frac{1}{2}$. **(c)** $P(0.5 < X < 1.3) = 0.4$.

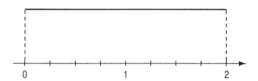

1.82. The mean and median both equal 0.5; the quartiles are $Q_1 = 0.25$ and $Q_3 = 0.75$.

1.83. (a) Mean is C, median is B (the right skew pulls the mean to the right). **(b)** Mean A, median A. **(c)** Mean A, median B (the left skew pulls the mean to the left).

1.84. Hint: Draw the curve first, then place the numbers below it. Students may at first make mistakes like drawing a half-circle instead of the correct "bell-shaped" curve, or being careless about locating the standard deviation.

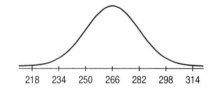

1.85. (a) The applet shows an area of 0.6826 between −1.000 and 1.000, while the 68–95–99.7 rule rounds this to 0.68. **(b)** Between −2.000 and 2.000, the applet reports 0.9544 (compared to the rounded 0.95 from the 68–95–99.7 rule). Between −3.000 and 3.000, the applet reports 0.9974 (compared to the rounded 0.997).

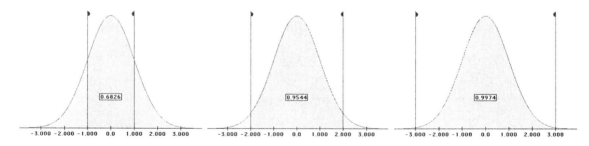

1.86. See the sketch of the curve in the solution to Exercise 1.84. **(a)** The middle 95% fall within two standard deviations of the mean: $266 \pm 2(16)$, or 234 to 298 days. **(b)** The shortest 2.5% of pregnancies are shorter than 234 days (more than two standard deviations below the mean).

1.87. (a) 99.7% of horse pregnancies fall within three standard deviations of the mean: $336 \pm 3(3)$, or 327 to 325 days. (b) About 16% are longer than 339 days, since 339 days or more corresponds to at least one standard deviation above the mean.

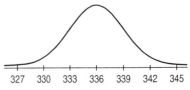

    Note: *This exercise did not ask for a sketch of the normal curve, but students should be encouraged to make such sketches anyway.*

1.88. (a) About 50% of samples give values above the mean (0.4). Since 0.43 is two standard deviations above the mean, about 2.5% of sample values are above 0.43. (b) 0.37 to 0.43—that is, $0.4 \pm 2(0.015)$.

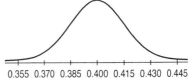

    Note: *As the text models, it is probably best to use decimals for these proportions rather than percentages (0.37 instead of 37%) to lessen the confusion with, for example, 95%.*

1.89. The z-scores are $z_w = \frac{72-64}{2.7} \doteq 2.96$ for women and $z_m = \frac{72-69.3}{2.8} \doteq 0.96$ for men. The z-scores tell us that six feet is quite tall for a woman, but not at all extraordinary for a man.

1.90. Because the quartiles of any distribution have 50% of observations between them, we seek to place the flags so that the reported area is 0.5. The closest the applet gets is an area of 0.5034, between -0.680 and 0.680. Thus, the quartiles of any normal distribution are about 0.68 standard deviations above and below the mean.

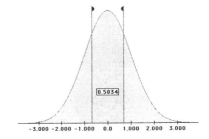

    Note: *Table A places the quartiles at about ± 0.67; other statistical software gives ± 0.6745.*

1.91. The mean and standard deviation are $\bar{x} = 5.4256$ and $s = 0.5379$. About 67.62% $(71/105 \doteq 0.6476)$ of the pH measurements are in the range $\bar{x} \pm s = 4.89$ to 5.96. About 95.24% $(100/105)$ are in the range $\bar{x} \pm 2s = 4.35$ to 6.50. All (100%) are in the range $\bar{x} \pm 3s = 3.81$ to 7.04.

1.92. (a) $Z < 1.85$: 0.9678. (b) $Z > 1.85$: 0.0322. (c) $Z > -0.66$: 0.7454. (d) $-0.66 < Z < 1.85$: $0.9678 - 0.2546 = 0.7132$.

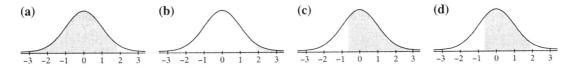

1.93. (a) $Z \leq -2$: 0.0228. (b) $Z \geq -2$: 0.9772. (c) $Z > 1.67$: 0.0475. (d) $-2 < Z < 1.67$: $0.9772 - 0.0475 = 0.9297$.

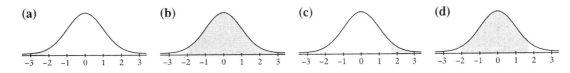

1.94. (a) 20% of the observations fall below −0.8416. (This is the 20th percentile of the standard normal distribution). **(b)** 30% of the observations fall above 0.5244 (the 70th percentile of the standard normal distribution).

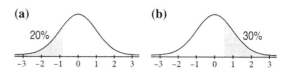

1.95. (a) $z = 0.8416$ has cumulative proportion 0.8 (that is, 0.8416 is the 80th percentile of the standard normal distribution). **(b)** If $z = 0.1257$, then $Z > z$ has proportion 0.45 (0.1257 is the 55th percentile).

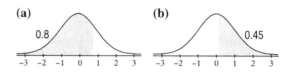

1.96. 70 is two standard deviations below the mean (that is, it has standard score $z = -2$), so about 2.5% (half of the outer 5%) of adults would have WAIS scores below 70.

1.97. 130 is two standard deviations above the mean (that is, it has standard score $z = 2$), so about 2.5% of adults would score at least 130.

1.98. Tonya's score standardizes to $z = \frac{1318-1026}{209} \doteq 1.3971$, while Jermaine's score corresponds to $z = \frac{27-20.8}{4.8} \doteq 1.2917$. Tonya's score is higher.

1.99. Jacob's score standardizes to $z = \frac{16-20.8}{4.8} = -1$, while Emily's score corresponds to $z = \frac{670-1026}{209} \doteq -1.7033$. Jacob's score is higher.

1.100. Jose's score standardizes to $z = \frac{1287-1026}{209} \doteq 1.2488$, so an equivalent ACT score is $20.8 + 1.2488 \times 4.8 \doteq 26.8$. (Of course, ACT scores are reported as whole numbers, so this would presumably be a score of 27.)

1.101. Maria's score standardizes to $z = \frac{28-20.8}{4.8} = 1.5$, so an equivalent SAT score is $1026 + 1.5 \times 209 = 1339.5$ (presumably reported as either 1339 or 1340.)

1.102. Tonya's score standardizes to $z = \frac{1318-1026}{209} \doteq 1.3971$; this is the 92nd percentile.

1.103. Jacob's score standardizes to $z = \frac{16-20.8}{4.8} = -1$; this is the 16th percentile.

1.104. A score of 1600 standardizes to $z = \frac{1600-1026}{209} \doteq 2.7368$. 99.7% of standard scores are below this level, so about 0.3% are above this level (and are therefore reported as 1600).

1.105. A score of 36 standardizes to $z = \frac{36-20.8}{4.8} \doteq 3.1667$. About 99.9% of standard scores are below this level, so about 0.1% are above this level (and are therefore reported as 36).

1.106. The top 10% corresponds to a standard score of $z = 1.2816$, which in turn corresponds to a score of $1026 + 1.2816 \times 209 \doteq 1294$ on the SAT.

1.107. The top 20% corresponds to a standard score of $z = 0.8416$, which in turn corresponds to a score of $20.8 + 0.8416 \times 4.8 \doteq 24.8$ (or 25) on the ACT.

1.108. The quartiles of a normal distribution are ± 0.6745 standard deviations from the mean, so for ACT scores, they are $20.8 \pm 0.6745 \times 4.8 = 17.6$ to 24.0.

1.109. The quintiles of the SAT score distribution are $1026 - 0.8416 \times 209 = 850$, $1026 - 0.2533 \times 209 = 973$, $1026 + 0.2533 \times 209 = 1079$, and $1026 + 0.8416 \times 209 = 1202$.

1.110. (a) 240 mg/dl standardizes to $z = \frac{240-185}{39} \doteq 1.41$, which has cumulative probability 0.9207, so about 8% of young women have levels over 240 mg/dl. (b) 200 mg/dl standardizes to $z = \frac{200-185}{39} \doteq 0.385$, which has cumulative probability 0.6499, so about 27% of young women have levels between 200 and 240 mg/dl.

1.111. 200 and 240 mg/dl standardize to $z = \frac{200-222}{37} \doteq -0.5946$ (cumulative probability 0.2761) and $z = \frac{240-222}{37} \doteq 0.4865$ (cumulative probability 0.6867). Therefore, about 31% of middle-aged men have levels over 240 mg/dl, and about 41% have levels between 200 and 240 mg/dl.

1.112. (a) About 0.6% of healthy young adults have osteoporosis (the cumulative probability below a standard score of -2.5 is 0.0062). (b) About 31% of this population of older women has osteoporosis: The BMD level which is 2.5 standard deviations below the young adult mean would standardize to -0.5 for these older women, and the cumulative probability for this standard score is 0.3085.

1.113. (a) About 3.3% of men score 750 or better: Among men, a score of 750 corresponds to standard score $z = \frac{750-537}{116} \doteq 1.8362$, for which the cumulative probability is 0.9668.
(b) About 1.2% of women score 750 or better: Among women, a score of 750 corresponds to standard score $z = \frac{750-503}{110} \doteq 2.2455$, for which the cumulative probability is 0.9876.

1.114. (a) The middle 95% of yearly returns is $8.3\% \pm 2(20.3\%) = -32.3\%$ to 48.9%. (b) A return of 0% corresponds to a standard score of $z = \frac{0-8.3}{20.3} \doteq -0.4089$, so the market is down in about 34% of all years. (c) A return of 25% corresponds to a standard score of $z = \frac{25-8.3}{20.3} \doteq 0.8227$, so the index gains at least 25% in about 20.5% of all years.

1.115. (a) About 5.2%: $x < 240$ corresponds to $z < -1.625$. Table A gives 5.16% for -1.63 and 5.26% for -1.62. Software (or averaging the two table values) gives 5.21%. (b) About 54.7%: $240 < x < 270$ corresponds to $-1.625 < z < 0.25$. The area to the left of 0.25 is 0.5987; subtracting the answer from part (a) leaves about 54.7%. (c) About 279 days or longer: Searching Table A for 0.80 leads to $z > 0.84$, which corresponds to $x > 266 + 0.84(16) = 279.44$. (Using the software value $z > 0.8416$ gives $x > 279.47$.)

1.116. (a) The quartiles for a standard normal distribution are ± 0.6745. (b) For a $N(\mu, \sigma)$ distribution, $Q_1 = \mu - 0.6745\sigma$ and $Q_3 = \mu + 0.6745\sigma$. (c) For human pregnancies, $Q_1 = 266 - 0.6745 \times 16 \doteq 255.2$ and $Q_3 = 266 + 0.67455 \times 16 \doteq 276.8$ days.

1.117. (a) As the quartiles for a standard normal distribution are ± 0.6745, we have $IQR = 1.3490$. (b) $c = 1.3490$: For a $N(\mu, \sigma)$ distribution, the quartiles are $Q_1 = \mu - 0.6745\sigma$ and $Q_3 = \mu + 0.6745\sigma$.

1.118. In the previous two exercises, we found that for a $N(\mu, \sigma)$ distribution, $Q_1 = \mu - 0.6745\sigma$, $Q_3 = \mu + 0.6745\sigma$, and $IQR = 1.3490\sigma$. Therefore, $1.5 \times IQR = 2.0235\sigma$, and the suspected outliers are below $Q_1 - 1.5 \times IQR = \mu - 2.698\sigma$, and above $Q_3 + 1.5 \times IQR = \mu + 2.698\sigma$. The percentage outside of this range is $2 \times 0.0035 = 0.70\%$.

1.119. The plot is nearly linear. Because heart rate is measured in whole numbers, there is a slight "step" appearance to the graph.

1.120. The shape of the quantile plot suggests that the data are right-skewed (as was observed in Exercises 1.24 and 1.44). This can be seen in the flat section in the lower left—these numbers were less spread out than they should be for normal data—and the three apparent outliers (the U.S., Canada, and Australia) that deviate from the line in the upper right; these were much larger than they would be for a normal distribution.

1.121. The plot is reasonably close to a line, apart from the stair-step appearance, presumably due to limited accuracy of the measuring instrument.

1.122. **(a)** is the graph of (3) the highway gas mileages: Aside from the Insight, these numbers are reasonably normal, and in this graph, the points fall close to a line aside from one high outlier. **(b)** is the graph of (1) the IQ data: This distribution was the most normal of the four, and this graph is almost a perfect line. **(c)** is the graph of (4) the call length data: The stemplot is right-skewed, with several high outliers (the outliers were not shown in the stemplot; rather they were listed after the plot). The skewness is visible in the flat section of this graph. **(d)** is the graph of (2) the tuition and fees data: The histogram showed three clusters, which are visible in the graph. The low and high clusters had peaks at their extremes; these show up in the flat sections in the lower left and upper right of the graph.

   Note: *Matching (a) and (c) is probably the most difficult decision. Aside from the reasons given above, students might also observe that graph (a) shows considerably fewer points than (c), which is consistent with the 21 two-seater cars in data set (3) versus the 80 call lengths for (4).*

1.123. See also the solution to Exercise 1.34. The plot suggests no major deviations from normality, although the three lowest measurements do not quite fall in line with the other points.

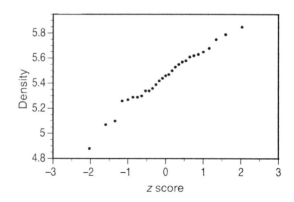

1.124. (a) All three quantile plots are below; the yellow variety is the nearest to a straight line. (b) The other two distributions are both slightly right-skewed (the lower-left portion of the graph is somewhat flat); additionally, the *bihai* variety appears to have a couple of high outliers.

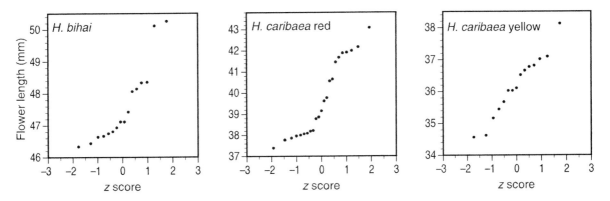

1.125. See also the solution to Exercise 1.60. The first plot (for never-logged areas) is nearly linear. The other two each show a low value, perhaps suggesting a slight skew to the left.

1.126. A stemplot from one sample is shown. Histograms will vary slightly but should suggest a bell curve. The normal probability plot shows something fairly close to a line but illustrates that, even for actual normal data, the tails may deviate slightly from a line.

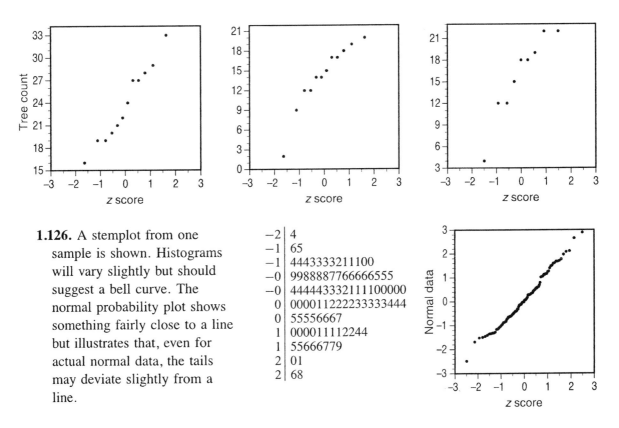

```
-2 | 4
-1 | 65
-1 | 4443333211100
-0 | 9988887766666555
-0 | 444443332111100000
 0 | 000011222233333444
 0 | 55556667
 1 | 000011112244
 1 | 55666779
 2 | 01
 2 | 68
```

1.127. A stemplot from one sample is shown. Histograms will vary slightly but should suggest the density curve of Figure 1.35 (but with more variation than students might expect). The normal quantile plot shows that, compared to a normal distribution, the uniform distribution does not extend as low or as high (not surprising, since all observations are between 0 and 1).

0	001245778
1	11223344666678999
2	56667888999
3	0112233345699
4	4556799
5	00233666899
6	00123589
7	002256688
8	13345557899
9	2446

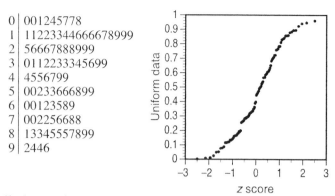

1.128. **(a)** & **(b)** Answers will vary. Definitions might be as simple as "free time," or "time spent doing something other than studying." For (b), it might be good to encourage students to discuss practical difficulties; for example, if we ask Sally to keep a log of her activities, the time she spends filling it out presumably reduces her available "leisure time."

1.129. Shown is a stemplot; a histogram should look similar to this. This distribution is relatively symmetric apart from one high outlier. Because of the outlier, the five-number summary is preferred:

22 23.735 24.31 24.845 28.55

(all in hours). Alternatively, the mean and standard deviation are $\bar{x} = 24.339$ and $s = 0.9239$ hours.

22	013
22	7899
23	000011222233344444
23	5556666666777777788888888999
24	000000111111122222222223333333333444444
24	5555555666666666677777778888888999999
25	00001111233344
25	56666889
26	2
26	56
27	2
27	
28	
28	5

1.130. Gender and automobile preference are categorical; age and household income are quantitative.

1.131. Many—but less than half—of these students were 19.

Note: *In fact, there had to be* at least *nine students who were 19, and no more than 111—the largest number only if the next youngest student was 43. If you have some particularly bright students, you might challenge them to prove this.*

1.132. Either a bar graph or a pie chart could be used. The given numbers sum to 58.3, so the "Other" category presumably includes the remaining 19.1 million subscribers.

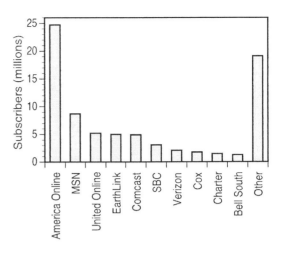

1.133. Women's weights are skewed to the right: This makes the mean higher than the median, and it is also revealed in the differences $M - Q_1 = 14.9$ pounds and $Q_3 - M = 24.1$ pounds.

1.134. **(a)** For car makes (a categorical variable), use either a bar graph or pie chart. For car age (a quantitative variable), use a histogram, stemplot, or boxplot. **(b)** Study time is quantitative, so use a histogram, stemplot, or boxplot. To show change over time, use a time plot (average hours studied against time). **(c)** Use a bar graph or pie chart to show radio station preferences. **(d)** Use a normal quantile plot to see whether the measurements follow a normal distribution.

1.135. **(a)** About 20% of low-income and 33% of high-income households consisted of two people. **(b)** The majority of low-income households, but only about 7% of high-income households, consist of one person. One-person households often have less income because they would include many young people who have no job, or have only recently started working. (Income generally increases with age.)

1.136. The counts given add to 6067, so the others received 626 spam messages. Either a bar graph or a pie chart would be appropriate. What students learn from this graph will vary; one observation might be that AA and BB (and perhaps some others) might need some advice on how to reduce the amount of spam they receive.

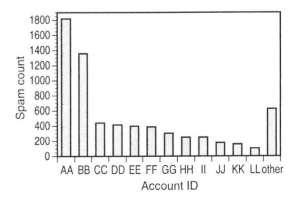

1.137. No, and no: It is easy to imagine examples of many different data sets with mean 0 and standard deviation 1—for example, $\{-1,0,1\}$ and $\{-2,0,0,0,0,0,0,0,2\}$.

Likewise, for any given five numbers $a \leq b \leq c \leq d \leq e$ (not all the same), we can create many data sets with that five number summary, simply by taking those five numbers and adding some additional numbers in between them, for example (in increasing order): 10, __, 20, __, __, 30, __, __, 40, __, 50. As long as the number in the first blank is between 10 and 20, and so on, the five-number summary will be 10, 20, 30, 40, 50.

1.138. In the first time plot, we see that numbers of eagle young begin to rise shortly after the ban in 1972. In the second time plot, the five highest DDE numbers occurred before 1972. (Note that the points in the second time plot have not been connected here; connecting the dots is confusing when there are multiple measurements in a year.)

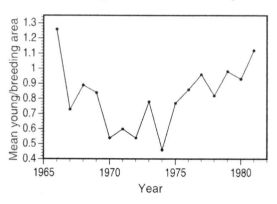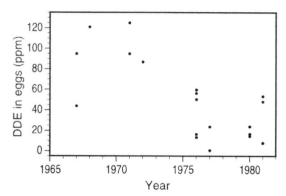

1.139. The time plot is shown below; because of the great detail in this plot, it is larger than other plots. Ruth's and McGwire's league-leading years are marked with different symbols. **(a)** During World War II (when many baseball players joined the military), the best home run numbers decline sharply and steadily. **(b)** Ruth seemed to set a new standard for other players; after his first league-leading year, he had ten seasons much higher than anything that had come before, and home run production has remained near that same level ever since (even the worst post-Ruth year—1945—had more home runs than the best pre-Ruth season). While some might argue that McGwire's numbers also raised the standard, the change is not nearly as striking, nor did McGwire maintain it for as long as Ruth did. (This is not necessarily a criticism of McGwire; it instead reflects that in baseball, as in many other endeavors, rates of improvement tend to decrease over time as we reach the limits of human ability.)

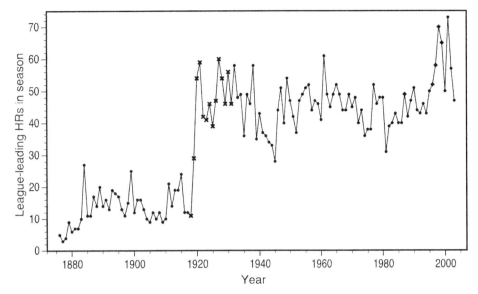

1.140. Bonds's mean changes from 36.56 to 34.41 home runs (a drop of 2.15), while his median changes from 35.5 to 34 home runs (a drop of 1.5). This illustrates that outliers affect the mean more than the median.

1	69
2	4
2	55
3	3344
3	77
4	02
4	5669
5	
5	
6	
6	
7	3

1.141. Recall the text's description of the effects of a linear transformation $x_{\text{new}} = a + bx$: The mean and standard deviation are each multiplied by b (technically, the standard deviation is multiplied by $|b|$, but this problem specifies that $b > 0$). Additionally, we add a to the (new) mean, but a does not affect the standard deviation. **(a)** The desired transformation is $x_{\text{new}} = -50 + 2x$; that is, $a = -50$ and $b = 2$. (We need $b = 2$ to double the standard deviation; as this also doubles the mean, we then subtract 50 to make the new mean 100.) **(b)** $x_{\text{new}} = -49.0909 + 1.8182x$; that is, $a = -49\frac{1}{11} \doteq -49.0909$ and $b = \frac{20}{11} \doteq 1.8182$. (This choice of b makes the new standard deviation 20 and the new mean $149\frac{1}{11}$; we then subtract 49.0909 to make the new mean 100.) **(c)** David's score—$2 \cdot 78 - 50 = 106$—is higher within his class than Nancy's score—$1.8182 \cdot 78 - 49.0909 \doteq 92.7$—is within her class. **(d)** From (c), we know that a third-grade score of 78 corresponds to a score of 106 from the $N(100, 20)$ distribution, which has a standard score of $z = \frac{106-100}{20} = 0.3$. (Alternatively, $z = \frac{78-75}{10} = 0.3$.) A sixth-grade score of 78 has standard score $z = \frac{92.7-100}{20} = \frac{78-82}{11} \doteq -0.36$. Therefore, about 62% of third graders and 36% of sixth graders score below 78.

1.142. Shown below are both quantile plots. Skewness shows up in a quantile plot as a flat tail; for right-skewness, that flat portion is at the beginning (the lower left).

The tornado data shows no clear outliers (the highest points appear to fit reasonably well with the nearby points in the plot). The three highest oil-well numbers appear to be outliers. (Incidentally, the 1.5 × *IQR* rule supports this conclusion.)

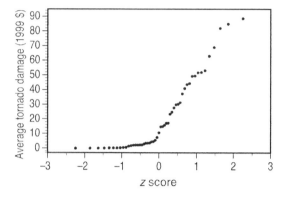
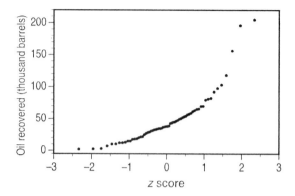

1.143. (a) Sketches may vary somewhat, but should be linear in the middle; the outliers would show up as a point in the lower left *below* the line (because low outliers are less than we expect them to be for a normal distribution), and a point in the upper right *above* the line (because high outliers are greater than we expect them to be). **(b)** The quantile plot for this data agrees with the expectations noted in (a).

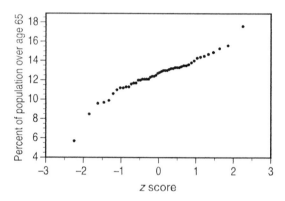

1.144. (a) Sketches should be linear in the middle. The heavy tails would show up flat sections in the lower left and upper right. The values in the tails are less spread out than we would expect for a normal distribution, so the line is less steep for low and high data values. **(b)** The quantile plot for this data does not clearly suggest heavy tails. (This is consistent with the text's statement: "Average returns... over longer periods of time become more normal.") There are no clear deviations from normality.

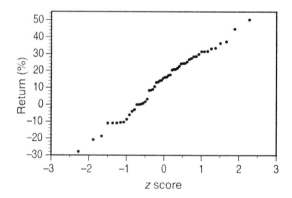

Note: *For an example of a quantile plot of a heavy-tailed distribution, see the tuition-and-fees data from Exercise 1.21; a quantile plot is shown in Figure 1.41(d), which accompanies Exercise 1.122.*

1.145. Results will vary. One set of 20 samples gave the results at the right (normal quantile plots are not shown).

Theoretically, $\bar{x}$ will have a $N(20, 1)$ distribution— so that about 99.7% of the time, one should find $\bar{x}$ between 17 and 23. Meanwhile, the theoretical distribution of s is nearly normal (slightly skewed) with mean $\doteq 4.9482$ and standard deviation $\doteq 0.7178$; about 99.7% of the time, s will be between 2.795 and 7.102. Note that "on the average," s underestimates σ (that is, $4.9482 < 5$). Unlike the mean $\bar{x}$, s is not an unbiased estimator of σ; in fact, for a sample of size n, the mean of s/σ is $\frac{\sqrt{2}\,\Gamma(n/2)}{\sqrt{n-1}\,\Gamma(n/2-1/2)}$. (This factor approaches 1 as n approaches infinity.) The proof of this fact is left as an exercise—for the instructor, not for the average student!

Means		Standard deviations	
18	589	3	8
19	00124	4	01
19	7789	4	22
20	1333	4	44455
20		4	66
21	223	4	9
21	5	5	000
		5	22
		5	45

1.146. Shown is a histogram with classes of width $10,000, which omits the 67 individuals with incomes over $410,000. A boxplot would also be an appropriate choice, although it would not show the cluster of individuals with incomes between $300,000 and $400,000.

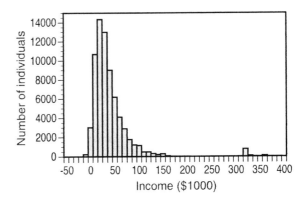

Because this distribution is skewed, the five-number summary is more appropriate than the mean:

   Min $= -\$23,980$, $Q_1 = \$22,000$, $M = \$35,000$, $Q_3 = \$53,000$, Max $= \$609,548$

For reference, the mean is $46,050 (larger than the median, as we would expect).

Note: *Processing this data file is no simple task; be sure that your students have adequate software. Some otherwise well-behaved software might choke on a data file as large as this. For example, Excel spreadsheets only allow 65,536 rows, so it would need to have this data set broken into at least two pieces.*

1.147. Men seem to have higher SATM scores than women; each number in the five-number summary is 40 to 60 points higher than the corresponding number for women. Women generally have higher GPAs than men, but the difference is less striking; in fact, the men's median is slightly higher.

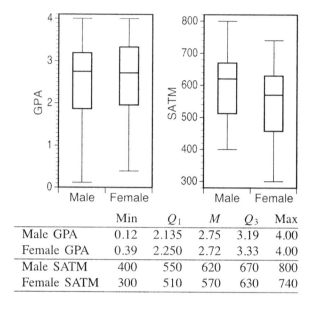

Quantile plots are shown below. Judging from these (and from the $1.5 \times IQR$ criterion), student 183 is an outlier for female SATM (300). For male GPA, outliers are students 127 (GPA 0.12) and 90 (GPA 0.4), and for female GPA, the outlier is student 188 (GPA 0.39). (Judgments of these may vary if the $1.5 \times IQR$ criterion is not used.)

	Min	Q_1	M	Q_3	Max
Male GPA	0.12	2.135	2.75	3.19	4.00
Female GPA	0.39	2.250	2.72	3.33	4.00
Male SATM	400	550	620	670	800
Female SATM	300	510	570	630	740

All four normal quantile plots look fairly linear, so students might judge all four data sets to be normal. However, both GPA sets—especially the male GPA—are somewhat left-skewed; there is some evidence of this in the long bottom tails of the GPA boxplots, as well as by the flatness in the upper right of their quantile plots.

Note: *In fact, statistical tests indicate that the male GPA numbers would not be likely to come from a normal distribution, even with the outliers omitted.*

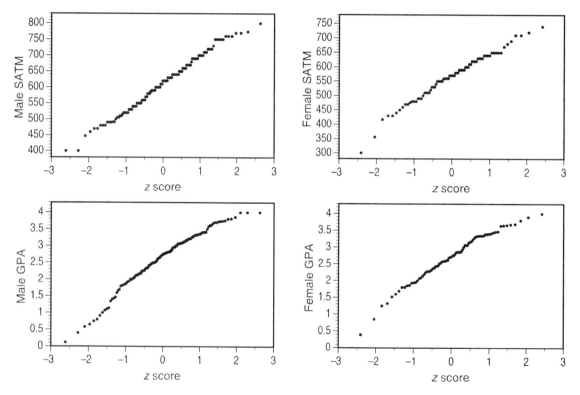

For answers to the EESEE Case Studies (exercises 148–150), see the instructor's version of EESEE.

Chapter 2 Solutions

2.1. **(a)** Time spent studying is explanatory; the grade is the response variable. **(b)** Explore the relationship; there is no reason to view one or the other as explanatory. **(c)** Rainfall is explanatory; crop yield is the response variable. **(d)** Explore the relationship. **(e)** Income is explanatory; years of education completed is the response variable.

2.2. Parents' income is explanatory, and college debt is the response. Both variables are quantitative. We would expect a negative association: Low income goes with high debt, high income with low debt.

2.3. **(a)** In general, we expect more intelligent children to be better readers, and less intelligent children to be weaker. The plot does show this positive association. **(b)** The four points are for children who have moderate IQs but poor reading scores. **(c)** The rest of the scatterplot is roughly linear, but quite weak (there would be a lot of variation about any line we draw through the scatterplot).

2.4. **(a)** From the scatterplot, we estimate 50% in 1954 and about −28% in 1974. (The data file `ex01-144.dat` gives the values 50.28% and −27.87%.) **(b)** The return on Treasury bills in 1981 was about 14.8%. **(c)** The scatterplot shows no clear pattern. (The statement that "high treasury bill returns tend to go with low returns on stocks" implies a negative association; there may be *some* suggestion of such a pattern, but it is extremely weak.)

2.5. **(a)** The response variable (estimated level) can only take on the values 1, 2, 3, 4, 5, so the points in the scatterplot must fall on one of those five levels. **(b)** The association is (weakly) positive. **(c)** The estimate is 4, which is an overestimate; that child had the lowest score on the test.

2.6. Ideally, the scales should be the same on both axes. The scatterplot shows a fairly strong, positive, linear association. Three countries (Tajikistan, Kazakhstan, Uzbekistan) reported 100% literacy for men and 99% literacy for women. Yemen (70% for men, 29% for women) might be considered an outlier.

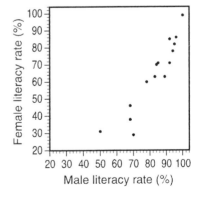

2.7. (a) If we used the number of males returning, then we might not see the relationship,
because areas with many breeding pairs
would correspondingly have more males that
might potentially return. (In the given numbers, the number of breeding pairs varies only
from 28 to 38, but considering hypothetical
data with 10 and 100 breeding pairs makes
more apparent the reason for using percents
rather than counts.) **(b)** Scatterplot on the
right. Mean responses are shown as crosses;

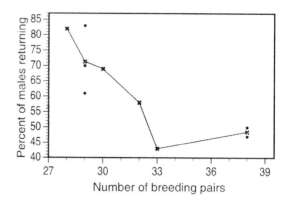

the mean responses with 29 and 38 breeding pairs are (respectively) 71.3333% and 48.5%
males returning. **(c)** The scatterplot does show the negative association we would expect if
the theory were correct.

2.8. (a) Two-seater cars are shown as filled circles, minicom-
pact cars as open circles. Ideally, the scales should be the
same on both axes. **(b)** The scatterplot shows a strong,
positive, linear association. Two-seater cars include several
vehicles with poor fuel efficiency (most notably, the Lamborghini and Ferrari models, and perhaps also the Maserati);
apart from these cars, the two sets of points show basically
the same relationship for both types of cars.

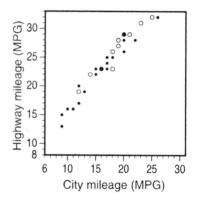

2.9. The scatterplot shows a fairly strong,
positive, linear association. There are no
particular outliers; each variable has low
and high values, but those points do not
deviate from the pattern of the rest. Social
exclusion does appear to trigger a pain
response.

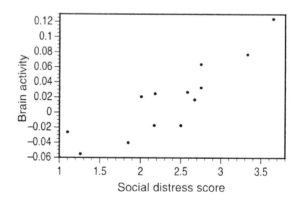

2.10. There appears to be a positive association between cycle length and day length, but it is quite weak: The points of the scatterplot are generally located along a positively-sloped line, but with a lot of spread around that line. (Ideally, both axes should have the same scale.)

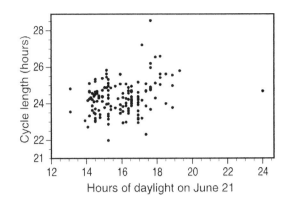

2.11. (Ideally, both graphs should have the same scale on both axes. However, this makes the graph dimensions rather awkward, so the graphs below do not reflect that ideal.) **(a)** The Lakers and the Knicks are high in both variables (but fit the pattern). The Grizzlies, Cavaliers, and Rockets have slightly higher values than their revenues would suggest. The association is positive and linear. **(b)** The Lakers and Knicks still stand out, as do the Bulls and Trailblazers, but the association is quite weak. (It hardly makes sense to speak of outliers when there is little or no pattern.) Revenue is a much better predictor of value.

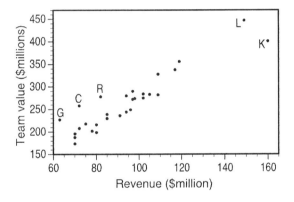
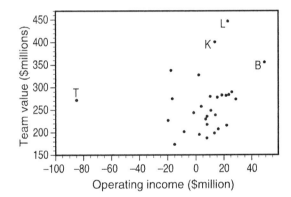

2.12. (a) MA angle is the explanatory variable, so it should be on the horizontal axis of the scatterplot. (This scatterplot has the same scale on both axes, because both variables are measured in degrees.) **(b)** The scatterplot shows a moderate-to-weak positive linear association, with one clear outlier (the patient with HAV angle 50°). **(c)** MA angle can be used to give (very rough) estimates of HAV angle, but the spread is so wide that they would not be too reliable.

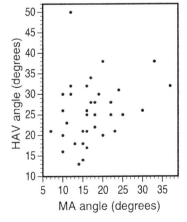

2.13. **(a)** Women are marked with filled circles, men with open circles. **(b)** The association is linear and positive. The women's points show a stronger association. As a group, males typically have larger values for both variables.

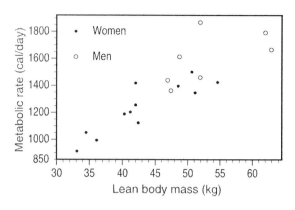

2.14. **(a)** At right; speed is explanatory, so it belongs on the *x*-axis. **(b)** The relationship is curved—low in the middle, higher at the extremes. Because low "mileage" is actually *good* (it means that we use less fuel to travel 100 km), this makes sense: moderate speeds yield the best performance. Note that 60 km/hr is about 37 mph. **(c)** Above-average (that is, bad) values of "fuel used" are found with both low and high values of "speed." **(d)** The relationship is very strong—there is little scatter around the curve, and it is very useful for prediction.

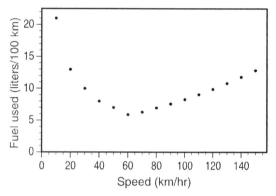

2.15. The plot shows a fairly steady rate of improvement until the mid-1980s, with much slower progress after that (the record has only been broken once since 1986).

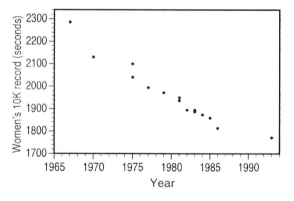

2.16. **(a)** In the scatterplot on the right, the open circles represent run 8905, the higher flow rate. **(b)** Icicles seem to grow faster when the water runs more slowly. (Note that there is no guarantee that the pattern we observe with these two flow rates applies to rates a lot faster than 29.6 mg/s, or slower than 11.9 mg/s.)

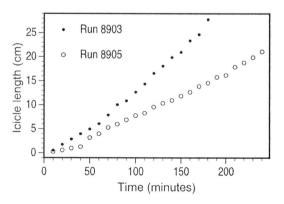

2.17. **(a)** Both men (filled circles) and women (open circles) show fairly steady improvement. Women have made more rapid progress, but their progress seems to have slowed, while men's records may be dropping more rapidly in recent years. **(b)** The data supports the first claim, but does not seem to support the second.

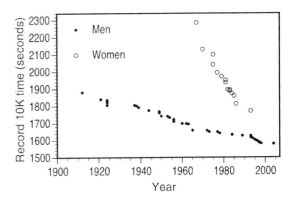

2.18. **(a)** The scatterplot on the right shows both the original data (circles) and the means (crosses). The means are 10.65, 10.43, 5.60, and 5.45 cm. **(b)** There is little difference in the growth when comparing 0 and 1000 nematodes, or 5000 and 10,000 nematodes — but the growth drops substantially between 1000 and 5000 nematodes.

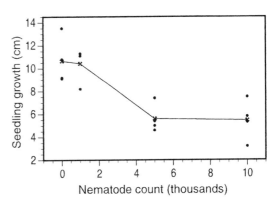

2.19. **(a)** Plot shown on the right. Means (plotted with crosses) are 30.96%, 32.76%, 54.31%, and 23.32%. (Note that the sectors on the horizontal axis are shown there in the order given in the text, but that is completely arbitrary.) **(b)** Technology had the highest average performance. **(c)** Referring to a positive or negative association only makes sense when both variables are quantitative. (There *is* an association here, but it cannot be called positive or negative.)

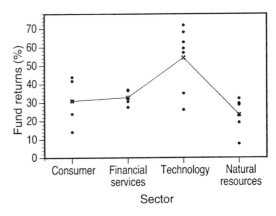

2.20. Methods of graphical analysis will vary; shown below are two possible approaches. On the left, for each sector, 2002 returns are shown as filled circles and 2003 returns are open circles. On the right is a scatterplot with 2002 return as the explanatory variable; the letters C, F, T, and N indicate the different fund types. The negative association in the second graph makes more clear something that can also be observed in the first graph: Generally, the worse a fund did in 2002, the better it did in 2003 (and vice versa).

```
−0 | 3
−0 |
 0 | 0
 0 | 223333
 0 | 444455555
 0 | 6
 0 | 9
 1 | 001
 1 | 2
```

Also shown (right) is a stemplot of the differences for each fund (that is, each fund's 2003 return minus its 2002 return). Only one fund return decreased; every other fund increased its return by between 8.3% and 122.4%.

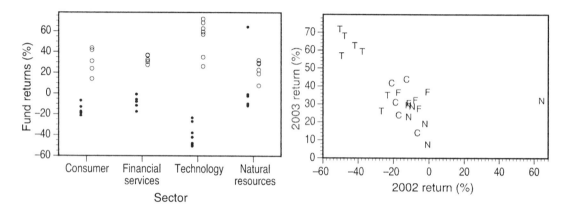

2.21. **(a)** Price is explanatory (and so is on the horizontal axis). The plot shows a positive linear association. **(b)** $\bar{x} = 50$ cents/lb and $s_x \doteq 16.3248$ cents/lb; $\bar{y} = 1.738\%$ and $s_y \doteq 0.9278\%$. The standardized values are below; the correlation is $r = 3.8206/4 = 0.955$. **(c)** Obviously, the calculator value should be the same.

z_x	z_y	$z_x z_y$
−1.2864	−1.3451	1.7303
−0.6126	−0.1595	0.0977
0.2450	−0.0517	−0.0127
0.3063	0.0884	0.0271
1.3476	1.4679	1.9783
		3.8206

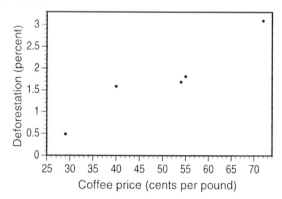

2.22. **(a)** The best guess is $r = 0.6$. There is far too much scatter for $r = 0.9$, and enough of a positive association that r must be more than 0.1. **(b)** The actual correlation is 0.6821.

2.23. The best guess is $r = 0.6$. There is far too much scatter for $r = 0.9$, and enough of a positive association that r must be more than 0.1.

2.24. **(a)** $r = 0.98$ goes with the Dividend Growth fund, which is most similar to the stocks represented by the S&P index. $r = 0.81$ goes with the Small Cap Stock fund; small U.S. companies should be somewhat similar to large U.S. companies. Finally, $r = 0.35$ goes with Emerging Markets, as these stocks would be the most different from those in the S&P index. **(b)** Positive correlations do not indicate that stocks went up. Rather, they indicate that when the S&P index rose, the other funds often did, too—and when the S&P index fell, the other funds were likely to fall.

2.25. r would not change; units do not affect correlation.

2.26. **(a)** See the solution to Exercise 2.20 for the scatterplot. (It is the second of the two graphs shown there.) **(b)** For all 23 funds, $r = -0.6230$; with the outlier removed, $r^* = -0.8722$. Removing the Gold fund makes the association stronger, because the remaining points are less scattered about a line drawn through the data points.

2.27. See also the solution to Exercise 2.11. **(a)** For team value and revenue, $r_1 = 0.9265$; for team value and operating income, $r_2 = 0.2107$. This agrees with conclusions from the scatterplots: revenue is a much better predictor of team value. **(b)** Without Portland (marked with a "T" in the scatterplot), $r_2 = 0.3469$. The removal of this point makes the scatterplot appear (slightly) more linear, so the association is stronger.

2.28. For Exercise 2.10, $r_1 = 0.2797$; for Exercise 2.16, $r_2 = 0.9958$ (run 8903) and $r_3 = 0.9982$ (run 8905).

2.29. **(a)** The scatterplot shows a moderate positive association, so r should be positive, but not close to 1. **(b)** The correlation is $r = 0.5653$. **(c)** r would not change if all the men were six inches shorter. A positive correlation does not tell us that the men were generally taller than the women; instead it indicates that women who are taller (shorter) than the average woman tend to date men who are also taller (shorter) than the average man. **(d)** r would not change, because it is unaffected by units. **(e)** r would be 1, as the points of the scatterplot would fall on a positively-sloped line.

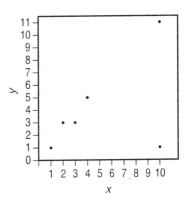

2.30. The correlation is $r \doteq 0.481$. The correlation is greatly lowered by the one outlier. Outliers tend to have fairly strong effects on correlation; it is even stronger here because there are so few observations.

2.31. (a) As two points determine a line, the correlation is always either -1 or 1. **(b)** Sketches will vary; an example is shown on the right. Note that the scatterplot must be positively sloped, but r is affected only by the scatter about a line drawn through the data points, not by the steepness of the slope. **(c)** The first nine points cannot be spread from the top to the bottom of the graph because in such a case the correlation cannot exceed about 0.66 (based on empirical evidence—that is, from a reasonable amount of playing around with the applet). One possibility

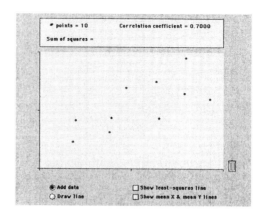

is shown below, left. **(d)** To have $r \doteq 0.7$, the curve must be higher at the right than at the left. One possibility is shown below, right.

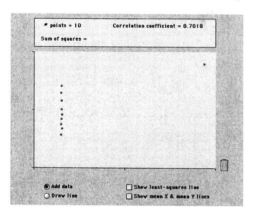
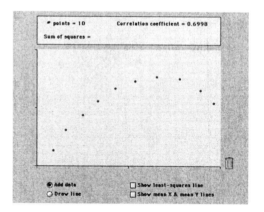

2.32. See the solution to Exercise 2.14 for the scatterplot. $r = -0.172$—it is close to zero, because the relationship is a curve rather than a line; correlation measures the degree of *linear* association.

2.33. (a) The Insight seems to fit the line suggested by the other points. **(b)** Without the Insight, $r = 0.9757$; with it, $r^* = 0.9934$. The Insight increases the strength of the association (the line is the same, but the scatter about that line is *relatively* less when the Insight is included).

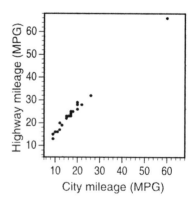

2.34. (a) The correlation will be closer to 1. One possible answer is shown below, left.
(b) Answers will vary, but the correlation will decrease, and can be made negative by

dragging the point down far enough (see below, right).

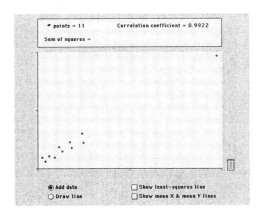
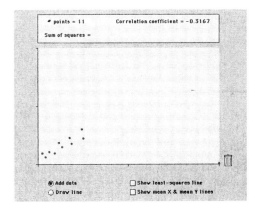

2.35. (Scatterplot not shown.) If the husband's age is y and the wife's x, the linear relationship $y = x + 2$ would hold, and hence $r = 1$ (because the slope is positive).

2.36. Explanations and sketches will vary, but should note that correlation measures the strength of the association, not the slope of the line. The hypothetical Funds A and B mentioned in the report, for example, might be related by a linear formula with slope 2 (or 1/2).

2.37. The person who wrote the article interpreted a correlation close to 0 as if it were a correlation close to -1 (implying a negative association between teaching ability and research productivity). Professor McDaniel's findings mean there is little linear association between research and teaching—for example, knowing that a professor is a good researcher gives little information about whether she is a good or bad teacher.

2.38. (a) Because gender has a categorical (nominal) scale, we cannot compute the correlation between sex and anything. (There is a strong *association* between gender and income. Some writers and speakers use "correlation" as a synonym for "association." It is much better to retain the more specific meaning.) **(b)** A correlation $r = 1.09$ is impossible because $-1 \leq r \leq 1$ always. **(c)** Correlation has no units, so $r = 0.23$ *bushel* is incorrect.

2.39. Both relationships (scatterplots below) are somewhat linear. The GPA/IQ scatterplot ($r = 0.6337$) shows a stronger association than GPA/self-concept ($r = 0.5418$). The two students with the lowest GPAs stand out in both plots; a few others stand out in at least one plot. Generally speaking, removing these points raises r (because the remaining points look more linear). An exception: removing the lower-left point in the self-concept plot decreases r, because the relative scatter of the remaining points is greater.

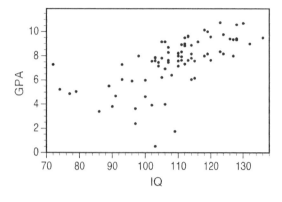

2.40. (a) The new speed and fuel consumption (respectively) values are $x^* = x \div 1.609$ and $y^* = y \times 1.609 \div 100 \div 3.785 \doteq 0.004251y$. (The factor of $1/100$ is needed since we were measuring fuel consumption in liters/100 km.) The transformed data has the same correlation as the original—$r = -0.172$ (computed in the solution to Exercise 2.32)—since a linear transformation does not alter the correlation. The scatterplot of the transformed data is not shown here;

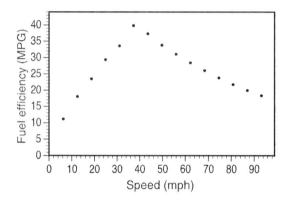

it resembles (except for scale) the plot shown in the solution to Exercise 2.14. **(b)** The new correlation is $r^* = -0.043$; the new plot is even less linear than the first.

2.41. (a) The predicted scores for $x = 90$ and $x = 140$ are
$$-33.4 + 0.882 \times 90 = 45.98 \text{ and}$$
$$-33.4 + 0.882 \times 140 = 90.08.$$
Plot the points $(90, 46)$ and $(140, 90)$ and draw the line connecting them. **(b)** If the reading score increases by 1 for each IQ point, the professor's line has slope 1. In order for an IQ of 100 to correspond to a reading score of 50, the equation must be reading score = IQ − 50.

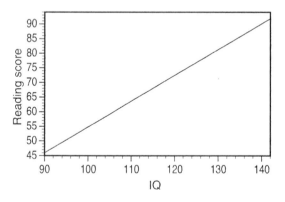

2.42. (a) The slope is 2.59, meaning that (on the average) team value rises 2.59 units (dollars, $million, or whatever) from each one-unit increase in revenue. (Most students may make this statement in terms of millions of dollars, as the table gives values with those units, but the ratio holds regardless of the unit, provided the same unit is used for both variables.) **(b)** The predicted value is $21.4 + 2.59 \times 149 = 407.31$ million dollars; the error is -39.69 million dollars. **(c)** The high correlation means that the line does a fairly good job of predicting value; specifically, the regression line explains about $r^2 \doteq 86\%$ of the variability in team value.

2.43. (a) The slope tells us that volume increases at an average rate of 4.2255 km³/year. (b) The estimate for 1780 is −271 km³; a negative number makes no sense in this context. (c) The estimate for 1990 is 617 km³. Based on the time plot, it appears that the actual discharge in 1990 was around 680 km³ (this is the value given in Table 1.4), so the prediction error is about 63 km³. (d) There are high spikes in the time plot in the two flood years.

2.44. (a) Because the slope is 0.0086 (in units of "proportion of perch eaten per perch count"), an increase of 10 in the perch count increases the proportion eaten by 0.086 (on the average). (b) When the perch count is 0, the equation tells us that 12% (0.12) of those perch will be eaten. Of course, 12% of 0 is 0, so one could argue that this is in some sense correct, but computing the proportion eaten would require dividing by zero.

2.45. (a) Time plot shown on the right, along with the regression line. (b) The means and standard deviations are $\bar{x} = 1987.7778$, $\bar{y} = 304.1111$, $s_x = 8.7003$, and $s_y = 3.4440$. With the correlation $r = 0.7268$, the slope and intercept are $b = r\,s_y/s_x = 0.2877$ and $a = \bar{y} - b\bar{x} = -267.78$. The equation is therefore $\hat{y} = 0.2877x - 267.78$; this line explains about $r^2 \doteq 53\%$ of the variation in score.

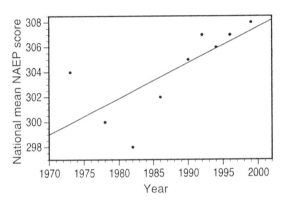

2.46. (a) The least-squares line is $\hat{y} = 0.7267x + 4.9433$. This is less steep than the line $y = x$, reflecting the observation that field measurements tend to be lower for greater depths. (b) The line $y = x$ has slope 1; the regression line has slope 0.7267. A slope of 1 would mean that for every additional unit of depth as measured in the laboratory, the field measurement would also increase by one unit. The slope of 0.7267 means that on the average, the field measurement increases by only 0.7267 units for every one unit in the lab

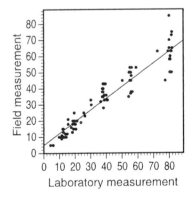

2.47. See also the solution to Exercise 2.9. (a) The regression equation is $\hat{y} = 0.06078x - 0.1261$. (b) Based on the "up-and-over" method, most students will probably estimate that $\hat{y} \doteq 0$; the regression formula gives $\hat{y} = -0.0045$. (c) The correlation is $r \doteq 0.8782$, so the line explains $r^2 = 77\%$ of the variation in brain activity.

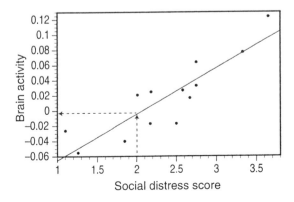

2.48. See also the solution to Exercise 2.12. **(a)** The regression line is $\hat{y} = 19.7 + 0.339x$. **(b)** For $x = 25°$, we predict $\hat{y} = 28.2°$. **(c)** The scatterplot shows a lot of spread, so predictions based on this line will not be very reliable. This is confirmed by the value of $r^2 = 9.1\%$; the straight-line relationship explains less than 10% of the variation in HAV angle.

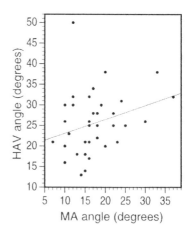

2.49. The regression equations are $\hat{y} = -2.39 + 0.158x$ (Run 8903, 11.9 mg/s) and $\hat{y} = -1.45 + 0.0911x$ (Run 8905, 29.6 mg/s). Therefore, the growth rates are (respectively) 0.158 cm/minute and 0.0911 cm/minute; this suggests that the faster the water flows, the more slowly the icicles grow.

2.50. (a) For all the funds, $\hat{y} = 29.2512 - 0.4501x$ (the dashed line in the plot); with the outlier omitted, the equation is $\hat{y} = 18.1106 - 0.9429x$ (the solid line). As in the solution to Exercise 2.20, the scatterplot uses the letters C, F, T, and N to indicate the fund type. **(b)** Because the least-squares criterion attempts to minimize the total squared distances from points to the line, the point for Fidelity Gold Fund pulls the line toward it.

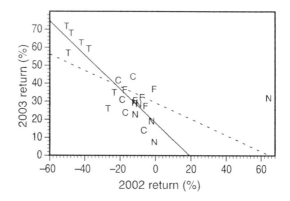

2.51. No, we could not predict stock returns accurately from Treasury bill returns: The scatterplot shows little or no association, and regression only explains 1.3% of the variation in stock return.

2.52. The means and standard deviations are $\bar{x} = 95$ min, $\bar{y} = 12.6611$ cm, $s_x = 53.3854$ min, and $s_y = 8.4967$ cm; the correlation is $r = 0.9958$.

   For predicting length from time, the slope and intercept are $b_1 = r\, s_y/s_x \doteq 0.158$ cm/min and $a_1 = \bar{y} - b_1\bar{x} \doteq -2.39$ cm, giving the equation $\hat{y} = -2.39 + 0.158x$ (as in Exercise 2.48).

   For predicting time from length, the slope and intercept are $b_2 = r\, s_x/s_y \doteq 6.26$ min/cm and $a_2 = \bar{x} - b_2\bar{y} \doteq 15.79$ min, giving the equation $\hat{x} = 15.79 + 6.26y$.

2.53. The means and standard deviations are: For lean body mass, $\bar{m} = 46.74$ and $s_m = 8.28$ kg, and for metabolic rate, $\bar{r} = 1369.5$ and $s_r = 257.5$ cal/day. The correlation is $r = 0.8647$. For predicting metabolic rate from body mass, the slope is $b_1 = r \cdot s_r/s_m \doteq 26.9$ cal/day per kg. For predicting body mass from metabolic rate, the slope is $b_2 = r \cdot s_m/s_r \doteq 0.0278$ kg per cal/day.

2.54. The correlation of IQ with GPA is $r_1 = 0.634$; for self-concept and GPA, $r_2 = 0.542$. IQ does a slightly better job; it explains about $r_1^2 = 40.2\%$ of the variation in GPA, while self-concept explains about $r_2^2 = 29.4\%$ of the variation.

2.55. Women's heights are the x values; men's are the y values. The slope is $b = (0.5)(2.7)/2.5 = 0.54$ and the intercept is $a = 68.5 - (0.54)(64.5) = 33.67$.

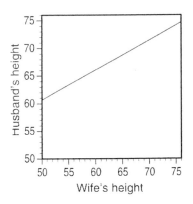

The regression equation is $\hat{y} = 33.67 + 0.54x$. Ideally, the scales should be the same on both axes. For a 67-inch tall wife, we predict the husband's height will be about 69.85 inches.

2.56. We have slope $b = r\, s_y/s_x$ and intercept $a = \bar{y} - b\bar{x}$, and $\hat{y} = a + bx$, so when $x = \bar{x}$,

$$\hat{y} = a + b\bar{x} = (\bar{y} - b\bar{x}) + b\bar{x} = \bar{y}.$$

(Note that the value of the slope does not actually matter.)

2.57. **(a)** $\bar{x} = 95$ min, $s_x = 53.3854$ min, $\bar{y} = 12.6611$ cm, and $s_y = 8.4967$ cm. The correlation $r \doteq 0.9958$ has no units. **(b)** Multiply the old values of $\bar{y}$ and s_y by 2.54: $\bar{y} = 32.1591$ and $s_y = 21.5816$ inches. The correlation r is unchanged. **(c)** The slope is $r\, s_y/s_x$; with s_y from part (b), this gives 0.4025 in/min. (Or, multiply by 2.54 the appropriate slope from the solution to Exercise 2.49.)

2.58. **(a)** The slope is $b = r\, s_y/s_x = (0.6)(8)/(30) = 0.16$, and the intercept is $a = \bar{y} - b\bar{x} = 30.2$. **(b)** Julie's predicted score is $\hat{y} = 78.2$. **(c)** $r^2 = 0.36$; only 36% of the variability in y is accounted for by the regression, so the estimate $\hat{y} = 78.2$ could be quite different from the real score.

2.59. $r = \sqrt{0.16} = 0.40$ (high attendance goes with high grades, so the correlation must be positive).

2.60. **(a)** In the scatterplot (shown on the right), open circles represent two observations. This plot does suggest a linear association between days stored and the logarithm of the concentration, which supports the simple exponential decay model. **(b)** The regression equation is $\log C = -0.0341 - 0.0005068t$; we therefore estimate k to be 0.0005068.

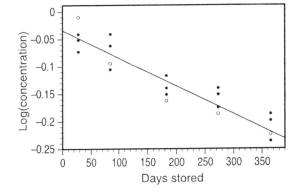

Note: *Students may need some help in performing this computation, especially in making sure that they compute the natural rather than the common logarithm. With most calculators and software, the correct function is "ln."*

2.61. **(a)** In the scatterplot on the right, open circles represent two observations. **(b)** The regression line slope is about 0.000051; the scatterplot suggests a nearly horizontal line (which would have slope 0). **(c)** Storing the oil doesn't help, as the total toxin level does not change over time; all that happens is the fenthion gradually changes to fenthion sulfoxide.

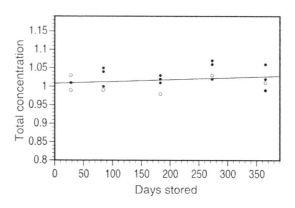

2.62. See also the solutions to Exercises 2.14 and 2.40. **(a)** Below, left. **(b)** The sum is −0.01. **(c)** The first two and last four residuals are positive, and those in the middle are negative. Plot below, right.

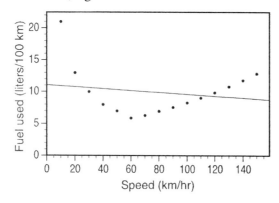
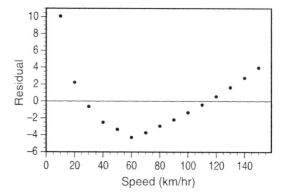

2.63. **(a)** Below, left. **(b)** This line is not a good summary of the pattern, because the pattern is curved rather than linear. **(c)** The sum is 0.01. The first two and last four residuals are negative, and those in the middle are positive. Plot below, right.

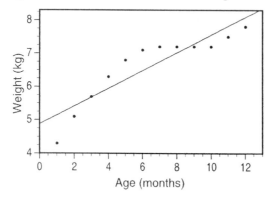
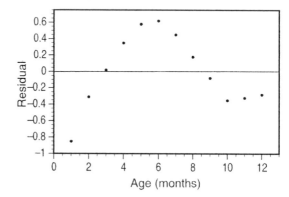

2.64. (a) The predicted concentration is $\hat{y} =$ 0.9524, so the residual is $0.99 - \hat{y} =$ 0.0376. **(b)** Rounding in the regression coefficients (slope and intercept) accounts for the difference between our residual (0.0376) and the value 0.0378 given in this list. The residuals do sum to 0. **(c)** In the residual plot, open circles represent two observations. There is a very slight curved pattern—high on the left and right, and low in the middle.

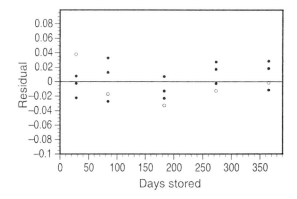

2.65. With individual children, the correlation would be smaller (closer to 0), because the additional variation of data from individuals would increase the "scatter" on the scatterplot, thus decreasing the strength of the relationship.

2.66. Presumably, those applicants who were hired would generally have been those who scored well on the test. As a result, we have little or no information on the job performance of those who scored poorly (and were therefore not hired). Those with higher test scores (who were hired) will likely have a range of performance ratings, so we will only see the various ratings for those with high scores, which will almost certainly show a weaker relationship than if we had performance ratings for all applicants.

2.67. For example, a student who in the past might have received a grade of B (and a lower SAT score) now receives an A (but has a lower SAT score than an A student in the past). While this is a bit of an oversimplification, this means that today's A students are yesterday's A and B students, today's B students are yesterday's C students, and so on. Because of the grade inflation, we are not comparing students with equal abilities in the past and today.

2.68. A simple example illustrates this nicely: Suppose that everyone's current salary is their age (in thousands of dollars); for example, a 52-year-old worker makes $52,000 per year. Everyone receives a $500 raise each year. That means that in two years, every worker's income has increased by $1000, but their age has increased by 2, so each worker's salary is not their age minus 1 (thousand dollars).

2.69. The correlation between BMR and fat gain is $r = 0.08795$; the slope of the regression line is $b = 0.000811$ kg/cal. These both show that BMR is less useful for predicting fat gain. The small correlation suggests a very weak linear relationship (explaining less than 1% of the variation in fat gain). The small slope means that changes in BMR have very little impact on fat gain; for example, increasing BMR by 100 calories changes fat gain by only 0.08 kg.

2.70. **(a)** The scatterplot of the data is below on the left. **(b)** The regression equation is
$\hat{y} = -14.4 + 46.6x$. **(c)** Residual plot below, right. The residuals for the extreme x-values
($x = 0.25$ and $x = 20.0$) are almost all positive; all those for the middle two x values are
negative.

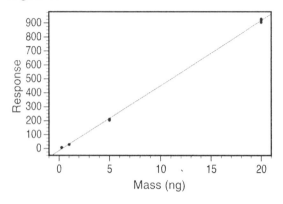
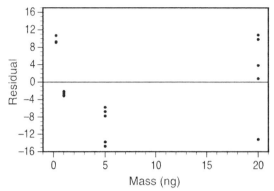

2.71. **(a)** There is a moderate positive relationship; player 7's point is an outlier. Ideally,
both scales should be equal. **(b)** The first
equation is the dashed line in the plot. It
omits the influential observation; the other
(solid) line is pulled toward the outlier.

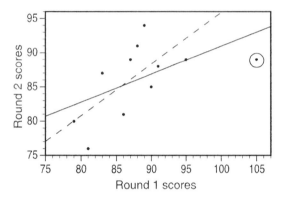

2.72. **(a)** Apart from the outlier—circled for
part (b)—the scatterplot shows a moderate
linear negative association. **(b)** With the
outlier, $r = -0.3387$; without it, $r^* =
-0.7866$. **(c)** The two regression formulas
are $\hat{y} = -492.6 - 33.79x$ (the solid line,
with all points), and $\hat{y} = -1371.6 - 75.52x$
(the dashed line, with the outlier omitted).
The omitted point is also influential, as it
has a noticeable impact on the line.

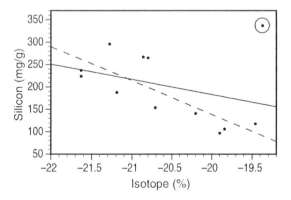

2.73. (a) Scatterplot below on the left. **(b)** The regression line is $\hat{y} = 6.47 + 1.01x$. The residual plot is below on the right. **(c)** The largest residuals are the Porsche Boxster (2.365) and Lamborghini Murcielago (−2.545). **(d)** The Insight is influential; it pulls the line toward its point, so that it not far from the regression line.

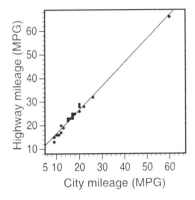 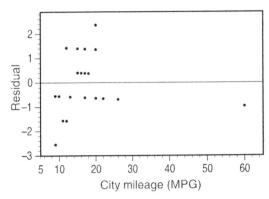

2.74. (a) Scatterplot below, left. The relationship seems linear. **(b)** The regression line is $\hat{y} = 1.77 + 0.0803x$ (y is stride rate, x is speed). **(c)** The residuals (reported by Minitab, then rounded to 3 decimal places) are 0.011, −0.001, −0.001, −0.011, −0.009, 0.003, 0.009. These add to 0.001. Results will vary with rounding, and also with the number of decimal places used in the regression equation. **(d)** Residuals are positive for low and high speeds, negative for moderate speeds; this suggests that a curve (like a parabola) may be a better fit. No observations are particularly influential; the line would change very little if we omitted any point.

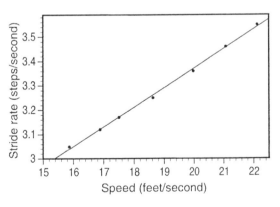 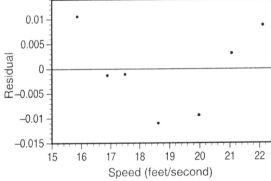

2.75. Without the Insight, $\hat{y} = 4.87 + 1.11x$ (the dashed line in the plot). For city mileages between 10 and 30 MPG, the difference in predicted highway mileage (with or without the Insight) is no more than 1.4 MPG, so the Insight is not very influential; it falls near the line suggested by the other points.

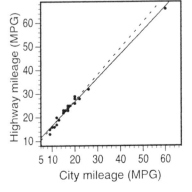

2.76. The correlation is $r = 0.999$. With individual runners, the correlation would be smaller (closer to 0), since using data from individual runners would increase the "scatter" on the scatterplot, thus decreasing the strength of the relationship.

2.77. **(a)** Drawing the "best line" by eye is a very inaccurate process; few people choose the best line (although you can get better at it with practice). **(b)** Most people tend to overestimate the slope for a scatterplot with $r \doteq 0.7$; that is, most students will find that the least-squares line is less steep than the one they draw.

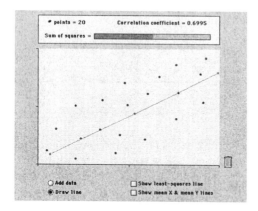 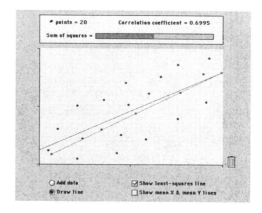

2.78. **(a)** Any point that falls exactly on the regression line will not increase the sum of squared vertical distances (which the regression line minimizes). Any other line—even if it passes through this new point—will necessarily have a higher total sum of squares. Thus, the regression line does not change. Possible output below, left. **(b)** Influential points are those whose x coordinates are outliers; this point is on the right side, while all others are on the left. Possible output below, right.

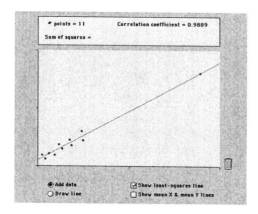 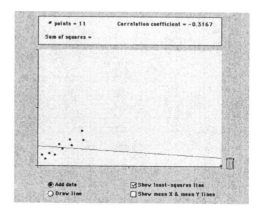

2.79. The plot shown is a very simplified (and not very realistic) example. Filled circles are economists in business; open circles are teaching economists. The plot should show positive association when either set of circles is viewed separately, and should show a large number of bachelor's degree economists in business and graduate degree economists in academia.

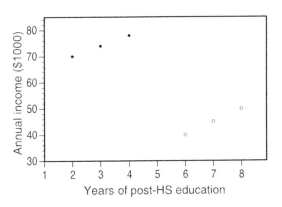

2.80. (a) To three decimal places, the correlations are all approximately 0.816 (for set D, r actually rounds to 0.817), and the regression lines are all approximately $\hat{y} = 3.000 + 0.500x$. For all four sets, we predict $\hat{y} \doteq 8$ when $x = 10$. (b) Below. (c) For Set A, the use of the regression line seems to be reasonable—the data do seem to have a moderate linear association (albeit with a fair amount of scatter). For Set B, there is an obvious *non*linear relationship; we should fit a parabola or other curve. For Set C, the point (13, 12.74) deviates from the (highly linear) pattern of the other points; if we can exclude it, the (new) regression formula would be very useful for prediction. For Set D, the data point with $x = 19$ is a very influential point—the other points alone give no indication of slope for the line. Seeing how widely scattered the y-coordinates of the other points are, we cannot place too much faith in the y-coordinate of the influential point; thus, we cannot depend on the slope of the line, and so we cannot depend on the estimate when $x = 10$. (We also have no evidence as to whether or not a line is an appropriate model for this relationship.)

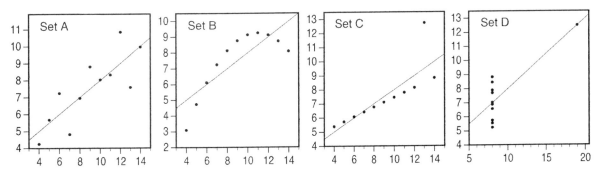

2.81. (a) As the slope of the line is negative, there is some support for this idea, but the relationship is quite weak. (b) There seems to be some suggestion of curvature, and there is considerably more scatter on the left side. This weakens the conclusion.

2.82. (a) Right-hand points are filled circles; left-hand points are open circles. **(b)** The right-hand points lie below the left-hand points. (This means the right-hand times are shorter, so the subject is right-handed.) There is no striking pattern for the left-hand points; the pattern for right-hand points is obscured because they are squeezed at the bottom of the plot. **(c)** Right hand: $\hat{y} = 99.4 + 0.0283x$ ($r = 0.305$, $r^2 = 9.3\%$). Left hand: $\hat{y} = 172 + 0.262x$

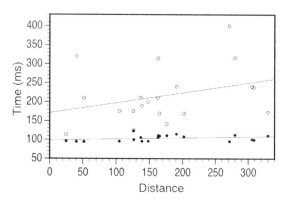

($r = 0.318$, $r^2 = 10.1\%$). The left-hand regression is slightly better, but neither is very good: distance accounts for only 9.3% (right) and 10.1% (left) of the variation in time. **(d)** The two residual plots are shown below; neither shows a systematic pattern.

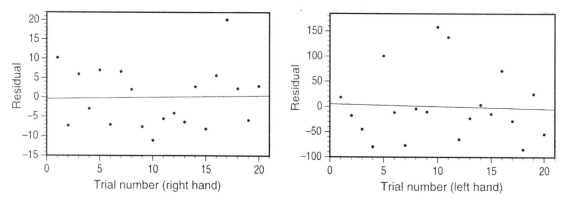

2.83. (a) There is clearly higher scatter for higher predicted values; the regression more accurately predicts low salaries than high salaries. **(b)** The residual plot is curved. Salaries are typically overestimated for players who are new to the majors, and for those who have been in the majors for 15 or more years (these residuals are mostly negative, meaning the predicted value is greater than the observed value). Those in for eight years will generally have their salaries underestimated; these residuals are mostly positive.

2.84. Responses will vary. For example, students who choose the online course might have more self-motivation, or have better computer skills. A diagram is shown on the right; the generic "Student characteristics" might be replaced with something more specific.

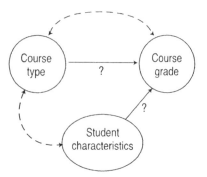

2.85. Age is one lurking variable: Married men would
generally be older than single men, so they would have
been in the work force longer, and therefore had more
time to advance in their careers. The diagram shown
on the right shows this lurking variable; other variables
could also be shown in place of "age."

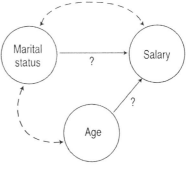

2.86. A large company has more workers who might be
laid off, and often pays more to its CEO (because,
presumably, there is more work involved in running a
large company than a small one). Smaller companies
typically pay less, and have fewer workers to lay off.

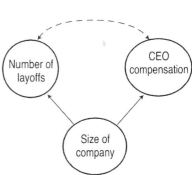

2.87. No: Self-confidence and improving fitness could be a common response to some other
personality trait, or high self-confidence could make a person more likely to join the
exercise program.

2.88. If a nation's population has high income, they have more money to spend on things that
can help to keep them healthy: health care, medicine, better food, better sanitation, and so
on. On the other hand, if a nation's population is healthy, they can spend less on health care
and instead put their money to more productive uses. Additionally, they miss fewer work
days, so they would typically earn more money.

2.89. Students with music experience may have other
advantages (wealthier parents, better school systems, and
so forth.). That is, experience with music may have been
a "symptom" (common response) of some other factor
that also tends to cause high grades.

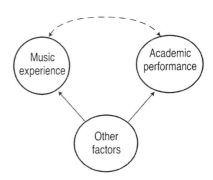

2.90. Two possibilities are that they might perform better simply because this is their second
attempt, or because they feel better prepared as a result of taking the course (whether or not
they really *are* better prepared).

2.91. The diagram below illustrates the confounding between exposure to chemicals and
standing up.

For 2.91.   *For 2.92.*

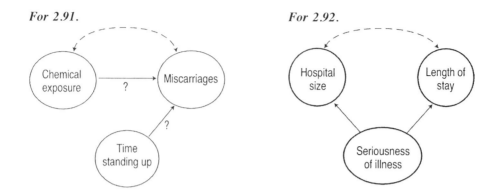

2.92. Patients suffering from more serious illnesses are more likely to go to larger hospitals (which may have more or better facilities) for treatment. They are also likely to require more time to recuperate afterwards.

2.93. Spending more time watching TV means that *less* time is spent on other activities; this may suggest lurking variables. For example, perhaps the parents of heavy TV watchers do not spend as much time at home as other parents. Also, heavy TV watchers would typically not get as much exercise.

2.94. In this case, there may be a causative effect, but in the direction opposite to the one suggested: People who are overweight are more likely to be on diets, and so choose artificial sweeteners over sugar. (Also, heavier people are at a higher risk to develop diabetes; if they do, they are likely to switch to artificial sweeteners.)

2.95. **(a)** Statements such as this typically mean that the risk of dying at a given age is half as great; that is, given two groups of the same age, where one group walks and the other does not, the walkers are half as likely to die in (say) the next year. **(b)** Men who choose to walk might also choose (or have chosen, earlier in life) other habits and behaviors that reduce mortality.

2.96. A reasonable explanation is that the cause-and-effect relationship goes in the other direction: Doing well makes students or workers feel good about themselves, rather than vice versa.

2.97. These results support the idea (the slope is negative, so variation decreases with increasing diversity), but the relationship is only moderately strong ($r^2 = 0.34$, so diversity only explains 34% of the variation in population variation).

    Note: *That last parenthetical comment is awkward and perhaps confusing, but is consistent with similar statements interpreting r^2.*

2.98. **(a)** A scatterplot of stock price growth against earnings growth shows a positive association, which supports the idea. Additionally, each y value is fairly similar to its x value, which indicates that stock price growth is roughly predicted by earnings growth (that is, $\hat{y} \approx x$)—this is a stronger statement than simply saying that the two variables have a positive association. **(b)** The regression explains $r^2 = 0.846 = 84.6\%$ of the variation in stock price growth. **(c)** The slope would be 1 (and the equation would be $\hat{y} = x$) because "stock prices exactly follow[ing] earnings" means that stock prices would change (increase or decrease)

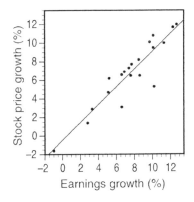

in exactly the same way that earnings change. The actual slope is 0.9552 (the full regression equation is $\hat{y} = 0.9552x - 0.4551$). **(d)** The correlation is $r = 0.9198$. With data from individual companies, the correlation would be much lower, because the additional variation of data from individuals would increase the "scatter" on the scatterplot, thus decreasing the strength of the relationship.

2.99. **(a)** One possible measure of the difference is the mean response: 106.2 spikes/second for pure tones and 176.6 spikes/second for monkey calls—an average of an additional 70.4 spikes/second. **(b)** The regression equation is $\hat{y} = 93.9 + 0.778x$. The third point (pure tone 241, call 485 spikes/second) has the largest residual; it is circled. The first point (474 and 500 spikes/second) is an outlier in the x direction; it is marked with a square. **(c)** The correlation drops only slightly (from 0.6386 to 0.6101) when the third point is removed; it drops more drastically (to 0.4793) without the first point. **(d)** Without the first point, the line is $\hat{y} = 101 + 0.693x$; without the third point, it is $\hat{y} = 98.4 + 0.679x$.

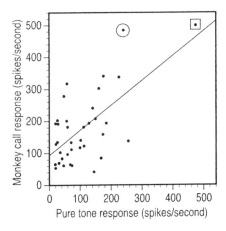

2.100. On the right is a scatterplot of MOR against MOE, showing a moderate, linear, positive association. The regression equation is $\hat{y} = 2653 + 0.004742x$; this regression explains $r^2 = 0.6217 \doteq 62\%$ of the variation in MOR. So, we can use MOE to get fairly good (though not perfect) predictions of MOR.

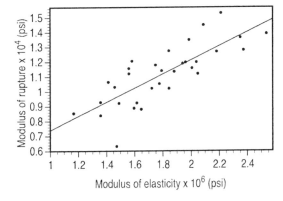

2.101. The quantile plot (right) is reasonably close to a straight line, so we have little reason to doubt that they come from a normal distribution.

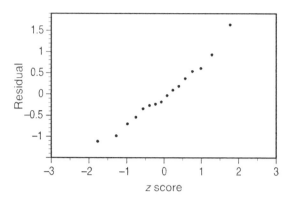

2.102. **(a)** The scatterplot is on the right. **(b)** The regression equation is $\hat{y} = 1.2027 + 0.3275x$. As we see from the scatterplot, the relationship is not too strong; the correlation ($r = 0.4916$, $r^2 = 0.2417$) confirms this.

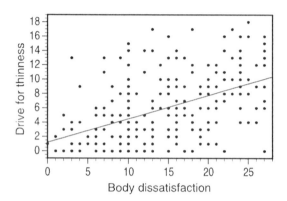

2.103. **(a)** Yes: The two lines appear to fit the data well. There do not appear to be any outliers or influential points. **(b)** Compare the slopes: before—0.189; after—0.157. (The units for these slopes are 100 ft³/day per degree-day/day; for students who are comfortable with units, 18.9 ft³ vs. 15.7 ft³ would be a better answer.) **(c)** Before: $\hat{y} = 1.089 + 0.189(35) = 7.704 = 770.4$ ft³. After: $\hat{y} = 0.853 + 0.157(35) = 6.348 = 634.8$ ft³. **(d)** This amounts to an additional ($1.20)(7.704 − 6.348) = $1.63 per day, or $50.44 for the month.

2.104. **(a)** $b = r \cdot s_y/s_x \doteq 1.1694$; $a = \bar{y} - b\bar{x} \doteq 0.3531$. The regression equation is $\hat{y} = 0.3531 + 1.1694x$; it explains $r^2 \doteq 27.6\%$ of the volatility in Philip Morris stock. **(b)** On the average, for every percentage-point rise in the S&P monthly return, Philip Morris stock returns rise about 1.17 percentage points. (And similarly, Philip Morris returns fall 1.17% for each 1% drop in the S&P index return.) **(c)** When the market is rising, the investor would like to earn money faster than the prevailing rate, and so prefers beta > 1. When the market falls, returns on stocks with beta < 1 will drop more slowly than the prevailing rate.

2.105. **(a)** Explanatory: weeds per meter (wpm). Response: corn yield. **(b)** The stemplots (below) give some evidence that yield decreases when there are more lamb's-quarter plants. **(c)** Scatterplot below. The regression equation is $\hat{y} = 166 - 1.10x$. Each additional lamb's-quarter per meter decreases yield by about 1.1 bushels/acre. **(d)** $\hat{y} = 166 - 1.10(6) = 159.4$ bushels/acre.

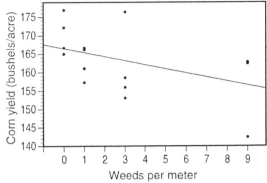

0 wpm		1 wpm		3 wpm		9 wpm	
14		14		14		14	2
14		14		14		14	
15		15		15	3	15	
15		15	7	15	69	15	
16		16	1	16		16	233
16	57	16	67	16		16	
17	2	17		17		17	
17	7	17		17	6	17	

2.106. **(a)** Below, left. **(b)** The regression equation is $\hat{y} = 1.71 + 0.0795x$. **(c)** Below, right. The points for the residuals, like those of the original data, are split with women above the line (zero), and men below. (Men are taller on the average, so they have longer legs, and therefore longer strides. Thus, they need fewer steps per second to run at a given speed.)

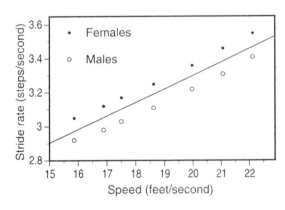

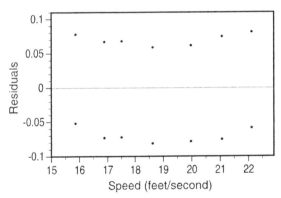

2.107. **(a)** Shown below are plots of count against time, and residuals against time for the regression, which gives the formula $\hat{y} = 259.58 - 19.464x$. Both plots suggest a curved relationship rather than a linear one. **(b)** With natural logarithms, the regression equation is $\hat{y} = 5.9732 - 0.2184x$; with common logarithms, $\hat{y} = 2.5941 - 0.09486x$. The second pair of plots below show the (natural) logarithm of the counts against time, suggesting a fairly linear relationship, and the residuals against time, which shows no systematic pattern. (If common logarithms are used instead of natural logs, the plots will look the same, except the vertical scales will be different.) The correlations confirm the increased linearity of the log plot: $r^2 = 0.8234$ for the original data, $r^2 = 0.9884$ for the log-data.

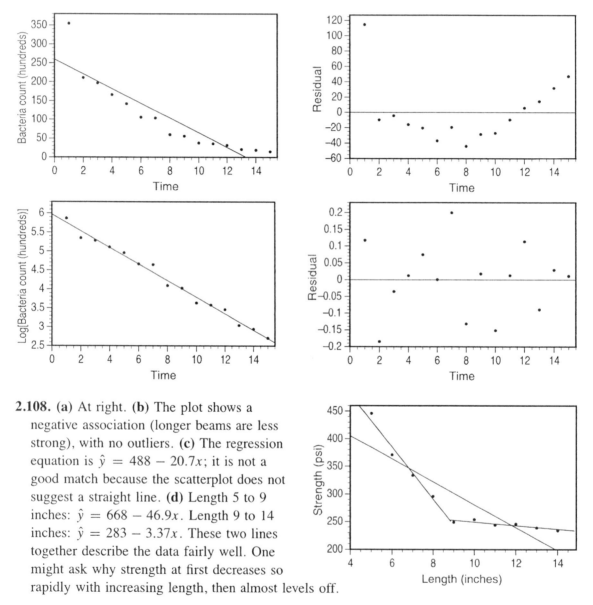

2.108. **(a)** At right. **(b)** The plot shows a negative association (longer beams are less strong), with no outliers. **(c)** The regression equation is $\hat{y} = 488 - 20.7x$; it is not a good match because the scatterplot does not suggest a straight line. **(d)** Length 5 to 9 inches: $\hat{y} = 668 - 46.9x$. Length 9 to 14 inches: $\hat{y} = 283 - 3.37x$. These two lines together describe the data fairly well. One might ask why strength at first decreases so rapidly with increasing length, then almost levels off.

2.109. In the mid-1990s, European and American stocks were only weakly linked, but now it is more common for them to rise and fall together. Thus investing in both types of stocks is not that much different from investing in either type alone.

2.110. The article is incorrect; a correlation of 0.8 means that a straight-line relationship explains about $r^2 = 64\%$ of the variation of European stock prices.

2.111. Number of firefighters and amount of damage both increase with the seriousness of the fire (that is, they are common responses to the fire's seriousness.)

2.112. Note that $\bar{y} = 46.6 + 0.41\bar{x}$. We predict that Octavio will score 4.1 points above the mean on the final exam: $\hat{y} = 46.6 + 0.41(\bar{x} + 10) = 46.6 + 0.41\bar{x} + 4.1 = \bar{y} + 4.1$. (Alternatively, because the slope is 0.41, we can observe that an increase of 10 points on the midterm yields an increase of 4.1 on the predicted final exam score.)

2.113. The scatterplot is not very promising. The regression equation is $\hat{y} = 1.28 + 0.00227x$; the correlation is $r = 0.252$, and the regression explains $r^2 = 6.3\%$ of the variation in GPA. By itself, SATM does not give reliable predictions of GPA.

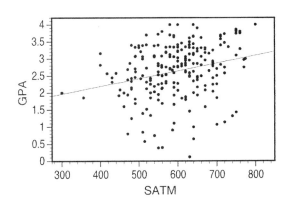

For answers to the EESEE Case Studies (exercises 114–117), see the instructor's version of EESEE.

Chapter 3 Solutions

3.1. Jamie and his friends do not constitute a random sample, and so would not be representative of the population of all "young people."

3.2. The anecdote describes a single unusual event. We would like data on deaths and injuries for occupants wearing/not wearing restraints for many accidents.

3.3. This is an observational study: No treatment was assigned to the subjects; we merely observed cell phone usage (and presence/absence of cancer). The explanatory variable is cell phone usage, and the response variable is whether or not a subject has brain cancer.

3.4. **(a)** No treatment is imposed on the subjects (children); they (or their parents) choose how much TV they watch. The explanatory variable is hours watching TV, and the response variable is "later aggressive behavior." **(b)** An adolescent who watches a lot of television probably is more likely to spend less time doing homework, playing sports, or having social interactions with peers. He or she may also have less contact with or guidance from his/her parents.

3.5. This is an experiment: Each subject is (presumably randomly) assigned to a group, each with its own treatment (computer animation or reading the textbook). The explanatory variable is the teaching method, and the response variable is the change in each student's test score.

3.6. **(a)** In this observational study, we do not know if the reduction in heart attack risk was due to hormones or other factors. An experiment would have involved taking a (very large) group of women, splitting them randomly into two groups; one would take hormones, and the other would not. The random allocation would allow us to conclude that, if we observed a difference in heart attack risk in either group, it could be attributed to the treatment.
(b) Possible characteristics might include socio-economic factors; for example, women who take hormones might be wealthier and therefore have better access to health care. There might also be biological factors; perhaps women who are more sensitive to menopause (and are therefore more likely to use hormones to relieve its symptoms) are also at less risk for heart attacks.

3.7. **(a)** In an observational study, we might take a sample and classify each subject as a wine drinker or a beer drinker. For an experiment, we would assign each subject to drink either wine or beer. In either case, we would then observe the health of the subjects over time.
(b) Wine drinkers might be wealthier, better educated, have white-collar jobs, and have different dietary habits ("beer and pretzels" vs. "wine and cheese").

3.8. This number is subject to change, as is the NCES web site. At the time of this writing, a search at the NCES web site for the phrase "undergraduates work part-time" yielded a document (dated February 1998) which included the following statement: "In 1992–93, 72 percent of the undergraduates in this analysis worked while enrolled, . . . an average of 31 hours per week and 88 percent of the months they were enrolled." Note that this was one of the top 10 results, but not the first result. A search at www.google.com for the same phrase also yielded many matches, at sites other than NCES, but this same document was conveniently at the top of the list.

3.9. Experimental units: Pine tree seedlings. Factor: Amount of light. Treatments: Full light, or shaded to 5% of normal. Response variable: Dry weight at end of study.

3.10. Experimental units: Middle schools. Factors: Physical activity program, and nutrition program. Treatments (four): Activity intervention, nutrition intervention, both interventions, and neither intervention. Response variables: Physical activity and lunchtime consumption of fat.

3.11. Subjects: Adults (or registered voters) from selected households. Factors: Level of identification, and offer of survey results. Treatments (six): Interviewer's name with results, interviewer's name without results, university name with results, university name without results, both names with results, both names without results. Response variable: Whether or not the interview is completed.

3.12. (a) The subjects are the physicians, the factor is medication (aspirin or placebo), and the response variable is health, specifically whether the subjects have heart attacks. **(b)** Below. **(c)** The difference in the number of heart attacks between the two groups was so great that it would rarely occur by chance if aspirin had no effect.

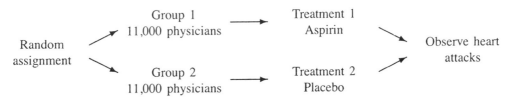

3.13. Assign nine subjects to each treatment. A diagram is below; if we assign labels 01 through 36, then line 130 gives:

Group 1		Group 2		Group 3	
05 Chen	32 Vaughn	31 Valasco	02 Asihiro	35 Willis	11 Fleming
16 Imrani	04 Bikalis	18 Kaplan	36 Zhang	21 Marsden	15 Hruska
17 James	25 Padilla	07 Duncan	23 O'Brian	26 Plochman	12 George
20 Maldonado	29 Trujillo	13 Han	27 Rosen	08 Durr	14 Howard
19 Liang		33 Wei		10 Farouk	

The other nine subjects are in Group 4. See note on page 50 about using Table B.

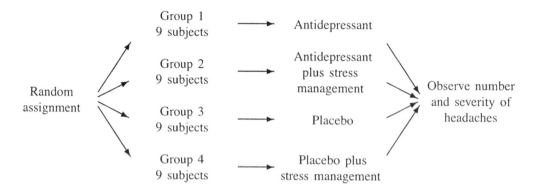

3.14. **(a)** A diagram is shown below. **(b)** Label the subjects from 01 through 20. From line 131, we choose

05, 19, 04, 20, 16, 18, 07, 13, 02, and 08;

that is, Decker, Travers, Chen, Ullmann, Quinones, Thompson, Fluharty, Lucero, Afifi, and Gerson for one group, and the rest for the other. See note on page 50 about using Table B.

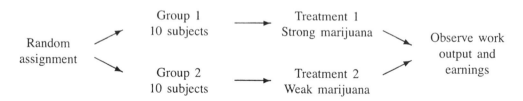

3.15. (a) Diagram below. (b) If we assign labels 01, ..., 18 and begin on line 142, then we select:

02, 08, 17, 10, 05, and 09 for Group 1;

06, 16, 01, 07, 18, and 15 for Group 2.

The remaining rats are assigned to the placebo group. See note on page 50 about using Table B.

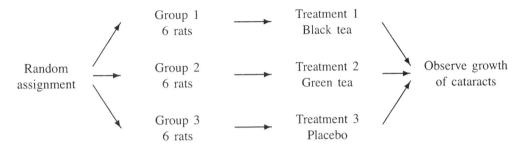

3.16. (a) Diagram below. (b) Using line 123 from Table B, the first four subjects are 102, 063, 035, and 090. See note on page 50 about using Table B.

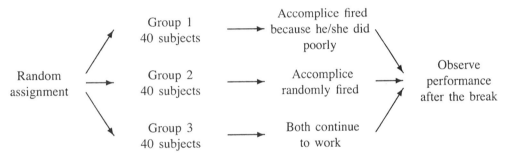

3.17. Diagram below. Starting at line 105, we choose:

07, 19, 14, 17, 13, 15 for Group 1,

08, 21, 20, 11, 24, 09 for Group 2,

06, 23, 16, 18, 12, 04 for Group 3,

and the rest for Group 4. See note on page 50 about using Table B.

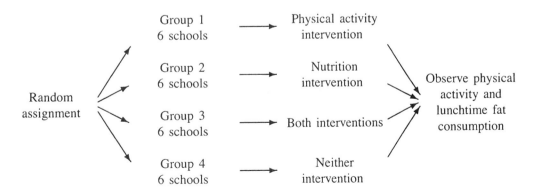

3.18. (a) The table below shows the 16 treatments—four levels for each of the two factors. (b) A diagram is not shown here (it is quite large). Five subjects are randomly assigned to each treatment; they read the ad for that treatment, and we record their attractiveness ratings for the ad. Using line 133, the first five subjects are 45, 74, 04, 18, and 07.

Factor B
Fraction of shoes on sale

		25%	50%	75%	100%
	20%	Treatment 1	Treatment 2	Treatment 3	Treatment 4
Factor A	40%	Treatment 5	Treatment 6	Treatment 7	Treatment 8
Discount level	60%	Treatment 9	Treatment 10	Treatment 11	Treatment 12
	80%	Treatment 13	Treatment 14	Treatment 15	Treatment 16

3.19. (a) There are three factors (roller type, dyeing cycle time, and temperature), each with two levels, for a total of $2^3 = 8$ treatments. The experiment therefore requires 24 fabric specimens. (b) In the interest of space, <u>only the top half of the diagram</u> is shown below. The other half consists of Groups 5 to 8, for which the treatments have natural bristle rollers instead of metal rollers.

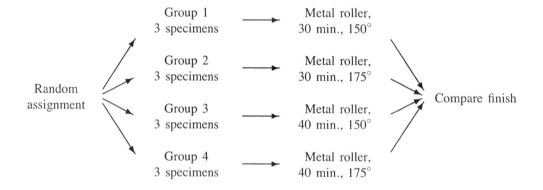

3.20. Population = 1 to 40 , Select a sample of size 20 , then click Reset and Sample .

3.21. (a) Population = 1 to 150 , Select a sample of size 25 , click Reset and Sample .
(b) Without resetting, click Sample again.

3.22. For a range of discounts, the attractiveness of the sale decreases slightly as the percentage of goods on sale increases. (The decrease is so small that it might not be significant.) With precise discounts, on the other hand, mean attractiveness increases with the percentage on sale. Range discounts are more attractive when only 25% of goods are marked down, while the precise discount is more attractive if 75% or 100% of goods are discounted.

3.23. The first design is an observational study. It is flawed because the women observed chose whether or not to take bee pollen; one might reasonably expect that people who choose to take bee pollen have other dietary or health habits that would differ from those who do not. The second design is an experiment; because the treatment is randomly assigned, the effect of other habits would be "diluted" because they would be more-or-less equally split between the two groups. Therefore, any difference in colon health between the two groups could be attributed to the treatment (bee pollen or not).

3.24. "Randomized" means that patients were randomly assigned to receive either the standard morphine treatment or CR morphine tablets. "Double blind" means that the treatment assigned to a patient was unknown to both the patient and those responsible for assessing the effectiveness of that treatment. (It is not clear how the treatment was hidden from the patients, because they would know when they received the morphine.) "Comparative" means researchers compared the effectiveness of two treatments, rather than simply trying to assess the effectiveness of one treatment—that is, researchers did not simply change over to CR morphine and try to judge if it was better than the standard treatment had been in the past.

3.25. (a) "Randomized" means that patients were randomly assigned to receive either Saint-John's-wort or a placebo. "Double blind" means that the treatment assigned to a patient was unknown to both the patient and those responsible for assessing the effectiveness of that treatment. "Placebo-controlled" means that some of the subjects were given placebos. Even though these possess no medical properties, some subjects may show improvement or benefits just as a result of participating in the experiment; the placebos allow those doing the study to observe this effect. **(b)** Diagram below.

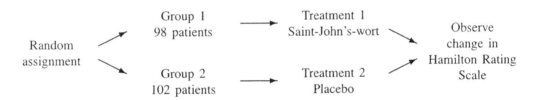

3.26. The mean Monday return for the first three weeks of the month was both different from zero and higher than the mean for the last two Mondays. However, the difference from zero was small enough that it might have occurred purely by chance (and so it gives no reason to suspect that the first three Mondays tend to produce negative returns). On the other hand, the difference between the first three Mondays and the last two Mondays was so large that it would rarely occur by chance, leading us to conclude that the last two Mondays really do (for whatever reason) tend to yield lower returns than the first three Mondays.

3.27. As described, there are two factors: ZIP code (three levels: none, 5-digit, 9-digit) and the day on which the letter is mailed (three levels: Monday, Thursday, or Saturday) for a total of 9 treatments. To control lurking variables, aside from mailing all letters to the same address, all letters should be the same size, and either printed in the same handwriting or typed. The design should also specify how many letters will be in each treatment group. Also, the letters should be sent randomly over many weeks.

3.28. Results will vary, but probability computations reveal that more than 97% of samples will have 7 to 13 fast-reacting subjects (and 99.6% of samples have 8 to 14 fast-reacting subjects). Additionally, if students average their 10 samples, nearly all students (more than 99%) should find that the average number of fast-reacting subjects is between 8.5 and 11.5.

   Note: *X, the number of fast-reacting subjects in the sample, has a hypergeometric distribution with parameters $N = 40$, $r = 20$, $n = 20$, so that $P(7 \leq X \leq 13) \doteq 0.974$. The theoretical average number of fast-reacting subjects is 10.*

3.29. Each player will be put through the sequence (100 yards, four times) twice—once with oxygen and once without, and we will observe the difference in their times on the final run. (If oxygen speeds recovery, we would expect that the oxygen-boosted time will be lower.) Randomly assign half of the players to use oxygen on the first trial, while the rest use it on the second trial. Trials should be on different days to allow ample time for full recovery.

   If we label the players 01 through 20 and begin on line 170, we choose 07, 13, 14, 02, 12, 20, 06, 08, 16, 03 to be in the oxygen-first group. See note on page 50 about using Table B.

3.30. The sketches requested in the problem are not shown here; random assignments will vary among students. **(a)** Label the circles 1 to 6, then randomly select three (using Table B, or simply by rolling a die) to receive the extra CO_2. Observe the growth in all six regions, and compare the mean growth within the three treated circles with the mean growth in the other three (control) circles. **(b)** Select pairs of circles in each of three different areas of the forest. For each pair, randomly select one circle to receive the extra CO_2 (using Table B or by flipping a coin). For each pair, compute the difference in growth (treated minus control).

3.31. (a) Randomly assign half the girls to get high-calcium punch, and the other half get low-calcium punch. The response variable is not clearly described in this exercise; the best we can say is "observe how the calcium is processed." **(b)** Randomly select half of the girls to receive high-calcium punch first, while the other half gets low-calcium punch first, then for each subject, compute the difference in the response variable for each level. This is a better design because it deals with person-to-person variation; the differences in responses for 60 individuals gives more precise results than the difference in the average responses for two groups of 30 subjects. **(c)** The first five subjects are 16, 34, 59, 44, and 21. In the CR design, the first group receives high-calcium punch all summer; in the matched pairs design, they receive high-calcium punch for the first part of the summer, and then low-calcium punch in the second half.

3.32. (a) Ordered by increasing weight, the five blocks are

(1)	Williams	22	Festinger	24	Hernandez	25	Moses	25
(2)	Santiago	27	Kendall	28	Mann	28	Smith	29
(3)	Brunk	30	Obrach	30	Rodriguez	30	Loren	32
(4)	Jackson	33	Stall	33	Brown	34	Dixon	34
(5)	Birnbaum	35	Tran	35	Nevesky	39	Wilansky	42

(b) The exact randomization will vary with the starting line in Table B. Different methods are possible; perhaps the simplest is to number from 1 to 4 within each block, then assign the members of block 1 to a weight-loss treatment, then assign block 2, and so on. For example, starting on line 133, we assign 4–Moses to treatment A, 1–Williams to B, and

3–Hernandez to C (so that 2–Festinger gets treatment D), then carry on for block 2, and so forth (either continuing on the same line or starting over somewhere else).

3.33. The simplest design would be a completely randomized design, assigning half of the women to take strontium renelate and half to take the placebo. A better design would block according to the medical center (and country); that is, randomly select for the strontium renelate group half the women from country A, half of those from country B, and so on. This blocking would take care of any differences in the level of medical care from one country to the next.

3.34. (a) This is a block design. (b) The diagram might be similar to the one below (which assumes equal numbers of subjects in each group). (c) The results observed in this study would rarely have occurred by chance if vitamin C were ineffective.

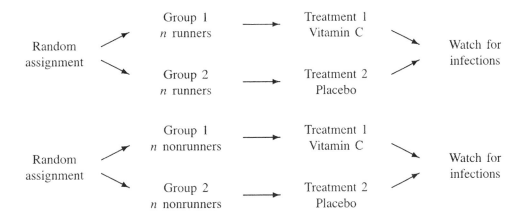

3.35. (a) False. Such regularity holds only in the long run. If it were true, you could look at the first 39 digits and know whether or not the 40th was a 0. (b) True. All pairs of digits (there are 100, from 00 to 99) are equally likely. (c) False. Four random digits have chance 1/10000 to be 0000, so this sequence will occasionally occur. 0000 is no more or less random than 1234 or 2718, or any other four-digit sequence.

3.36. The population is (all) local businesses. The sample is the 73 businesses that return the questionnaire, *or* the 150 businesses selected. The nonresponse rate is $51.3\% = \frac{77}{150}$.

Note: *The definition of "sample" makes it somewhat unclear whether the sample includes all the businesses selected, or only those which responded. My inclination is toward the latter (the smaller group), which is consistent with the idea that the sample is "a part of the population that we actually examine."*

3.37. (a) The population is adult residents of the U.S. The sample size is 1002. (b) Perhaps people are more inclined to respond with the first or last option they hear. Rotating the order of the options would cancel out any effect on the response of such inclinations.

3.38. Exact descriptions of the populations may vary. (a) Adult residents of the U.S. (b) All pieces of wood in the lot. (c) All U.S. households.

3.39. **(a)** The population is (something like) adult residents of the U.S. **(b)** The nonresponse rate is $\frac{669}{1800} \doteq 37.2\%$. **(c)** This question will likely have response bias; specifically, many people will give an inaccurate count of how many movies they have seen in the past year.

3.40. Numbering from 01 to 33 alphabetically (down the columns), we enter Table B at line 117 and choose
   16=Fairington, 32=Waterford Court, 18=Fowler, 06=Briarwood, 23=Mayfair Village.
See note on page 50 about using Table B.

3.41. Numbering from 01 to 32 alphabetically (down the columns), we enter Table B at line 139 and choose
   04=Bell, 10=Fernandez, 17=Johnson, 19=Molina, 12=Gandhi,
   32=Zhao, 13=Garcia, 18=Kim, 24=Prince, 28=Samuels.
See note on page 50 about using Table B.

3.42. Population = 1 to **33** , Select a sample of size **5** , then click **Reset** and **Sample** .

3.43. With the applet: Population = 1 to **371** , Select a sample of size **25** , then click **Reset** and **Sample** . With Table B, line 149 gives the codes labeled 353, 246, 027, 038, and 207.

3.44. One could use the labels already assigned to the blocks, but that would mean skipping a lot of four-digit combinations that do not correspond to any block. An alternative would be to drop the second digit and use labels 100,101,102,. . . ,105; 200,. . . ,211; 300,. . . ,325. But by far the simplest approach is to assign labels 01, . . . , 44 (in numerical order by the four-digit numbers already assigned), enter the table at line 125, and select:
   21 (#3002), 37 (#3018), 18 (#2011), 44 (#3025), and 23 (#3004).
See note on page 50 about using Table B.

3.45. If one always begins at the same place, then the results could not really be called random.

3.46. The sample will vary with the starting line in Table B. The simplest method is to use the last digit of the numbers assigned to the blocks in Group 1 (that is, assign the labels 0–5), then choose one of those blocks; use the last two digits of the blocks in Group 2 (00–11) and choose two of those, and finally use the last two digits of the blocks in Group 3 (00–25) and choose three of them.

3.47. **(a)** If we choose one of the first 45 students, and then every 45th name after that, we will have a total of $\frac{9000}{45} = 200$ names. **(b)** Label the first 45 names 01–45. Beginning at line 145, the first number we find is 19, so we choose names 19, 64, 109, ...

3.48. Considering the 9000 students of Exercise 3.47, each student is equally likely; specifically, each name has chance 1/45 of being selected. To see this, note that each of the first 45 has chance 1/45 because one is chosen at random. But each student in the second 45 is chosen exactly when the corresponding student in the first 45 is, so each of the second

45 also has chance 1/45. And so on.

This is not an SRS because the only possible samples have exactly one name from the first 45, one name from the second 45, and so on; that is, there are only 45 possible samples. An SRS could contain *any* 200 of the 9000 students in the population.

3.49. (a) This is a stratified random sample. **(b)** Label from 01 through 25; beginning at line 111, we choose

12 (559), 04 (209), 11 (805), 19 (562), 02 (707),

06 (925), 08 (650), 25 (619), 17 (626), and 14 (661).

3.50. Assign labels 01–36 for the Climax 1 group, 01–72 for the Climax 2 group, and so on. Then beginning at line 162, choose

34, 14, 15, 36 from the Climax 1 group, and (continuing on in Table B) choose

23, 36, 21, 11, 55, 27, 14 from the Climax 2 group,

28, 31, 09 from the Climax 3 group, and

03, 41, 37, 16 from the mature secondary group.

See note on page 50 about using Table B.

3.51. Label the students 01, . . . , 30 and use Table B. Then label the faculty 0, . . . , 9 and use the table again. (You could also label the faculty from 01 to 10, but that would needlessly require two-digit labels.)

Note: *Students often try some fallacious method of choosing both samples simultaneously. We simply want to choose two separate SRSs: one from the students and one from the faculty. See note on page 50 about using Table B.*

3.52. Each student has a 10% chance: 3 out of 30 over-21 students, and 2 of 20 under-21 students. This is not an SRS because not every group of 5 students can be chosen; the only possible samples are those with 3 older and 2 younger students.

3.53. Label the 500 midsize accounts from 001 to 500, and the 4400 small accounts from 0001 to 4400. On line 115, we first encounter numbers 417, 494, 322, 247, and 097 for the midsize group, then 3698, 1452, 2605, 2480, and 3716 for the small group. See note on page 50 about using Table B.

3.54. The higher no-answer was probably the second period—more families are likely to be gone for vacations, and so on. Nonresponse of this type might underrepresent those who are more affluent (and are able to travel). In general, high nonresponse rates always make results less reliable, because we do not know what information we are missing.

3.55. (a) This design would omit households without telephones or with unlisted numbers. Such households would likely be made up of poor individuals (who cannot afford a phone), those who choose not to have phones, and those who do not wish to have their phone numbers published. **(b)** Those with unlisted numbers would be included in the sampling frame when a random-digit dialer is used.

3.56. **(a)** There were 14,484 responses. (Note that we have no guarantee that these came from 14,484 distinct people; some may have voted more than once.) **(b)** This voluntary response sample collects only the opinions of those who visit this site and feel strongly enough to respond.

3.57. **(a)** This will almost certainly produce a positive response, because it draws the dubious conclusion that cell phones *cause* brain cancer. Some people who drive cars, or eat carrots, or vote Republican develop brain cancer, too. Do we conclude that these activities should come with warning labels, also? **(b)** The phrasing of this question will tend to make people respond in favor of national health insurance: It lists two benefits of such a system, and no arguments from the other side of the issue. **(c)** This sentence is so convoluted and complicated that it is almost unreadable, and is also vague (what sort of 'economic incentives'? How much would this cost?). A better phrasing might be, "Would you be willing to pay more for the products you buy if the extra cost were used to conserve resources by encouraging recycling?" That is still vague, but less so, and is written in plain English.

3.58. The first wording brought the higher numbers in favor of a tax cut; "new government programs" has considerably less appeal than the list of specific programs given in the second wording.

3.59. Children from larger families will be overrepresented in such a sample. Student explanations of why will vary; a simple illustration can aid in understanding this effect. Suppose that there are 100 families with children; 60 families have one child, and the other 40 have three. Then there are a total of 180 children (an average of 1.8 children per family), and *two-thirds* of those children come from families with three children. Therefore, if we had a class (a sample) chosen from these 180 children, only one-third of the class would answer "one" to the teacher's question, and the rest would say "three." This would give an average of about 2.3 children per family.

3.61. Responses to public opinion polls can be affected by things like the wording of the question, as was the case here: Both statements address the question of how to distribute wealth in a society, but subtle (and not-so-subtle) slants in the wording suggest that the public holds conflicting opinions on the subjects.

3.62. 621 is a statistic (related to the sample of 2000 phone numbers); 35% is a parameter (related to the population of all residential phone numbers).

3.63. 72% is a statistic (related to the sample of 663 registered voters); 56% is a parameter (related to the population of all registered voters).

3.64. Both 40.2% and 31.7% are statistics (related, respectively, to the samples of small-class and large-class black students).

3.65. Both 283 and 311 pushes per minute are statistics (related to one sample: the subjects with placebo, and the same subjects with caffeine).

3.66. (a) High bias, high variability (many are low, wide scatter). (b) Low bias, low variability, (close to parameter, little scatter). (c) Low bias, high variability (neither too low nor too high, wide scatter). (d) High bias, low variability (too high, little scatter).

Note: *Make sure that students understand that "high bias" means that the values are far from the parameter, not that they are too high.*

3.67. (a) The sample size for Hispanics was smaller. Smaller sample sizes give less information about the population, and therefore lead to larger margins of error (with the same confidence level). (b) The sample size was so small, and the margin of error so large, that the results could not be viewed as an accurate reflection of the population of Cubans.

3.68. No: With sufficiently large populations ("at least 100 times larger than the sample"), the variability (and margin of error) depends on the sample size.

3.69. (a) Because the smallest population is still more than 100 times the sample size, the variability will be (approximately) the same for all states. (b) Yes, it will change—the sample size would vary from 500 in Wyoming to 35,000 in California, so the margin of error would be smaller in larger states.

3.70. (a) The population is Ontario residents; the sample is the 61,239 people interviewed. (b) The sample size is very large, so if there were large numbers of both sexes in the sample—this is a safe assumption because we are told this is a "random sample"—these two numbers should be fairly accurate reflections of the values for the whole population.

3.71. See also the solution to Exercise 1.146. (a) Answers will vary, but almost all means will be between $25,000 and $80,000 (see Figure 3.14 in the text). (b) For samples of size 25, means range from $25,000 to $80,000; for samples of size 100, the range is $35,000 to $65,000 (although very few means exceeded $60,000). This illustrates that sampling variability decreases as sample size increases. (c) Based on the histogram, the mean is between $45,000 and $50,000. (The actual mean of the 71,076 incomes is $46,050.)

3.72. (a) Answers will vary. If, for example, eight heads are observed, then $\hat{p} = \frac{8}{20} = 0.4 = 40\%$. (b) Note that all the leaves in the stemplot should be either 0 or 5, since all possible $\hat{p}$-values end in 0 or 5. For comparison, here is a histogram of the sampling distribution (assuming p

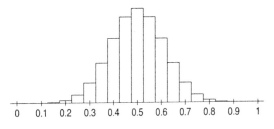

really is 0.5). An individual student's stemplot will probably only roughly approximate this distribution, but pooled efforts should be fairly close.

3.73. (a) The histogram should be centered at about 0.6 (with quite a bit of spread). For reference, the theoretical histogram is shown below on the left; student results should have a similar appearance. (b) The histogram should be centered at about 0.2 (with quite a bit of spread). The theoretical histogram is shown below on the right.

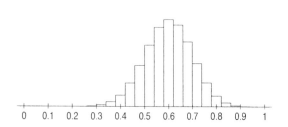 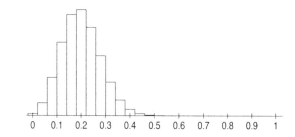

3.74. (a) The histogram of this theoretical sampling distribution is shown (on the right) for reference. (b) This theoretical sampling distribution is shown below on the left. Students should observe that their two stemplots have clearly different centers (near 0.6 and 0.3, respectively), but similar spreads. (c) The

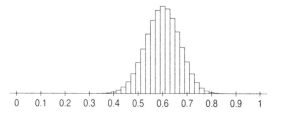

theoretical sampling distribution is below on the right. Compared to the distribution of (a), this has the same center, but is about half as wide; that is, the spread is about half as much when the sample size is multiplied by 4. (The vertical scale of this graph is not the same as the other two; it should be about twice as tall as it is, since it is only about half as wide.)

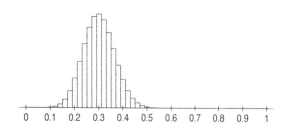 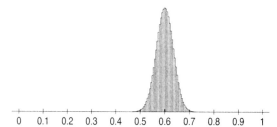

3.75. (a) The scores will vary depending on the starting row. Note that the smallest possible mean is 61.75 (from the sample 58, 62, 62, 65) and the largest is 77.25 (from 73, 74, 80, 82). (b) Answers will vary; shown below are two views of the (exact) sampling distribution. The first shows all possible values of the experiment (so the first rectangle is for 61.75, the next is for 62.00, etc.); the other shows values grouped from 61 to 61.75, 62 to 62.75, etc. (which makes the histogram less bumpy). The tallest rectangle in the first picture is 8 units; in the second, the tallest is 28 units.

   Note: *These histograms were found by considering all $\binom{10}{4} = 210$ of the possible* *samples. It happens that half (105) of those samples yield a mean smaller than 69.4 and half yield a greater mean.*

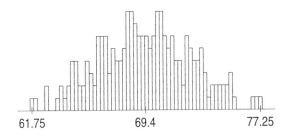 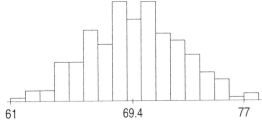

3.76. Student results will vary greatly, and ten values of $\bar{x}$ will give little indication of the appearance of the sampling distribution. In fact, the sampling distribution of $\bar{x}$ is approximately normal with a mean of 50.5 and a standard deviation of about 8.92; this approximating normal distribution is shown on the right (above). Therefore, nearly every sample of size 10 would yield a mean between 23 and 78.

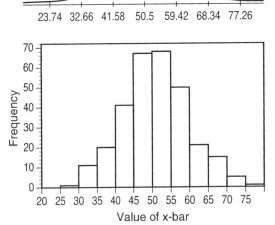

The shape of the sampling distribution becomes more apparent if the results of many students are pooled. Below on the right is an example based on 300 sample means, which might arise from pooling all the results in a class of 30.

Note: *Because the values in these samples are not independent (there can be no repeats), a stronger version of the central limit theorem is needed to determine that the sampling distribution is approximately normal. Confirming the standard deviation given above is a reasonably difficult exercise even for a mathematics major.*

3.77. (a) Below is the population stemplot (which gives the same information as a histogram). The (population) mean GPA is $\mu \doteq 2.6352$, and the standard deviation is $\sigma \doteq 0.7794$. [Technically, we should take $\sigma \doteq 0.7777$, which comes from dividing by n rather than $n - 1$, but few (if any) students would know this, and it has little effect on the results.]
(b) & (c) Results will vary; these histograms are not shown. Not every sample of size 20 could be viewed as "generally representative of the population," but most should bear at least some resemblance to the population distribution.

```
0 | 134
0 | 567889
1 | 0011233444
1 | 5566667888888888999999
2 | 000000000111111111222222222333333333344444444
2 | 5555555555555566666666777777777777778888888888888999999
3 | 000000000000001111111111122222222223333333333333333344444444
3 | 5566666666677777788889
4 | 0000
```

3.78. (a) Shown for reference is a histogram of the approximate sampling distribution of $\bar{x}$. This distribution is difficult to find exactly, but based on 1000 simulated samples, it is approximately normal with mean 2.6352 (the same as μ) and standard deviation $s_{\bar{x}} \doteq 0.167$. (Therefore, $\bar{x}$ will almost

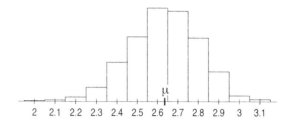

always be between 2.13 and 3.14.) **(b)** Results may vary, but most students should see no strong suggestion of bias. **(c)** Student means and standard deviations will vary, but for most (if not all) students, their values should meet the expectations (close to $\mu \doteq 2.6352$ and less than $\sigma \doteq 0.78$).

   Note: *Observe that the distribution of $\bar{x}$ is slightly left-skewed, but less than the population distribution. Also note that $s_{\bar{x}}$, the standard deviation of the sampling distribution, is smaller than $\sigma/\sqrt{20} \doteq 0.174$, since we are sampling without replacement.*

3.79. (a) The simplest approach is to label from 00001 through 14959, and then take five digits at a time from the table. A few clever students might think of some ways to make this process more efficient, such as taking the first random digit chosen as "0" if it is even and "1" if odd. (This way, fewer numbers need to be ignored.) **(b)** Using labels 00001–14959, we choose 03638, 07871, and 12193. Students who try an alternate approach may have a different sample.

3.80. (a) Possible response variables: Whether or not a subject has a job within some period of time, number of hours worked during some period, length of time before subject became employed. For the design, randomly assign about one-third of the group (3,355 subjects) to each treatment, and observe the chosen response variables after a suitable amount of time. **(b)** The simplest approach is to label from 00001 through 10065, and then take five digits at a time from the table. (This means we have to skip about 90% of the five-digit sets, as only those beginning with 0 [and a few beginning with 1] are useful.) With this approach, we choose 00850, 02182, and 00681 (the last of these is on line 172). More efficient labellings are possible and will lead to different samples.

3.81. (a) A matched pairs design (two halves of the same board would have similar properties). **(b)** A sample survey (with a stratified sample: smokers and nonsmokers). **(c)** A block design (blocked by gender).

3.82. (a) In a serious case, when the patient has little chance of surviving, a doctor might choose not to recommend surgery; it might be seen as an unnecessary measure, bringing expense and a hospital stay with little benefit to the patient. **(b)** Diagram below.

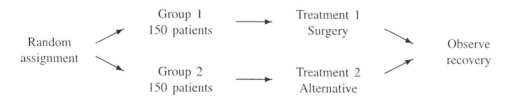

3.83. This is an experiment, because each subject is (randomly, we assume) assigned to a treatment. The explanatory variable is the price history seen by the subject (steady prices or fluctuating prices), and the response variable is the price the subject expects to pay.

3.84. (a) A sample survey: We want to gather information about a population (U.S. residents) based on a sample. **(b)** An experiment: We want to establish a cause-and-effect relationship between teaching method and amount learned. **(c)** An observational study: There is no particular population from which we will sample; we simply observe "your teachers," much like an animal behavioral specialist might study animals in the wild.

3.86. Each subject should taste both kinds of cheeseburger, in a randomly selected order, and then be asked about preference. Both burgers should have the same "fixings" (ketchup, mustard, etc.). Because some subjects might be able to identify the cheeseburgers by appearance, one might need to take additional steps (such as blindfolding or serving only the center part of the burger) in order to make this a true "blind" experiment.

3.87. The two factors are gear (three levels) and steepness of the course (number of levels not specified). Assuming there are at least three steepness levels—which seems like the smallest reasonable choice—that means at least nine treatments. Randomization should be used to determine the order in which the treatments are applied. Note that we must allow ample recovery time between trials, and it would be best to have the rider try each treatment several times.

3.89. (a) One possible population: all full-time undergraduate students in the fall term on a list provided by the registrar. **(b)** A stratified sample with 125 students from each year is one possibility. **(c)** Mailed (or e-mailed) questionnaires might have high nonresponse rates. Telephone interviews exclude those without phones and may mean repeated calling for those who are not home. Face-to-face interviews might be more costly than your funding will allow. There might also be some response bias: Some students might be hesitant about criticizing the faculty (while others might be far too eager to do so).

3.90. (a) The treatment combinations are shown in the table on the right, and the design is diagrammed below. **(b)** Larger samples give more information; in particular, with large samples, we reduce the variability in the

		Injection	Skin patch	IV drip
Factor A **Dosage**	5 mg	Treatment 1	Treatment 2	Treatment 3
	10 mg	Treatment 4	Treatment 5	Treatment 6

Factor B
Administration method

observed mean concentrations, so that we can have more confidence that the differences we might observe are due to the treatment applied rather than random fluctuation.

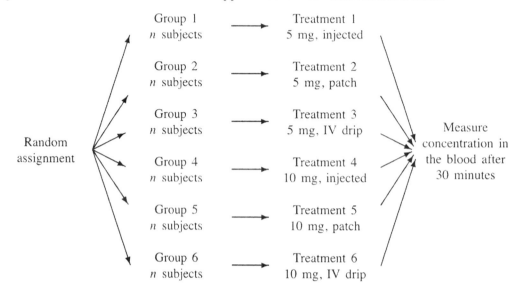

3.91. (a) The factors are storage method (three levels: fresh, room temperature for one month, refrigerated for one month) and preparation method (two levels: cooked immediately, or after one hour). There are therefore six treatments (summarized in the table on the right). The response variables are the tasters' color and flavor ratings. **(b)** Randomly allocate n

	Cooked immediately	Wait one hour
Fresh	Treatment 1	Treatment 2
Stored	Treatment 3	Treatment 4
Refrigerated	Treatment 5	Treatment 6

potatoes to each of the six groups, then compare ratings. (Diagram not shown.) **(c)** For each taster, randomly choose the order in which the fries are tasted.

3.92. Use a block design: Separate men and women, and randomly allocate each gender among the six treatments.

3.93. Voluntary response samples are affected by strong feelings, promotional campaigns, and possibly multiple votes from one individual. Furthermore, online polls are also likely to overrepresent the opinions of the more technologically sophisticated (i.e., the "nerds"), which might account for tech hero Torvalds' advantage over figures like Mandela and Diana.

3.94. Parents who fail to return the consent form may be more likely to place less priority on education, and therefore may give their children less help with homework, and so forth. Including those children in the control group is likely to lower that group's score.

Note: *This is a generalization, to be sure: We are not saying that* every *such parent does not value education, only that the percentage of this group that highly values education will almost certainly be lower than that percentage of the parents who return the form.*

3.95. The latter method (CASI) will show a higher percentage of drug use, because respondents will generally be more comfortable (and more assured of anonymity) about revealing embarrassing or illegal behavior to a computer than to a person, so they will be more likely to be honest.

For answers to the EESEE Case Studies (exercises 96–99), see the instructor's version of EESEE.

Chapter 4 Solutions

4.1. Long trials of this experiment often approach 40% heads. One theory attributes this surprising result to a "bottle-cap effect" due to an unequal rim on the penny. We don't know. But a teaching assistant claims to have spent a profitable evening at a party betting on spinning coins after learning of the effect.

4.2. Note that in this experiment, factors other than the nickel's characteristics might affect the outcome. For example, if the surface used is not quite level, there will be a tendency for the penny to fall in the "downhill" direction.

4.3. The table on the right shows information from www.mms.com as of this writing. The exercise specified M&M's Milk Chocolate Candies, but based on these numbers, results will be similar for other popular varieties. Of course, answers will vary, but students who take reasonably large samples should get results close to the numbers in this

M&M's variety	Blue %
Milk Chocolate	24%
Peanut	23%
Almond	20%
Peanut Butter	20%
Crispy	17%

table. (For example, samples of size 50 will almost always be within ±12%, while size 75 should give results within ±10%.)

4.4. In the long run, of a large number of hands of five cards, the fraction containing two pairs will be about 1/21. It does not mean that exactly one out of 21 hands contains two pairs; that would mean, for example, that if you've been dealt 20 hands without two pairs, that you could count on the next hand having two pairs.

4.5. **(a)** Most answers will be between 35% and 65%. **(b)** Based on 10,000 simulated trials—more than students are expected to do—there is about an 80% chance of having a longest run of four or more (i.e., either making or missing four shots in a row), a 54% chance of getting five or more, a 31% chance of getting six or more, and a 16% chance of getting seven or more. The average ("expected") longest run length is about six.

4.6. **(a)** – **(c)** Results will vary, but after n tosses, the distribution of the proportion $\hat{p}$ is approximately normal with mean 0.5 and standard deviation $1/(2\sqrt{n})$, while the distribution of the count of heads is approximately normal with mean $0.5n$ and standard deviation $\sqrt{n}/2$, so using the 68–95–99.7 rule, we have the re-

n	99.7% Range for $\hat{p}$	99.7% Range for count
40	0.5 ± 0.237	20 ± 9.5
120	0.5 ± 0.137	60 ± 16.4
240	0.5 ± 0.097	120 ± 23.2
480	0.5 ± 0.068	240 ± 32.9

sults shown in the table on the right. Note that the range for $\hat{p}$ gets narrower, while the range for the count gets wider.

4.7. The true probability (assuming perfectly fair dice) is $1 - \left(\frac{5}{6}\right)^4 \doteq 0.5177$, so students should conclude that the probability is "quite close to 0.5."

4.8. **(a)** The distribution of this proportion is roughly normal with mean 0.3 and standard deviation 0.1, so the 25 results can be quite variable. A stemplot for one set of 25 trials is shown. **(b)** With 200 tosses, the standard deviation drops to about 0.032, so the stemplot should be much less spread out. (Note the different "scales" in these two stemplots: The first ranges from 0.10 to 0.55, and the second from 0.235 to 0.355.)

20 tosses		200 tosses	
1	0	23	5
1	5	24	
2	0	25	
2	5555	26	00
3	0000000	27	55
3	5555	28	055
4	00000	29	0055
4	5	30	05
5		31	0005
5	5	32	00
		33	55
		34	
		35	055

4.9. **(a)** One such histogram is shown below on the left. It should appear approximately normal with center near 0.3 and standard deviation about 0.1, so it will typically range from about 0.1 to 0.5. **(b)** Now the histogram (sample below, right) should appear to be roughly normal with mean 0.3 and standard deviation about 0.026, spread from about 0.22 to 0.38. **(c)** Both distributions are roughly normal with center near 0.3, but as expected, the larger sample leads to much less variability.

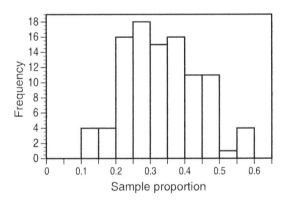 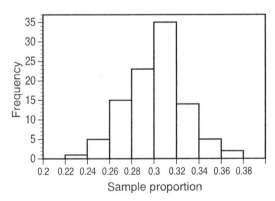

4.10. **(a)** $S = \{F, M\}$ or {female, male}. **(b)** $S = \{6, 7, \ldots, 20\}$. **(c)** $S = \{$All numbers between 2.5 and 6 l/min$\}$. **(d)** $S = \{$All numbers (or all whole numbers) between __ and __ bpm$\}$. (Choices of upper and lower limits will vary.)

4.11. **(a)** $S = \{$right, left$\}$. **(b)** $S = \{$All numbers between __ and __ cm$\}$. (Choices of upper and lower limits will vary.) **(c)** $S = \{$all numbers greater than or equal to 0$\}$, or $S = \{0, 0.01, 0.02, 0.03, \ldots\}$. **(d)** $S = \{$all numbers between 0 and 1440$\}$. (There are 1440 minutes in one day, so this is the *largest* upper limit we could choose; many students will likely give a smaller upper limit.)

4.12. **(a)** The table on the right illustrates the 16 possible pair combinations in the sample space. **(b)** Add 1 to each pair-total on the right: $S = \{3, 4, 5, 6, 7, 8, 9\}$.

4.13. (a) The given probabilities have sum 0.96, so P(type AB) = 0.04. **(b)** P(type O or B) = $0.45 + 0.11 = 0.56$.

4.14. P(both are type O) = $(0.45)(0.35) = 0.1575$. P(both are the same type) = $(0.45)(0.35) + (0.40)(0.27) + (0.11)(0.26) + (0.04)(0.12) = 0.2989$.

4.15. (a) Legitimate. **(b)** Not legitimate: The total is more than 1. **(c)** Legitimate.

4.16. (a) The given probabilities have sum 0.89, so P(other language) = 0.11. **(b)** P(not English) = $1 - 0.59 = 0.41$. (Or, add the other three probabilities.)

4.17. (a) The given probabilities have sum 0.72, so this probability must be 0.28. **(b)** P(at least a high school education) = $1 - P$(has not finished HS) = $1 - 0.12 = 0.88$. (Or, add the other three probabilities.)

4.18. (a) The given probabilities have sum 0.81, so P(other topic) = 0.19. **(b)** P(adult or scam) = $0.145 + 0.142 = 0.287$.

> **Note:** *An underlying assumption here is that each piece of spam falls into exactly one category.*

4.19. If P(Red Sox win) = P(Angels win) = x, then P(Athletics win) = P(White Sox win) = $\frac{1}{3}x$, and $0.6 + x + x + \frac{1}{3}x + \frac{1}{3}x = 1$. Therefore $\frac{8}{3}x = 0.4$, so $x = 0.15$. Thus the whole set of probabilities is

Team	Yankees	Red Sox	Angels	Athletics	White Sox
Probability	0.6	0.15	0.15	0.05	0.05

4.20. See also the solution to Exercise 4.12. As all faces are equally likely and the dice are independent, each of the 16 possible pairings is equally likely, so (for example) the probability of a total of 5 is 3/16, because 3 pairings add to 4 (and then we add 1). The complete set of probabilities is shown in the table.

Total	Probability
3	1/16
4	2/16
5	3/16
6	4/16
7	3/16
8	2/16
9	1/16

4.21. The probabilities of 2, 3, 4 and 5 are unchanged (1/6), so $P(\boxed{\cdot}$ or $\boxed{:\,:})$ must still be 1/3. If $P(\boxed{:\,:}) = 0.2$, then $P(\boxed{\cdot}) = \frac{1}{3} - 0.2 = 0.1\overline{3}$ (or $\frac{2}{15}$).

Face	$\boxed{\cdot}$	$\boxed{\cdot\,}$	$\boxed{\cdot\cdot}$	$\boxed{:\cdot}$	$\boxed{:\cdot}$	$\boxed{:\,:}$
Probability	$0.1\overline{3}$	1/6	1/6	1/6	1/6	0.2

4.22. (a) It is legitimate because every person must fall into exactly one category, and the probabilities add to 1. **(b)** $P(A) = 0.125 = 0.000 + 0.003 + 0.060 + 0.062$. **(c)** B^c is the event "the person chosen is not white." $P(B^c) = 1 - P(B) = 1 - (0.060 + 0.691) = 0.249$. **(d)** $P(A^c$ and $B) = 0.691$ is the probability that a randomly chosen American is a non-Hispanic white.

4.23. For example, the probability for O-positive blood is $(0.45)(0.84) = 0.378$, and for O-negative it is $(0.45)(0.16) = 0.072$.

Blood type	O+	O–	A+	A–	B+	B–	AB+	AB–
Probability	0.3780	0.0720	0.3360	0.0640	0.0924	0.0176	0.0336	0.0064

4.24. We found in Exercise 4.22 that $P(A) = 0.125$ and that $P(B) = 0.751$. (We actually computed $P(B^c) = 0.249$.) Because $P(A)P(B) \doteq 0.094$ is not equal to $P(A \text{ and } B) = 0.060$ (from the table in Exercise 4.22), A and B are *not* independent.

4.25. (a) All are equally likely; the probability is $1/38$. (b) Because 18 slots are red, the probability of a red is $P(\text{red}) = \frac{18}{38} \doteq 0.474$. (c) There are 12 winning slots, so $P(\text{win a column bet}) = \frac{12}{38} \doteq 0.316$.

4.26. (a) There are six arrangements of the digits 1, 2, and 3 (123, 132, 213, 231, 312, 321), so that $P(\text{win}) = \frac{6}{1000} = 0.006$. (b) With the digits 1, 1, and 2, there are only three distinct arrangements (112, 121, 211), so $P(\text{win}) = \frac{3}{1000} = 0.003$.

4.27. (a) There are $10^4 = 10,000$ possible PINs (0000 through 9999).* (b) The probability that a PIN has *no* 0s is 0.9^4 (because there are 9^4 PINs that can be made from the nine nonzero digits), so the probability of at least one 0 is $1 - 0.9^4 = 0.3439$.

*If we assume that PINs cannot have leading 0s, then there are only 9000 possible codes (1000–9999), and the probability of at least one 0 is $1 - \frac{9^4}{9000} = 0.271$.

4.28. $P(\text{none are O-negative}) = (1 - 0.07)^{10} \doteq 0.4840$, so $P(\text{at least one is O-negative}) \doteq 1 - 0.4840 = 0.5160$.

4.29. If we assume that each site is independent of the others (and that they can be considered as a random sample from the collection of sites referenced in scientific journals), then $P(\text{all seven are still good}) = 0.87^7 \doteq 0.3773$.

4.30. (a) About 0.33: $P(\text{no calls reach a live person}) \doteq (1 - 0.2)^5 = 0.8^5 = 0.32768$.
(b) About 0.66: $P(\text{no NY calls reach a live person}) \doteq 0.92^5 \doteq 0.65908$.

4.31. This computation would only be correct if the events "a randomly selected person is at least 75" and "a randomly selected person is a woman" were independent. This is likely not true; in particular, as women have a greater life expectancy than men, this fraction is probably greater than 3%.

4.32. As $P(R) = \frac{2}{6}$ and $P(G) = \frac{4}{6}$, and successive rolls are independent, the respective probabilities are $\left(\frac{2}{6}\right)^4 \left(\frac{4}{6}\right) = \frac{2}{243} \doteq 0.00823$, $\left(\frac{2}{6}\right)^4 \left(\frac{4}{6}\right)^2 = \frac{4}{729} \doteq 0.00549$, and $\left(\frac{2}{6}\right)^5 \left(\frac{4}{6}\right) = \frac{2}{729} \doteq 0.00274$.

4.33. (a) $(0.65)^3 \doteq 0.2746$ (under the random walk theory). (b) 0.35 (because performance in separate years is independent). (c) $(0.65)^2 + (0.35)^2 = 0.545$.

4.34. For any event A, along with its complement A^c, we have $P(S) = P(A \text{ or } A^c)$ because "$A \text{ or } A^c$" includes all possible outcomes (that is, it is the entire sample space S). By Rule 2, $P(S) = 1$, and by Rule 3, $P(A \text{ or } A^c) = P(A) + P(A^c)$, because A and A^c are disjoint. Therefore, $P(A) + P(A^c) = 1$, from which Rule 4 follows.

4.35. Note that $A = (A \text{ and } B) \text{ or } (A \text{ and } B^c)$, and the events $(A \text{ and } B)$ and $(A \text{ and } B^c)$ are disjoint, so Rule 3 says that

$$P(A) = P\big((A \text{ and } B) \text{ or } (A \text{ and } B^c)\big) = P(A \text{ and } B) + P(A \text{ and } B^c).$$

If $P(A \text{ and } B) = P(A)P(B)$, then we have

$$P(A \text{ and } B^c) = P(A) - P(A)P(B) = P(A)(1 - P(B)),$$

which equals $P(A)P(B^c)$ by the complement rule.

4.36. (a) Hannah and Jacob's children can have alleles AA, BB, or AB, so they can have blood type A, B, or AB. (The table on the right shows the possible combinations.) **(b)** Either note that the four combinations in the table are equally likely, or compute:

	A	B
A	AA	AB
B	AB	BB

$$P(\text{type A}) = P(\text{A from Hannah and A from Jacob}) = P(A_H)P(A_J) = 0.5^2 = 0.25$$
$$P(\text{type B}) = P(\text{B from Hannah and B from Jacob}) = P(B_H)P(B_J) = 0.5^2 = 0.25$$
$$P(\text{type AB}) = P(A_H)P(B_J) + P(B_H)P(A_J) = 2 \cdot 0.25 = 0.5.$$

4.37. (a) Nancy and David's children can have alleles BB, BO, or OO, so they can have blood type B or O. (The table on the right shows the possible combinations.) **(b)** Either note that the four combinations in the table are equally likely, or compute $P(\text{type O}) = P(\text{O from Nancy and O from David}) = 0.5^2 = 0.25$, and $P(\text{type B}) = 1 - P(\text{type O}) = 0.75$.

	B	O
B	BB	BO
O	BO	OO

4.38. Any child of Jennifer and José has a 50% chance of being type A (alleles AA or AO), and each child inherits alleles independently of other children, so $P(\text{both are type A}) = 0.5^2 = 0.25$. For one child, we have $P(\text{type A}) = 0.5$ and $P(\text{type AB}) = P(\text{type B}) = 0.25$, so that $P(\text{both have same type}) = 0.5^2 + 0.25^2 + 0.25^2 = 0.375 = \frac{3}{8}$.

	A	O
A	AA	AO
B	AB	BO

4.39. (a) Any child of Jasmine and Joshua has an equal (1/4) chance of having blood type AB, A, B, or O (see the allele combinations in the table). Therefore, $P(\text{type O}) = 0.25$. **(b)** $P(\text{all three have type O}) = 0.25^3 = 0.015625 = \frac{1}{64}$. $P(\text{first has type O, next two do not}) = 0.25 \cdot 0.75^2 = 0.140625 = \frac{9}{64}$.

	A	O
B	AB	BO
O	AO	OO

4.40. The RPE rating in (b) is discrete, because the description says that it "ranges in whole-number steps from 6 ... to 20." VO2 and maximum heart rate are continuous.

   Note: *In practice, heart rate is given as a whole number, for example, "60 bpm" rather than "59.63 bpm." For this reason, the argument could be made that this is discrete. In fact, since we cannot measure anything with infinite precision, one could say that, in practice, everything is discrete. Be aware that this distinction can be somewhat unclear to students; you (the instructor) will need to decide how to handle this.*

4.41. (a) "At least one nonword error" is the event "$X \geq 1$" (or "$X > 0$").
$P(X \geq 1) = 1 - P(X = 0) = 0.9$. **(b)** "$X \leq 2$" is "no more than two nonword errors," or "fewer than three nonword errors." $P(X \leq 2) = P(X = 0) + P(X = 1) + P(X = 2) = 0.1 + 0.2 + 0.3 = 0.6$. $P(X < 2) = P(X = 0) + P(X = 1) = 0.1 + 0.2 = 0.3$.

4.42. About 0.017: $P(Y > 300) = P\left(\frac{Y-266}{16} > \frac{300-266}{16}\right) = P(Z > 2.125)$. Software gives 0.0168; Table A gives 0.0166 for -2.13 and 0.0170 for -2.12 (so the average is again 0.0168).

4.43. The two histograms are shown below. Rented housing typically has fewer rooms, and its distribution is considerably more skewed than the owned-housing distribution.

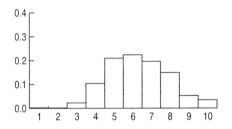 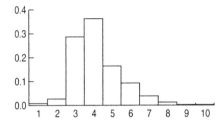

4.44. The two histograms are shown below. The most obvious difference is that a "family" must have at least two people. Otherwise, the family-size distribution has slightly larger probabilities for 2, 3, or 4, while for large family/household sizes, the differences between the distributions are small.

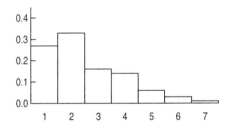 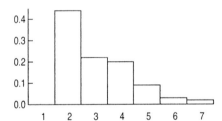

4.45. (a) "The unit has 5 or more rooms" is "$X \geq 5$" or "$X > 4$." $P(X \geq 5) = 0.210 + 0.224 + 0.197 + 0.149 + 0.053 + 0.035 = 0.868$. **(b)** "$X > 5$" is "the unit has more than 5 (or at least 6) rooms." $P(X > 5) = 0.658$. **(c)** With discrete distributions, one must pay attention to whether or not the endpoints should be included in the probability computation. (That is, pay attention to whether you have "greater than" or "greater than or equal to.")

4.46. (a) "More than one person lives in this household" is "$Y > 1$" or "$Y \geq 2$."
$P(Y > 1) = 1 - P(Y = 1) = 1 - 0.27 = 0.73$. **(b)** $P(2 < Y \leq 4) = P(Y = 3 \text{ or } Y = 4) = 0.16 + 0.14 = 0.30$. **(c)** $P(Y \neq 2) = 1 - P(Y = 2) = 1 - 0.33 = 0.67$.

4.47. (a) $P(T = 2) = P(\text{your friend breaks the chain}) = 1 - 0.37 = 0.63$. $P(T = 3) = P(\text{your friend's friend breaks the chain}) = (0.37)(0.63) = 0.2331$. **(b)** $P(T \leq 4)$ is the probability that the message stops before reaching the fifth person—that is, one of the first three people to receive it breaks the chain. $P(T \leq 4) = 0.63 + (0.37)(0.63) + (0.37)(0.37)(0.63) \doteq 0.9493$.

4.48. (a) The pairs are given below. We must assume that we can distinguish between, e.g., "(1,2)" and "(2,1)"; otherwise the outcomes are not equally likely. **(b)** Each pair has probability 1/36. **(c)** The value of X is given below each pair. For the distribution (given below), we see (for example) that there are four pairs that add to 5, so $P(X = 5) = \frac{4}{36}$. Histogram below, right. **(d)** $P(7 \text{ or } 11) = \frac{6}{36} + \frac{2}{36} = \frac{8}{36} = \frac{2}{9}$. **(e)** $P(\text{not } 7) = 1 - \frac{6}{36} = \frac{5}{6}$.

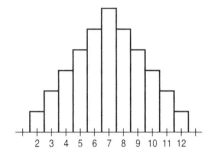

(1,1)	(1,2)	(1,3)	(1,4)	(1,5)	(1,6)
2	3	4	5	6	7
(2,1)	(2,2)	(2,3)	(2,4)	(2,5)	(2,6)
3	4	5	6	7	8
(3,1)	(3,2)	(3,3)	(3,4)	(3,5)	(3,6)
4	5	6	7	8	9
(4,1)	(4,2)	(4,3)	(4,4)	(4,5)	(4,6)
5	6	7	8	9	10
(5,1)	(5,2)	(5,3)	(5,4)	(5,5)	(5,6)
6	7	8	9	10	11
(6,1)	(6,2)	(6,3)	(6,4)	(6,5)	(6,6)
7	8	9	10	11	12

Value of X	2	3	4	5	6	7	8	9	10	11	12
Probability	$\frac{1}{36}$	$\frac{2}{36}$	$\frac{3}{36}$	$\frac{4}{36}$	$\frac{5}{36}$	$\frac{6}{36}$	$\frac{5}{36}$	$\frac{4}{36}$	$\frac{3}{36}$	$\frac{2}{36}$	$\frac{1}{36}$

4.49. The possible values of Y are 1,2,3,...,12, each with probability 1/12. Aside from drawing a diagram showing all the possible combinations, one can reason that the first (regular) die is equally likely to show any number from 1 through 6. Half of the time, the second roll shows 0, and the rest of the time it shows 6. Each possible outcome therefore has probability $\frac{1}{6} \cdot \frac{1}{2}$.

4.50. The table on the right shows the additional columns to add to the table given in the solution to Exercise 4.48. There are 48 possible (equally-likely) combinations.

Value of X	2	3	4	5	6	7	8	9	10	11	12	13	14
Probability	$\frac{1}{48}$	$\frac{2}{48}$	$\frac{3}{48}$	$\frac{4}{48}$	$\frac{5}{48}$	$\frac{6}{48}$	$\frac{6}{48}$	$\frac{6}{48}$	$\frac{5}{48}$	$\frac{4}{48}$	$\frac{3}{48}$	$\frac{2}{48}$	$\frac{1}{48}$

(1,7)	(1,8)
8	9
(2,7)	(2,8)
9	10
(3,7)	(3,8)
10	11
(4,7)	(4,8)
11	12
(5,7)	(5,8)
12	13
(6,7)	(6,8)
13	14

4.51. **(a)** W can be 0, 1, 2, or 3. **(b)** See the top two lines of the table below. **(c)** The distribution is given in the bottom two lines of the table. For example, $P(W = 0) = (0.73)(0.73)(0.73) \doteq 0.3890$, and in the same way, $P(W = 3) = 0.27^3 \doteq 0.1597$. For $P(W = 1)$, note that each of the three arrangements that give $W = 1$ have probability $(0.73)(0.73)(0.27) = 0.143883$, so $P(W = 1) = 3(0.143883) \doteq 0.4316$. Similarly, $P(W = 2) = 3(0.73)(0.27)(0.27) \doteq 0.1597$.

Arrangement	DDD	DDF	DFD	FDD	FFD	FDF	DFF	FFF
Probability	0.3890	0.1439	0.1439	0.1439	0.0532	0.0532	0.0532	0.0197
Value of W	0	1			2			3
Probability	0.3890	0.4316			0.1597			0.0197

4.52. Let "S" mean that a student supports funding and "O" mean that the student opposes funding. **(a)** $P(SSO) = (0.6)(0.6)(0.4) = 0.144$. **(b)** See the top two lines of the table below. **(c)** The distribution is given in the bottom two lines of the table. For example, $P(X = 0) = (0.6)(0.6)(0.6) = 0.216$, and in the same way, $P(X = 3) = 0.4^3 = 0.064$. For $P(X = 1)$, note that each of the three arrangements that give $X = 1$ have probability 0.144, so $P(X = 1) = 3(0.144) = 0.432$. Similarly, $P(X = 2) = 3(0.6)(0.4)(0.4) = 0.288$. **(d)** A majority means $X \geq 2$; $P(X \geq 2) = 0.288 + 0.064 = 0.352$.

Arrangement	SSS	SSO	SOS	OSS	OOS	OSO	SOO	OOO
Probability	0.216	0.144	0.144	0.144	0.096	0.096	0.096	0.064
Value of X	0	1			2			3
Probability	0.216	0.432			0.288			0.064

4.53. **(a)** $P(X < 0.5) = 0.5$. **(b)** $P(X \leq 0.5) = 0.5$. **(c)** For continuous random variables, "equal to" has no effect on the probability; that is, $P(X = c) = 0$ for any value of c.

4.54. **(a)** $P(X \geq 0.27) = 0.73$. **(b)** $P(X = 0.27) = 0$. **(c)** $P(0.27 < X < 1.27) = P(0.27 < X < 1) = 0.73$. **(d)** $P(0.1 \leq X \leq 0.2 \text{ or } 0.8 \leq X \leq 0.9) = 0.1 + 0.1 = 0.2$. **(e)** $P(\text{not } [0.3 \leq X \leq 0.8]) = 1 - P(0.3 \leq X \leq 0.8) = 1 - 0.5 = 0.5$.

4.55. **(a)** The height should be $\frac{1}{2}$, since the area under the curve must be 1. The density curve is at the right. **(b)** $P(Y \leq 1) = \frac{1}{2}$. **(c)** $P(0.5 < Y < 1.3) = 0.4$. **(d)** $P(Y \geq 0.8) = 0.6$.

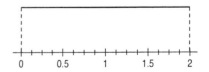

0   0.5   1   1.5   2

4.56. (a) The area of a triangle is $\frac{1}{2}bh = \frac{1}{2}(2)(1) = 1$. (b) $P(Y < 1) = 0.5$.
(c) $P(Y < 0.5) = 0.125$.

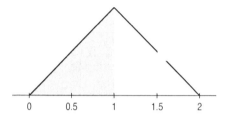   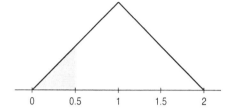

4.57. $P(8 \leq \bar{x} \leq 10) = P\left(\frac{8-9}{0.075} \leq \frac{\bar{x}-9}{0.075} \leq \frac{10-9}{0.075}\right) = P(-13.3 \leq Z \leq 13.3)$. This probability is essentially 1; $\bar{x}$ will almost certainly estimate μ within ± 1 (in fact, it will almost certainly be much closer than this).

4.58. (a) $P(0.52 \leq \hat{p} \leq 0.60) = P\left(\frac{0.52-0.56}{0.019} \leq \frac{\hat{p}-0.56}{0.019} \leq \frac{0.60-0.56}{0.019}\right) = P(-2.11 \leq Z \leq 2.11) = 0.9826 - 0.0174 = 0.9652$. (b) $P(\hat{p} \geq 0.72) = P\left(\frac{\hat{p}-0.56}{0.019} \geq \frac{0.72-0.56}{0.019}\right) = P(Z \geq 8.42)$; this is basically 0.

4.59. The average grade is $\mu = (0)(0.01) + (1)(0.05) + (2)(0.30) + (3)(0.43) + (4)(0.21) = 2.78$.

4.60. The mean number of nonword errors is $(0)(0.1)+(1)(0.2)+(2)(0.3)+(3)(0.3)+(4)(0.1) = 2.1$, and the mean number of word errors is $(0)(0.4) + (1)(0.3) + (2)(0.2) + (3)(0.1) = 1$.

4.61. For owner-occupied units, the mean is

$$(1)(0.003) + (2)(0.002) + (3)(0.023) + (4)(0.104) + (5)(0.210)+$$

$$(6)(0.224) + (7)(0.197) + (8)(0.149) + (9)(0.053) + (10)(0.035) = 6.284 \text{ rooms.}$$

For rented units, the mean is

$$(1)(0.008) + (2)(0.027) + (3)(0.287) + (4)(0.363) + (5)(0.164)+$$

$$(6)(0.093) + (7)(0.039) + (8)(0.013) + (9)(0.003) + (10)(0.003) = 4.187 \text{ rooms.}$$

This agrees with the observation in Exercise 4.43 that rented housing typically has fewer rooms.

4.62. (a) The mean of Y is $\mu_Y = 1$—the obvious balance point of the triangle. (b) Both X_1 and X_2 have mean $\mu_{X_1} = \mu_{X_2} = 0.5$, and $\mu_Y = \mu_{X_1} + \mu_{X_2}$.

4.63. The owned-unit distribution seems to be more spread out, and the two standard deviations confirm this impression: $\sigma_o \doteq 1.6399$ and $\sigma_r \doteq 1.3077$ rooms. The full details of these computations are not shown, but for example the variance of the number of rooms in an owner-occupied unit looks like this:

$$\sigma_o^2 = (1 - \mu_o)^2(0.003) + (2 - \mu_o)^2(0.008) + \cdots + (10 - \mu_o)^2(0.035) \doteq 2.6893,$$

and in the same way, $\sigma_r^2 \doteq 1.7100$. Taking square roots completes the task.

4.64. Let N and W be nonword and word error counts. In Exercise 4.60, we found $\mu_N = 2.1$ errors and $\mu_W = 1$ error. The variances of these distributions are

$\sigma_N^2 = 1.29$ and $\sigma_W^2 = 1$, so the standard deviations are $\sigma_N = 1.1358$ and $\sigma_W = 1$ errors. The mean total error count is $\mu_N + \mu_W = 3.1$ errors for both cases. **(a)** If error counts are independent, $\sigma_{N+W}^2 = \sigma_N^2 + \sigma_W^2 = 2.29$ and $\sigma_{N+W} = 1.5133$ errors. (Note we add the *variances*, not the standard deviations.) **(b)** With $\rho = 0.5$, $\sigma_{N+W}^2 = \sigma_N^2 + \sigma_W^2 + 2\rho\sigma_N\sigma_W = 2.29 + 1.1358 = 3.4258$, and $\sigma_{N+W} = 1.8509$ errors.

4.65. (a) Over two days, the value of this stock changes by a factor of $1.3^2 = 1.69, 0.75^2 = 0.5625$, or $1.3 \times 0.75 = 0.75 \times 1.3 = 0.975$. Therefore, the possible values and probabilities are as given in the table on the right. The stock gains value only 25% of the time. **(b)** The mean value is $1050.625.

Value	$562.50	$975	$1690
Probability	0.25	0.5	0.25

    Note: *Each of the four possible pairs—fall/fall, fall/rise, rise/fall, and rise/rise—are equally likely.*

4.66. We are trying to estimate the probabilities in the distribution of first digits among the invoices. If we have inaccurate estimates, then small differences between the observed probabilities and those of Benford's law can be attributed to that inaccuracy; we would need to see very large discrepancies before we could conclude that the invoices were faked. We can get better (more accurate) estimates by taking more invoices; this would mean that it would be easier to detect a set of faked invoices.

4.67. (a) The mean for one coin is $\mu_1 = (0)\left(\frac{1}{2}\right) + (1)\left(\frac{1}{2}\right) = 0.5$ and the variance is $\sigma_1^2 = (0 - 0.5)^2\left(\frac{1}{2}\right) + (1 - 0.5)^2\left(\frac{1}{2}\right) = 0.25$, so the standard deviation is $\sigma_1 = 0.5$. **(b)** Multiply μ_1 and σ_1^2 by 4: $\mu_4 = 4\mu_1 = 2$ and $\sigma_4^2 = 4\sigma_1^4 = 1$, so $\sigma_4 = 1$. **(c)** The computations (not shown here) are more tedious, but the results are the same. Note that because of the symmetry of the distribution, we do not need to compute the mean to see that $\mu_4 = 2$; this is the obvious balance point of the probability histogram in Figure 4.7.

4.68. If S and R are the results from the six- and eight-sided dice (respectively), then $\mu_S = 3.5$ and $\mu_E = 4.5$ by symmetry (this can be confirmed by computation). Therefore, $\mu_{S+E} = 8$. For the variances,

$$\sigma_S^2 = (1 - 3.5)^2\left(\frac{1}{6}\right) + (2 - 3.5)^2\left(\frac{1}{6}\right) + (3 - 3.5)^2\left(\frac{1}{6}\right) +$$
$$(4 - 3.5)^2\left(\frac{1}{6}\right) + (5 - 3.5)^2\left(\frac{1}{6}\right) + (6 - 3.5)^2\left(\frac{1}{6}\right) = \frac{35}{12} \doteq 2.9167,$$

and by similar computations, $\sigma_E^2 = 5.25$. Therefore, $\sigma_{S+E}^2 = 8\frac{1}{6} \doteq 8.1667$, and the standard deviation is $\sigma_{S+E} \doteq 2.8577$.

4.69. With R as the rod length and B_1 and B_2 the bearing lengths, we have $\mu_{B_1+R+B_2} = 10 + 2 \cdot 2 = 14$ cm and $\sigma_{B_1+R+B_2} = \sqrt{0.005^2 + 2 \cdot 0.001^2} \doteq 0.005196$ cm.

4.70. (a) $d_1 = 2\sigma_R = 0.010$ cm and $d_2 = 2\sigma_B = 0.002$ cm. **(b)** The natural tolerance of the assembled parts is $2\sigma_{B_1+R+B_2} \doteq 0.01039$ cm.

4.71. (a) Not independent: Knowing the total X of the first two cards tells us something about the total Y for three cards. (b) Independent: Separate rolls of the dice should be independent.

4.72. (a) Independent: Weather conditions a year apart should be independent. (b) Not independent: Weather patterns tend to persist for several days; today's weather tells us something about tomorrow's. (c) Not independent: The two locations are very close together, and would likely have similar weather conditions.

4.73. (a) The total mean is $11 + 20 = 31$ seconds. (b) No: Changing the standard deviations does not affect the means. Reducing variation is useful, though, because it increases the consistency of the process; for example, we could more reliably predict how many units could be assembled during a shift. (c) The mean does not change, because correlation does not affect the total mean.

4.74. Divide the given values by 2.54: $\mu \doteq 69.6063$ in and $\sigma \doteq 2.8346$ in.

4.75. If the two times are independent, the total standard deviation is

$$\sigma_{total} = \sqrt{\sigma_{pos}^2 + \sigma_{att}^2} = \sqrt{2^2 + 8^2} = \sqrt{68} \doteq 8.2462 \text{ seconds.}$$

With correlation 0.3, we have

$$\sigma_{total} = \sqrt{\sigma_{pos}^2 + \sigma_{att}^2 + 2\rho\sigma_{pos}\sigma_{att}} = \sqrt{68 + 2(0.3)(2)(8)} = \sqrt{77.6} \doteq 8.8091 \text{ seconds.}$$

With a positive correlation, if the first task takes longer, the second often does, too, while a shorter time for the first task often means the second time is shorter. Consequently, there is an increased chance of extreme (long or short) times, increasing the spread of the distribution.

4.76. (a) $\mu_Y = \frac{1}{2}(\mu_{X_1} + \mu_{X_2}) = 100$ m, and $\sigma_Y = \frac{1}{2}\sigma_{X_1+X_2} = \frac{1}{2}\sqrt{1.2^2 + 0.85^2} \doteq 0.7353$ m.

(b) $\mu_W = \frac{1}{3}\mu_{X_1} + \frac{2}{3}\mu_{X_2} = 100$ m, and $\sigma_W = \sqrt{\left(\frac{1}{3}\right)^2 \sigma_{X_1}^2 + \left(\frac{2}{3}\right)^2 \sigma_{X_2}^2} \doteq 0.6936$ m.

4.77. With $\rho = 1$, we have

$$\sigma_{X+Y}^2 = \sigma_X^2 + \sigma_Y^2 + 2\rho\sigma_X\sigma_Y = \sigma_X^2 + \sigma_Y^2 + 2\sigma_X\sigma_Y = (\sigma_X + \sigma_Y)^2,$$

and of course $\sigma_{X+Y} = \sqrt{(\sigma_X + \sigma_Y)^2} = \sigma_X + \sigma_Y$.

4.78. The mean of X is $(\mu - \sigma)(0.5) + (\mu + \sigma)(0.5) = \mu$, and the standard deviation is $\sqrt{(\mu - \sigma - \mu)^2(0.5) + (\mu + \sigma - \mu)^2(0.5)} = \sqrt{\sigma^2} = \sigma$.

4.79. Although the probability of having to pay for a total loss for one or more of the 12 policies is very small, if this were to happen, it would be financially disastrous. On the other hand, for thousands of policies, the law of large numbers says that the average claim on many policies will be close to the mean, so the insurance company can be assured that the premiums they collect will (almost certainly) cover the claims.

4.80. The total loss T for 12 fires has mean $\mu_T = 12 \cdot \$250 = \$3000$, and standard deviation $\sigma_T = \sqrt{12 \cdot \$300^2} \doteq \$1039$. The average loss is $T/12$, so $\mu_{T/12} = \frac{1}{12}\mu_T = \$250$ and $\sigma_{T/12} = \frac{1}{12}\sigma_T = \$86.60$.

4.81. (a) Add up the given probabilities and subtract from 1; this gives P(man does not die in the next five years) $= 0.99749$. **(b)** The distribution of income (or loss) is given below. Multiplying each possible value by its probability gives the mean intake $\mu \doteq \$623.22$.

Age at death	21	22	23	24	25	Survives
Loss or income	$-\$99,825$	$-\$99,650$	$-\$99,475$	$-\$99,300$	$-\$99,125$	$\$875$
Probability	0.00039	0.00044	0.00051	0.00057	0.00060	0.99749

4.82. The mean μ of the company's "winnings" (premiums) and their "losses" (insurance claims) is positive. Even though the company will lose a large amount of money on a small number of policyholders who die, it will gain a small amount on the majority. The law of large numbers says that the average "winnings" minus "losses" should be close to μ, and overall the company will almost certainly show a profit.

4.83. With $R = 0.8W + 0.2Y$, we have $\mu_R = 0.8\mu_W + 0.2\mu_Y = 11.116\%$ and

$$\sigma_R = \sqrt{(0.8\sigma_W)^2 + (0.2\sigma_Y)^2 + 2\rho_{WY}(0.8\sigma_W)(0.2\sigma_Y)} \doteq 15.9291\%.$$

4.84. With $\rho_{WY} = 0$, the standard deviation drops to $\sqrt{(0.8\sigma_W)^2 + (0.2\sigma_Y)^2} \doteq 14.3131\%$. The mean is unaffected by the correlation.

4.85. With $R = 0.6W + 0.2X + 0.2Y$, we have $\mu_R = 0.6\mu_W + 0.2\mu_X + 0.2\mu_Y = 10.184\%$ and

$$\begin{aligned} \sigma_R^2 &= (0.6\sigma_W)^2 + (0.2\sigma_X)^2 + (0.2\sigma_Y)^2 \\ &\quad + 2\rho_{WX}(0.6\sigma_W)(0.2\sigma_X) + 2\rho_{WY}(0.6\sigma_W)(0.2\sigma_Y) + 2\rho_{XY}(0.2\sigma_X)(0.2\sigma_Y) \\ &\doteq 152.3788 \end{aligned}$$

so that $\sigma_R \doteq 12.3442\%$. The benefit of this diversification is reduced variability (σ_R is smaller than either σ_W and σ_Y), but the mean return is reduced because of the inclusion of the Bond Fund.

4.86. $P(A \text{ or } B) = P(A) + P(B) - P(A \text{ and } B) = 0.138 + 0.261 - 0.082 = 0.317$.

4.87. $P(A \mid B) = \dfrac{P(A \text{ and } B)}{P(B)} = \dfrac{0.082}{0.261} \doteq 0.3142$. If A and B were independent, then $P(A \mid B)$ would equal $P(A)$, and also $P(A \text{ and } B)$ would equal the product $P(A)P(B)$.

4.88. (a) {*A* and *B*}: household is both prosperous and educated; $P(A \text{ and } B) = 0.082$ (given). **(b)** {*A* and B^c}: household is prosperous but not educated; $P(A \text{ and } B^c) = P(A) - P(A \text{ and } B) = 0.056$. **(c)** {$A^c$ and *B*}: household is not prosperous but is educated; $P(A^c \text{ and } B) = P(B) - P(A \text{ and } B) = 0.179$. **(d)** {$A^c$ and B^c}: household is neither prosperous nor educated; $P(A^c \text{ and } B^c) = 0.683$ (so that the probabilities add to 1).

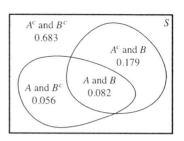

4.89. (a) "The vehicle is a car" $= A^c$; $P(A^c) = 1 - P(A) = 1 - 0.69 = 0.31$. **(b)** "The vehicle is an imported car"

	$P(A) = \mathbf{0.69}$	$P(A^c) = 0.31$
$P(B) = 0.22$	$P(A \text{ and } B) = 0.14$	$P(A^c \text{ and } B) = 0.08$
$P(B^c) = \mathbf{0.78}$	$P(A \text{ and } B^c) = \mathbf{0.55}$	$P(A^c \text{ and } B^c) = 0.23$

$= A^c$ and *B*. To find this probability, note that we have been given $P(B^c) = 0.78$ and $P(A \text{ and } B^c) = 0.55$. From this we can determine that $78\% - 55\% = 23\%$ of vehicles sold were domestic cars—that is, $P(A^c \text{ and } B^c) = 0.23$—so $P(A^c \text{ and } B) = P(A^c) - P(A^c \text{ and } B^c) = 0.31 - 0.23 = 0.08$.

  Note: *The table shown here summarizes all that we can determine from the given information* (**bold**).

4.90. Let *A* be the event "income $\geq$ \$1 million" and *B* be "income $\geq$ \$100,000." Then "*A* and *B*" is the same as *A*, so

$$P(A \mid B) = \frac{P(A)}{P(B)} = \frac{\dfrac{240{,}000}{129{,}075{,}000}}{\dfrac{10{,}855{,}000}{129{,}075{,}000}} = \frac{240{,}000}{10{,}855{,}000} \doteq 0.02211.$$

4.91. See also the solution to Exercise 4.89, especially the table of probabilities given there. **(a)** $P(A^c \mid B) = \dfrac{P(A^c \text{ and } B)}{P(B)} = \dfrac{0.08}{0.22} \doteq 0.3636$. **(b)** The events A^c and *B* are *not* independent; if they were, $P(A^c \mid B)$ would be the same as $P(A^c) = 0.31$.

4.92. To find the probabilities in this Venn diagram, begin with $P(A \text{ and } B \text{ and } C) = 0$ in the center of the diagram. Then each of the two-way intersections $P(A \text{ and } B)$, $P(A \text{ and } C)$, and $P(B \text{ and } C)$ go in the remainder of the overlapping areas; if $P(A \text{ and } B \text{ and } C)$ had been something other than 0, we would have subtracted this from each of the two-way intersection probabilities to find, for example, $P(A \text{ and } B \text{ and } C^c)$. Next, determine $P(A \text{ only})$ so that the total probability of the regions that make up the event *A* is 0.6. Finally, $P(\text{none}) = P(A^c \text{ and } B^c \text{ and } C^c) = 0$ because the total probability inside the three sets *A*, *B*, and *C* is 1.

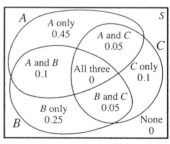

4.93. We seek $P(\text{at least one offer}) = P(A \text{ or } B \text{ or } C)$; we can find this as $1 - P(\text{no offers}) = 1 - P(A^c \text{ and } B^c \text{ and } C^c)$. We see in the Venn diagram of Exercise 4.92 that this probability is 1.

4.94. This is $P(A \text{ and } B \text{ and } C^c)$. As was noted in Exercise 4.92, because $P(A \text{ and } B \text{ and } C) = 0$, this is the same as $P(A \text{ and } B) = 0.1$.

4.95. $P(B \mid C) = \dfrac{P(B \text{ and } C)}{P(C)} = \dfrac{0.05}{0.2} = 0.25$. $P(C \mid B) = \dfrac{P(B \text{ and } C)}{P(B)} = \dfrac{0.05}{0.4} = 0.125$.

4.96. Let W be the event "the person is a woman" and P be "the person earned a professional degree." **(a)** $P(W) = \dfrac{1119}{1944} \doteq 0.5756$. **(b)** $P(W \mid P) = \dfrac{39/1944}{83/1944} = \dfrac{39}{83} \doteq 0.4699$. **(c)** W and P are *not* independent; if they were, the two probabilities in (a) and (b) would be equal.

4.97. Let M be the event "the person is a man" and B be "the person earned a bachelor's degree." **(a)** $P(M) = \dfrac{825}{1944} \doteq 0.4244$. **(b)** $P(B \mid M) = \dfrac{559/1944}{825/1944} = \dfrac{559}{825} \doteq 0.6776$.
(c) $P(M \text{ and } B) = P(M) \, P(B \mid M) \doteq (0.4244)(0.6776) \doteq 0.2876$. This agrees with the directly computed probability: $P(M \text{ and } B) = \dfrac{559}{1944} \doteq 0.2876$.

4.98. Each unemployment rate is computed as shown on the right. (Alternatively, subtract the number employed from the number in the labor force, then divide that difference by the number in the labor force.) Because these rates (probabilities) are different, education level and being employed are not independent.

Did not finish HS	$1 - \dfrac{11.552}{12.623} \doteq 0.0848$
HS/no college	$1 - \dfrac{36.249}{38.210} \doteq 0.0513$
Some college	$1 - \dfrac{32.429}{33.928} \doteq 0.0442$
College graduate	$1 - \dfrac{39.250}{40.414} \doteq 0.0288$

4.99. (a) Add up the numbers in the first and second columns. We find that there are 186,210 thousand (that is, over 186 million) people aged 25 or older, of which 125,175 thousand are in the labor force, so $P(L) = \dfrac{125.175}{186.210} \doteq 0.6722$.
(b) $P(L \mid C) = \dfrac{P(L \text{ and } C)}{P(C)} = \dfrac{40.414}{51.568} \doteq 0.7837$. **(c)** L and C are *not* independent; if they were, the two probabilities in (a) and (b) would be equal.

4.100. For the first probability, add up the numbers in the third column. We find that there are 119,480 thousand (that is, over 119 million) employed people aged 25 or older. Therefore, $P(C \mid E) = \dfrac{P(C \text{ and } E)}{P(E)} = \dfrac{39.250}{119.480} \doteq 0.3285$.
For the second probability, we use the total number of college graduates in the population: $P(E \mid C) = \dfrac{P(C \text{ and } E)}{P(C)} = \dfrac{39.250}{51.568} \doteq 0.7611$.

4.101. The population includes retired people who have left the labor force. Retired persons are more likely than other adults to have not completed high school; consequently, a relatively large number of retired persons fall in the "did not finish high school" category.
Note: *Details of this lurking variable can be found in the Current Population Survey annual report on "Educational Attainment in the United States." For 2003, this report says that among the 65-and-over population, about 29% have not completed high school, compared to about 15% of the under-65 group.*

4.102. By the multiplication rule, $P(E \text{ and } W) = P(E) \, P(W \mid E) = (0.15)(0.8) = 0.12$.
Therefore, $P(E \mid W) = \dfrac{P(E \text{ and } W)}{P(W)} = \dfrac{0.12}{0.6} = 0.2$.

4.103. Tree diagram at right. The numbers on the right side of the tree are found by the multiplication rule; for example, P("nonword error" and "caught") $= P(N \text{ and } C) = P(N) P(C \mid N) = (0.25)(0.9) = 0.225$. A proofreader should catch about $0.225 + 0.525 = 0.75 = 75\%$ of all errors.

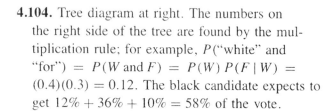

4.104. Tree diagram at right. The numbers on the right side of the tree are found by the multiplication rule; for example, P("white" and "for") $= P(W \text{ and } F) = P(W) P(F \mid W) = (0.4)(0.3) = 0.12$. The black candidate expects to get $12\% + 36\% + 10\% = 58\%$ of the vote.

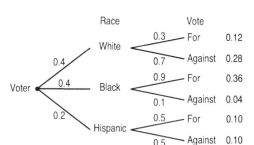

4.105. Although this exercise does not call for a tree diagram, one is shown at right. The numbers on the right side of the tree are found by the multiplication rule; for example, P("regular" and "$\geq \$20$") $= P(R \text{ and } T) = P(R) P(T \mid R) = (0.4)(0.3) = 0.12$. The probability that the next customer pays at least \$20 is $P(T) = 0.12 + 0.175 + 0.15 = 0.445$.

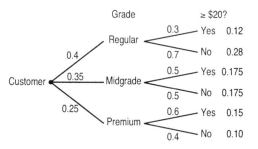

4.106. $P(B \mid F) = \dfrac{P(B \text{ and } F)}{P(F)} = \dfrac{0.36}{0.58} \doteq 0.6207$—about 62%.

4.107. $P(P \mid T) = \dfrac{P(P \text{ and } T)}{P(T)} = \dfrac{0.15}{0.445} \doteq 0.3371$—about 34%.

4.108. With B, M, and D representing the three kinds of degrees, and W meaning the degree recipient was a woman, we have been given

$$P(B) = 0.73, \quad P(M) = 0.21, \quad P(D) = 0.06,$$
$$P(W \mid B) = 0.48, \quad P(W \mid M) = 0.42, \quad P(W \mid D) = 0.29.$$

Therefore, we find $P(W) = P(W \text{ and } B) + P(W \text{ and } M) + P(W \text{ and } D) = P(B) P(W \mid B) + P(M) P(W \mid M) + P(D) P(W \mid D) = 0.456$, so

$$P(B \mid W) = \frac{P(B \text{ and } W)}{P(W)} = \frac{P(B) P(W \mid B)}{P(W)} = \frac{0.3504}{0.456} \doteq 0.7684.$$

4.109. (a) Her brother has type aa, and he got one allele from each parent. But neither parent is albino, so neither could be type aa. **(b)** The table on the right shows the possible combinations, each of which is equally likely, so $P(aa) = 0.25$, $P(Aa) = 0.5$, and $P(AA) = 0.25$. **(c)** Beth is either AA or Aa, and $P(AA \mid \text{not } aa) = \frac{0.25}{0.75} = \frac{1}{3}$ while $P(Aa \mid \text{not } aa) = \frac{0.50}{0.75} = \frac{2}{3}$.

	A	a
A	AA	Aa
a	Aa	aa

4.110. (a) If Beth is Aa, then the first table on the right gives the (equally likely) allele combinations for a child, so P(child is non-albino | Beth is Aa) $= \frac{1}{2}$. If Beth is AA, then as the

	A	a
a	Aa	aa
a	Aa	aa

	A	A
A	Aa	Aa
A	Aa	Aa

second table shows, their child will definitely be type Aa (and non-albino), so P(child is non-albino | Beth is AA) $= 1$. **(b)** We have

$$P(\text{child is non-albino}) = P(\text{child } Aa \text{ and Beth } Aa) + P(\text{child } Aa \text{ and Beth } AA)$$
$$= P(\text{Beth } Aa) \, P(\text{child } Aa \mid \text{Beth } Aa) + P(\text{Beth } AA) \, P(\text{child } Aa \mid \text{Beth } AA)$$
$$= \tfrac{2}{3} \cdot \tfrac{1}{2} + \tfrac{1}{3} \cdot 1 = \tfrac{2}{3}.$$

Therefore, $P(\text{Beth is } Aa \mid \text{child is } Aa) = \frac{1/3}{2/3} = \frac{1}{2}$.

4.111. Let T be the event "test is positive" and C be the event "Jason is a carrier." Since the given information says that the test is never positive for noncarriers, it clearly must be the case that $P(C \mid T) = 1$.

To confirm this, note that (if there is no human error), we have $P(T \text{ and } C^c) = 0$, and $P(T) = P(T \text{ and } C) + P(T \text{ and } C^c) = P(T \text{ and } C) = P(T) \, P(T \mid C) = (0.04)(0.9) = 0.036$. Therefore, $P(C \mid T) = \dfrac{P(C \text{ and } T)}{P(T)} = \dfrac{0.036}{0.036} = 1$.

4.112. Let C be the event that Julianne is a carrier, and let D be the event that Jason's and Julianne's child has the disease. We have been given $P(C) = \frac{2}{3}$, $P(D \mid C) = \frac{1}{4}$, and $P(D \mid C^c) = 0$. Therefore, $P(D^c) = P(C) \, P(D^c \mid C) + P(C^c) \, P(D^c \mid C^c) = \left(\frac{2}{3}\right)\left(\frac{3}{4}\right) + \left(\frac{1}{3}\right)(1) = \frac{1}{2} + \frac{1}{3} = \frac{5}{6}$, and $P(C \mid D^c) = \frac{1/2}{5/6} = \frac{3}{5}$.

4.113. Let C be the event "Toni is a carrier," T be the event "Toni tests positive," and D be "her son has DMD." We have $P(C) = \frac{2}{3}$, $P(T \mid C) = 0.7$, and $P(T \mid C^c) = 0.1$. Therefore, $P(T) = P(T \text{ and } C) + P(T \text{ and } C^c) = P(C) \, P(T \mid C) + P(C^c) \, P(T \mid C^c) = \left(\frac{2}{3}\right)(0.7) + \left(\frac{1}{3}\right)(0.1) = 0.5$, and

$$P(C \mid T) = \frac{P(T \text{ and } C)}{P(C)} = \frac{(2/3)(0.7)}{0.5} = \frac{14}{15} \doteq 0.9333.$$

4.114. $P(\text{A}) = P(\text{B}) = \cdots = P(\text{F}) = \frac{0.72}{6} = 0.12$ and $P(1) = P(2) = \cdots = P(8) = \frac{1-0.72}{8} = 0.035$.

4.115. (a) All probabilities are greater than or equal to 0, and their sum is 1. **(b)** Let R_1 be Taster 1's rating and R_2 be Taster 2's rating. Add the probabilities on the diagonal (upper left to lower right): $P(R_1 = R_2) = 0.03 + 0.08 + 0.25 + 0.20 + 0.06 = 0.62$. **(c)** $P(R_1 > 3) = 0.39$ (the sum of the ten numbers in the bottom two rows), and $P(R_2 > 3) = 0.39$ (the sum of the ten numbers in the right two rows). Note that because the matrix is symmetric (relative to the main diagonal), these probabilities agree.

4.116. (a) $\mu_X = (1)(0.1) + (1.5)(0.2) + (2)(0.4) + (4)(0.2) + (10)(0.1) = 3$ million dollars and $\sigma_X = \sqrt{(1-3)^2(0.1) + (1.5-3)^2(0.2) + (2-3)^2(0.4) + (4-3)^2(0.2) + (10-3)^2(0.1)} = \sqrt{6.35} \doteq 2.5199$ million dollars. **(b)** $\mu_Y = \mu_{0.9X-0.2} = 0.9\mu_X - 0.2 = 2.5$ million dollars, and $\sigma_Y = \sigma_{0.9X-0.2} = 0.9\sigma_X \doteq 2.2679$ million dollars.

4.117. (a) The probability of winning nothing is $1 - \left(\frac{1}{10,000} + \frac{1}{1,000} + \frac{1}{100} + \frac{1}{20}\right) = 0.9389$.

(b) The mean is $\mu = (\$1000)\left(\frac{1}{10,000}\right) + (\$200)\left(\frac{1}{1,000}\right) + (\$50)\left(\frac{1}{100}\right) + (\$10)\left(\frac{1}{20}\right) = \$1.30$.

(c) $\sigma^2 = (\$998.70)^2\left(\frac{1}{10,000}\right) + (\$198.70)^2\left(\frac{1}{1,000}\right) + (\$48.70)^2\left(\frac{1}{100}\right) + (\$8.70)^2\left(\frac{1}{20}\right) = 168.31$, so $\sigma \doteq \$12.9734$.

4.118. As $\sigma_{a+bX} = b\sigma_X$ and $\sigma_{c+dY} = d\sigma_Y$, we need $b = \frac{100}{108}$ and $d = \frac{100}{109}$. With these choices for b and d, we have $\mu_{a+bX} = a + b\mu_X \doteq a + 409.2593$, so $a \doteq 90.7407$, and $\mu_{c+dX} = c + d\mu_Y \doteq c + 519.2661$, so $c \doteq -19.2661$.

4.119. This is the probability of 19 (independent) losses, followed by a win; by the multiplication rule, this is $0.994^{19} \cdot 0.006 \doteq 0.005352$.

4.120. (a) $P(\text{win the jackpot}) = \left(\frac{1}{20}\right)\left(\frac{9}{20}\right)\left(\frac{1}{20}\right) = 0.001125$. **(b)** The other symbol can show up on the middle wheel, with probability $\left(\frac{1}{20}\right)\left(\frac{11}{20}\right)\left(\frac{1}{20}\right) = 0.001375$, or on either of the outside wheels, with probability $\left(\frac{19}{20}\right)\left(\frac{9}{20}\right)\left(\frac{1}{20}\right) = 0.021375$. Therefore, combining all three cases, we have $P(\text{exactly two bells}) = 0.001375 + 2 \cdot 0.021375 = 0.044125$.

4.121. Let R_1 be Taster 1's rating and R_2 be Taster 2's rating. $P(R_1 = 3) = 0.01 + 0.05 + 0.25 + 0.05 + 0.01 = 0.37$, so

$$P(R_2 > 3 \mid R_1 = 3) = \frac{P(R_2 > 3 \text{ and } R_1 = 3)}{P(R_1 = 3)} = \frac{0.05 + 0.01}{0.37} \doteq 0.1622.$$

4.122. Let F be "adult is a full-time student," P be "adult is a part-time student," N be "adult is not a student," and A be "adult accesses Internet from someplace other than work or home."

We were given $P(F) = 0.041$ and $P(P) = 0.029$, so that $P(N) = 1 - 0.041 - 0.029 = 0.93$. Also, $P(A \mid F) = 0.58$, $P(A \mid P) = 0.30$, and $P(A \mid N) = 0.21$. Therefore $P(A) = P(F)\,P(A \mid F) + P(P)\,P(A \mid P) + P(N)\,P(A \mid N) \doteq 0.22778$—about 22.8%.

4.123. Note first that $P(A) = \frac{1}{2}$ and $P(B) = \frac{2}{4} = \frac{1}{2}$. Now $P(B \text{ and } A) = P(\text{both coins are heads}) = 0.25$, so $P(B \mid A) = \frac{P(B \text{ and } A)}{P(A)} = \frac{0.25}{0.5} = 0.5 = P(B)$.

4.124. The event $\{Y < 1/2\}$ is the bottom half of the square, while $\{Y > X\}$ is the upper left triangle of the square. They overlap in a triangle with area $1/8$, so

$$P(Y < \tfrac{1}{2} \mid Y > X) = \frac{P(Y < \frac{1}{2} \text{ and } Y > X)}{P(Y > X)} = \frac{1/8}{1/2} = \frac{1}{4}.$$

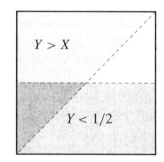

4.125. The response will be "no" with probability $0.35 = (0.5)(0.7)$. If the probability of plagiarism were 0.2, then P(student answers "no") $= 0.4 = (0.5)(0.8)$. If 39% of students surveyed answered "no," then we estimate that $2 \cdot 39\% = 78\%$ have *not* plagiarized, so about 22% have plagiarized.

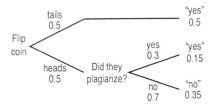

Chapter 5 Solutions

5.1. (a) This could be reasonably viewed as binomial with $n = 500$ and $p = 1/12$, because there is a fixed number (500) of independent trials with the same chance of success ($1/12$) on each try. **(b)** Not binomial: There is no fixed number of attempts (n). **(c)** Not binomial: There are no separate "trials" or "attempts" being observed here.

5.2. (a) No: There is no fixed number of observations. **(b)** A binomial distribution is reasonable here; a "large city" will have a population over 1000 (10 times as big as the sample). **(c)** In a "Pick 3" game, Joe's chance of winning the lottery is the same every week, so assuming that a year consists of 52 weeks (observations), this would be binomial.

5.3. (a) C, the number caught, is binomial with $n = 20$ and $p = 0.7$. M, the number missed, is binomial with $n = 20$ and $p = 0.3$. **(b)** Referring to Table C, we find $P(M \geq 9) = 0.0654 + 0.0308 + 0.0120 + 0.0039 + 0.0010 + 0.0002 = 0.1133$.

5.4. (a) X, the number of auction site visitors, is binomial with $n = 12$ and $p = 0.5$. **(b)** Referring to Table C, we find $P(X \geq 8) = 0.1208 + 0.0537 + 0.0161 + 0.0029 + 0.0002 = 0.1937$. (Software: 0.19385.)

5.5. (a) The mean of C is $(20)(0.7) = 14$ errors caught, and for M the mean is $(20)(0.3) = 6$ errors missed. **(b)** The standard deviation of C (or M) is $\sigma = \sqrt{(20)(0.7)(0.3)} \doteq 2.0494$ errors. **(c)** With $p = 0.9$, $\sigma = \sqrt{(20)(0.9)(0.1)} \doteq 1.3416$ errors; with $p = 0.99$, $\sigma \doteq 0.4450$ errors. σ decreases toward 0 as p approaches 1.

5.6. (a) The mean of X is $(12)(0.5) = 6$; the mean of $\hat{p}$ is 0.5. **(b)** The mean of X increases with n; it is 60 with $n = 120$, and 600 with $n = 1200$. The mean of $\hat{p}$ is 0.5 for any value of n.

5.7. $m = 10$: From Table C, we see that $P(X \geq 10) = 0.0479$ and $P(X \geq 9) = 0.1133$. (Software gives $P(X \geq 10) = 0.04796$, but the conclusion is the same.)

5.8. (a) The population (the 75 members of the fraternity) is only three times the size of the sample. Our rule of thumb says that this ratio should be at least 20. **(b)** Our rule of thumb for the normal approximation calls for np and $n(1 - p)$ to be at least 10; we have $np = (500)(0.002) = 1$.

5.9. The count of 0s among n random digits has a binomial distribution with $p = 0.1$. **(a)** P(at least one 0) $= 1 - P$(no 0) $= 1 - (0.9)^5 \doteq 0.4095$. (Or take 0.5905 from Table C and subtract from 1.) **(b)** $\mu = (40)(0.1) = 4$.

5.10. One sample of 15 flips is shown on the right. Results will vary quite a bit; Table C shows that 99.5% of the time, there will be 4 or fewer bad records in a sample of 15.

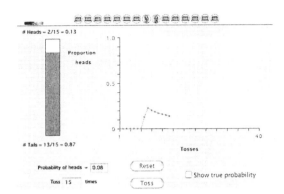

Out of 20 samples, most students should see 3 to 12 samples with exactly one bad record. That is, N, the number of samples with one bad record, has a binomial distribution with parameters $n = 20$ and $p = 0.3734$, and $P(3 \leq N \leq 12) = 0.9818$.

5.11. (a) For Mark McGwire, $\mu_H = (509)(0.116) = 59.044$ home runs. (b) The exact answer (using software) is 0.0764. For the normal approximation, we compute $\sigma_H = \sqrt{(509)(0.116)(0.884)} \doteq 7.225$, so

$$P(H \geq 70) = P\left(\frac{H-59.044}{7.225} \geq \frac{70-59.044}{7.225}\right) = P(Z \geq 1.52) \doteq 0.0643.$$

If we use the continuity correction,

$$P(H \geq 69.5) = P\left(\frac{H-59.044}{7.225} \geq \frac{69.5-59.044}{7.225}\right) = P(Z \geq 1.45) \doteq 0.0735.$$

(c) Regardless of the approach used to compute the probability, $P(H_2 \geq 73) < 0.000005$ — basically 0.

5.12. (a) $n = 6$ and $p = 0.65$. (b) The distribution is below; the histogram is on the right. (c) $\mu = np = 3.9$ years. (d) $\sigma = \sqrt{np(1-p)} \doteq 1.1683$ years; one standard deviation from μ means $P(3 \leq X \leq 5) = 0.8072$.

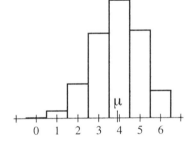

x	0	1	2	3	4	5	6
$P(X = x)$	.0018	.0205	.0951	.2355	.3280	.2437	.0754

5.13. (a) $n = 4$ and $p = 1/4 = 0.25$. (b) The distribution is below; the histogram is on the right. (c) $\mu = np = 1$.

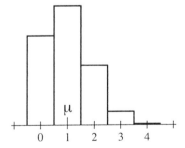

x	0	1	2	3	4
$P(X = x)$	.3164	.4219	.2109	.0469	.0039

5.14. For $\hat{p}$, $\mu = 0.49$ and $\sigma = \sqrt{p(1-p)/n} \doteq 0.01576$. As $\hat{p}$ is approximately normally distributed with this mean and standard deviation, we find

$$P(0.46 < \hat{p} < 0.52) \doteq P(-1.90 < Z < 1.90) = 0.9426$$

(Exact calculation gives 0.94565.)

5.15. Recall that $\hat{p}$ is approximately normally distributed with mean $\mu = p$ and standard deviation $\sqrt{p(1-p)/n}$. (a) With $p = 0.30$, $\sigma \doteq 0.01441$, so $P(0.29 < \hat{p} < 0.31) =$

$P(-0.69 < Z < 0.69) = 0.5098$. (Exact computation gives 0.50735.) **(b)** With $p = 0.06$, $\sigma \doteq 0.00747$, so $P(0.05 < \hat{p} < 0.07) = P(-1.34 < Z < 1.34) = 0.8198$. (Exact computation gives 0.81527.) **(c)** $P(-0.01 < \hat{p} - p < 0.01)$ increases to 1 as p gets closer to 0. (This is because σ also gets close to 0, so that $0.01/\sigma$ grows.)

5.16. When $n = 250$, the distribution of $\hat{p}$ is approximately normal with mean 0.49 and standard deviation 0.03162 (about twice that in Exercise 5.14). When $n = 4000$, the standard deviation drops to 0.00790 (half as big as in Exercise 5.14). Therefore,

$$n = 250 : \qquad P(0.46 < \hat{p} < 0.52) \doteq P(-0.95 < Z < 0.95) = 0.6578$$

$$n = 4000 : \qquad P(0.46 < \hat{p} < 0.52) \doteq P(-3.80 < Z < 3.80) = 0.9998$$

Larger samples give a better probability that $\hat{p}$ will be close to the true proportion p. (Exact calculation of the first probability gives 0.68853, but this more accurate answer does not change our conclusion.)

5.17. **(a)** $\hat{p} = \frac{62}{100} = 0.62$. **(b)** We want $P(X \leq 62)$ or $P(\hat{p} \leq 0.62)$. The first can be found exactly (using a binomial distribution), or we can

			Continuity correction	
Exact prob.	Table normal	Software normal	Table normal	Software normal
0.1690	0.1446	0.1438	0.1685	0.1693

compute either using a normal approximation (with or without the continuity correction). All possible answers are shown on the right. **(c)** The sample results are lower than the national percentage, but the sample was so small that such a difference could arise by chance even if the true campus proportion is the same.

5.18. As $\sigma_{\hat{p}} = \sqrt{p(1-p)/n}$, we have $0.005^2 = (0.49)(0.51)/n$, so $n = 9996$.

5.19. **(a)** $p = 1/4 = 0.25$. **(b)** $P(X \geq 10) = 0.0139$. **(c)** $\mu = np = 5$ and $\sigma = \sqrt{np(1-p)} = \sqrt{3.75} \doteq 1.9365$ successes. **(d)** No: The trials would not be independent, because the subject may alter his/her guessing strategy based on this information.

5.20. **(a)** $\mu = (1500)(0.7) = 1050$ and $\sigma = \sqrt{315} \doteq 17.7482$ students. **(b)** $P(X \geq 1000) \doteq P(Z \geq -2.82) = 0.9976$ (0.9978 with continuity correction; see the first line of the table on the right).

		Continuity correction	
Table normal	Software normal	Table normal	Software normal
0.9976	0.9976	0.9978	0.9978
0.2810	0.2802	0.2877	0.2892

(c) $P(X \geq 1201) \doteq P(Z \geq 8.51) < 0.00005$ (it's *very* small). **(d)** With $n = 1700$, $P(X \geq 1201) \doteq P(Z \geq 0.58) = 0.2810$. Other answers are shown in the second line of the table on the right.

5.21. **(a)** X, the count of successes, has a binomial distribution with mean $\mu_X = np = (1000)(1/5) = 200$ and $\sigma_X = \sqrt{(1000)(0.2)(0.8)} \doteq 12.6491$ successes. **(b)** For $\hat{p}$, the mean is $\mu_{\hat{p}} = p = 0.2$ and $\sigma_{\hat{p}} = \sqrt{(0.2)(0.8)/1000} \doteq 0.01265$. **(c)** $P(\hat{p} > 0.24) \doteq P(Z > 3.16) = 0.0008$. (Exact computation gives 0.00111; using $P(X \geq 240)$ with the continuity correction gives 0.0009.) **(d)** From a standard normal distribution, $P(Z > 2.326) = 0.01$, so the subject must score 2.326 standard deviations above the mean: $\mu_{\hat{p}} + 2.326\sigma_{\hat{p}} = 0.2294$. This corresponds to 230 or more successes.

5.22. (a) M has a binomial distribution with $n = 30$ and $p = 0.7$, so $P(M = 20) = \binom{30}{20}(0.7)^{20}(0.3)^{10} \doteq 0.1416$. (b) $P(\text{1st woman is the 4th call}) = (0.7)^3(0.3) = 0.1029$.

5.23. (a) $p = \frac{23,772,494}{209,128,094} \doteq 0.1137$. (b) If B is the number of blacks, then B has a binomial distribution with parameters $n = 1500$ and $p \doteq 0.1137$, so the mean is $np \doteq 170.5$ blacks. (c) $P(B \le 170) \doteq P(Z < -0.04) = 0.4840$. See the table on the right for alternate answers.

Exact prob.	Table normal	Software normal	Continuity correction Table normal	Continuity correction Software normal
0.5038	0.4840	0.4834	0.5000	0.4996

Note: *In (b), the population is at least 20 times as large as the sample, so our "rule of thumb" for using a binomial distribution is satisfied. In fact, the mean would be the same even if we could not use a binomial distribution, but we need to have a binomial distribution for part (c), so that we can approximate it with a normal distribution—which we can safely do, because both np and $n(1 - p)$ are much greater than 10.*

5.24. (a) $\binom{n}{n} = \frac{n!}{n!\,0!} = 1$. The only way to distribute n successes among n observations is for all observations to be successes. (b) $\binom{n}{n-1} = \frac{n!}{(n-1)!\,1!} = \frac{n \cdot (n-1)!}{(n-1)!} = n$. To distribute $n - 1$ successes among n observations, the one failure must be either observation $1, 2, 3, \ldots$, $n - 1$, or n. (c) $\binom{n}{k} = \frac{n!}{k!\,(n-k)!} = \frac{n!}{(n-k)!\,[n-(n-k)]!} = \binom{n}{n-k}$. Distributing k successes is equivalent to distributing $n - k$ failures.

5.25. (a) $P(\hat{p} \le 0.70) = P(X \le 70)$ is on line 1. (b) $P(\hat{p} \le 0.70) = P(X \le 175)$ is on line 2. (c) For a test with 400 questions, the standard deviation of $\hat{p}$ would be half as big as the standard deviation of $\hat{p}$ for a test with 100 questions: With $n = 100$, $\sigma = \sqrt{(0.75)(0.25)/100} \doteq 0.04330$; and with $n = 400$, $\sigma = \sqrt{(0.75)(0.25)/400} \doteq 0.02165$.

Table normal	Software normal	Continuity correction Table normal	Continuity correction Software normal
0.1251	0.1241	0.1492	0.1493
0.0336	0.0339	0.0401	0.0398

(d) Yes: Regardless of p, n must be quadrupled to cut the standard deviation in half.

5.26. (a) $P(\text{first } \boxdot \text{ appears on toss 2}) = \left(\frac{5}{6}\right)\left(\frac{1}{6}\right) = \frac{5}{36}$.

(b) $P(\text{first } \boxdot \text{ appears on toss 3}) = \left(\frac{5}{6}\right)\left(\frac{5}{6}\right)\left(\frac{1}{6}\right) = \frac{25}{216}$.

(c) $P(\text{first } \boxdot \text{ appears on toss 4}) = \left(\frac{5}{6}\right)^3\left(\frac{1}{6}\right)$.

$P(\text{first } \boxdot \text{ appears on toss 5}) = \left(\frac{5}{6}\right)^4\left(\frac{1}{6}\right)$.

5.27. Y has possible values $1, 2, 3, \ldots$. $P(\text{first } \boxdot \text{ appears on toss } k) = \left(\frac{5}{6}\right)^{k-1}\left(\frac{1}{6}\right)$.

5.28. (a) $\sigma_{\bar{x}} = \sigma/\sqrt{3} = 10/\sqrt{3} \doteq 5.7735$ mg. (b) Solve $10/\sqrt{n} = 5$: $\sqrt{n} = 2$, so $n = 4$. The average of several measurements is more likely than a single measurement to be close to the mean.

5.29. Mean $\mu = 40.125$ mm and standard deviation $\sigma/\sqrt{4} = 0.001$ mm.

5.30. In Exercise 5.28, we found that $\sigma_{\bar{x}} \doteq 5.7735$ mg, so $\bar{x}$ has a $N(4600 \text{ mg}, 5.7735 \text{ mg})$ distribution. **(a)** On the right. The normal curve for $\bar{x}$ should be "taller and skinnier" (specifically, taller by a factor of $\sqrt{3}$, and skinnier by a factor of $1/\sqrt{3}$, although this detail will not be exact in a student's sketch). **(b)** The probability that an individual measurement misses the true mass by 10 mg—one standard deviation—is about 32% (by the 68–95–99.7

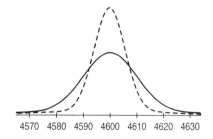

4570 4580 4590 4600 4610 4620 4630

rule), or 0.3174 (using Table A). **(c)** 10 mg is $10/\sigma_{\bar{x}} \doteq 1.73$ standard deviations for the distribution of $\bar{x}$, so $P(\bar{x} < 4590 \text{ or } \bar{x} > 4610) = P(Z < -1.73 \text{ or } Z > 1.73) = 0.0836$ using Table A, or 0.0833 using software.

5.31. In Exercise 5.29, we found that $\sigma_{\bar{x}} = 0.001$ mm, so $\bar{x}$ has a $N(40.125 \text{ mm}, 0.001 \text{ mm})$ distribution. **(a)** On the right. The normal curve for $\bar{x}$ should be taller by a factor of 2, and skinnier by a factor of 0.5. **(b)** The probability that an individual axle diameter differs from the target by at least 0.004 mm—two standard deviations—is about 5% (by the 68–95–99.7 rule), or 0.0456 (using Table A). **(c)** 0.004 mm is four standard deviations for the

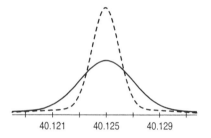

40.121   40.125   40.129

distribution of $\bar{x}$, so this probability is $P(Z < -4 \text{ or } Z > 4) < 0.0001$.

5.32. **(a)** If T is the total number of lightning strikes (in one year), then $\mu_T = 10 \times 6 = 60$ strikes and $\sigma_T = \sqrt{10} \times 2.4 \doteq 7.5895$ strikes. **(b)** If $\bar{x}$ is the mean number of strikes per square kilometer (that is, $\bar{x} = T/10$), then $\mu_{\bar{x}} = 6$ strikes/km^2 and $\sigma_{\bar{x}} = 2.4/\sqrt{10} \doteq 0.7589$ strikes/km^2.

5.33. **(a)** $\bar{x}$ is not systematically higher than or lower than μ; that is, it has no particular tendency to underestimate or overestimate μ. **(b)** With large samples, $\bar{x}$ is more likely to be close to μ, because with a larger sample comes more information (and therefore less uncertainty).

5.34. **(a)** $P(X \geq 23) \doteq P(Z \geq \frac{23-20.8}{4.8}) = P(Z \geq 0.46) = 0.3428$ (with software: 0.3234). Because ACT scores are reported as whole numbers, we might instead compute $P(X \geq 22.5) \doteq P(Z \geq 0.35) = 0.3632$ (software: 0.3616). **(b)** $\mu_{\bar{x}} = 20.8$ and $\sigma_{\bar{x}} = \sigma/\sqrt{25} = 0.96$. **(c)** $P(\bar{x} \geq 23) \doteq P(Z \geq \frac{23-20.8}{0.96}) = P(Z \geq 2.29) = 0.0110$. (In this case, it is not appropriate to find $P(\bar{x} \geq 22.5)$, unless $\bar{x}$ is rounded to the nearest whole number.) **(d)** Because individual scores are only roughly normal, the answer to (a) is approximate. The answer to (c) is also approximate, but should be more accurate because $\bar{x}$ should have a distribution that is closer to normal.

5.35. **(a)** $\mu_{\bar{x}} = 0.5$ and $\sigma_{\bar{x}} = \sigma/\sqrt{50} = 0.7/\sqrt{50} \doteq 0.09899$. **(b)** Because this distribution is only approximately normal, it would be quite reasonable to use the 68–95–99.7 rule to give a rough estimate: 0.6 is about one standard deviation above the mean, so the probability should be about 0.16 (half of the 32% that falls outside ± 1 standard deviation). Alternatively, $P(\bar{x} > 0.6) \doteq P(Z > \frac{0.6-0.5}{0.09899}) = P(Z > 1.01) = 0.1562$.

5.36. (a) $\mu = (4)(0.21) + (3)(0.43) + (2)(0.30) + (1)(0.05) + (0)(0.01) = 2.78$
and $\sigma = \sqrt{0.7516} \doteq 0.8669$. (b) $\mu_{\bar{x}} = \mu = 2.78$ and $\sigma_{\bar{x}} = \sigma/\sqrt{50} \doteq 0.1226$.
(c) $P(X \geq 3) = 0.21 + 0.43 = 0.64$, and $P(\bar{x} \geq 3) \doteq P(Z \geq \frac{3-2.78}{0.1226} = P(Z \geq 1.79) = 0.0367$
(software value: 0.0364).

5.37. Let X be Sheila's measured glucose level. (a) $P(X > 140) = P(Z > 1.5) = 0.0668$.
(b) If $\bar{x}$ is the mean of four measurements (assumed to be independent), then $\bar{x}$ has a
$N(125, 10/\sqrt{4})$ or $N(125 \text{ mg/dl}, 5 \text{ mg/dl})$ distribution, and $P(\bar{x} > 140) = P(Z > 3) = 0.0013$.

5.38. (a) $\mu_X = (\$500)(0.001) = \$0.50$ and $\sigma_X = \sqrt{249.75} \doteq \$15.8035$. (b) In the long run,
Joe makes about 50 cents for each \$1 ticket. (c) If $\bar{x}$ is Joe's average payoff over a year,
then $\mu_{\bar{x}} = \mu = \$0.50$ and $\sigma_{\bar{x}} = \sigma_X/\sqrt{365} \doteq \$0.8272$. The central limit theorem says that $\bar{x}$
is approximately normally distributed (with this mean and standard deviation). (d) Using this
normal approximation, $P(\bar{x} > \$1) \doteq P(Z > 0.60) = 0.2743$ (software: 0.2728).

    Note: *Joe comes out ahead if he wins at least once during the year. This probability is
easily computed as $1 - (0.999)^{365} \doteq 0.3059$. The distribution of $\bar{x}$ is different enough from a
normal distribution so that answers given by the approximation are not as accurate in this
case as they are in many others.*

5.39. The mean of four measurements has a $N(125 \text{ mg/dl}, 5 \text{ mg/dl})$ distribution, and
$P(Z > 1.645) = 0.05$ if Z is $N(0, 1)$, so $L = 125 + 1.645 \cdot 5 = 133.225$ mg/dl.

5.40. $\bar{x}$ is approximately normal with mean 1.6 and standard deviation $1.2/\sqrt{200} \doteq$
0.08485 flaws/yd^2, so $P(\bar{x} > 2) \doteq P(Z > 4.71) = 0$ (essentially).

5.41. If W is total weight, and $\bar{x} = W/19$, then

$$P(W > 4000) = P(\bar{x} > 210.5263) \doteq P(Z > \tfrac{210.5263-190}{35/\sqrt{19}}) = P(Z > 2.56) = 0.0052$$

(software: 0.0053).

5.42. (a) Although the probability of having to pay for a total loss for one or more of the 12
policies is very small, if this were to happen, it would be financially disastrous. On the other
hand, for thousands of policies, the law of large numbers says that the average claim on
many policies will be close to the mean, so the insurance company can be assured that the
premiums they collect will (almost certainly) cover the claims. (b) The central limit theorem
says that, in spite of the skewness of the population distribution, the average loss among
10,000 policies will be approximately normally distributed with mean \$250 and standard
deviation $\sigma/\sqrt{10,000} = \$1000/100 = \$10$. Since \$275 is 2.5 standard deviations above the
mean, the probability of seeing an average loss over \$275 is about 0.0062.

5.43. Over 45 years, $\bar{x}$ (the mean return) is approximately normal with $\mu_{\bar{x}} = 9.2\%$ and
$\sigma_{\bar{x}} = 20.6\%/\sqrt{45} \doteq 3.0709\%$, so $P(\bar{x} > 15\%) = P(Z > 1.89) = 0.0294$, and
$P(\bar{x} < 5\%) = P(Z < -1.37) = 0.0853$.

    Note: *We have to assume that returns in separate years are independent.*

5.44. Let D be the shaft diameter, so that D has a $N(2.45 \text{ cm}, 0.01 \text{ cm})$ distribution.
(a) 99.38% fit into the hole: $P(D \leq 2.475) = P(Z \leq \frac{2.475 - 2.45}{0.01}) = P(Z \leq 2.50) = 0.9938$.
(b) 96.16%: If H is the hole diameter, then $H - D$ has a normal distribution with mean
$2.5 - 2.45 = 0.05$ cm and standard deviation $\sqrt{0.01^2 + 0.01^2} \doteq 0.01414$ cm. Therefore,
$P(H - D \geq 0.025) = P(Z \geq \frac{0.025 - 0.05}{0.01414}) = P(Z \geq -1.77) \doteq 0.9616$ (software: 0.9615).

5.45. (a) The mean of five untreated specimens has a standard deviation of $2.3/\sqrt{5} \doteq$
1.0286 lbs, so $P(\bar{x}_u > 50) = P(Z > \frac{50 - 58}{1.0286}) = P(Z > -7.78)$, which is basically 1. (b) The
mean of $\bar{x}_u - \bar{x}_t$ is $58 - 30 = 28$ lbs, and the standard deviation is $\sqrt{2.3^2/5 + 1.6^2/5} \doteq$
1.2530 lbs, so $P(\bar{x}_u - \bar{x}_t > 25) = P(Z > \frac{25 - 28}{1.2530}) = P(Z > -2.39) = 0.9916$ (software:
0.9917).

5.46. (a) The central limit theorem says that the sample means will be roughly
normal. Note that the distribution of individual scores cannot have extreme outliers,
because all scores are between 1 and 7. (b) For *Journal* scores, $\bar{y}$ has mean 4.8
and standard deviation $1.5/\sqrt{30} \doteq 0.2739$. For *Enquirer* scores, $\bar{x}$ has mean 2.4
and standard deviation $1.6/\sqrt{30} \doteq 0.2921$. (c) $\bar{y} - \bar{x}$ has (approximately) a normal
distribution with mean 2.4 and standard deviation $\sqrt{1.5^2/30 + 1.6^2/30} \doteq 0.4004$.
(d) $P(\bar{y} - \bar{x} \geq 1) = P(Z \geq \frac{1 - 2.4}{0.4004}) = P(Z \geq -3.50) \doteq 0.9998$.

5.47. (a) $\bar{y}$ has a $N(\mu_Y, \sigma_Y/\sqrt{m})$ distribution and $\bar{x}$ has a $N(\mu_X, \sigma_X/\sqrt{n})$ distribution.
(b) $\bar{y} - \bar{x}$ has a normal distribution with mean $\mu_Y - \mu_X$ and standard deviation
$\sqrt{\sigma_Y^2/m + \sigma_X^2/n}$.

5.48. We have been given $\mu_X = 9\%$, $\sigma_X = 20\%$, $\mu_Y = 10\%$, $\sigma_Y = 17\%$, and $\rho = 0.6$.
(a) Linda's return $R = 0.8X + 0.2Y$ has mean $\mu_R = 0.8\mu_X + 0.2\mu_Y = 9.2\%$ and standard
deviation $\sigma_R = \sqrt{(0.8\sigma_X)^2 + (0.2\sigma_Y)^2 + 2\rho(0.8\sigma_X)(0.2\sigma_Y)} \doteq 18.2439\%$. (b) $\bar{R}$, the average
return over 20 years, has approximately a normal distribution with mean 9.2% and standard
deviation $\sigma_R/\sqrt{20} \doteq 4.0795\%$, so $P(\bar{R} < 5\%) \doteq P(Z < -1.03) \doteq 0.1515$ (software gives
0.1516). (c) After a 12% gain in the first year, Linda would have $1120; with a 6% gain in
the second year, her portfolio would be worth $1187.20. By contrast, two years with a 9%
return would make her portfolio worth $1188.10.

     Note: *As the text suggests, the appropriate average for this situation is (a variation
on) the* geometric mean, *computed as* $\sqrt{(1.12)(1.06)} - 1 \doteq 8.9587\%$. *Generally, if the
sequence of annual returns is* $r_1, r_2, \ldots, r_k$ *(expressed as decimals), the mean return is*
$\sqrt[k]{(1 + r_1)(1 + r_2) \cdots (1 + r_k)} - 1$. *It can be shown that the geometric mean is always
smaller than the arithmetic mean, unless all the returns are the same.*

5.49. The total height H of the four rows has a normal distribution with mean
$4 \times 8 = 32$ inches and standard deviation $0.1\sqrt{4} = 0.2$ inch. $P(H < 31.5 \text{ or } H > 32.5) =$
$1 - P(31.5 < H < 32.5) = 1 - P(-2.50 < Z < 2.50) = 1 - 0.9876 = 0.0124$.

5.50. The mean monthly fee for 500 households has approximately a $N(\$28, \$10/\sqrt{500}) =$
$N(\$28, \$0.4472)$ distribution, so $P(\bar{x} > \$29) \doteq P(Z > 2.24) \doteq 0.0125$ (software: 0.0127).

5.51. (a) Yes; this rule works for any random variables X and Y. **(b)** No; this rule requires that X and Y be independent. The incomes of two married people are certainly not independent, as they are likely to be similar in many characteristics that affect income (for example, educational background).

5.52. For each step of the random walk, the mean is $\mu = (1)(0.75) + (-1)(0.25) = 0.5$, the variance is $\sigma^2 = (1 - 0.5)^2(0.75) + (-1 - 0.5)^2(0.25) = 0.75$, and the standard deviation is $\sigma = \sqrt{0.75} \doteq 0.8660$. Therefore, $Y/500$ has approximately a $N(0.5, 0.03873)$ distribution, and $P(Y \geq 200) = P(\frac{Y}{500} \geq 0.4) \doteq P(Z \geq -2.58) = 0.9951$.

   Note: *The number R of right-steps has a binomial distribution with $n = 500$ and $p = 0.75$. $Y \geq 200$ is equivalent to taking at least 350 right-steps, so we can also compute this probability as $P(R \geq 350)$, for which software gives the exact value 0.99517.*

5.53. Out of six independent drivers, the number A who have an accident in the same year has a binomial distribution with $n = 6$ and $p = 0.2$, so $P(A \geq 3) = 0.0989$ (using Table C, software, or a calculator). Six roommates could not be considered independent, as they were not randomly chosen from the population of all drivers.

5.54. (a) Ramon's score is about the 64th percentile: $P(X \leq 1100) \doteq P(Z \leq \frac{1100-1026}{209}) = P(Z \leq 0.35) = 0.6368$ (software: 0.6384). Note that a continuity correction would be reasonable here, as SAT scores are reported as whole numbers; that is, we could compute $P(Z \leq \frac{1100.5-1026}{209}) = P(Z \leq 0.36) = 0.6406$ (software: 0.6393). **(b)** $\bar{x} = 1100$ is about the 99.9th percentile: $\bar{x}$ is approximately normal with mean 1026 and standard deviation $209/\sqrt{70} \doteq 24.9803$, so $P(\bar{x} \leq 1100) \doteq P(Z \leq 2.96) = 0.9985$. (The continuity correction would not be appropriate in this case.) **(c)** The first answer is less accurate: The distribution of an individual's score (like Ramon's) might not be normal, but the central limit theorem says that the distribution of $\bar{x}$ will be close to normal.

5.55. (a) Out of ten independent vehicles, the number X with one person has a binomial distribution with $n = 10$ and $p = 0.7$, so $P(X \geq 6) = 0.8497$ (using Table C, software, or a calculator). **(b)** Y (the number of one-person cars in a sample of 100) has a binomial distribution with $n = 100$ and $p = 0.7$. Regardless of the approach used—normal approximation, or exact computation using software or a calculator—$P(Y \geq 51)$ is very close to 1 (the exact value is 0.99998).

5.56. This would not be surprising: Assuming that all the authors are independent (for example, none were written by siblings or married couples), we can view the nine names as being a random sample, so that the number N of occurrences of the ten most common names would have a binomial distribution with $n = 9$ and $p = 0.056$. Then $P(N = 0) = (1 - 0.056)^9 \doteq 0.5953$.

5.57. The probability that the first digit is 1, 2, or 3 is $0.301 + 0.176 + 0.125 = 0.602$, so the number of invoices for amounts beginning with these digits should have a binomial distribution

Table normal	Software normal	Continuity correction Table normal	Continuity correction Software normal
0.0062	0.0062	0.0068	0.0067

with $n = 1200$ and $p = 0.602$. More usefully, the proportion $\hat{p}$ of such invoices should have approximately a normal distribution with mean $p = 0.602$ and standard deviation $\sqrt{p(1-p)/1200} \doteq 0.01413$, so $P(\hat{p} \le \frac{680}{1200}) \doteq P(Z \le -2.50) = 0.0062$. Alternate answers shown on the right.

5.58. (a) If R is the number of red-blossomed plants out of a sample of 8, then $P(R = 6) = 0.3115$, using a binomial distribution with $n = 8$ and

Exact prob.	Table normal	Software normal	Continuity correction Table normal	Continuity correction Software normal
0.99542	0.9951	0.9951	0.9966	0.9966

$p = 0.75$. (For Table C, use $p = 0.25$ and find $P(X = 2)$, where $X = 8 - R$ is the number of flowers with nonred blossoms.) (b) With $n = 80$, the mean number of red-blossomed plants is $np = 60$. (c) If R_2 is the number of red-blossomed plants out of a sample of 80, then $P(R_2 \ge 50) \doteq P(Z \ge -2.58) = 0.9951$.

5.59. If $\bar{x}$ is the average weight of 12 eggs, then $\bar{x}$ is $N(65 \text{ g}, 5/\sqrt{12} \text{ g})$ or $N(65 \text{ g}, 1.4434 \text{ g})$, and $P(\frac{750}{12} < \bar{x} < \frac{825}{12}) \doteq P(-1.73 < Z < 2.60) = 0.9535$ (software: 0.9537).

5.60. (a) X has a binomial distribution with $n = 1555$ and $p = 0.2$. (b) $P(X \le 300) \doteq P(Z \le -0.7) = 0.2420$ (or see the table).

Exact prob.	Table normal	Software normal	Continuity correction Table normal	Continuity correction Software normal
0.25395	0.2420	0.2428	0.2514	0.2528

Note: *Actually, X has a hypergeometric distribution, but the size of the population (all Internet users) is so much larger than the sample that the binomial distribution is an extremely good approximation.*

5.61. (a) No. Possible reasons: One could never have $X = 0$. There is no fixed number of "attempts" here. Solving $np = 1.5$ and $\sqrt{np(1-p)} = 0.75$ gives $p = 0.625$ and $n = 2.4$. (b) No: A count assumes only whole-number values, so it cannot be normally distributed. (c) $\bar{x}$ is approximately $N(1.5, 0.75/\sqrt{700})$ or $N(1.5, 0.02835)$. (d) $P(\text{more than } 1075 \text{ in } 700 \text{ cars}) = P(\bar{x} > \frac{1075}{700}) \doteq P(Z > 1.26) = 0.1038$ (software: 0.1039). We could also do a continuity correction for this question: $P(700\bar{x} > 1075.5) \doteq P(Z > 1.29) = 0.0985$ (software: 0.0994).

5.62. The probability that an airman completes a tour of duty without being on a lost aircraft is $0.95^{30} \doteq 0.2146$.

5.63. If $\hat{p}$ is the sample proportion who have been on a diet, then $\hat{p}$ has approximately a $N(0.70, 0.02804)$ distribution, so $P(\hat{p} \ge 0.75) \doteq P(Z \ge 1.78) = $

Exact prob.	Table normal	Software normal	Continuity correction Table normal	Continuity correction Software normal
0.0329	0.0301	0.0298	0.0344	0.0347

0.0375 (software: 0.0373). Alternatively, as $\hat{p} \ge 0.75$ is equivalent to 201 or more dieters in the sample, we can compute this probability using the binomial distribution; these answers are shown in the table.

5.64. (a) The machine that makes the caps and the machine that applies the torque are not the same. **(b)** T (torque) is $N(7, 0.9)$ and S (cap strength) is $N(10, 1.2)$, so $T - S$ is $N(7 - 10, \sqrt{0.9^2 + 1.2^2}) = N(-3 \text{ inch} \cdot \text{lb}, 1.5 \text{ inch} \cdot \text{lb})$. The probability that the cap breaks is $P(T > S) = P(T - S > 0) = P(Z > 2.00) = 0.0228$.

5.65. The center line is $\mu_{\bar{x}} = \mu = 4.22$ and the control limits are $\mu \pm 3\sigma/\sqrt{5} = 4.0496$ to 4.3904.

5.66. (a) $\bar{x}$ has a $N(32, 6/\sqrt{23}) = N(32, 1.2511)$ distribution, and $\bar{y}$ has a $N(29, 5/\sqrt{23})$ or $N(29, 1.0426)$ distribution, and **(b)** $\bar{y} - \bar{x}$ has a $N(29 - 32, \sqrt{5^2/23 + 6^2/23})$ or $N(-3, 1.6285)$ distribution. **(c)** $P(\bar{y} \geq \bar{x}) = P(\bar{y} - \bar{x} \geq 0) = P(Z \geq 1.84) = 0.0329$ (software: 0.0327).

5.67. (a) $\hat{p}_F$ is approximately $N(0.82, 0.01718)$ and $\hat{p}_M$ is approximately $N(0.88, 0.01453)$. **(b)** When we subtract two independent normal random variables, the difference is normal. The new mean is the difference of the two means ($0.88 - 0.82 = 0.06$), and the new variance is the sum of the variances ($0.01453^2 + 0.01718^2 = 0.0005064$), so $\hat{p}_M - \hat{p}_F$ is approximately $N(0.06, 0.02250)$. **(c)** $P(\hat{p}_F > \hat{p}_M) = P(\hat{p}_M - \hat{p}_F < 0) \doteq P(Z < -2.67) = 0.0038$.

Chapter 6 Solutions

6.1. The 95% confidence interval is $76 \pm 12 = 64$ to 88. (The sample size is not needed.)

6.2. Greater than 12: A wider margin of error is needed in order to be more confident that the interval includes the true mean.

6.3. The margins of error are $1.96 \times 5/\sqrt{n}$, which yields 3.10, 2.19, 1.55, and 0.98. (And, of course, all intervals are centered at 50.) Interval width decreases with increasing sample size.

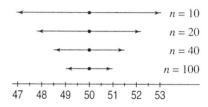

6.4. The margins of error are $z^* \times 15/\sqrt{25} = 3z^*$. With z^* equal to 1.282, 1.645, 1.960, and 2.576, this yields 3.846, 4.935, 5.880, and 7.728. (And, of course, all intervals are centered at 70.) Increasing confidence makes the interval wider.

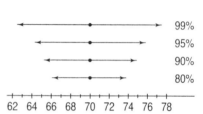

6.5. The margin of error is 2.29 U/l, and the 95% confidence interval is $13.2 \pm (1.96)(6.5/\sqrt{31}) = 13.2 \pm 2.29 = 10.91$ to 15.49 U/l.

6.6. The 95% confidence interval is $33.4 \pm (1.96)(19.6/\sqrt{31}) = 33.4 \pm 6.90 = 26.50$ to 40.30 ng/ml.

6.7. The margin of error is 3.01 U/l, and the 99% confidence interval is $13.2 \pm (2.576)(6.5/\sqrt{31}) = 13.2 \pm 3.01 = 10.19$ to 16.21 U/l. This interval is wider than the 95% interval.

6.8. The 90% confidence interval is $33.4 \pm (1.645)(19.6/\sqrt{31}) = 33.4 \pm 5.79 = 27.61$ to 39.19 ng/ml. This interval is narrower than the 95% interval.

6.9. Scenario (B) has a smaller margin of error. Both samples would have the same value of z^* (1.96), but the value of σ would be smaller for (B), because we would have less variability in height for students in a single grade level.

6.10. The 95% confidence interval is $\$580 \pm (1.96)(\$90/\sqrt{10}) = \$580 \pm \$55.78 = \$524.22$ to $\$635.78$.

6.11. No: This is a range of values for the mean rent, not for individual rents.
   Note: *To find a range to include 95% of all rents, we should take $\mu \pm 2\sigma$, where μ is the (unknown) mean rent for all apartments, and σ is the standard deviation for all apartments (assumed to be \$90 in Exercise 6.10). If μ were equal to \$580, for example, this range would be \$400 to \$760.*

6.12. If the distribution were roughly normal, the 68–95–99.7 rule says that 68% of all measurements should be in the range 13.8 to 53.0 ng/ml, 95% should be between −5.8 and 72.6 ng/ml, and 99.7% should be between −25.4 and 92.2 ng/ml. Because the measurements cannot be negative, this suggests that the distribution must be skewed to the right. The normal confidence interval should be fairly accurate nonetheless, because the sample mean $\bar{x}$ will still be roughly normal because of the central limit theorem.

6.13. (a) The 95% confidence interval is $80 \pm (1.96)(35/\sqrt{25}) = 80 \pm 13.72 = 66.28$ to 93.72 minutes. **(b)** No: This is a range of values for the mean study time, not for individual study times. (See also the solution to Exercise 6.11.)

6.14. (a) Divide both quantities by 60: $\bar{x} = \frac{80}{60} \doteq 1.3333$ hr and $\sigma = \frac{35}{60} \doteq 0.5833$ hr. **(b)** The 95% confidence interval is $1.3333 \pm (1.96)(0.5833/\sqrt{25}) = 1.3333 \pm 0.229 = 1.105$ to 1.562 hours. **(c)** Convert the interval from the previous exercise into hours: $\frac{66.28}{60} \doteq 1.105$ hr and $\frac{93.72}{60} \doteq 1.562$ hr.

6.15. (a) The standard deviation of $\bar{x}$ is $\sigma_{\bar{x}} = \sigma/\sqrt{200} \doteq 2.1920$ cal/day. **(b)** The probability is about 0.95 that $\bar{x}$ is within 4.3840 cal/day (two standard deviations) of the population mean μ. **(c)** About 95% of all samples will capture the true mean of calories consumed per day in the interval $\bar{x} \pm$ 4.3840 cal/day. Some students may use 1.96 rather than 2 and answer 4.2964. (This is the whole idea behind a confidence interval: Probability tells us that $\bar{x}$ is usually close to μ. That is equivalent to saying that μ is usually close to $\bar{x}$.)

6.16. (a) The standard deviation of $\bar{x}$ is $\sigma_{\bar{x}} = \sigma/\sqrt{20} \doteq 0.6485$ MPG. **(b)** The mean is $\bar{x} = 18.48$ MPG, and the 95% confidence interval is $18.48 \pm (1.96)(2.9/\sqrt{20}) = 18.48 \pm 1.27 = 17.21$ to 19.75 MPG.

6.17. The mean is $\bar{x} = 30.8$ MPH, and the 95% confidence interval is $30.8 \pm (1.96)(10.3/\sqrt{20}) = 30.8 \pm 4.5142 = 26.2858$ to 35.3142 MPH.

6.18. The mean $\bar{x} = 30.8$ MPH converts to 49.28 KPH, and the margin of error 4.5142 MPH converts to 7.2227 KPH. The new interval is therefore 42.0573 to 56.5027 KPH.

6.19. The mean is $\bar{x} \doteq 35.0909$, and the 95% confidence interval is $35.0909 \pm (1.96)(11/\sqrt{44}) = 35.0909 \pm 3.2503 = 31.8406$ to 38.3412.

6.20. One sample screen is shown below (left), and a sample stemplot of results in shown on the right. The number of hits will vary, but the distribution should follow a binomial distribution with $n = 50$ and $p = 0.95$, so we expect the average number of hits to be about 47.5. We also find that about 99.7% of individual counts should be 43 or more, and the mean hit count for 30 samples should be approximately normal with mean 47.5 and standard deviation 0.2814—so almost all sample means should be between 46.66 and 48.34.

```
44 | 00
45 | 0000
46 | 00
47 | 00000000
48 | 000000
49 | 000
50 | 00000
```

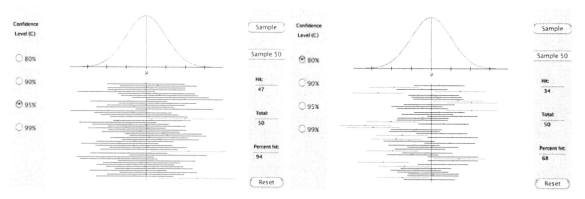

6.21. One sample screen is shown above (right), and a sample stemplot of results in shown on the right. The number of hits will vary, but the distribution should follow a binomial distribution with $n = 50$ and $p = 0.8$, so we expect the average number of hits to be about 40. We also find that about 99.7% of individual counts should be between 32 and 48, and the mean hit count for 30 samples should be approximately normal with mean 40 and standard deviation 0.5164—so almost all sample means should be between 38.45 and 41.55.

```
31 | 0
32 |
33 |
34 | 00
35 | 0
36 | 000
37 | 00
38 | 00
39 | 00
40 | 0000
41 | 0000
42 | 00000
43 | 0
44 | 00
45 | 0
```

6.22. $n = \left(\dfrac{1.96 \times \$9000}{\$400} \right)^2 = 1944.81$—take $n = 1945$.

6.23. It will be smaller, because we require less precision (and therefore need less information). Specifically, because the desired margin of error is twice as large, the sample size will be about one-fourth as large as before: $n = \left(\dfrac{1.96 \times \$9000}{\$800} \right)^2 \doteq 486.20$—take $n = 487$.

6.24. $n = \left(\dfrac{1.645 \times \$90}{\$20} \right)^2 \doteq 54.80$—take $n = 55$.

6.25. $n = \left(\dfrac{1.96 \times 6.5}{2.0} \right)^2 \doteq 40.58$—take $n = 41$.

6.26. If we start with a sample of size k and lose 20% of the sample, we will end with $0.8k$. Therefore, we need to *increase* the sample size by *25%*—that is, start with a sample of size $k = 1.25n$—so that we end with $(0.8)(1.25n) = n$. With $n = 41$, that means we should initially sample 52 subjects.

6.27. This is probably not a confidence interval; it is not intended to give an estimate of the mean income, but rather it gives the range of incomes earned by all (or most) telemarketers working for this company.

6.28. (a) The 98% confidence interval is $10.0023 \pm (2.326)(0.0002/\sqrt{5}) = 10.0023 \pm 0.0002 = 10.0021$ to 10.0025 g. **(b)** $n = \left(\frac{(2.326)(0.0002)}{0.0001}\right)^2 \doteq 21.64$ — take $n = 22$.

6.29. The number of hits has a binomial distribution with parameters $n = 4$ and $p = 0.95$, so the number of misses is binomial with $n = 4$ and $p = 0.05$. We can therefore use Table C to answer these questions. **(a)** The probability that all cover their means is $0.95^4 \doteq 0.8145$. (Or use Table C to find the probability of 0 misses.) **(b)** The probability that at least three cover their means is $0.95^4 + 4(0.05)(0.95^3) \doteq 0.9860$. (Or use Table C to find the probability of 0 or 1 misses.)

6.30. (a) The 95% confidence interval would be $0.80 \pm 0.04 = 0.76$ to 0.84. **(b)** The confidence interval methods used here require that the results come from an SRS of the population (which presumably is "the newspaper's readers"). This sample cannot be viewed as an SRS.

6.31. (a) The results will vary from one sample to the next; one sample will not perfectly represent the population. **(b)** The method used gives correct results 95% of the time. **(c)** The 95% confidence interval is $37\% \pm 3\% = 34\%$ to 40%. **(d)** Yes; some fans would change their responses based on what they are currently watching.

6.32. (a) Our hypothesis should be "some claim about the population." Whether or not it rains tomorrow is not such a statement. Put another way, hypothesis testing — at least as described in this text — does not deal with random outcomes, but rather with statements that are either true or false. Rain (or not) is a random outcome. **(b)** The standard deviation of the sample mean is $15/\sqrt{20}$. **(c)** The null hypothesis should be a statement about μ, not $\bar{x}$.

6.33. (a) H_0 and H_a have been switched: The null hypothesis should be a statement of "no change." **(b)** H_0 should concern μ, not $\bar{x}$. **(c)** A P-value of 0.95 is not significant by any reasonable standard.

6.34. (a) One possibility: If μ_1 is the mean change in bone density for a sample of rats eating a high-soy diet, and μ_2 is the mean change for a control group, we could test H_0: $\mu_1 = \mu_2$ vs. H_a: $\mu_1 \neq \mu_2$. (The alternative might be one-sided, for example, $\mu_1 > \mu_2$.) We could also state hypotheses which refer to a single mean μ, if we simply look at change for one group of rats (with no control group). **(b)** If μ is the mean rating for all students, we could test H_0: $\mu = 0$ vs. H_a: $\mu > 0$. **(c)** With μ as the mean score of all of this TA's students, we test H_0: $\mu = 75$ vs. H_a: $\mu > 75$.

6.35. (a) If μ is the population mean proportion of food expenditures in restaurants (that is, this is the average of the fraction r/f for all local households, where f is total food expenditures, and r is restaurant food expenditures), then we test H_0: $\mu = 0.3$ vs. H_a: $\mu \neq 0.3$. **(b)** H_0: $\mu = 20$ seconds vs. H_a: $\mu < 20$ seconds. **(c)** If μ is the mean DXA reading for the phantom, we test H_0: $\mu = 1.3$ g/cm^2 vs. H_a: $\mu \neq 1.3$ g/cm^2.

   Note: *For (a), the hypotheses could be stated in terms of a proportion p, but note that this kind of proportion is fundamentally different from proportions in binomial populations. The latter proportions represent the probability of success in independent trials; in this case, we are measuring a fraction of total food expenditures.*

6.36. (a) H_0: $\mu_A = \mu_B$; H_a: $\mu_A > \mu_B$, where μ_A is the mean score for group A and μ_B is the group B mean. **(b)** H_0: $\rho = 0$; H_a: $\rho > 0$, where ρ is the (population) correlation between GPA and self-esteem. **(c)** H_0: $p_m = p_f$; H_a: $p_m < p_f$, where p_m is the proportion of males who name English as their favorite subject, and p_f is that proportion for females.

6.37. (a) H_0: $\mu = \$72,500$; H_a: $\mu > \$72,500$. **(b)** H_0: $\mu = 1.8$ hr; H_a: $\mu \neq 1.8$ hr.

6.38. $P(Z > 2.3) = 0.0107$, so the two-sided P-value is $2(0.0107) = 0.0214$.

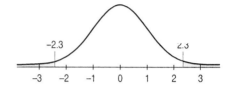

6.39. $P(Z < -1.4) = 0.0808$, so the two-sided P-value is $2(0.0808) = 0.1616$.

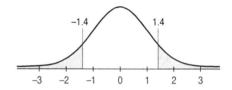

6.40. (a) No, we do not reject H_0 at $\alpha = 0.05$. **(b)** No, we do not reject H_0 at $\alpha = 0.01$. **(c)** We have $P = 0.082$; to reject, we need $P < \alpha$.

6.41. (a) Yes, we reject H_0 at $\alpha = 0.05$. **(b)** No, we do not reject H_0 at $\alpha = 0.01$. **(c)** We have $P = 0.032$; to reject, we need $P < \alpha$.

6.42. (a) For H_a: $\mu > \mu_0$, the P-value is $P(Z > 1.6) = 0.0548$.
(b) For H_a: $\mu < \mu_0$, the P-value is $P(Z < 1.6) = 0.9452$.
(c) For H_a: $\mu \neq \mu_0$, the P-value is $2P(Z > 1.6) = 2(0.0548) = 0.1096$.

6.43. (a) For H_a: $\mu > \mu_0$, the P-value is $P(Z > -1.6) = 0.9452$.
(b) For H_a: $\mu < \mu_0$, the P-value is $P(Z < -1.6) = 0.0548$.
(c) For H_a: $\mu \neq \mu_0$, the P-value is $2P(Z < -1.6) = 2(0.0548) = 0.1096$.

6.44. Recall the statement from the text: "A level α two-sided significance test rejects a hypothesis H_0: $\mu = \mu_0$ exactly when the value μ_0 falls outside a level $1 - \alpha$ confidence interval for μ." **(a)** Yes, 30 is in the 95% confidence interval, because $P = 0.09$ means that we would not reject H_0 at $\alpha = 0.05$. **(b)** No, 30 is not in the 90% confidence interval, because we would reject H_0 at $\alpha = 0.10$.

6.45. Recall the statement from the text: "A level α two-sided significance test rejects a hypothesis H_0: $\mu = \mu_0$ exactly when the value μ_0 falls outside a level $1 - \alpha$ confidence interval for μ." **(a)** No, 30 is not in the 95% confidence interval, because $P = 0.04$ means that we would reject H_0 at $\alpha = 0.05$. **(b)** No, 30 is not in the 90% confidence interval, because we would also reject H_0 at $\alpha = 0.10$.

6.46. (a) If the alternative is two-sided, the answer is *yes*; see the quote from the text in the solutions to Exercises 6.44 and 6.45 for an explanation. If H_a is one-sided, then the answer depends on its direction: If H_a is $\mu > 68$, the answer is *no*. If H_a is $\mu < 68$, the answer is *yes*, because the given interval suggests $\bar{x} = 61$ and the standard error of the mean is about 2 (or less, if the interval were constructed using the t distribution rather than the normal distribution), so $\bar{x}$ is 3.5 standard errors from 68. **(b)** Regardless of the alternative, we would not reject H_0, because 62 falls well inside the confidence interval.

6.47. (a) Regardless of the alternative, we would not reject H_0, because 13 falls well inside the confidence interval. **(a)** If the alternative is two-sided, the answer is *yes*; see the quote from the text in the solutions to Exercises 6.44 and 6.45 for an explanation. If H_a is one-sided, then the answer depends on its direction: If H_a is $\mu < 10$, the answer is *no*. If H_a is $\mu > 10$, the answer is *yes*, because the given interval suggests $\bar{x} = 13.5$ and the standard error of the mean is about 0.9 (or less, if the interval were constructed using the t distribution rather than the normal distribution), so $\bar{x}$ is 3.8 standard errors from 10.

6.48. The study presumably examined malarial infection rates in two groups of subjects—one with bed nets, and one without. The observed difference between the two groups were so large that they would be unlikely to occur by chance if bed nets had no effect. Specifically, if the groups were the same, and we took many samples, the difference in malarial infections would be so large less than 0.1% of the time.

6.49. Even if the two groups (the health and safety class, and the statistics class) had the same level of alcohol awareness, there might be some difference in our sample due to chance. The difference observed was large enough that it would rarely arise by chance. The reason for this difference might be that health issues related to alcohol use are probably discussed in the health and safety class.

6.50. Even if scores had not changed over time, random fluctuation might cause the mean in 2003 to be different from the 2000 mean. However, in this case the difference was so great that it is unlikely to have occurred by chance; specifically, such a difference would arise less than 5% of the time if the actual mean had not changed. We therefore conclude that the mean did change from 2000 to 2003.

6.51. If the mean score for all Boston students were 287, then by chance we might expect to see a sample mean of 262. In fact, there is greater than a 5% chance of this happening, so we do not consider a mean of 262 to be strong enough evidence to conclude that Boston's mean is less than 287.

6.52. If μ is the mean north-south location, the hypotheses are H_0: $\mu = 100$ vs. H_a: $\mu \neq 100$. For testing these hypotheses, we find $z = \frac{99.74 - 100}{58/\sqrt{584}} \doteq -0.11$. This is not significant—$P = 2(0.4562) = 0.9124$—so we have no reason to doubt a uniform distribution based on this test.

6.53. If μ is the mean east-west location, the hypotheses are H_0: $\mu = 100$ vs. H_a: $\mu \neq 100$ (as in the previous exercise). For testing these hypotheses, we find $z = \frac{113.8 - 100}{58/\sqrt{584}} \doteq 5.75$. This is highly significant ($P < 0.0001$), we conclude that the trees are not uniformly spread from east to west.

6.54. For testing these hypotheses, we find $z = \frac{10.2-8.9}{2.5/\sqrt{6}} \doteq 1.27$. This is not significant ($P = 0.1020$); there is not enough evidence to conclude that these sonnets were not written by our poet.

6.55. (a) $z = \frac{132.2-115}{30/\sqrt{25}} \doteq 2.87$, so the P-value is $P = P(Z > 2.87) = 0.0021$. This is strong evidence that the older students have a higher SSHA mean. **(b)** The important assumption is that this is an SRS from the population of older students. We also assume a normal distribution, but this is not crucial provided there are no outliers and little skewness.

6.56. (a) $H_0: \mu = 9.5$ mg/dl vs. $H_a: \mu \neq 9.5$ mg/dl. **(b)** $z = \frac{9.57-9.5}{0.4/\sqrt{160}} \doteq 2.21$, so the P-value is $P = 2P(Z > 2.21) = 0.0272$. This is pretty strong evidence that μ is different from (greater than) 9.5 mg/dl. **(c)** The 95% confidence interval is $9.57 \pm (1.96)(0.4/\sqrt{160}) = 9.57 \pm 0.062 = 9.508$ to 9.632.

6.57. (a) $H_0: \mu = 32$; $H_a: \mu > 32$. **(b)** $\bar{x} = 35.090-$, so $z = \frac{35.0909-32}{11/\sqrt{44}} \doteq 1.86$ and $P = 0.0314$. This is fairly good evidence that children in this district have a mean score higher than the national average—observations this extreme would occur in only about 3 out of 100 samples if H_0 were true.

6.58. A sample screen (for $\bar{x} = 1$) is shown below on the left. As one can judge from the shading under the normal curve, $\bar{x} = 0.5$ is not significant, but 0.6 is. (In fact, the cutoff is about 0.52, which is approximately $1.645/\sqrt{10}$.)

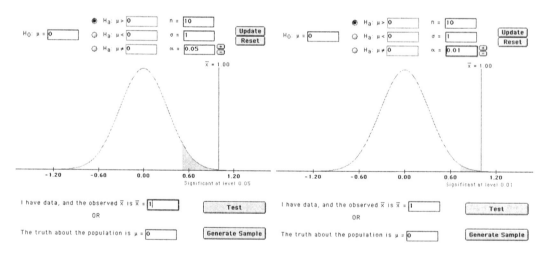

6.59. See the sample screen (for $\bar{x} = 1$) above on the right. As one can judge from the shading under the normal curve, $\bar{x} = 0.7$ is not significant, but 0.8 is. (In fact, the cutoff is about 0.7354, which is approximately $2.326/\sqrt{10}$.) Smaller α means that $\bar{x}$ must be farther away from μ_0 in order to reject H_0.

6.60. A sample screen (for $x = 0.4$) is shown on the right. The P-values given by the applet are listed in the table below; as $\bar{x}$ moves farther away from μ_0, P decreases.

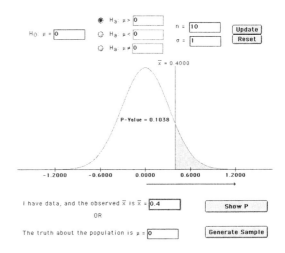

$\bar{x}$	P	$\bar{x}$	P
0.1	0.3745	0.6	0.0287
0.2	0.2643	0.7	0.0136
0.3	0.1711	0.8	0.0057
0.4	0.1038	0.9	0.0022
0.5	0.0571	1	0.0008

6.61. Either compare with the critical values in Table D, or determine the P-value (0.0401). **(a)** Yes, because $z > 1.645$ (or because $P < 0.05$). **(b)** No, because $z < 2.326$ (or because $P > 0.01$).

6.62. (a) $z = \frac{0.4365 - 0.5}{0.2887/\sqrt{100}} \doteq -2.20$. For the other parts of this problem, either compare this with the critical values in Table D, or determine the P-value (0.0278). **(b)** This result is significant at the 5% level because $z < -1.960$ (or because $P < 0.05$). **(c)** It is not significant at 1% because $z \geq -2.576$ (or because $P > 0.01$).

6.63. When a test is significant at the 1% level, it means that if the null hypothesis were true, outcomes similar to those seen are expected to occur less than once in 100 repetitions of the experiment or sampling. "Significant at the 5% level" means we have observed something that occurs in less than 5 out of 100 repetitions (when H_0 is true). Something that occurs "less than once in 100 repetitions" also occurs "less than 5 times in 100 repetitions," so significance at the 1% level implies significance at the 5% level (or any higher level).

6.64. Something that occurs "less than 5 times in 100 repetitions" is not necessarily as rare as something that occurs "less than once in 100 repetitions," so a test that is significant at 5% is not necessarily significant at 1%.

6.65. Using Table D or software, we find that the 0.005 critical value test is 2.576, and the 0.0025 critical value is 2.807. Therefore, if $2.576 < |z| < 2.807$—that is, either $2.576 < z < 2.807$ or $-2.807 < z < -2.576$—then z would be significant at the 1% level but not at the 0.5% level.

6.66. As $-4.3 < -3.291$, the two-sided P-value is $P < 2(0.0005) = 0.001$.

6.67. As $0.22 < 0.674$, the one-sided P-value is $P > 0.25$.

6.68. (a) Reject H_0 if $z > 1.645$. **(b)** Reject H_0 if $|z| > 1.960$. **(c)** For tests at a fixed significance level (α), we reject H_0 when we observe values of our statistic that are so extreme (far from the mean, or other "center" of the sampling distribution) that they would rarely occur when H_0 is true. (Specifically, they occur with probability no greater than α.) For a two-sided alternative, we split the rejection region—this set of extreme values—into two pieces, while with a one-sided alternative, all the extreme values are in one piece, which is twice as large (in area) as either of the two pieces used for the two-sided test.

6.69. Because $1.282 < 1.34 < 1.645$, the P-value is between $2(0.05) = 0.10$ and $2(0.10) = 0.20$. From Table A, $P = 2(0.0901) = 0.1802$.

6.70. Because the alternative is two-sided, the answer is the same for $z = -1.34$: $-1.282 > -1.34 > -1.645$, so Table D says that $0.10 < P < 0.20$, and Table A gives $P = 2(0.0901) = 0.1802$.

6.71. (a) The 95% confidence interval is $104.1\overline{3} \pm (1.96)(9/\sqrt{12}) = 104.1\overline{3} \pm 5.0922 = 99.0411$ to 109.2256 pCi/L. **(b)** We test H_0: $\mu = 105$ pCi/L vs. H_a: $\mu \neq 105$ pCi/L. Because 105 is in the interval from (a), we do not have enough evidence to reject H_0.

6.72. Finding something to be "statistically significant" is not really useful unless the significance level is sufficiently small. While there is some freedom to decide what "sufficiently small" means, $\alpha = 0.5$ would lead your team to incorrectly rejecting H_0 half the time, so it is clearly a bad choice. (This approach would be essentially equivalent to flipping a coin to make your decision!)

6.73. The first test was barely significant at $\alpha = 0.05$, while the second was significant at any reasonable α.

6.74. We expect 50 tests to be statistically significant: Each of the 1000 tests has a 5% chance of being significant, so the number of significant tests has a binomial distribution with $n = 1000$ and $p = 0.05$, for which the mean is $np = 50$.

6.75. $P = 0.00001 = \frac{1}{100,000}$, so we would need $n = 100,000$ tests in order to expect one P-value of this size (assuming that all null hypotheses are true). That is why we reject H_0 when we see P-values such as this: It indicates that our results would rarely happen if H_0 were true.

6.76. The study may have rejected $\mu = \mu_0$ (or some other null hypothesis), but with such a large sample size, such a rejection might occur even if the actual mean (or other parameter) differs only slightly from μ_0. For example, there might be no practical importance to the difference between $\mu = 10$ and $\mu = 10.5$.

6.77. We expect more variation with small sample sizes, so even a large difference between $\bar{x}$ and μ_0 (or whatever measures are appropriate in our hypothesis test) might not turn out to be significant. If we were to repeat the test with a larger sample, the decrease in the standard error might give us a small enough P-value to reject H_0.

6.78. $P = 0.95$ means that we have no reason to doubt the null hypothesis. Specifically, results like those observed in the sample would occur 95% of the time when H_0 is true.

6.81. When many variables are examined, "significant" results will show up by chance, so we should not take it for granted that the variables identified are really indicative of future success. In order to decide if they are appropriate, we should track this year's trainees, and compare the success of those from urban/suburban backgrounds with the rest, and likewise compare those with a degree in a technical field with the rest.

6.82. (a) $z = \frac{483-480}{100/\sqrt{100}} = 0.3$, so $P = P(Z > 0.3) = 0.3821$. **(b)** $z = \frac{483-480}{100/\sqrt{1000}} \doteq 0.95$, so $P = P(Z > 0.95) = 0.1711$. **(c)** $z = \frac{483-480}{100/\sqrt{10000}} = 3$, so $P = P(Z > 3) = 0.0013$.

6.83. The interval is $483 \pm (2.576)(100/\sqrt{n})$. $n = 100$: 457.24 to 508.76. $n = 1000$: 474.85 to 491.15. $n = 10,000$: 480.42 to 485.58.

6.84. (a) $z = \frac{496.4-480}{100/\sqrt{100}} = 1.64$. This is not significant at $\alpha = 0.05$, because $z < 1.645$ (or $P = 0.0505$). **(b)** $z = \frac{496.5-480}{100/\sqrt{100}} = 1.65$. This *is* significant at $\alpha = 0.05$, because $z > 1.645$ (or $P = 0.0495$).

6.86. Using $\alpha/7 \doteq 0.007143$ as the cutoff, the second ($P = 0.003$), fourth ($P = 0.004$), and seventh ($P = 0.001$) are significant.

6.87. Using $\alpha/10 = 0.005$ as the cutoff, we reject the fourth ($P = 0.004$), fifth ($P = 0.001$), and ninth ($P = 0.002$).

6.88. With all 50 states (plus Puerto Rico) listed in the table, we have information about the entire population in question; no statistical procedures are needed (or meaningful).

6.90. The power of this study is far lower than what is generally desired—for example, it is well below the "80% standard" mentioned in the text. Twenty percent power for the specified effect means that, if the effect is present, we will only detect it 20% of the time. With such a small chance of detecting an important difference, the study should probably not be run (unless the sample size is increased to give sufficiently high power).

6.91. A larger sample gives more information and therefore gives a better chance of detecting a given alternative; that is, larger samples give more power.

6.92. The power for $\mu = -10$ is the same as the power for $\mu = 10$, because both alternatives are an equal distance from the null value of μ. (The symmetry of two-sided tests with the normal distribution means that we only need to consider the size of the difference, not the direction.)

6.93. The power for $\mu = 80$ will be higher than 0.5, because larger differences are easier to detect.

6.94. The applet (or other software) gives the power as about 0.061.

   Note: *At the time these solutions were prepared, the* Power *applet would not allow sample sizes over 50. If that is still the case, students can be directed to use the online power calculators at* http://calculators.stat.ucla.edu/powercalc. *For this problem, choose "Normal: 1 sample."*

6.95. The applet (or other software) gives the power as about 0.99. (See the note in the previous solution.)

6.96. (a) $\alpha = P(\text{Type I error}) = P(\bar{x} > 43.12 \text{ when } \mu = 40)$

$$= P(Z > \tfrac{43.12-40}{60/\sqrt{1000}}) = P(Z > 1.64) = 0.0505 \text{ (software: 0.0500).}$$

   (b) $P(\text{Type II error when } \mu = 45) = P(\bar{x} \le 43.12 \text{ when } \mu = 45)$

$$= P(Z \le \tfrac{43.12-45}{60/\sqrt{1000}}) = P(Z < -0.99) = 0.1611 \text{ (software: 0.1609).}$$

   (c) $P(\text{Type II error when } \mu = 50) = P(\bar{x} < 43.12 \text{ when } \mu = 50)$

$$= P(Z \le \tfrac{43.12-50}{60/\sqrt{1000}}) = P(Z < -3.63) = 0.0001.$$

   (d) The sample size ($n = 1000$) is so large that the mean will be very close to normal.

6.97. $z \ge 2.326$ is equivalent to $\bar{x} \ge 450 + 2.326(100/\sqrt{500}) \doteq 460.4$, so the power is

$$P(\text{reject } H_0 \text{ when } \mu = 462) = P(\bar{x} \ge 460.4 \text{ when } \mu = 462)$$

$$= P\left(Z \ge \tfrac{460.4-462}{100/\sqrt{500}}\right) \doteq P(Z \ge -0.36) = 0.6406.$$

(Software gives the power as 0.6394.) This is not too bad, but a bit less than the "80% power" standard.

6.98. (a) $P(\text{Type I error}) = P(X = 0 \text{ or } X = 1 \text{ when the distribution is } p_0) = 0.2.$
   (b) $P(\text{Type II error}) = P(X > 1 \text{ when the distribution is } p_1) = 0.5.$

6.99. (a) H_0: The patient is ill (or "the patient should see a doctor"); H_a: The patient is healthy (or "the patient should not see a doctor"). A Type I error means a false negative—clearing a patient who should be referred to a doctor. A Type II error is a false positive—sending a healthy patient to the doctor. **(b)** One might wish to lower the probability of a false negative so that most ill patients are treated, especially for serious diseases that require fast treatment. On the other hand, if resources (for example, money or medical personnel) are limited, or for less serious health problems, lowering the probability of false positives might be desirable.

   Note: *For (a), there is no clear choice for which should be the null hypothesis in this case. Because the subjects have no specific medical complaints,* H_0 *might be "the patient is healthy." This choice may also be affected by the factors considered in part (b).*

6.100. (a) Because all standard deviations and sample sizes are the same, the margin of error for all intervals is $(1.96)(4.5)/\sqrt{750} \doteq 0.3221$ months. The confidence intervals are listed in the table below. **(b)** Plot below. **(c)** The mean number of months of full-time employment shows a steady increase over time, at an average rate of about 0.8 months per year.

Age (years)	Average months worked
18	2.58 to 3.22
19	3.88 to 4.52
20	4.68 to 5.32
21	4.98 to 5.62
22	6.08 to 6.72
23	7.08 to 7.72
24	8.18 to 8.82
25	8.58 to 9.22
26	8.98 to 9.62

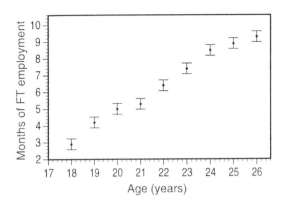

6.101. (a) Because all standard deviations and sample sizes are the same, the margin of error for all intervals is $(1.96)(19)/\sqrt{180} \doteq 2.7757$. The confidence intervals are listed in the table below. **(b)** The plot below shows the error bars for the confidence intervals of (a), and also for part (c). The limits for (a) are the thicker lines which do not extend as far above and below the mean. **(c)** With $z^* = 2.40$, the margin of error for all intervals is $(2.40)(19)/\sqrt{180} \doteq 3.3988$. The confidence intervals are listed in the table below and are shown in the plot (the thinner lines with the wider dashes). **(d)** When we use $z^* = 2.40$ to adjust for the fact that we are making three "simultaneous" confidence intervals, the margin of error is larger, so the intervals overlap more.

Workplace size	Mean SCI
< 50	64.45 to 70.01
50–200	67.59 to 73.15
> 200	72.05 to 77.61
< 50	63.83 to 70.63
50–200	66.97 to 73.77
> 200	71.43 to 78.23

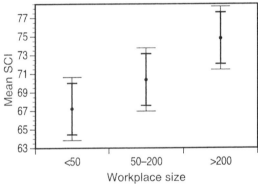

6.102. Shown below is a sample screenshot from the applet and an example of what the resulting plot might look like. Most students (99.7% of them) should find that their final proportion is between 0.90 and 1; 90% will have a proportion between 0.925 and 0.975.

Note: *For each n (number of intervals), the number of "hits" would have a binomial distribution with p = 0.95, but these counts would not be independent; for example, if we knew there were 28 hits after 30 tries, we would know that there could be no more than 38 after 40 tries.*

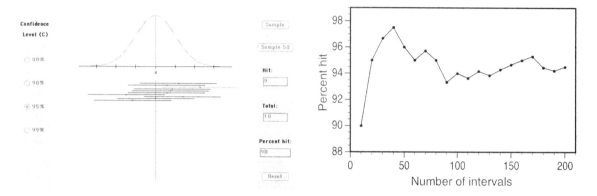

6.103. A sample screenshot and example plot are not shown but would be similar to those shown above for the previous exercise. Most students (99.4% of them) should find that their final proportion is between 0.84 and 0.96; 85% will have a proportion between 0.87 and 0.93.

6.104. For $n = 10$, $z = \frac{5-0}{17/\sqrt{10}} \doteq 0.93$, for which $P = 0.1762$. For the other sample sizes, the computations are similar; the resulting table and graphs are shown below. We see that sample size increases the value of the test statistic (assuming the mean is the same), which in turn decreases the size of the P-value.

n	z	P
10	0.93	0.1762
20	1.32	0.0934
30	1.61	0.0537
40	1.86	0.0314
50	2.08	0.0188

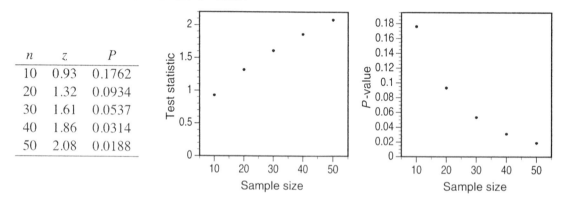

6.105. (a) $\bar{x} = 5.\overline{3}$ mg/dl, so $\bar{x} \pm 1.960\sigma/\sqrt{6}$ is 4.6132 to 6.0534 mg/dl. (b) To test H_0: $\mu = 4.8$ mg/dl vs. H_a: $\mu > 4.8$ mg/dl, we compute $z = \frac{\bar{x}-4.8}{0.9/\sqrt{6}} \doteq 1.45$ and $P \doteq 0.0735$. This is not strong enough to reject H_0.

   Note: *The confidence interval in (a) would allow us to say without further computation that, against a two-sided alternative, we would have $P > 0.05$. Because we have a one-sided alternative, we could conclude from the confidence interval that $P > 0.025$, but that is not enough information to draw a conclusion.*

6.106. (a) The 95% confidence interval is $140 \pm (1.96)(8/\sqrt{16}) = 140 \pm 3.92 = 136.08$ to 143.92 mg/g. (b) Our hypotheses are H_0: $\mu = 135$ mg/g vs. H_a: $\mu > 135$ mg/g. The test statistic is $z = \frac{140-135}{8/\sqrt{16}} = 2.50$, so the P-value is $P = P(Z > 2.50) = 0.0062$. This is strong evidence against H_0; we conclude that the mean cellulose content is higher than 135 mg/g. (c) We must assume that the 16 cuttings in our sample are an SRS. Because our sample is not too large, the population should be normally distributed, or at least not extremely nonnormal.

6.107. (a) The stemplot is reasonably symmetric for such a small sample.
(b) $\bar{x} = 30.6\ \mu\text{g/l}$; $30.6 \pm (1.96)(7/\sqrt{10})$ gives 26.2614 to 34.9386 $\mu\text{g/l}$.
(c) H_0: $\mu = 25\ \mu\text{g/l}$; H_a: $\mu > 25\ \mu\text{g/l}$. $z = \frac{30.6-25}{7/\sqrt{10}} \doteq 2.53$, so $P = 0.0057$.
(We knew from (b) that it had to be smaller than 0.025). This is fairly strong evidence against H_0; the beginners' mean threshold is higher than 25 $\mu\text{g/l}$.

```
2 | 04
2 | 5
3 | 0123
3 | 56
4 | 0
```

6.108. (a) The intended population is probably "the American public"; the population that was actually sampled was "citizens of Indianapolis (with listed phone numbers)." (b) Take $\bar{x} \pm 1.96s/\sqrt{201}$. Food stores: 15.22 to 22.12. Mass merchandisers: 27.77 to 36.99. Pharmacies: 43.68 to 53.52. (c) The confidence intervals do not overlap at all; in particular, the *lower* confidence limit of the rating for pharmacies is higher than the *upper* confidence limit for the other stores. This indicates that the pharmacies are *really* rated higher.

6.109. (a) Under H_0, $\bar{x}$ has a $N(0\%, 53\%/\sqrt{104}) \doteq$ $N(0\%, 5.1971\%)$ distribution. (b) $z = \frac{6.8-0}{53/\sqrt{104}} \doteq 1.31$, so $P = P(Z > 1.31) = 0.0951$. (c) This is not significant at $\alpha = 0.05$. The study gives *some* evidence of increased compensation, but it is not very strong; similar results would happen almost 10% of the time just by chance.

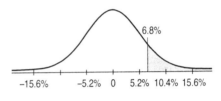

6.110. No: "Significant at $\alpha = 0.05$" *does* mean that the null hypothesis is unlikely, but only in the sense that the evidence (from the sample) would not occur very often if H_0 were true. There is no probability associated with H_0 [unless one is a Bayesian statistician]; it is either true or it is not.

6.111. Yes. That's the heart of why we care about statistical significance. Significance tests allow us to discriminate between random differences ("chance variation") that might occur when the null hypothesis is true, and differences that are unlikely to occur when H_0 is true.

6.112. For each sample, find $\bar{x}$, then take $\bar{x} \pm 1.96(5/\sqrt{12}) = \bar{x} \pm 2.829$.
We "expect" to see that 95 of the 100 intervals will include 20 (the true value of μ); binomial computations show that (about 99% of the time) 90 or more of the 100 intervals will include 20.

6.113. For each sample, find $\bar{x}$, then compute $z = \frac{\bar{x}-20}{5/\sqrt{12}}$. Choose a significance level α and the appropriate cutoff point—for example, with $\alpha = 0.10$, reject H_0 if $|z| > 1.645$; with $\alpha = 0.05$, reject H_0 if $|z| > 1.96$.
If, for example, $\alpha = 0.05$, we "expect" to reject H_0 (that is, make the wrong decision) only 5 of the 100 times.

6.114. For each sample, find $\bar{x}$, then compute $z = \frac{\bar{x}-18}{5/\sqrt{12}}$. Choose a significance level α and the appropriate cutoff point (z^*)—for example, with $\alpha = 0.10$, reject H_0 if $|z| > 1.645$; with $\alpha = 0.05$, reject H_0 if $|z| > 1.96$.

Because the true mean is 20, $Z = \frac{\bar{x}-20}{5/\sqrt{12}}$ has a $N(0, 1)$ distribution, so the probability that we will accept H_0 is $P\left(-z^* < \frac{\bar{x}-18}{5/\sqrt{12}} < z^*\right) = P(-z^* < Z + 1.3856 < z^*) = P(-1.3856 - z^* < Z < -1.3856 + z^*)$. If $\alpha = 0.10$ ($z^* = 1.645$), this probability is $P(-3.03 < Z < 0.26) = 0.6014$; if $\alpha = 0.05$ ($z^* = 1.96$), this probability is $P(-3.35 < Z < 0.57) = 0.7153$. For smaller α, the probability will be larger. Thus we "expect" to (wrongly) accept H_0 a majority of the time, and correctly reject H_0 about 40% of the time or less. (The probability of rejecting H_0 is essentially the power of the test against the alternative $\mu = 20$.)

6.116. The listing below shows the statements ordered from largest to smallest means (that is, with the highest level of agreement at the top) for both age groups. Lines are drawn in the list to show sets of similar complaints for both groups; for example, the top complaint is the same for both groups, and the next set is the same (although the order is different). Restauranteurs wishing to make their businesses attractive to older customers should probably pay the most attention to the top of this list. (Note that those statements which are in the bottom half of the list have ratings of just over 3 or less. On a 1-to-5 scale, "3" is a neutral response.)

Ages 50–64	Ages 65–79
I would rather be served . . .	I would rather be served . . .
I would rather pay the server . . .	Tables are too close together.
Tables are too close together.	Print size is not large enough.
Print size is not large enough.	Background music is often too loud.
Most restaurants are too noisy.	I would rather pay the server . . .
Background music is often too loud.	Most restaurants are too noisy.
Restaurants are too smoky.	Tables are too small.
Service is too slow.	Restaurants are too smoky.
Tables are too small.	Service is too slow.
Glare makes menus difficult to read.	Glare makes menus difficult to read.
Most restaurants are too dark.	It is difficult to hear the service staff.
It is difficult to hear the service staff.	Most restaurants are too dark.
Colors make menus difficult to read.	Colors make menus difficult to read.

In comparing the means, we use a two-sided alternative, because we have no prior expectation that the differences should be either positive or negative. As the text says, the z statistics are found by taking the differences between the means and dividing by 0.08; for example, the first is $z = \frac{2.75-2.93}{0.08} \doteq -2.25$, for which $P = 0.0244$. Those with P-values less than 0.05 are marked with an asterisk. Because we are performing 13 tests, a P-value below 0.05 should not be viewed as establishing significance. Using the Bonferroni approach (see Exercise 6.86), we would be willing to declare as significant any differences with $P < 0.05/13 \doteq 0.0038$; these are marked with two asterisks. Given the clustering of complaints noted in the list above, it is not too surprising that few differences are significant. Two of these three differences suggest that the older group may have more concerns about noise level and hearing.

	Statement	z	P	
Ambience:	Most restaurants are too dark.	-2.25	0.0244	*
	Most restaurants are too noisy.	-1.25	0.2113	
	Background music is often too loud.	-3.50	0.0005	**
	Restaurants are too smoky.	0.62	0.5353	
	Tables are too small.	-2.38	0.0173	*
	Tables are too close together.	-0.25	0.8026	
Menu design:	Print size is not large enough.	-1.13	0.2585	
	Glare makes menus difficult to read.	-2.50	0.0124	*
	Colors of menus make them difficult to read.	-2.38	0.0173	*
Service:	It is difficult to hear the service staff.	-4.38	0.0000	**
	I would rather be served than serve myself.	1.13	0.2585	
	I would rather pay the server than a cashier.	5.00	0.0000	**
	Service is too slow.	0.37	0.7114	

Chapter 7 Solutions

7.1. (a) A stemplot (right) reveals that the distribution has two peaks and a high value (not quite an outlier). Both the stemplot and quantile plot show that the distribution is not normal. **(b)** Maybe: We have a large enough sample to overcome the nonnormal distribution, but we are sampling from a small population. **(c)** The mean is $\bar{x} = 27.29$ cm, $s \doteq 17.7058$ cm, and the margin of error is $t^* \cdot s/\sqrt{40}$:

```
0 | 222244
0 | 579
1 | 0113
1 | 678
2 | 2
2 | 6679
3 | 112
3 | 5789
4 | 0033444
4 | 7
5 | 112
5 |
6 |
6 | 9
```

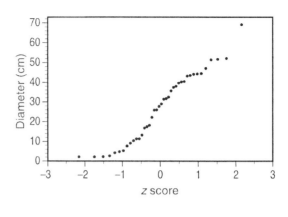

	df	t^*	Interval
Table D	30	2.042	$27.29 \pm 5.7167 = 21.57$ to 33.01 cm
Software	39	2.0227	$27.29 \pm 5.6626 = 21.63$ to 32.95 cm

(d) One could argue for either answer. We chose a random sample from this tract, so the main question is, can we view trees in this tract as being representative of trees elsewhere?

7.2. (a) The distribution is extremely skewed to the right, with two or three high outliers. **(b)** Means are typically *not* the best measure of center for skewed distributions. **(c)** The mean CRP is $\bar{x} \doteq 10.0323$ mg/l, $s \doteq 16.5632$ mg/l, and the margin of error is $t^* \cdot s/\sqrt{40}$:

	df	t^*	Interval
Table D	30	2.042	$\bar{x} \pm 5.3477 = 4.68$ to 15.38 mg/l
Software	39	2.0227	$\bar{x} \pm 5.2972 = 4.74$ to 15.33 mg/l

The skewness of the distribution makes this methodology somewhat suspect.

```
0 | 00000000000000003334
0 | 55555677899
1 | 2
1 | 5
2 | 02
2 | 6
3 | 0
3 |
4 |
4 | 6
5 |
5 | 9
6 |
6 |
7 | 3
```

7.3. Shown are the results for taking *natural* logarithms; common (base 10) logarithms would differ by a factor of about 0.434.
(a) The distribution is still skewed to the right, but considerably less so than the original data. There do not appear to be any outliers in the transformed data (although the group of 0s stands out). **(b)** Means are typically *not* the best measure of center for skewed distributions. **(c)** The mean log-CRP is $\bar{x} \doteq 1.4952$, $s \doteq 1.3912$, and the margin of error is $t^* \cdot s/\sqrt{40}$:

```
0 | 0000000000000000
0 |
1 |
1 | 555788888
2 | 001233
2 | 58
3 | 0134
3 | 8
4 | 13
```

	df	t^*	Interval
Table D	30	2.042	$1.4952 \pm 0.4492 = 1.0460$ to 1.9443
Software	39	2.0227	$1.4952 \pm 0.4449 = 1.0502$ to 1.9401

After undoing the transformation (that is, exponentiating these limits and then subtracting 1), this is about 1.85 to 5.99 mg/l.

7.4. The distribution is skewed to the right, with two peaks—clearly not normal. However, the sample size of 40 should be sufficient to overcome this, so the t methods should be fairly reliable. The mean is $\bar{x} = 0.76475$ μmol/l, $s \doteq 0.3949$ μmol/l, and the margin of error is $t^* \cdot s/\sqrt{40}$:

```
0 | 2333333333333
0 | 455
0 | 6667
0 | 88889999
1 | 00011111
1 | 23
1 | 4
1 |
1 | 9
```

	df	t^*	Interval
Table D	30	2.042	$0.76475 \pm 0.1275 = 0.6372$ to 0.8923 μmol/l
Software	39	2.0227	$0.76475 \pm 0.1263 = 0.6384$ to 0.8911 μmol/l

7.5. (a) The distribution is not normal—there were lots of 1s and 10s—but the nature of the scale means that there can be no extreme outliers, so with a sample of size 60, the t methods should be acceptable. **(b)** The mean is $\bar{x} \doteq 5.9$, $s \doteq 3.7719$, and the margin of error is $t^* \cdot s/\sqrt{60}$:

```
 1 | 0000000000000000
 2 | 0000
 3 | 0
 4 | 0
 5 | 00000
 6 | 000
 7 | 0
 8 | 000000
 9 | 00000
10 | 000000000000000000
```

	df	t^*	Interval
Table D	50	2.009	$5.9 \pm 0.9783 = 4.9217$ to 6.8783
Software	59	2.0010	$5.9 \pm 0.9744 = 4.9256$ to 6.8744

(c) Because this is not a random sample, it may not represent other children well.

7.6. (a) The distribution is irregularly spread from 13.6 to 22.6 MPG. Though not normal, it is not particularly skewed, and has no outliers. **(b)** The *t* methods should be acceptable: The sample size (20) is not very large, but is probably large enough to overcome the minor departures from normality. (For many distributions with little or no skew, the distribution of the mean can be quite close to normal for *n* as small as 10.) **(c)** $\bar{x} = 18.48$ MPG, $s \doteq 3.1158$ MPG, and the standard error is $SE_{\bar{x}} \doteq 0.6967$ MPG. With df = 19, $t^* = 2.093$, so the margin of error is $t^*SE_{\bar{x}} \doteq 1.4582$ MPG, and the 95% confidence interval is 17.0218 to 19.9382 MPG. **(d)** It might be risky to view 20 readings from a single vehicle as a representative sample from other vehicles. It would be better to take samples from a number of vehicles.

13	6
14	368
15	668
16	
17	2
18	07
19	144
20	9
21	05
22	4566

7.7. (a) The distribution is clearly not normal but has no outliers. **(b)** The *t* methods should be acceptable: The sample size (20) is not very large but is probably large enough to overcome the minor departures from normality. (For many distributions with little or no skew, the distribution of the mean can be quite close to normal for *n* as small as 10.) **(c)** $\bar{x} = 30.8$ MPH, $s \doteq 11.2041$ MPH, and the standard error is $SE_{\bar{x}} \doteq 2.5053$ MPH. With df = 19, $t^* = 2.093$, so the margin of error is $t^*SE_{\bar{x}} \doteq 5.2436$ MPH, and the 95% confidence interval is 25.5564 to 36.0436 MPH. **(d)** No; driving speed probably depends on the driver more than on the car.

1	668999
2	11
2	9
3	144
3	5679
4	3
4	589

7.8. (a) The distribution cannot be normal, because all values must be (presumably) integers between 0 and 4. **(b)** The sample size (282) should make the *t* methods appropriate, because the distribution of ratings can have no outliers. **(c)** The margin of error is $t^* \cdot s/\sqrt{282}$, which is either 0.1611 (Table D) or 0.1591 (software):

	df	t^*	Interval
Table D	100	2.626	$2.22 \pm 0.1611 = 2.0589$ to 2.3811
Software	281	2.5934	$2.22 \pm 0.1591 = 2.0609$ to 2.3791

(d) The sample might not represent children from other locations well (or perhaps more accurately, it might not represent well the opinions of parents of children from other locations).

7.9. These intervals are constructed as in the previous exercise, except for the choice of t^*. We see that the width of the interval increases with confidence level.

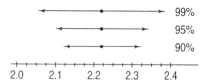

		df	t^*	Interval
90% confidence	Table D	100	1.660	$2.22 \pm 0.1018 = 2.1182$ to 2.3218
	Software	281	1.6503	$2.22 \pm 0.1012 = 2.1188$ to 2.3212
95% confidence	Table D	100	1.984	$2.22 \pm 0.1217 = 2.0983$ to 2.3417
	Software	281	1.9684	$2.22 \pm 0.1207 = 2.0993$ to 2.3407

7.10. (a) & (b) For example, the weight change for Subject 1 is $61.7 - 55.7 = 6$ kg. The mean change is $\bar{x} = 4.73125$ kg and the standard deviation is $s \doteq 1.7457$ kg. (c) $SE_{\bar{x}} = s/\sqrt{16} \doteq 0.4364$ kg; for df $= 15$, $t^* = 2.131$, so the margin of error for 95% confidence is ± 0.9300 (software: ± 0.9302). Based on a method that gives correct results 95% of the time, the mean weight change is 3.8012 to 5.6613 kg (software: 3.8010 to 5.6615 kg). (d) $\bar{x} = 10.40875$ lb, $s \doteq 3.8406$ lb, and the 95% confidence interval is 8.3626 to 12.4549 lb (software: 8.3622 to 12.4553 lb). (e) H_0 is $\mu = 16$ lb. The test statistic is $t \doteq -5.823$ with df $= 15$, which is highly significant evidence ($P < 0.0001$) against H_0 (unless H_a is $\mu > 16$ lb). (f) The data suggest that the excess calories were not converted into weight; the subjects must have used this energy some other way. (See the next exercise for more information.)

7.11. (a) $t = \frac{328 - 0}{256/\sqrt{16}} \doteq 5.1250$ with df $= 15$, for which $P \doteq 0.0012$. There is strong evidence of a change in NEAT. (b) With $t^* = 2.131$, the 95% confidence interval is 191.6 to 464.4 cal/day. This tells us how much of the additional calories might have been burned by the increase in NEAT: It consumed 19% to 46% of the extra 1000 cal/day.

7.12. (a) If μ represents the average percentage change from last month to this month, we test H_0: $\mu = 0\%$ vs. H_a: $\mu \neq 0\%$. A two-sided alternative is the best choice, because (before looking at the data) we had no reason to suspect a change in one direction or the other. (b) $t = \frac{3.8 - 0}{12/\sqrt{40}} \doteq 2.0028$. Table D (with df $= 30$) tells us that $P > 0.05$; software (df $= 39$) says $P = 0.0522$. This is not quite significant at the 5% level. (With a one-sided alternative, the P-value is 0.0261, and we would reject H_0.) (c) Even if we had rejected H_0, this would only mean that the *average* change was nonzero; this does not guarantee that each *individual* store changed.

7.13. (a) For a t distribution with df $= 4$, the P-value is 0.0704—not significant at the 5% level. See sketch on the right (above). (b) For a t distribution with df $= 9$, the P-value is 0.0368, which is significant at the 5% level. See sketch on the right (below). A larger sample size means that there is less variability in the sample mean, so the t statistic is less likely to be large when H_0 is true. Note that even with these computer-produced graphs of these t distributions, it is difficult to see the subtle difference between them: The "tails" 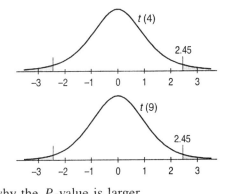 of the $t(4)$ distribution are slightly "heavier," which is why the P-value is larger.

7.14. This t distribution with df $= 1999$ is virtually indistinguishable from a $N(0, 1)$ distribution. The 0.5% critical value is 2.5783 (or 2.581, using df $= 1000$ from Table D, or 2.576 using a normal distribution).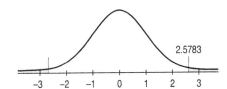

7.15. The 1% critical value for a *t* distribution with
df = 1999 is 2.3282 (or 2.330, using df = 1000 from
Table D, or 2.326 using a normal distribution). Only
one of the one-sided options is shown; the other is
simply the mirror image of this sketch.

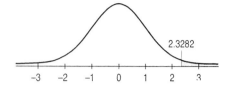

7.16. Because the value of $\bar{x}$ is positive, which supports the direction of the alternative
($\mu > 0$), the *P*-value for the one-sided test is half as big as that for the two-sided test:
$P = 0.04$.

7.17. $\bar{x} = -12.3$ would support the alternative $\mu < 0$,
and for that alternative, the *P*-value would still be
0.04. For the alternative $\mu > 0$ given in Exercise 7.16,
the *P*-value is 0.96. Note that in the sketch shown,
no scale has been given, because in the absence of

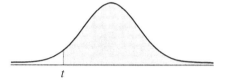

a sample size, we do not know the degrees of freedom. Nevertheless, the *P*-value for the
alternative $\mu > 0$ is the area above the computed value of the test statistic *t*, which will be
the opposite of that found when $\bar{x} = 12.3$. As the area below *t* is 0.04, the area above this
point must be 0.96.

7.18. (a) Use df = 19: $t^* = 2.093$. **(b)** Use df = 29: $t^* = 1.699$. **(c)** Use df = 40: $t^* = 1.303$.
(Using software, the appropriate critical value for df = 49 is $t^* = 1.299$.)

7.19. Software values (rounded to three decimal places) are given in the table below. As
sample size increases, t^* approaches 1.960 (the critical value for a normal distribution).

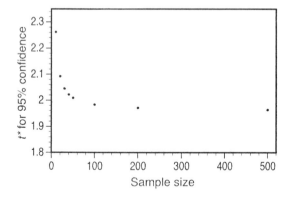

n	df	t^*
10	9	2.262
20	19	2.093
30	29	2.045
40	39	2.023
50	49	2.010
100	99	1.984
200	199	1.972
500	499	1.965

7.20. (a) df = 14. **(b)** $2.145 < t < 2.264$. **(c)** For
$t^* = 2.145$, $p = 0.025$; for $t^* = 2.264$, $p = 0.02$.
(d) $0.02 < P < 0.025$. **(e)** On the right. **(f)** $t = 2.15$
is significant at 5% but not at 1%. **(g)** From software,
$P \doteq 0.0248$.

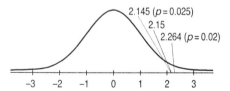

7.21. (a) df = 29. (b) $1.311 < t < 1.699$; for $t^* = 1.311$, $p = 0.10$; for $t^* = 1.699$, $p = 0.05$. (c) Because the alternative is two-sided, we double the right-tail probabilities to find the *P*-value: $0.10 < P < 0.20$. (d) $t = 1.35$ is not significant at 10% or 5%. (e) On the right. (f) From software, $P \doteq 0.1875$.

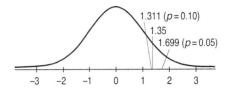

7.22. (a) df = 11. (b) Because $3.106 < |t| < 3.497$, the *P*-value is between $0.0025 < P < 0.005$. (c) From software, $P \doteq 0.0042$.

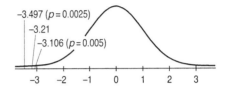

7.23. Let *P* be the given (two-sided) *P*-value, and suppose that the alternative is $\mu > \mu_0$. If $\bar{x}$ is greater than μ_0, this supports the alternative over H_0. However, if $\bar{x} < \mu_0$, we would not take this as evidence against H_0, because $\bar{x}$ is on the "wrong" side of μ_0. So, if the value of $\bar{x}$ is on the "correct" side of μ_0, the one-sided *P*-value is simply $P/2$. However, if the value of $\bar{x}$ is on the "wrong" side of μ_0, the one-sided *P*-value is $1 - P/2$ (which will always be at least 0.5, so it will never indicate significant evidence against H_0).

7.24. (a) The stemplot (right) shows a high outlier (3223 mg/day). A normal quantile plot (not shown) suggests no other major departures from normality. Apart from the outlier, the data are spread from 350 to 1475 mg/day. (b) $\bar{x} = 901.85$ and $s \doteq 467.9059$ mg/day. A normal distribution with this mean and standard deviation is shown below on the left; note that it is spread much more widely than the stemplot, and a large part of the probability falls on negative numbers (which make no sense for calcium intake). (c) From Table D, we use df = 30 and $t^* = 2.042$; with software, we have df = 39 and $t^* = 2.0227$. Based on this sample, we can be 95% confident that the mean calcium intake for these women is between 750.7779 and 1052.9221 mg/day (software: 752.2066 to 1051.4934 mg/day). (d) Without the outlier, $\bar{x} = 842.3333$ and $s \doteq 281.5660$ mg/day. This normal distribution (below, right) looks much more like the stemplot. The Table D critical value is the same; the software critical value for df = 38 is 2.0244. The 95% confidence interval is now 750.2664 to 934.4002 (software: 751.0602 to 933.6065) mg/day. The lower limits changed very little, but because the standard deviation is smaller without the outlier, these intervals are much narrower. (e) One argument against extending these results to other women would be that knowing calcium intake is being observed would almost certainly alter one's behavior.

```
0 | 3
0 | 444455555
0 | 66667777
0 | 8888899999
1 | 00111
1 | 22222
1 | 4
1 |
1 |
2 |
2 |
2 |
2 |
2 |
3 |
3 | 2
```

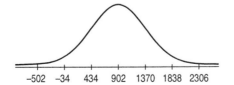

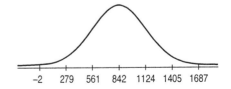

7.25. **(a)** We test H_0: $\mu = 1000$ mg vs. H_a: $\mu \neq$
1000 mg. (Some students might elect to use the one-
sided alternative $\mu < 1000$ mg.) **(b)** With $\bar{x} = 901.85$
and $s \doteq 467.9056$, we find $t = -1.327$ (df $= 39$), for
which software gives $P = 0.1923$. (For a one-sided

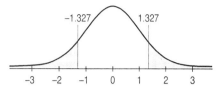

alternative, the P-value is half this big.) **(c)** Based on this test, we do not reject the null
hypothesis; we do not have enough evidence to conclude that mean calcium intake differs
from 1000 mg/day. **(d)** For the sign test (Minitab output below), we find $P = 0.0166$. This
rejects H_0 (the median equals 1000), while the t test does not reject its H_0 because of the
high outlier in the data.

Minitab output

```
Sign test of median = 1000 versus  N.E.   1000


              N  BELOW  EQUAL  ABOVE  P-VALUE     MEDIAN
Calcium      40    28      0    12    0.0166      828.0
```

7.26. The 99% confidence interval is $3.9 \pm t^*(0.98/\sqrt{1406})$.
With Table D (df $= 1000$ and $t^* = 2.581$), this is 3.8325 to 3.9675.
With software (df $= 1405$ and $t^* = 2.5793$), this is 3.8326 to 3.9674.

7.27. **(a)** The differences are spread from -0.018 to 0.020 g, with mean $\bar{x} =$
-0.0015 and standard deviation $s \doteq 0.0122$ g. A stemplot is shown on the right;
the sample is too small to make judgments about skewness or symmetry. **(b)** For
H_0: $\mu = 0$ vs. H_a: $\mu \neq 0$, we find $t = \frac{-0.0015-0}{s/\sqrt{8}} \doteq -0.347$ with df $= 7$, for
which $P = 0.7388$. We cannot reject H_0 based on this sample. **(c)** The 95%
confidence interval is $-0.0015 \pm (2.365)(0.0122/\sqrt{8}) = -0.0015 \pm 0.0102 =$
-0.0117 to 0.0087 g. **(d)** The subjects from this sample may be representative
of future subjects, but the test results and confidence interval are suspect because
this is not a random sample.

```
-1 85
-1
-0 65
-0
 0 2
 0 55
 1
 1
 2 0
```

7.28. **(a)** The differences are spread from -31 to 45 g/cm^2, with mean $\bar{x} = 4.625$
and standard deviation $s \doteq 26.8485$ g/cm^2. A stemplot is shown on the right;
the sample is too small to make judgments about skewness or symmetry. **(b)** For
H_0: $\mu = 0$ vs. H_a: $\mu \neq 0$, we find $t = \frac{4.625-0}{s/\sqrt{8}} \doteq 0.487$ with df $= 7$, for which
$P = 0.6410$. We cannot reject H_0 based on this sample. **(c)** The 95% confidence
interval is $4.625 \pm (2.365)(26.8485/\sqrt{8}) = 4.625 \pm 22.4494 = -17.8244$ to
27.0744 g/cm^2. **(d)** See the answer to part (d) of the previous exercise.

```
-3 1
-2 8
-1
-0 4
 0 16
 1 3
 2
 3 5
 4 5
```

7.29. (a) A stemplot (right) or histogram shows the distribution to be left-skewed, spread from −3 to 9. **(b)** The mean is $\bar{x} \doteq 3.6176$ and the standard deviation is $s \doteq 3.0552$. **(c)** The 95% confidence interval is $\bar{x} \pm t^*(s/\sqrt{34})$. With Table D (df = 30 and $t^* = 2.042$), this is 2.5477 to 4.6876. With software (df = 33 and $t^* = 2.0345$), this is 2.5516 to 4.6837.

```
-3 | 0
-2 | 00
-1 | 0
-0 | 0
 0 | 0
 1 | 0
 2 | 000
 3 | 00000
 4 | 0000000
 5 | 00
 6 | 000
 7 | 00000
 8 |
 9 | 00
```

7.30. The neurobiological arguments suggest that there should be improvement, so we use a one-sided alternative: H_0: $\mu = 0$ vs. H_a: $\mu > 0$. For this test, we find $t = \frac{3.6176-0}{3.0552/\sqrt{34}} \doteq 6.904$ with df = 33, for which the P-value is very small ($P < 0.0005$), so we reject H_0. The confidence interval in part (c) of the previous exercise tells us that we can be 95% confident that the improvement is between about 2.5 and 4.7 points. (Based on that confidence interval, we could have determined that $P < 0.025$, and guessed that the actual value of P was quite a bit smaller, but we could not have made a very accurate estimate.)

7.31. We test H_0: $\mu = 0$ vs. H_a: $\mu < 0$, where μ is the mean change in vitamin C content. Subtract "After" from "Before" to give −53, −52, −57, −52, and −61 mg/100g. Then $\bar{x} = -55$, $s \doteq 3.9370$, and $\text{SE}_{\bar{x}} \doteq 1.7607$ mg/100g, so $t \doteq -31.24$, which is significant for any reasonable α (using df = 4). Cooking does decrease the vitamin C content.

7.32. (a) With $\bar{x} = -55$, $s \doteq 3.9370$, and df = 4, we have $t^* = 2.776$, so the 95% confidence interval is −59.89 to −50.11 mg/100g. **(b)** The "After" measurements are 20.4%, 27.6%, 29.6%, 36.7%, and 17.3% of the specification. For these percents, $\bar{x} \doteq 26.3265\%$, $s \doteq 7.6836\%$, and $\text{SE}_{\bar{x}} \doteq 3.4362\%$—and of course df and t^* are the same as in (a)—so the interval is 16.79% to 35.87% of the specification.

7.33. (a) To test H_0: $\mu = 0$ vs. H_a: $\mu > 0$, we find $t = \frac{565}{267/\sqrt{500}} \doteq 47.32$; because P is tiny, we reject H_0 (at $\alpha = 0.01$, or any reasonable choice of α) and conclude that the new policy would increase credit card usage. **(b)** The 95% confidence interval is $\bar{x} \pm t^*(s/\sqrt{500})$. With Table D (df = 100 and $t^* = 1.984$), this is \$541.31 to \$588.69. With software (df = 499 and $t^* = 1.9647$), this is \$541.54 to \$588.46. **(c)** The sample size is very large, and we are told that we have an SRS. This means that outliers are the only potential snag, and there are none. **(d)** Make the offer to an SRS of n customers, and choose another SRS of size n as a control group. (Or, randomly allocate our SRS of 500 into two groups of 250 each.) Compare the mean increase for the two groups.

7.34. (a) $\bar{x} = 5.3\overline{6}$ mg/dl and $s \doteq 0.6653$ mg/dl, so $\text{SE}_{\bar{x}} \doteq 0.2716$ mg/dl. **(b)** For df = 5, we have $t^* = 2.015$, so the interval is 4.819 to 5.914 mg/dl.

7.35. To test H_0: $\mu = 4.8$ mg/dl vs. H_a: $\mu > 4.8$ mg/dl, we find $t = \frac{5.3\overline{6}-4.8}{0.2716} \doteq 2.086$. For df $= 5$, Table D shows that $0.025 < P < 0.05$ (software gives $P = 0.0457$). This is fairly strong, though not overwhelming, evidence that the patient's phosphate level is above normal.

7.36. (a) For df $= 26$, we have $t^* = 2.056$, so the 95% confidence interval is $114.9 \pm (2.056)(9.3/\sqrt{27}) = 111.22$ to 118.58 mm Hg. **(b)** The essential assumption is that the 27 men tested can be regarded as an SRS from a population, such as all healthy white males in a stated age group. The assumption that blood pressure in this population is normally distributed is *not* essential, because $\bar{x}$ from a sample of size 27 will be roughly normal in any event, as long as the population is not too greatly skewed and has no outliers.

7.37. (a) At right. **(b)** To test H_0: $\mu = 105$ vs. H_a: $\mu \neq 105$, we find $\bar{x} = 104.1\overline{3}$ and $s \doteq 9.3974$ pCi/l, so $t = \frac{\bar{x}-105}{s/\sqrt{12}} \doteq -0.32$. With df $= 11$, we have $P = 0.7554$, which gives us little reason to doubt that $\mu = 105$ pCi/l.

9	1
9	5679
10	134
10	5
11	1
11	9
12	2

7.38. A stemplot of these call lengths can be seen in Figure 1.4 of the text. The distribution is sharply right-skewed, with one clear outlier (2631 minutes). In fact, based on the $1.5 \times IQR$ criterion, the top eight call lengths are outliers. The mean and standard deviation are $\bar{x} = 196.575$ and $s \doteq 342.0215$ min. The five-number summary (all in minutes) is Min $= 1$, $Q_1 = 54.5$, $M = 103.5$, $Q_3 = 200$, Max $= 2631$.

With Table D (df $= 70$ and $t^* = 1.994$), the 95% confidence interval for μ is 120.3261 to 272.8239 min. With software (df $= 79$ and $t^* = 1.9905$), it is 120.4618 to 272.6882 min. Given the sharp skewness of the data, and the large number of outliers, we should be quite cautious in using this interval for inference.

7.39. (a) For the factory data:
$\bar{x} \doteq 42.8519$ and $s \doteq 4.7935$ mg/100g.
For Haiti:
$\bar{x} \doteq 37.5185$ and $s \doteq 2.4396$ mg/100g.
For the change (Haiti minus Factory):
$\bar{x} = -5.\overline{3}$ and $s \doteq 5.5884$ mg/100g.
Stemplots are shown on the right. The change distribution is moderately right-skewed, but t procedures should be fairly reliable for all three of these distributions.
(b) We wish to test H_0: $\mu = 0$ mg/100g vs. H_a: $\mu < 0$ mg/100g, where μ is the

Factory		Haiti		Change	
3	2	34	000	−1	4
3		35	00000	−1	3322
3	77	36	0	−1	
3	88999	37	0000	−0	9988
4	001	38	000000	−0	7776666
4	233	39	0	−0	5444
4	444455	40	0000	−0	2
4	77	41	00	−0	1
4	89	42		0	1
5	00	43	0	0	33
5	2			0	4
				0	
				0	8

mean change. **(c)** $t = -4.96$ with df $= 26$, which has $P < 0.0001$. The mean is significantly less than 0. **(d)** See the Minitab output. Note that there is no simple relationship between the Factory and Haiti confidence intervals, and the Change interval; the latter cannot be determined by looking at the first two.

Minitab output

```
– – – – – – – – – – – – –   Significance Test   – – – – – – – – – – – – – –
Test of mu = 0.00 vs mu < 0.00

Variable      N     Mean    StDev   SE Mean        T    P-Value
Change       27    -5.33     5.59      1.08    -4.96     0.0000


– – – – – – – – – – – –   Confidence Intervals   – – – – – – – – – – – –
Variable      N     Mean    StDev   SE Mean       95.0 % C.I.
Factory      27   42.852    4.793     0.923   ( 40.955,  44.749)
Haiti        27   37.519    2.440     0.469   ( 36.553,  38.484)
Change       27    -5.33     5.59      1.08   (  -7.54,   -3.12)
```

7.40. With all 50 states listed in the table, we have information about the entire population in question; no statistical procedures are needed (or meaningful).

7.41. (a) We test H_0: $\mu = 0$ vs. H_a: $\mu > 0$, where μ is the mean change in score (that is, the mean improvement). **(b)** The distribution is slightly left-skewed, with mean $\bar{x} = 2.5$ and $s \doteq 2.8928$. **(c)** $t = \frac{2.5-0}{s/\sqrt{20}} \doteq 3.8649$, df $= 19$, and $P = 0.00052$; there is strong evidence of improvement in listening test scores. **(d)** With df $= 19$, we have $t^* = 2.093$, so the 95% confidence interval is 1.1461 to 3.8539.

```
-0 | 6
-0 |
-0 |
-0 | 0
 0 | 0011
 0 | 222333333
 0 |
 0 | 66666
```

7.42. The distribution is slightly left-skewed, with mean $\bar{x} = 1.45$ and $s \doteq 3.2032$. To test for improvement, we take H_0: $\mu = 0$ vs. H_a: $\mu > 0$, where μ is the mean change in score (that is, the mean improvement). We find $t = \frac{1.45-0}{s/\sqrt{20}} \doteq 2.0244$, df $= 19$, $P = 0.0286$. This is significant evidence (at $\alpha = 0.05$) of improvement in listening test scores. For a 95% confidence interval, we have $t^* = 2.093$, so the interval is -0.0491 to 2.9491.

```
-0 | 54
-0 | 32
-0 | 11
 0 | 11
 0 | 2223333
 0 | 4455
 0 | 7
```

7.43. The distribution is fairly symmetrical with no outliers. The mean IQ is $\bar{x} = 114.98\overline{3}$ and the standard deviation is $s \doteq 14.8009$. The 95% confidence interval is $\bar{x} \pm t^*(s/\sqrt{60})$. With Table D (df $= 50$ and $t^* = 2.009$), this is 111.1446 to 118.8221. With software (df $= 59$ and $t^* = 2.0010$), this is 111.1598 to 118.8068. Because all students in the sample came from the same school, this *might* adequately describe the mean IQ at this school, but the sample could not be considered representative of all fifth graders.

```
 8 | 12
 8 | 9
 9 | 04
 9 | 67
10 | 01112223
10 | 568999
11 | 0002233444
11 | 5677788
12 | 223444
12 | 56778
13 | 01344
13 | 6799
14 | 2
14 | 5
```

7.44. We test H_0: median $= 0$ vs. H_a: median $\neq 0$. The Minitab output below gives $P = 1$, because there were four positive and four negative differences, giving us no reason to doubt H_0. The t test P-value was 0.7388.

Minitab output

```
Sign test of median = 0.00000 versus  N.E.  0.00000

             N  BELOW  EQUAL  ABOVE  P-VALUE    MEDIAN
opdiff       8      4      0      4   1.0000  -0.00150
```

7.45. We test H_0: median $= 0$ vs. H_a: median $\neq 0$. There were three negative and five positive differences, so the P-value is $2P(X \geq 5)$ for a binomial distribution with parameters $n = 8$ and $p = 0.5$. From Table C or software (Minitab output below), we have $P = 0.7266$, which gives no reason to doubt H_0. The t test P-value was 0.6410.

Minitab output

```
Sign test of median = 0.00000 versus  N.E.  0.00000

             N  BELOW  EQUAL  ABOVE  P-VALUE   MEDIAN
opdiff       8      3      0      5   0.7266    3.500
```

7.46. We test H_0: median $= 0$ vs. H_a: median < 0. All five differences were negative, so the P-value is $P(X \geq 5)$ for a binomial distribution with parameters $n = 5$ and $p = 0.5$, which is 0.0312. This is significant evidence (at $\alpha = 0.05$) of a decrease in vitamin C content. The t test P-value was much smaller ($P < 0.0001$).

Minitab output

```
Sign test of median = 0.00000 versus  L.T.  0.00000

             N  BELOW  EQUAL  ABOVE  P-VALUE   MEDIAN
VitCDiff     5      5      0      0   0.0312   -53.00
```

7.47. (a) We test H_0: median $= 0$ vs. H_a: median > 0, or H_0: $p = 1/2$ vs. H_a: $p > 1/2$.
(b) Two of the 34 differences are zero; of the other 32, 28 are positive. For a $B(32, 0.5)$ distribution, the mean and standard deviation are 16 and 2.8284, so 28 positive differences standardizes to $z = 4.24$, for which $P < 0.0001$, and we reject H_0. (If we use the continuity correction, $z = 4.07$ and the conclusion is the same.)

7.48. We test H_0: median $= 0$ vs. H_a: median > 0, or H_0: $p = 1/2$ vs. H_a: $p > 1/2$. Three of the 20 differences are zero; of the other 17, 16 are positive. The P-value is $P(X \geq 16)$ for a $B(17, 0.5)$ distribution. While Table C cannot give us the exact value of this probability, if we weaken the evidence by pretending that the three zero differences were negative and look at the $B(20, 0.5)$ distribution, we can estimate that $P < 0.0059$—enough information to reject the null hypothesis. In fact, the P-value is 0.0001.

Minitab output

```
Sign test of median = 0.00000 versus  G.T.  0.00000

             N  BELOW  EQUAL  ABOVE  P-VALUE   MEDIAN
gain        20      1      3     16   0.0001    3.000
```

7.49. We test H_0: median $= 0$ vs. H_a: median > 0, or H_0: $p = 1/2$ vs. H_a: $p > 1/2$. Fourteen of the 20 differences are positive (none are zero). The P-value is $P(X \geq 14)$ for a $B(20, 0.5)$ distribution; Table C (or software) gives this value as $P = 0.0577$—not quite significant evidence of improvement.

Minitab output

```
Sign test of median = 0.00000 versus  G.T.   0.00000

           N  BELOW  EQUAL  ABOVE   P-VALUE     MEDIAN
gain      20     6      0     14    0.0577      2.000
```

7.50. After taking logarithms, the 90% confidence interval is $\bar{x} \pm t^*(s/\sqrt{5})$. For $df = 4$, $t^* = 2.132$, and the confidence

Log	$\bar{x}$	s	Confidence interval
Common	2.5552	0.0653	2.4930 to 2.6175
Natural	5.8836	0.1504	5.7403 to 6.0270

intervals are as shown in the table. (As we would expect, after exponentiating to undo the logarithms, both intervals are equivalent except for rounding differences: 311.2 to 414.5 hours.)

7.51. The standard deviation for the given data was $s \doteq 0.012224$. With $t = \dfrac{x}{s/\sqrt{15}}$, $\alpha = 0.05$, and $df = 14$, we reject H_0 if $|t| \geq 2.145$, which means $|\bar{x}| \geq (2.145)(s/\sqrt{15})$, or $|\bar{x}| \geq 0.00677$. Assuming $\mu = 0.002$:

$$P(|\bar{x}| \geq 0.00677) = 1 - P\left(-0.00677 \leq \bar{x} \leq 0.00677\right)$$

$$= 1 - P\left(\frac{-0.00677 - 0.002}{s/\sqrt{15}} \leq \frac{\bar{x} - 0.002}{s/\sqrt{15}} \leq \frac{0.00677 - 0.002}{s/\sqrt{15}}\right)$$

$$= 1 - P\left(-2.78 \leq Z \leq 1.51\right)$$

$$= 1 - (0.9345 - 0.0027) \doteq 0.07$$

The power is about 7% against this alternative—not surprising, given the small sample size, and the fact that the difference (0.002) is small relative to the standard deviation.

   Note: *You can find a collection of online power calculators for various types of statistical tests at* `http://calculators.stat.ucla.edu/powercalc/`. *Note that for one-sample tests, this page gives slightly different answers from those found by the method described in the text; for this problem, it gives the power as about 0.09. The online calculator, like other statistical software, uses a "noncentral t distribution" (used in the text for two-sample power problems) rather than a normal distribution, resulting in more accurate answers. In most situations, the practical conclusions drawn from the power computations are the same regardless of the method used.*

7.52. We will reject H_0 when $t = \dfrac{\bar{x}}{s/\sqrt{n}} \geq t^*$, where t^* is the appropriate critical value for the chosen sample size. This corresponds to $\bar{x} \geq 10t^*/\sqrt{n}$, so the power against $\mu = 2$ is

$$P(\bar{x} \geq 10t^*/\sqrt{n}) = P\left(\frac{\bar{x} - 2}{10/\sqrt{n}} \geq \frac{10t^*/\sqrt{n} - 2}{10/\sqrt{n}}\right)$$

$$= P\left(Z \geq t^* - 0.2\sqrt{n}\right)$$

n	t^*	$t^* - 0.2\sqrt{n}$	Power
50	1.6766	0.2623	0.3965
75	1.6657	-0.0663	0.5264
100	1.6604	-0.3396	0.6329
125	1.6572	-0.5788	0.7186
150	1.6551	-0.7943	0.7865
151	1.6551	-0.8026	0.7889
152	1.6550	-0.8108	0.7912
153	1.6549	-0.8189	0.7936
154	1.6549	-0.8271	0.7959
155	1.6548	-0.8352	0.7982
156	1.6547	-0.8433	0.8005

For $\alpha = 0.05$, the table on the right shows the power for a variety of sample sizes, and we see that $n \geq 156$ achieves the desired 80% power.

   Note: *Some power analysis software will determine the required sample size to achieve a specified level of power. For example, the online calculator noted above calculates the appropriate sample size to be 155.926.*

7.53. (a) The distribution cannot be normal, because all numbers are integers. **(b)** The t procedures should be appropriate, because we have two large samples, with no outliers. **(c)** $H_0: \mu_I = \mu_C$; H_a:

df	t^*	Confidence interval
354.0	1.9667	0.5143 to 0.9857
164	1.9745	0.5134 to 0.9866
100	1.984	0.5122 to 0.9878

$\mu_I > \mu_C$ (or $\mu_I \neq \mu_C$). The one-sided alternative reflects the researchers' (presumed) belief that the intervention would increase scores on the test. The two-sided alternative allows for the possibility that the intervention might have had a negative effect.
(d) $SE_D = \sqrt{s_I^2/n_I + s_C^2/n_C} \doteq 0.1198$ and $t = (\bar{x}_I - \bar{x}_C)/SE_D \doteq 6.258$. Regardless of how we compute degrees of freedom (df $\doteq$ 354 or 164), the P-value is very small: $P < 0.0001$. We reject H_0 and conclude that the intervention increased test scores. **(e)** The interval is $\bar{x}_I - \bar{x}_C \pm t^* SE_D$; the value of t^* depends on the df (see the table), but note that in every case the interval rounds to 0.51 to 0.99. **(f)** The results for this sample may not generalize well to other areas of the country.

7.54. (a) The distribution cannot be normal, because all numbers are integers. **(b)** The t procedures should be appropriate, because we have two large samples, with no outliers. **(c)** $H_0: \mu_I = \mu_C$; H_a:

df	t^*	Confidence interval
341.8	1.9669	0.1932 to 0.6668
164	1.9745	0.1922 to 0.6678
100	1.984	0.1911 to 0.6689

$\mu_I > \mu_C$ (or $\mu_I \neq \mu_C$). The one-sided alternative reflects the researchers' (presumed) belief that the intervention would increase self-efficacy scores. The two-sided alternative allows for the possibility that the intervention might have had a negative effect.
(d) $SE_D = \sqrt{s_I^2/n_I + s_C^2/n_C} \doteq 0.1204$ and $t = (\bar{x}_I - \bar{x}_C)/SE_D \doteq 3.571$. Regardless of how we compute degrees of freedom (df $\doteq$ 341.8 or 164), the (one-sided) P-value is about 0.0002. We reject H_0 and conclude that the intervention increased self-efficacy scores. **(e)** The interval is $\bar{x}_I - \bar{x}_C \pm t^* SE_D$; the value of t^* depends on the df (see the table), but note that in every case the interval rounds to 0.19 to 0.67. **(f)** As in the previous exercise, the results for this sample may not generalize well to other areas of the country.

7.55. (a) This may be near enough to an SRS, if this company's working conditions were similar to that of other workers. **(b)** $SE_D \doteq 0.7626$; regardless of how we choose df, the interval rounds to 9.99 to

df	t^*	Confidence interval
137.1	1.9774	9.9920 to 13.0080
114	1.9810	9.9893 to 13.0107
100	1.984	9.9870 to 13.0130

13.01 mg.y/m^3. **(c)** A one-sided alternative would seem to be reasonable here; specifically, we would likely expect that the mean exposure for outdoor workers would be lower. For testing H_0, we find $t = 15.08$, for which $P < 0.0001$ with either df = 137 or 114 (and for either a one- or two-sided alternative). We have strong evidence that outdoor concrete workers have lower dust exposure than the indoor workers. **(d)** The sample sizes are large enough that skewness should not matter.

7.56. With the given standard deviations, $SE_D \doteq 0.2653$; regardless of how we choose df, a 95% confidence interval for the difference in means rounds to 4.37 to 5.43 mg.y/m^3. With the null

df	t^*	Confidence interval
121.5	1.9797	4.3747 to 5.4253
114	1.9810	4.3744 to 5.4256
100	1.984	4.3736 to 5.4264

hypothesis $H_0: \mu_i = \mu_o$ (and either a one- or two-sided alternative, as in the previous exercise), we find $t = 18.47$, for which $P < 0.0001$ regardless of df and the chosen alternative. We have strong evidence that outdoor concrete workers have lower respirable dust exposure than the indoor workers.

7.57. To find a confidence interval $(\bar{x}_1 - \bar{x}_2) \pm t^* \mathrm{SE}_D$, we need either:

- sample sizes and standard deviations—in which case we could find the interval in the usual way;
- t and df—because $t = (\bar{x}_1 - \bar{x}_2)/\mathrm{SE}_D$, so we could compute $\mathrm{SE}_D = (\bar{x}_1 - \bar{x}_2)/t$ and use df to find t^*;
- or df and a more accurate P-value—from which we could determine t, and then proceed as above.

The confidence interval could give us useful information about the magnitude of the difference (although with such a small P-value, we do know that a 95% confidence interval would not include 0).

7.58. (a) The 68–95–99.7 rule suggests that the distributions are not normal: If they were normal, then (for example) 95% of 7-to-10-year-olds drink between -13.2 and 29.6 oz of sweetened drinks per day.

df	t^*	Confidence interval
7.8	2.3159	-16.4404 to 3.8404
4	2.7764	-18.4571 to 5.8571
4	2.776	-18.4551 to 5.8551

As negative numbers do not make sense (unless some children are regurgitating sweetened drinks), the distributions must be right-skewed. **(b)** We find $\mathrm{SE}_D \doteq 4.3786$ and $t \doteq -1.439$, with either df $\doteq 7.8$ ($P = 0.1890$) or df $= 4$ ($P = 0.2236$). We do not have enough evidence to reject H_0. **(c)** The possible 95% confidence intervals are given in the table. (The two different intervals for df $= 4$ are using t^* from software, and from Table D.) **(d)** Because the distributions are not normal, and the samples are small, the t procedures are questionable for these data. **(e)** Because this group is not an SRS—and indeed might not be random in any way—we would have to be very cautious about extending these results to other children.

7.59. (a) Hypotheses should involve μ_1 and μ_2 (population means) rather than $\bar{x}_1$ and $\bar{x}_2$ (sample means). **(b)** The samples are not independent; we would need to compare the 10 boys to the 10 girls. **(c)** We need P to be small (for example, less than 0.05) to reject H_0. A large P-value like this gives no reason to doubt H_0.

7.60. (a) Because 0 is not in the confidence interval, we would reject H_0 at the 5% level. **(b)** Larger samples generally give smaller margins of error (at the same confidence level, and assuming that the standard deviations for the large and small samples are about the same). One explanation for this is that larger samples give more information, and therefore offer more precise results. Alternatively, in looking at the formula for a two-sample confidence interval, we see that $\mathrm{SE}_D = \sqrt{s_1^2/n_1 + s_2^2/n_2}$, so that if n_1 and n_2 are increased, the standard error decreases.

> **Note:** *For (a), we can even make some specific statements about t and its P-value: The confidence interval tells us that $\bar{x}_1 - \bar{x}_2 = 1.95$, and the margin of error is 0.35. As t^* for a 95% confidence interval is at least 1.96, $\mathrm{SE}_D = \frac{0.35}{t^*}$ is less than about 0.179, and the t-statistic $t = 1.95/\mathrm{SE}_D$ is at least 10.9. (The largest possible value of t, for df $= 1$, is about 70.8.) A little experimentation with different df reveals that $P < 0.009$ for all df, and if df > 4, then $P < 0.0001$.*

7.61. (a) We can reject H_0: $\mu_1 = \mu_2$ in favor of the two-sided alternative at the 5% level, and even at the 1% level, because $P < 0.005$. **(b)** We do not reject H_0; a negative

t-statistic means that $\bar{x}_1 < \bar{x}_2$, which certainly does not make us reject H_0 in favor of $\mu_1 - \mu_2 > 0$—that is, $\mu_1 > \mu_2$. (In fact, $P = 0.9975$.)

7.62. We find $SE_D \doteq 2.2091$. The options for the 95% confidence interval for $\mu_1 - \mu_2$ are shown on the right. A 99% confidence interval would include more values (it would be wider), because

df	t^*	Confidence interval
94.9	1.9853	-24.3856 to -15.6144
49	2.0096	-24.4393 to -15.5607
40	2.021	-24.4645 to -15.5355

increasing our confidence level means that we need a larger margin of error.

7.63. (a) Use a two-sided alternative (H_a: $\mu_1 \neq \mu_2$), because we (presumably) have no prior suspicion that one design will be better than the other. (b) Both sample sizes are the same ($n_1 = n_2 = 30$), so the appropriate degrees of freedom would be df $= 30 - 1 = 29$. (c) Because $2.045 < t < 2.150$, and the alternative is two-sided, Table D tells us that the P-value is $0.04 < P < 0.05$. (Software gives $P = 0.0485$.)

7.64. For a two-sided test at $\alpha = 0.05$, we need $|t| > t^*$, where $t^* = 2.045$ is the 0.025 critical value for a t distribution with df $= 29$.

7.65. This is a matched-pairs design; for example, Monday sales are (at least potentially) not independent of one another. The correct approach would be to use one-sample t methods on the seven differences (Monday sales for design 1 minus Monday sales for design 2, Tuesday-1 minus Tuesday-2, and so on).

7.66. (a) Results for this randomization will depend on the technique used. (b) $SE_D \doteq 0.5235$, and the options for the 95% confidence interval are given on the right. (c) Because 0 falls outside the 95%

df	t^*	Confidence interval
12.7	2.1651	0.6667 to 2.9333
9	2.2622	0.6159 to 2.9841
9	2.262	0.6160 to 2.9840

confidence interval, the P-value is less than 0.05, so we would reject H_0. (For reference, $t \doteq 3.439$ and the actual P-value is either 0.0045 or 0.0074, depending on which df we use.)

7.67. The next ten employees who need screens might not be an independent group—perhaps they all come from the same department, for example. Randomization reduces the chance that we end up with such unwanted groupings.

7.68. (a) We test H_0: $\mu_0 = \mu_3$ vs. H_a: $\mu_0 > \mu_3$. For the two samples, we find $\bar{x}_0 = 48.705$, $s_0 = 1.5344$, $\bar{x}_3 = 21.795$, and $s_3 = 0.7707$ mg/100g; thus $SE_D \doteq 1.2142$ and $t = 22.16$. This gives either

df	t^*	Confidence interval
1.47	4.7037	21.1988 to 32.6212
1	6.3137	19.2439 to 34.5761
1	6.314	19.2436 to 34.5764

$P = 0.0080$ (df $= 1.47$) or $P = 0.0143$ (df $= 1$); either way, this is fairly strong evidence that vitamin C is lost in storage. (b) Options for the 90% confidence interval for $\mu_0 - \mu_3$ are given in the table.

7.69. (a) This is now a matched-pairs design: The immediate and three-days-later numbers are not independent. (b) The vitamin C content changed by -26.37 and -27.45 mg/100g, for which $\bar{x} = -26.91$ and $s \doteq 0.7637$ mg/100g. Then $t = \frac{\bar{x}}{s/\sqrt{2}} \doteq -49.83$ with df $= 1$, for which $P = 0.0064$. The 90% confidence interval for the change in vitamin C content is -30.3196 to -23.5004 mg/100g.

7.70. (a) We test H_0: $\mu_0 = \mu_3$ vs. H_a: $\mu_0 > \mu_3$. For the two samples, we find $\bar{x}_0 = 95.3$, $s_0 = 0.9899$, $\bar{x}_3 = 95.85$, and $s_3 = 2.1920$ mg/100g. Because $\bar{x}_3 > \bar{x}_0$, we have no evidence against H_0; further

df	t^*	Confidence interval
1.39	4.9847	-9.0276 to 7.9276
1	6.3137	-11.2880 to 10.1880
1	6.314	-11.2884 to 10.1884

analysis is not necessary. (However, just for reference, $t = -0.323$.) **(b)** Options for the 90% confidence interval for $\mu_0 - \mu_3$ are given in the table.

7.71. Small samples may lead to rejection of H_0, if (as in Exercise 7.68) the evidence is very strong. (The weakness of small samples is that they are not very powerful; the rejection in 7.68 occurred because the evidence suggests that the true means are quite different.)

7.72. (a) The null hypothesis is $\mu_1 = \mu_2$; the alternative can be either two- or one-sided. (It might be a reasonable expectation that $\mu_1 > \mu_2$.) We find $SE_D \doteq 0.2796$ and $t = 8.369$. Regardless of df

df	t^*	Confidence interval
121.5	1.9797	1.7865 to 2.8935
60	2.0003	1.7807 to 2.8993
60	2.000	1.7808 to 2.8992

and H_a, the conclusion is the same: P is very small, and we conclude that *WSJ* ads are more trustworthy. **(b)** Possible 95% confidence intervals are given in the table; all place the difference in trustworthiness at between about 1.8 and 2.9 points. **(c)** Advertising in *WSJ* is seen as more reliable than advertising in the *National Enquirer*—a conclusion that probably comes as a surprise to no one.

7.73. (a) Good statistical practice dictates that the alternative hypothesis should be chosen without looking at the data; we should only choose a one-sided alternative if we have some reason to expect it *before* looking at the sample results. **(b)** The correct P-value is twice that reported for the one-tailed test: $P = 0.12$.

7.74. To support the alternative $\mu_1 > \mu_2$, we need to see $\bar{x}_1 > \bar{x}_2$, so that $t = (\bar{x}_1 - \bar{x}_2)/SE_D$ must be positive. **(a)** If $t = 1.81$, the one-sided P-value is half of the reported two-sided value: $P = 0.035$. We therefore reject H_0 at $\alpha = 0.05$. **(b)** $t = -1.81$ does not support H_a; the one-sided P-value is 0.965. We do not reject H_0 at $\alpha = 0.05$ (or any other reasonable choice of α).

7.75. (a) The north distribution (five-number summary 2.2, 10.2, 17.05, 39.1, 58.8 cm) is right-skewed, while the south distribution (2.6, 26.1, 37.70, 44.6, 52.9 cm) is left-skewed. Stemplots and boxplots are shown on the right. **(b)** The methods of this section seem to be appropriate in spite of the skewness, because the sample sizes are relatively large, and there are not outliers in either distribution. **(c)** H_0: $\mu_n = \mu_s$; H_a: $\mu_n \neq \mu_s$; we should use a two-sided alternative, because we have no reason (before looking at the data) to expect a difference in a particular direction. **(d)** The means and standard deviations are $\bar{x}_n = 23.7$, $s_n \doteq 17.5001$, $\bar{x}_s = 34.5\bar{3}$, and

North		South
43322	0	2
65	0	57
443310	1	2
955	1	8
	2	13
8755	2	689
0	3	2
996	3	566789
43	4	003444
6	4	578
4	5	0112
85	5	

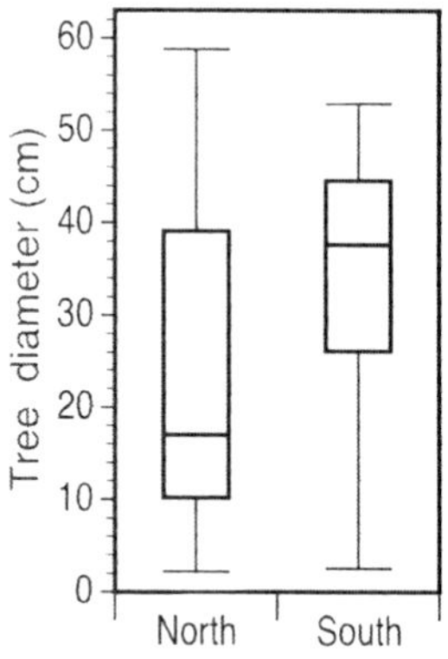

df	t^*	Confidence interval
55.7	2.0035	-19.0902 to -2.5765
29	2.0452	-19.2624 to -2.4043
29	2.045	-19.2614 to -2.4053

$s_s \doteq 14.2583$ cm. Then $SE_D \doteq 4.1213$, so $t = -2.629$ with df = 55.7 ($P = 0.011$) or df = 29 ($P = 0.014$). We conclude that the means are different (specifically, the south mean is greater than the north mean). **(e)** See the table for possible 95% confidence intervals.

7.76. (a) The east distribution (five-number summary 2.3, 6.7, 19.65, 38.7, 51.1 cm) is right-skewed, while the west distribution (2.9, 20.4, 33.20, 42.1, 58.0 cm) is left-skewed. Stemplots and boxplots are shown on the right. **(b)** The methods of this section seem to be appropriate in spite of the skewness, because the sample sizes are relatively large, and there are not outliers in either distribution. **(c)** H_0: $\mu_e = \mu_w$; H_a: $\mu_e \neq \mu_w$; we should use a two-sided alternative, because we have no reason (before looking at the data) to expect a difference in a particular direction. **(d)** The means and standard deviations are $\bar{x}_e = 21.71\bar{6}$, $s_e \doteq 16.0743$, $\bar{x}_w = 30.28\bar{3}$,

East		West
222	0	233
9566655	0	
3100	1	11
7	1	78
33222	2	0011
	2	55
11	3	00
98	3	555669
333	4	023444
86	4	1
1	5	78

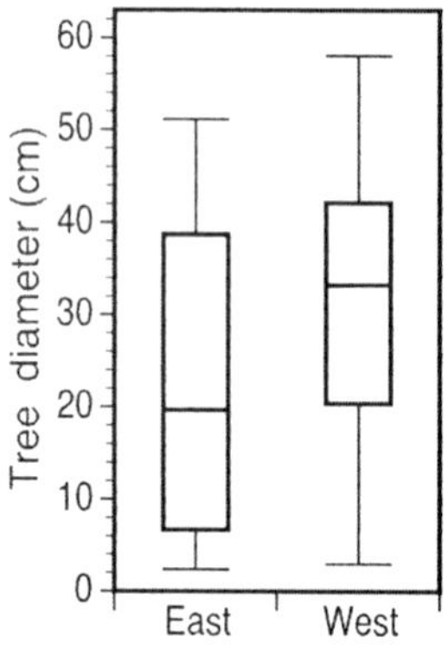

df	t^*	Confidence interval
57.8	2.0018	-16.6852 to -0.4481
29	2.0452	-16.8613 to -0.2720
29	2.045	-16.8604 to -0.2730

and $s_w \doteq 15.3314$ cm. Then $SE_D \doteq 4.0556$, so $t = -2.112$ with df = 57.8 ($P = 0.0390$) or df = 29 ($P = 0.0434$). We conclude that the means are different at $\alpha = 0.05$ (specifically, the west mean is greater than the east mean). **(e)** See the table for possible 95% confidence intervals.

7.77. (a) Control scores are fairly symmetrical, while piano scores are slightly left-skewed. Scores in the piano group are generally higher than scores in the control group. (b) Below. (c) We test H_0: $\mu_p = \mu_c$ vs. H_a: $\mu_p > \mu_c$. With the values in the table below, $SE_D \doteq 0.6387$, and $t = 5.06$. Whether df $= 33$ or df $= 61.7$, $P < 0.0001$, so we reject H_0 and conclude that piano lessons improved the test scores.

Control		Piano
0	−6	
	−5	
0	−4	
000	−3	0
00	−2	00
0000000	−1	0
00000	−0	0
000000	0	0
000000	1	0
0000000	2	000
0	3	00000
000	4	0000000
0	5	00
	6	000
	7	00000
	8	
	9	00

	n	$\bar{x}$	s	$SE_{\bar{x}}$
Piano	34	3.6176	3.0552	0.5240
Control	44	0.3863	2.4229	0.3653

7.78. The possible 95% confidence intervals for $\mu_p - \mu_c$ are given in the table on the right.

df	t^*	Confidence interval
61.7	1.9992	1.9544 to 4.5082
33	2.0345	1.9318 to 4.5308
30	2.042	1.9270 to 4.5355

7.79. Having the control group in 7.77 and 7.78 makes our conclusions more reliable, since it accounts for increases in scores that may come about simply from the passage of time. Between significance tests and confidence intervals, preferences might vary somewhat. Arguably, there is an advantage to the test since we have a one-sided alternative; the confidence interval by its nature is two-sided.

7.80. (a) The back-to-back stemplot shows a roughly normal shape for the healthy firms, while failed-firm ratios are generally lower and have an irregular (and slightly right-skewed) distribution. (b) H_0: $\mu_h = \mu_f$ vs. H_a: $\mu_h > \mu_f$. Summary statistics for the two groups are below; the t value is 7.90, with either df $= 32$ or df $= 81.7$. Either way, $P < 0.0005$, so we conclude that failed firms' ratios are lower. (c) One cannot impose the "treatments" of failure or success on a firm.

Failed		Healthy
11100	0	1
22	0	2
5544	0	
6	0	66
9999988888	0	899999
111111	1	00011
33	1	2223
4	1	4445555
6	1	66666777
	1	88888889999
0	2	0000111
	2	222223
	2	455
	2	6677
	2	8
	3	01

	n	$\bar{x}$	s	$SE_{\bar{x}}$
Healthy	68	1.726	0.639	0.078
Failed	33	0.824	0.481	0.084

7.81. (a) $SE_D \doteq 3.0175$. Answers will vary with the df used; see the table. (b) Because of random fluctuations between stores, we might (just by chance) have seen a rise in the average number of units sold even if actual mean sales had remained unchanged—or even if they dropped slightly.

df	t^*	Confidence interval
104.6	1.9829	−2.9834 to 8.9834
54	2.0049	−3.0497 to 9.0497
50	2.009	−3.0621 to 9.0621

7.82. (a) We test H_0: $\mu_p = \mu_o$ vs. H_a: $\mu_p < \mu_o$.
$SE_D \doteq 52.4710$ and $t = -7.34$, which gives
$P < 0.0001$ whether df $= 140.6$ or df $= 133$.
Cocaine use is associated with lower birth

df	t^*	Confidence interval
140.6	1.9770	−488.7342 to −281.2658
133	1.9780	−488.7856 to −281.2144
100	1.984	−489.1026 to −280.8974

weights. **(b)** The interval is $(\bar{x}_p - \bar{x}_o) \pm t^*SE_D$. Answers will vary with the degrees of freedom used; see the table. **(c)** The "Other" group may include drug users, since some in it were not tested. Among drug users, there may have been other ("confounding") factors that affected birthweight. Note that in this situation, an experiment is out of the question.

7.83. (a) We test H_0: $\mu_b = \mu_f$; H_a: $\mu_b > \mu_f$.
$SE_D \doteq 0.5442$ and $t = 1.654$, for which $P = 0.0532$
(df $= 37.6$) or 0.0577 (df $= 18$); there is not quite
enough evidence to reject H_0 at $\alpha = 0.05$. **(b)** The

df	t^*	Confidence interval
37.6	2.0251	−0.2021 to 2.0021
18	2.1009	−0.2434 to 2.0434
18	2.101	−0.2434 to 2.0434

confidence interval depends on the degrees of freedom used; see the table. **(c)** We need two independent SRSs from normal populations.

7.84. (a) Using a back-to-back stemplot, we see that both distributions are slightly skewed to the right, and have one or two moderately high outliers. Normal quantile plots (not shown) are fairly linear. A t procedure may be (cautiously) used in spite of the skewness, because the sum of the sample sizes is almost 40. **(b)** We test H_0: $\mu_w = \mu_m$ vs. H_a: $\mu_w > \mu_m$. Summary statistics (below) lead to $SE_D \doteq 9.6327$ and $t = 2.056$, so $P = 0.0236$ (df $= 35.6$) or $P = 0.0277$ (df $= 17$). This gives fairly strong evidence—significant at 5% but not 1%—that the women's mean is higher. **(c)** Possible 90% confidence intervals for $\mu_m - \mu_w$ are given below on the right.

Women		Men
	7	05
	8	8
	9	12
931	10	489
5	11	3455
966	12	6
77	13	2
80	14	06
442	15	1
55	16	9
8	17	
	18	07
	19	
0	20	

	n	$\bar{x}$	s
Women	18	141.05	26.4363
Men	20	121.25	32.8519

df	t^*	Confidence interval
35.6	1.6889	−36.0735 to −3.5376
17	1.7396	−36.5627 to −3.0484
17	1.740	−36.5665 to −3.0446

7.85. The standard deviations $s_1 = 1.15$ and $s_2 = 1.16$
are very similar, and the sample sizes are quite large,
so the pooled procedures should be fairly reliable.

df	t^*	Confidence interval
375	1.9663	0.5141 to 0.9859
100	1.984	0.5120 to 0.9880

$s_p = \sqrt{\frac{(n_1-1)s_1^2+(n_2-1)s_2^2}{n_1+n_2-2}} \doteq 1.1556$, so the standard error is $SE_D = s_p\sqrt{\frac{1}{n_1} + \frac{1}{n_2}} \doteq 0.1200$.
For the hypothesis test, we find $t = 6.251$, df $= 375$, and $P < 0.0001$ (so we conclude that the intervention increased test scores). The 95% confidence interval is $\bar{x}_1 - \bar{x}_2 \pm t^*SE_D$, for which the two possible intervals (with software, or with Table D) are shown in the table. These results are nearly the same as in Exercise 7.53.

7.86. The standard deviations $s_1 = 1.19$ and $s_2 = 1.12$ are fairly similar, and the sample sizes are quite large, so the pooled procedures should be fairly reliable.

df	t^*	Confidence interval
375	1.9663	0.1950 to 0.6650
100	1.984	0.1929 to 0.6671

$s_p = \sqrt{\frac{(n_1-1)s_1^2+(n_2-1)s_2^2}{n_1+n_2-2}} \doteq 1.1511$, so the standard error is $\text{SE}_D = s_p\sqrt{\frac{1}{n_1} + \frac{1}{n_2}} \doteq 0.1195$. For the hypothesis test, we find $t = 3.598$, df $= 375$, and $P = 0.0002$ (for a one-sided alternative); we conclude that the intervention increased self-efficacy scores. The 95% confidence interval is $\bar{x}_1 - \bar{x}_2 \pm t^*\text{SE}_D$, for which the two possible intervals (with software, or with Table D) are shown in the table. These results are nearly the same as in Exercise 7.54.

7.87. The pooled standard deviation is $s_p \doteq 15.9617$, and the standard error is $\text{SE}_D \doteq 4.1213$. For the significance test, $t = -2.629$, df $= 58$, and $P =$

df	t^*	Confidence interval
58	2.0017	-19.0830 to -2.5837
50	2.009	-19.1130 to -2.5536

0.0110, so we have fairly strong evidence (though not quite significant at $\alpha = 0.01$) that the south mean is greater than the north mean. Possible answers for the confidence interval (with software, and with Table D) are given in the table. All results are similar to those found in Exercise 7.75.

Note: *If $n_1 = n_2$ (as in this case), the standard error and t statistic are the same for the usual and pooled procedures. The degrees of freedom will usually be different (specifically, df is larger for the pooled procedure, unless $s_1 = s_2$ and $n_1 = n_2$).*

7.88. The standard deviations $s_1 \doteq 16.0743$ and $s_2 \doteq 15.3314$ are similar, and the sample sizes are equal, so the pooled procedures should be acceptable. The

df	t^*	Confidence interval
58	2.0017	-16.6848 to -0.4485
50	2.009	-16.7144 to -0.4190

pooled standard deviation is $s_p \doteq 15.7073$ and the standard error is $\text{SE}_D \doteq 4.0556$. For the significance test, $t = -2.112$, df $= 58$, and $P = 0.0390$, so we have fairly strong evidence (significant at 5% but not 1%) that the west mean is greater than the east mean. Possible answers for the confidence interval (with software, and with Table D) are given in the table. All results are similar to those found in Exercise 7.76.

Note: *See the comment above regarding the pooled procedures when $n_1 = n_2$.*

7.89. With $s_n \doteq 17.5001$, $s_s \doteq 14.2583$ and $n_n = n_s = 30$, we have $s_n^2/n_n \doteq 10.2085$ and $s_s^2/n_s \doteq 6.7767$, so

$$\text{df} = \frac{\left(\frac{s_n^2}{n_n} + \frac{s_s^2}{n_s}\right)^2}{\frac{1}{n_n-1}\left(\frac{s_n^2}{n_n}\right)^2 + \frac{1}{n_s-1}\left(\frac{s_s^2}{n_s}\right)^2} \doteq \frac{(10.2085 + 6.7767)^2}{\frac{1}{29}(10.2085^2 + 6.7767^2)} \doteq 55.7251.$$

7.90. With $s_e \doteq 16.0743$, $s_w \doteq 15.3314$ and $n_e = n_w = 30$, we have $s_e^2/n_e \doteq 8.6128$ and $s_w^2/n_w \doteq 7.8351$, so

$$\text{df} = \frac{\left(\frac{s_e^2}{n_e} + \frac{s_w^2}{n_w}\right)^2}{\frac{1}{n_e-1}\left(\frac{s_e^2}{n_e}\right)^2 + \frac{1}{n_w-1}\left(\frac{s_w^2}{n_w}\right)^2} \doteq \frac{(8.6128 + 7.8351)^2}{\frac{1}{29}(8.6128^2 + 7.8351^2)} \doteq 57.8706.$$

7.91. (a) With $s_i \doteq 7.8$, $n_i = 115$, $s_o \doteq 3.4$ and $n_o = 220$, we have $s_i^2/n_i \doteq 0.5290$ and $s_o^2/n_o \doteq 0.05455$, so

$$\text{df} \doteq \frac{(0.5290 + 0.05455)^2}{\dfrac{0.5290^2}{114} + \dfrac{0.05455^2}{219}} \doteq 137.0661.$$

	df	t^*	Confidence interval
Part (d)	333	1.9671	10.2931 to 12.7069
	100	1.984	10.2827 to 12.7173
Part (e)	333	1.9671	4.5075 to 5.2925
	100	1.984	4.5042 to 5.2958

(b) $s_p = \sqrt{\dfrac{(n_i-1)s_i^2 + (n_o-1)s_o^2}{n_i + n_o - 2}} \doteq 5.3320$, which is slightly closer to s_o (the standard deviation from the larger sample). **(c)** With no assumption of equality, $\text{SE}_1 = \sqrt{s_i^2/n_i + s_o^2/n_o} \doteq 0.7626$. With the pooled method, $\text{SE}_2 = s_p\sqrt{1/n_i + 1/n_o} \doteq 0.6136$. **(d)** With the pooled standard deviation, $t \doteq 18.74$ and df = 333, for which $P < 0.0001$, and the 95% confidence interval is as shown in the table. With the smaller standard error, the t value is larger (it had been 15.08), and the confidence interval is narrower. The P-value is also smaller (although both are less than 0.0001). **(e)** With $s_i \doteq 2.8$, $n_i = 115$, $s_o \doteq 0.7$ and $n_o = 220$, we have $s_i^2/n_i \doteq 0.06817$ and $s_o^2/n_o \doteq 0.002227$, so

$$\text{df} \doteq \frac{(0.06817 + 0.002227)^2}{\dfrac{0.06817^2}{114} + \dfrac{0.002227^2}{219}} \doteq 121.5030.$$

The pooled standard deviation is $s_p \doteq 1.7338$; the standard errors are $\text{SE}_1 = 0.2653$ (with no assumptions) and $\text{SE}_2 = 0.1995$ (assuming equal standard deviations). The pooled t is 24.56 (df = 333, $P < 0.0001$), and the 95% confidence intervals are shown in the table. The pooled and usual t procedures compare similarly to the results for part (d): t is larger, and the interval is narrower.

7.92. (a) For a two-sided test with df = 1, the critical value is $t^* = 12.71$. **(b)** With the pooled procedures, df = 2 and the critical value is $t^* = 4.303$. **(c)** The smaller critical value with the pooled approach means that a smaller t-value (that is, weaker evidence) is needed to reject H_0.

7.93. (a) Use an $F(4, 4)$ critical value: 9.60. **(b)** Use an $F(9, 9)$ critical value: 4.03. **(c)** Use an $F(25, 25)$ critical value: 2.23. **(d)** The ratio decreases with increasing sample size.

7.94. (a) $F = \frac{9.3}{3.1} = 3$. **(b)** For 15 and 9 degrees of freedom, we need $F > 3.77$ to reject H_0 at the 5% level (with a two-sided alternative). **(c)** We do not have enough evidence to conclude that the standard deviations are different. (Software gives $P = 0.1006$.)

7.95. The test statistic is $F = \frac{1.16^2}{1.15^2} \doteq 1.0175$ with df 211 and 164. Table E tells us that $P > 0.20$, while software gives $P = 0.9114$. The distributions are not normal ("total score was an integer between 0 and 6"), so the test may not be reliable (although with s_1 and s_2 so close, the conclusion is probably correct). To reject at the 5% level, we would need $F > F^*$, where $F^* = 1.46$ (using df 120 and 100 from Table E) or $F^* = 1.3392$ (using software). As $F = s_2^2/s_1^2$, we would need $s_2^2 > s_1^2 F^*$, or $s_2 > 1.15\sqrt{F^*}$, which is about 1.3896 (Table E) or 1.3308 (software).

7.96. The test statistic is $F = \frac{1.19^2}{1.12^2} \doteq 1.1289$ with df 164 and 211. Table E tells us that $P > 0.2$, while software gives $P = 0.4063$. We cannot conclude that the standard deviations are different. The distributions are not normal (because all responses are integers from 1 to 5), so the test may not be reliable.

7.97. The test statistic is $F = \frac{7.8^2}{3.7^2} \doteq 5.2630$ with df 114 and 219. Table E tells us that $P < 0.002$, while software gives $P < 0.0001$; we have strong evidence that the standard deviations differ. The authors described the distributions as somewhat skewed, so the normality assumption may be violated.

7.98. The test statistic is $F = \frac{2.8^2}{0.7^2} = 16$ with df 114 and 219. Table E tells us that $P < 0.002$, while software gives $P < 0.0001$; we have strong evidence that the standard deviations differ. We have no information about the normality of the distributions, so it is difficult to determine how reliable these conclusions are. (We can observe that for Exercise 7.55, $\bar{x}_1 - 3s_1$ and $\bar{x}_2 - 3s_2$ were both negative, hinting at the skewness of those distributions. For Exercise 7.56, this is not the case, suggesting that these distributions might not be as skewed.)

7.99. The test statistic is $F \doteq \frac{17.5001^2}{14.2583^2} \doteq 1.5064$ with df 29 and 29. Table E tells us that $P > 0.2$, while software gives $P = 0.2757$; we cannot conclude that the standard deviations differ. The stemplots and boxplots of the north/south distributions in Exercise 7.75 do not appear to be normal (north was right-skewed, south was left-skewed), so the results may not be reliable.

7.100. The test statistic is $F \doteq \frac{16.0743^2}{15.3314^2} \doteq 1.0993$ with df 29 and 29. Table E tells us that $P > 0.2$, while software gives $P = 0.8006$; we cannot conclude that the standard deviations differ. The stemplots and boxplots of the east/west distributions in Exercise 7.76 do not appear to be normal (east was right-skewed, west was left-skewed), so the results may not be reliable.

7.101. (a) H_0: $\sigma_m = \sigma_w$; H_a: $\sigma_m > \sigma_w$. (b) $F \doteq \frac{32.8519^2}{26.4363^2} \doteq 1.5443$ from an $F(19, 17)$ distribution. (c) Using the $F(15, 17)$ entry in the table, we find $P > 0.10$ (in fact, $P = 0.1862$). We do not have enough evidence to conclude that men's SSHA scores are more variable.

7.102. (a) With an $F(1, 1)$ distribution with a two-sided alternative, we need the critical value for $p = 0.025$: $F^* = 647.79$. This is a very low-power test, since large differences between σ_1 and σ_2 would rarely be detected. (b) To test H_0: $\sigma_1 = \sigma_2$ vs. H_a: $\sigma_1 \neq \sigma_2$, we find $F \doteq \frac{1.5344^2}{0.7707^2} \doteq 3.9634$. Not surprisingly, we do not reject H_0.

7.103. (a) For two samples of size 20, we have $\delta = \frac{10}{20\sqrt{2/20}} \doteq 1.5811$. With df $= 38$, $t^* = 2.0244$ (or 2.042 for df $= 30$ from Table D). The approximate power is $P(z > t^* - \delta) = 0.3288$ (0.3228 using Tables A and D). Software computation of the power (using a noncentral t distribution) gives 0.3379. (b) With $n_1 = n_2 = 60$, we have $\delta = \frac{10}{20\sqrt{2/60}} \doteq 2.7386$, df $= 118$, and $t^* = 1.9803$ (or 1.984 for df $= 100$ from Table D). The approximate power is $P(z > t^* - \delta) = 0.7759$ (0.7734 using Tables A and D). Software computation of the power (using a noncentral t distribution) gives 0.7753. **(c)** Samples of size 60 would give a reasonably good chance of detecting a difference of 20 cm.

G•Power output

```
Post-hoc analysis for "t-Test (means)", two-tailed:
Alpha: 0.0500
Power (1-beta): 0.3379
Effect size "d": 0.5000
Total sample size: 40 (n 1:20, n 2: 20)
Critical value: t(38) = 2.0244
Delta: 1.5811


Power (1-beta): 0.7753
Effect size "d": 0.5000
Total sample size: 120 (n 1:60, n 2: 60)
Critical value: t(118) = 1.9803
Delta: 2.7386
```

7.104. The four standard deviations from Exercises 7.75 and 7.76 are $s_n \doteq 17.5001$, $s_s \doteq 14.2583$, $s_e \doteq 16.0743$, and $s_w \doteq 15.3314$ cm. Using a larger σ for planning the study is advisable because it provides a conservative (safe) estimate of the power. For example, if we choose a sample size to provide 80% power, and the true σ is smaller than that used for planning, the actual power of the test is greater than the desired 80%.

	Power with $n =$	
σ	20	60
15	0.5334	0.9527
16	0.4809	0.9255
17	0.4348	0.8928
18	0.3945	0.8560

Results of additional power computations will depend on what students consider to be "other reasonable values of σ." Shown in the table are some possible answers using the normal approximation. (Powers computed using the noncentral t distribution are slightly greater.)

7.105. We reject H_0 if $t > t^*$, where $t^* = 1.6552$ for df $= 148$. (If using Table D, $t^* = 1.660$ for df $= 100$.) The noncentrality parameter is $\delta = \dfrac{350}{650\sqrt{2/75}} \doteq 3.2974$. The normal approximation for the power is $P(Z > t^* - \delta) \doteq P(Z > -1.64) = 0.9495$ for either choice of t^*. Software (see output below) gives 0.9492.

G•Power output

```
Post-hoc analysis for "t-Test (means)", one-tailed:
Alpha: 0.0500
Power (1-beta): 0.9492
Effect size "d": 0.5385
Total sample size: 150 (n 1:75, n 2: 75)
Critical value: t(148) = 1.6552
Delta: 3.2974
```

7.106. $\delta = 350/(650\sqrt{2/n}) \doteq 0.3807\sqrt{n}$. The table shows the values of δ, the t^* values (for df $= 38, 78, 118, 158, 198,$ and 238), and the power computed using the normal approximation ("Power[1]") and the G•Power software ("Power[2]"). The plot also includes points for $n = 30, 50, 70, 90,$ and 110. To reliably detect a difference of 350 g, we should choose at least $n = 40$. (This number will vary based on what we consider to be "reliable.")

n	δ	t^*	Power[1]	Power[2]
20	1.7028	1.6860	0.5067	0.5110
40	2.4081	1.6646	0.7714	0.7710
60	2.9493	1.6579	0.9017	0.9010
80	3.4055	1.6546	0.9600	0.9596
100	3.8075	1.6526	0.9844	0.9842
120	4.1709	1.6513	0.9941	0.9940

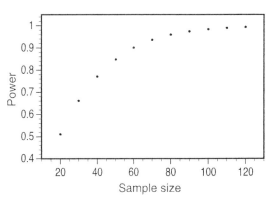

7.107. The standard error is $650\sqrt{2/n}$, and df $= 2n - 2$. The df, critical values, and margins of error are given in the table. (Note that these are 0.025 critical values, appropriate for a 95% confidence interval, rather than the 0.05 critical values needed for a one-sided hypothesis test.) The plot of margin of error against sample size below also includes points for $n = 30, 50, 70, 90$, and 110.

n	df	t^*	m.e.
20	38	2.0244	416.1
40	78	1.9908	289.4
60	118	1.9803	235.0
80	158	1.9751	203.0
100	198	1.9720	181.3
120	238	1.9700	165.3

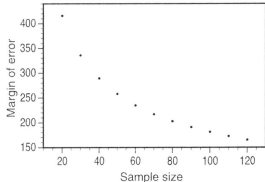

7.108. (a) The noncentrality parameter is $\delta = \dfrac{1.5}{1.6\sqrt{2/65}} \doteq 5.3446$. With such a large value of δ, the value of t^* (1.9787 for df $= 128$, or 1.984 for df $= 100$ from Table D) does not matter very much. The normal approximation for the power is $P(Z > t^* - \delta) \doteq 0.9996$ for either choice of t^*. Software (see output below) gives the same result. **(b)** For samples of size 100, $\delta \doteq 6.6291$, and once again the value of t^* makes little difference; the power is very close to 1 (using the normal approximation or software). **(c)** Because the effect is large relative to the standard deviation, small samples are sufficient. (Even samples of size 20 will detect this difference with probability 0.8236.)

G•Power output

```
Post-hoc analysis for "t-Test (means)", two-tailed:
Alpha: 0.0500
Power (1-beta): 0.9996
Effect size "d": 0.9375
Total sample size: 130 (n 1:65, n 2: 65)
Critical value: t(128) = 1.9787
Delta: 5.3446

Power (1-beta): 1.0000
Effect size "d": 0.9375
Total sample size: 200 (n 1:100, n 2: 100)
Critical value: t(198) = 1.9720
Delta: 6.6291
```

7.109. (a) The mean difference in body weight change (with wine minus without) was $\bar{x}_1 = 0.4 - 1.1 = -0.7$ kg, with standard error $SE_1 = 8.6/\sqrt{14} \doteq 2.2984$ kg. The mean difference in caloric intake was $\bar{x}_2 = 2589 - 2575 = 14$ cal, with $SE_2 = 210/\sqrt{14} \doteq 56.1249$ cal. **(b)** The t statistics $t_i = \bar{x}_i/SE_i$, both with df $= 13$, are $t_1 = -0.3046$ ($P_1 = 0.7655$) and $t_2 = 0.2494$ ($P_2 = 0.8069$). **(c)** For df $= 13$, $t^* = 2.160$, so the 95% confidence intervals $\bar{x}_i \pm t^*SE_i$ are -5.6646 to 4.2646 kg (-5.6655 to 4.2655 with software) and -107.2297 to 135.2297 cal (-107.2504 to 135.2504 with software). **(d)** Students might note a number of factors in their discussions; for example, all subjects were males, weighing 68 to 91 kg (about 150 to 200 lb), which may limit how widely we can extend these conclusions.

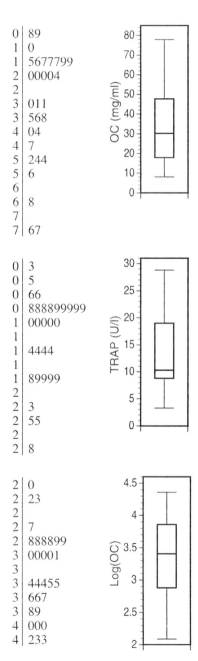

7.110. (a) A stemplot and boxplot are shown on the right; the distribution is right-skewed, with $n = 31$ and $\bar{x} \doteq 33.4161$, $s = 19.6097$, Min $= 8.1$, $Q_1 = 17.9$, $M = 30.2$, $Q_3 = 47.7$, Max $= 77.9$ mg/ml. **(b)** Using $t^* = 2.042$ from Table D, the 95% confidence interval is 26.2242 to 40.6081 mg/ml. With $t^* = 2.0423$ from software, the interval is 26.2232 to 40.6090 mg/ml. Because the sample size is fairly large, and there are no extreme outliers, the t procedures should be safe, provided the 31 women in the study can be considered an SRS.

7.111. (a) A stemplot and boxplot are shown on the right; the distribution is somewhat right-skewed with no extreme outliers, with $n = 31$ and $\bar{x} \doteq 13.2484$, $s = 6.5282$, Min $= 3.3$, $Q_1 = 8.8$, $M = 10.3$, $Q_3 = 19$, Max $= 28.8$ U/l. **(b)** Using $t^* = 2.042$ from Table D, the 95% confidence interval is 10.8541 to 15.6426 U/l. With $t^* = 2.0423$ from software, the interval is 10.8538 to 15.6430 U/l. Because the sample size is fairly large, and there are no extreme outliers, the t procedures should be safe, provided the 31 women in the study can be considered an SRS.

7.112. (a) A stemplot and boxplot are shown on the right. The distribution is now roughly symmetrical (perhaps slightly left-skewed), with $n = 31$ and $\bar{x} \doteq 3.3379$, $s = 0.6085$, Min $= 2.09$, $Q_1 = 2.88$, $M = 3.41$, $Q_3 = 3.86$, Max $= 4.36$. **(b)** Using either $t^* = 2.042$ (Table D) or $t^* = 2.0423$ (software), the 95% confidence interval is 3.1147 to 3.5611. The t procedures should be safe, provided the 31 women can be considered an SRS. **(c)** All three numbers are lower than in Exercise 7.110: $e^{\bar{x}} \doteq 28.1605$ mg/ml, while exponentiating the confidence interval yields 22.5271 to 35.2027 mg/ml.

7.113. (a) A stemplot and boxplot are shown on the right. The distribution is now slightly left-skewed, with $n = 31$ and $\bar{x} \doteq 2.4674$, $s = 0.4979$, Min $= 1.19$, $Q_1 = 2.17$, $M = 2.33$, $Q_3 = 2.94$, Max $= 3.36$. **(b)** Using either $t^* = 2.042$ (Table D) or $t^* = 2.0423$ (software), the 95% confidence interval is 2.2848 to 2.6501. The t procedures should be safe, provided the 31 women can be considered an SRS. **(c)** All three numbers are lower than in Exercise 7.111: $e^{\bar{x}} \doteq 11.7921$ U/l, while exponentiating the confidence interval yields 9.8236 to 14.1549 U/l.

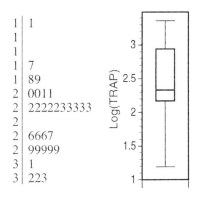

```
1 | 1
1 |
1 |
1 | 7
1 | 89
2 | 0011
2 | 2222233333
2 |
2 | 6667
2 | 99999
3 | 1
3 | 223
```

7.114. The mean is $\bar{x} \doteq 26.8437$ cm, $s \doteq 18.3311$ cm, and the margin of error is $t^* \cdot s/\sqrt{584}$:

	df	t^*	Interval
Table D	100	1.984	$26.8437 \pm 1.5050 = 25.3387$ to 28.3486 cm
Software	583	1.9640	$26.8437 \pm 1.4898 = 25.3538$ to 28.3335 cm

The confidence interval is much narrower with the whole data set, largely because the standard error is about one-fourth what it was with a sample of size 40. The distribution of the 584 measurements is right-skewed (although not as much as the smaller sample). If we can view these trees as an SRS of similar stands—a fairly questionable assumption—the t procedures should be fairly reliable because of the large n. See the solution to Exercise 7.116 for an examination of the distribution.

7.115. For north/south differences, the test of H_0: $\mu_n = \mu_s$ gives $t = -7.15$ with df $= 575.4$ or 283; either way, $P < 0.0001$, so we reject H_0. The 95% confidence interval is given in the table below. For east/west differences, $t = -3.69$ with df $= 472.7$ or 230; either way, $P \doteq 0.0003$, so we reject H_0. See the table below for the 95% confidence interval. The larger data set results in smaller standard errors (both are near 1.5, compared to about 4 in Exercises 7.75 and 7.76), meaning that t is larger and the margin of error is smaller.

	$\bar{x}$	s	n
North	21.7990	18.9230	300
South	32.1725	16.0763	284
East	24.5785	17.7315	353
West	30.3052	18.7264	231

	df	t^*	Confidence interval
N–S	575.4	1.9641	-13.2222 to -7.5248
	283	1.9684	-13.2285 to -7.5186
	100	1.984	-13.2511 to -7.4960
E–W	472.7	1.9650	-8.7764 to -2.6770
	230	1.9703	-8.7847 to -2.6687
	100	1.984	-8.8059 to -2.6475

7.116. The histograms and quantile plots are shown below, and the means and medians are given in the table on the right, and are marked on the histograms. (The plots were created using natural logarithms; for common logs, the appearance would be roughly the same except for scale.) The transformed data does not look notably more normal; it is left-skewed instead of right-skewed. The t procedures should be fairly dependable anyway because of the large sample size, but only if we can view the data as an SRS from some population.

	$\bar{x}$	M
Original	26.8437	26.15
Natural log	2.9138	3.2638
Common log	1.2654	1.4175

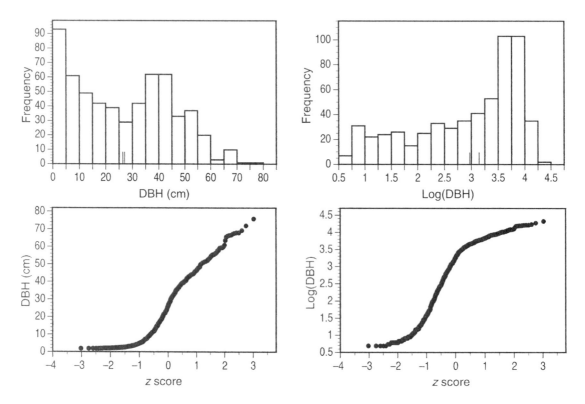

7.117. The mean and standard deviation of the 25 numbers are $\bar{x} \doteq 78.32\%$ and $s \doteq 33.3563\%$, so the standard error is $\mathrm{SE}_{\bar{x}} \doteq 6.6713\%$. For df $= 24$, Table D gives $t^* = 2.064$, so the 95% confidence interval is $\bar{x} \pm 13.7695\% = 64.5505\%$ to 92.0895% (with software, $t^* = 2.0639$ and the interval is $\bar{x} \pm 13.7688\% = 64.5512\%$ to 92.0888%). This seems to support the retailer's claim: 65% to 93% of the time, the original supplier's price was higher.

7.118. **(a)** We are interested in weight change; the pairs are the "before" and "after" measurements. **(b)** The mean weight change was a loss. The exact amount lost is not specified, but it was large enough so that it would rarely happen by chance for an ineffective weight-loss program. **(c)** Comparing to a $t(40)$ distribution in Table D, we find $P < 0.0005$ for a one-sided alternative ($P < 0.0010$ for a two-sided alternative). Software reveals that it is even smaller than that: about 0.000013 (or 0.000026 for a two-sided alternative).

7.119. Back-to-back stemplot below. The distributions appear similar; the most striking difference is the relatively large number of boys with low GPAs. Testing

	n	GPA $\bar{x}$	s	IQ $\bar{x}$	s
Boys	47	7.2816	2.3190	110.96	12.121
Girls	31	7.6966	1.7208	105.84	14.271

the difference in GPAs (H_0: $\mu_b = \mu_g$; H_a: $\mu_b < \mu_g$), we obtain $\text{SE}_D \doteq 0.4582$ and $t = -0.91$, which is not significant, regardless of whether we use df $= 74.9$ ($P = 0.1839$) or 30 ($0.15 < P < 0.20$). The confidence interval for the difference $\mu_b - \mu_g$ in GPAs is -1.3278 to 0.4978 (df $= 74.9$) or -1.3506 to 0.5206 (df $= 30$).

For the difference in IQs, we find $\text{SE}_D \doteq 3.1138$. For testing H_0: $\mu_b = \mu_g$ vs. H_a: $\mu_b > \mu_g$, we find $t = 1.64$, which is fairly strong evidence, although it is not quite significant at the 5% level: $P = 0.0528$ (df $= 56.9$) or $0.05 < P < 0.10$ (df $= 30$). The confidence interval for the difference $\mu_b - \mu_g$ in IQs is -1.1175 to 11.3535 (df $= 56.9$) or -1.2404 to 11.4764 (df $= 30$).

```
GPA:        Girls |   | Boys
                  | 0 | 5
                  | 1 | 7
                  | 2 | 4
              4   | 3 | 689
              7   | 4 | 068
            952   | 5 | 0
           4200   | 6 | 019
      988855432   | 7 | 1124556666899
         998731   | 8 | 001112238
          95530   | 9 | 1113445567
             17   |10 | 57
```

```
IQ:         Girls |   | Boys
               42 | 7 |
                  | 7 | 79
                  | 8 |
               96 | 8 |
               31 | 9 | 03
               86 | 9 | 77
           433320 |10 | 0234
              875 |10 | 556667779
         44422211 |11 | 00001123334
               98 |11 | 556899
                0 |12 | 03344
                8 |12 | 67788
               20 |13 |
                  |13 | 6
```

7.120. The median self-concept score is 59.5. Back-to-back stemplot (below) suggests that high self-concept students have a higher mean GPA and IQ. Testing H_0: $\mu_{\text{low}} = \mu_{\text{high}}$ vs. H_a: $\mu_{\text{low}} \neq \mu_{\text{high}}$ for GPAs leads to $\text{SE}_D \doteq 0.4167$ and $t = 4.92$, which is quite significant ($P < 0.0005$ regardless of df). The confidence interval for the difference $\mu_{\text{high}} - \mu_{\text{low}}$ in GPAs is shown in the table.

	n	GPA $\bar{x}$	s	IQ $\bar{x}$	s
High SC	39	8.4723	1.3576	114.23	10.381
Low SC	39	6.4208	2.2203	103.62	13.636

	df	t^*	Confidence interval
GPA	62.9	1.9984	1.2188 to 2.8843
	38	2.0244	1.2079 to 2.8951
	30	2.042	1.2006 to 2.9025
IQ	70.9	1.9940	5.1436 to 16.0871
	38	2.0244	5.0601 to 16.1707
	30	2.042	5.0118 to 16.2190

For the difference in IQs, we find $\text{SE}_D \doteq 2.7442$. For testing H_0: $\mu_{\text{low}} = \mu_{\text{high}}$ vs. H_a: $\mu_{\text{low}} \neq \mu_{\text{high}}$, we find $t = 3.87$, which is quite significant ($P < 0.0006$ regardless of df). The confidence interval for the difference $\mu_{\text{high}} - \mu_{\text{low}}$ in IQs is shown in the table.

In summary, both differences are significant; with 95% confidence, high self-concept students have a mean GPA that is 1.2 to 2.9 points higher, and their mean IQ is 5 to 16 points higher.

GPA:	Low SC		High SC
	5	0	
	7	1	
	4	2	
	864	3	9
	8760	4	
	9520	5	
	94000	6	12
	986655421	7	1234556688899
	887321100	8	112399
	97	9	0111334455556
		10	1577

IQ:	Low SC		High SC
	42	7	
	97	7	
		8	
	96	8	3
	310	9	3
	776	9	8
	44300	10	22333
	9877766	10	55567
	44432100	11	00111222334
	99985	11	568
	4	12	00334
	7	12	67888
		13	02
		13	6

7.121. It is reasonable to have a prior belief that people who evacuated their pets would score higher, so we test H_0: $\mu_1 = \mu_2$ vs. H_a: $\mu_1 > \mu_2$. We find $SE_D \doteq 0.4630$ and $t = 3.65$, which gives $P < 0.0005$ no matter how we choose degrees of freedom (115 or 237.0). As one might suspect, people who evacuated their pets have a higher mean score.

df	t^*	Confidence interval
237.0	1.9700	0.7779 to 2.6021
115	1.9808	0.7729 to 2.6071
100	1.984	0.7714 to 2.6086

One might also compute a 95% confidence interval for the difference; these are given in the table.

7.122. (a) "se" is standard error (of the mean). To find s, multiply the standard error by $\sqrt{n}$. **(b)** No: We test H_0: $\mu_d = \mu_c$ vs. H_a: $\mu_d < \mu_c$, for which $SE_D \doteq 65.1153$ and $t \doteq -0.3532$, so $P = 0.3623$ (df $= 173.9$) or 0.3625 (df $= 82$)—in either case, there is little evidence against H_0. **(c)** The evidence is not

		Calories		Alcohol	
	n	$\bar{x}$	s	$\bar{x}$	s
Drivers	98	2821	435.58	0.24	0.59397
Conductors	83	2844	437.30	0.39	1.00215

df	t^*	Confidence interval
128.4	2.6146	−0.4776 to 0.1776
82	2.6371	−0.4804 to 0.1804
80	2.639	−0.4807 to 0.1807

very significant: To test H_0: $\mu_d = \mu_c$ vs. H_a: $\mu_d \neq \mu_c$, $SE_D \doteq 0.1253$, $t \doteq -1.1971$, for which $P = 0.2335$ (df $= 128.4$) or 0.2348 (df $= 82$). **(d)** The 95% confidence interval is $0.39 \pm t^*(0.11)$. With Table D, $t^* = 1.990$ (df $= 80$) and the interval is 0.1711 to 0.6089 g; with software, $t^* = 1.9893$ (df $= 82$) and the interval is 0.1712 to 0.6088 g. **(e)** The 99% confidence interval is $(0.24 - 0.39) \pm t^* \sqrt{0.06^2 + 0.11^2}$; see the table.

7.123. The similarity of the sample standard deviations suggests that the population standard deviations are likely to be similar. The pooled standard deviation is $s_p \doteq 436.368$, and $t \doteq -0.3533$, so $P = 0.3621$ (df $= 179$)—still not significant.

7.124. (a) The sample sizes (98 and 83) are quite large, so the t test should be reasonably safe (provided there are no extreme outliers). **(b)** Large samples do not make the F test more reliable when the underlying distributions are skewed, so it should not be used.

7.125. No: What we have is nothing like an SRS of the population of Islamic men. (Additionally, the average of the 17 numbers in Table 1.2 would not really be an appropriate measure of the literacy rate among Islamic men; it would not take into account the different population sizes in the 17 countries.)

7.126. (a) A histogram (below, left) shows that the distribution is strongly right-skewed. Aside from the mean 68.4674 and median 47.96 shown in the histogram, $s \doteq 59.3906$ ppb. **(b)** The skewness, and more importantly the outliers in the distribution, make the t procedures questionable. The sample size *might* be enough to overcome this. **(c)** The 95% confidence interval is either 54.1678 to 82.7669 ($t^* = 2.000$ with df = 60 from Table D) or 54.2002 to 82.7345 ($t^* = 1.9955$ with df = 68 from software). This interval does *not* include 95% of the observations, nor should we expect it to; a confidence interval is a range of values for the *mean*, not for individual observations. **(d)** The logPCB distribution (histogram below, right) appears to be much more like a normal distribution. The mean is $\bar{x} \doteq 3.9171$, the median is $M \doteq 3.8704$, and $s \doteq 0.8020$. (This assumes natural logarithms; for common logs, multiply these numbers by 0.4343.) A 95% confidence interval for the mean is 3.7239 to 4.1101 ($t^* = 2.000$ with df = 60 from Table D) or 3.7244 to 4.1097 ($t^* = 1.9955$ with df = 68 from software). These limits translate to 41.4 to 60.9 ppb. (Note that the mean of the original data is not in this interval—an indication of the strength of the skew.) The t procedures are almost certainly more appropriate for the transformed data, as the outliers and skewness are no longer present after taking logarithms. **(e)** Visiting this web site should give your students a glimpse at the details of planning a major statistical study.

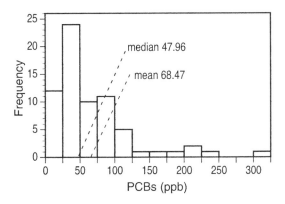 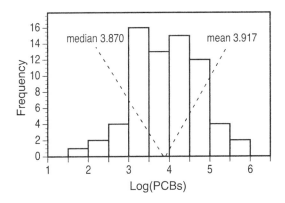

7.127. (a) A histogram (below, left) shows that the distribution is strongly right-skewed. Aside from the mean 1.7182 and median 1.2633 shown in the histogram, $s \doteq 1.3428$. **(b)** The sample size should be enough to overcome the skewness. (Unlike the PCB levels in the previous exercise, this distribution has no outliers.) **(c)** The 95% confidence interval is either 1.3949 to 2.0415 ($t^* = 2.000$ with df = 60 from Table D) or 1.3956 to 2.0408 ($t^* = 1.9955$ with df = 68 from software). This interval does *not* include 95% of the observations, nor should we expect it to; a confidence interval is a range of values for the *mean*, not for individual observations. **(d)** The logTEQPCB distribution (histogram below, right) is left-skewed, although it may be somewhat more normal than the untransformed data. The mean is $\bar{x} \doteq 0.1542$, the median is $M \doteq 0.2337$, and $s \doteq 1.0176$. (This assumes natural logarithms; for common logs, multiply these numbers by 0.4343.) A 95% confidence interval for the mean is -0.0908 to 0.3992 ($t^* = 2.000$ with df = 60 from Table D) or -0.0902 to 0.3987 ($t^* = 1.9955$ with df = 68 from software). These limits translate to 0.914 to 1.490. (Note that the mean of the original data is not in this interval—an indication of the strength of the skew.)

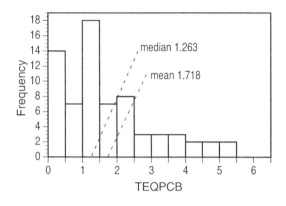

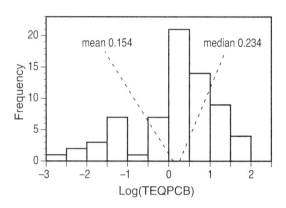

7.128. For the 35 noninfected children (low CRP), $\bar{x}_1 \doteq 0.7780$ and $s_1 \doteq 0.3359$; for the 55 infected children, $\bar{x}_2 \doteq 0.6198$ and $s_2 \doteq 0.3397$. Back-to-back stemplot or other comparison of the two distributions shows that both distributions are right-skewed, and the infected group has a high outlier. We cautiously use t procedures: The 95% confidence interval for $\mu_1 - \mu_2$ is:

df	t^*	Confidence interval
73.2	1.9929	0.0128 to 0.3036
34	2.0322	0.0099 to 0.3064
30	2.042	0.0092 to 0.3072

High CRP		Low CRP
6443	2	3
9888766554433310	3	1455559
211000	4	69
976652	5	89
998877	6	2777
8	7	0
742221	8	368
77	9	0499
96	10	0248
953	11	1357
30	12	2
	13	6
	14	4
	15	
	16	
	17	
	18	
0	19	

The researchers were interested in testing H_0: $\mu_1 = \mu_2$ vs. H_a: $\mu_1 > \mu_2$. For this test, we find $t = 2.168$, for which $P = 0.0167$ (df = 73.2) or $P = 0.0186$ (df = 34). We have significant evidence at $\alpha = 0.05$ and conclude that retinol levels are lower in recently infected children.

7.129. The stemplot on the right shows that the distribution is slightly right-skewed with one high outlier. Only 17 of the 90 children had AGP levels above 1 g/l (although 9 more had levels above 0.9). The mean AGP level for the sample was $\bar{x} = 0.8043$ g/l, and the standard deviation was $s \doteq 0.2765$ g/l. A 95% confidence interval for the population mean was 0.7463 to 0.8623 g/l ($t^* = 1.990$, df = 80 from Table D) or 0.7464 to 0.8622 g/l ($t^* = 1.9870$, df = 89 from software).

3	03
4	11355588899
5	45566899
6	011133557788999
7	00333366678
8	001224557999
9	00000126667999
10	256
11	11467888
12	
13	344
14	04
15	
16	
17	
18	2

7.130. **(a)** Stemplot and quantile plot below. There is a high outlier (2.94 g/mi), but otherwise the distribution looks reasonably normal. **(b)** The summary statistics and possible intervals are:

	n	$\bar{x}$	s	95% confidence interval
All points	46	1.3287	0.4844	1.1844 to 1.4730 (df = 40)
				1.1848 to 1.4725 (df = 45)
No outlier	45	1.2929	0.4239	1.1652 to 1.4206 (df = 40)
				1.1655 to 1.4202 (df = 44)

(c) We test H_0: $\mu = 1$; H_a: $\mu > 1$. If we include the outlier, $t \doteq 4.60$; without it, $t \doteq 4.64$. Either way, $P < 0.0005$. To the supervisor, we explain that if mean NOX emissions were only 1 g/mi (or less), we would almost never see average emissions as high as these. Therefore, we must conclude that mean emissions are higher than 1 g/mi; based on the evidence, we believe that the mean is between about 1.2 and 1.5 g/mi.

```
0 | 455
0 | 6777
0 | 899
1 | 0011111
1 | 222223333333
1 | 4444445
1 | 777
1 | 888
2 | 0
2 | 22
2 |
2 |
2 |
2 | 9
```

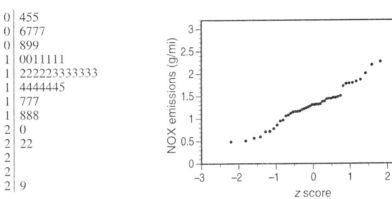

7.131. **(a)** We test H_0: $\mu_B = \mu_D$ vs. H_a: $\mu_B < \mu_D$. Pooling might be appropriate for this problem, in which case $s_p \doteq 6.5707$. Whether or not we pool, $SE_D \doteq 1.9811$ and $t \doteq 2.87$ with df = 42 (pooled), 39.3, or 21, so

	n	$\bar{x}$	s
Basal	22	41.0455	5.6356
DRTA	22	46.7273	7.3884
Strat	22	44.2727	5.7668

$P = 0.0032$, or 0.0033, or 0.0046. We conclude that the mean score using DRTA is higher than the mean score with the Basal method. The difference in the average scores is 5.68; options for a 95% confidence interval for the difference $\mu_D - \mu_B$ are given in the table below. **(b)** We test H_0: $\mu_B = \mu_S$ vs. H_a: $\mu_B < \mu_S$. If we pool, $s_p \doteq 5.7015$. Whether or not we pool, $SE_D \doteq 1.7191$ and $t \doteq 1.88$ with df = 42, 42.0, or 21, so $P = 0.0337$, or 0.0337, or 0.0372. We conclude that the mean score using Strat is higher than the Basal mean score. The difference in the average scores is 3.23; options for a 95% confidence interval for the difference $\mu_S - \mu_B$ are given in the table below.

df	t^*	Confidence interval for $\mu_D - \mu_B$	df	t^*	Confidence interval for $\mu_S - \mu_B$
39.3	2.0223	1.6754 to 9.6882	42.0	2.0181	−0.2420 to 6.6966
21	2.0796	1.5618 to 9.8018	21	2.0796	−0.3477 to 6.8023
21	2.080	1.5610 to 9.8026	21	2.080	−0.3484 to 6.8030
42	2.0181	1.6837 to 9.6799	42	2.0181	−0.2420 to 6.6965
40	2.021	1.6779 to 9.6857	40	2.021	−0.2470 to 6.7015

7.132. (a) Back-to-back stemplot below; summary statistics on the right. With a pooled standard deviation, $s_p \doteq 83.6388$, $t \doteq 4.00$

	n	SATM $\bar{x}$	SATM s	SATV $\bar{x}$	SATV s
Men	145	611.772	84.0206	508.841	94.3485
Women	79	565.025	82.9294	496.671	89.3849

with df $= 222$, so $P < 0.0001$. Without pooling, $SE_D \doteq 11.6508$, $t \doteq 4.01$ with df $= 162.2$, and again $P < 0.0001$ (or, with df $= 78$, we conclude that $P < 0.0005$). The test for equality of standard deviations gives $F \doteq 1.03$ with df 144 and 78; the P-value is 0.9114, so the pooled procedure should be appropriate. In either case, we conclude that male mean SATM scores are higher than female mean SATM scores. Options for a 95% confidence interval for the male $-$ female difference are given in the table below. **(b)** With a pooled standard deviation, $s_p \doteq 92.6348$, $t \doteq 0.94$ with df $= 222$, so $P = 0.3485$. Without pooling, $SE_D \doteq 12.7485$, $t \doteq 0.95$ with df $= 162.2$, so $P = 0.3410$ (or, with df $= 78$, $P = 0.3426$). The test for equality of standard deviations gives $F \doteq 1.11$ with df 144 and 78; the P-value is 0.6033, so the pooled procedure should be appropriate. In either case, we cannot see a difference between male and female mean SATV scores. Options for a 95% confidence interval for the male $-$ female difference are given in the table below. **(c)** The results may generalize fairly well to students in different years, less well to students at other schools, and probably not very well to college students in general.

df	t^*	Confidence interval for SATM $\mu_M - \mu_F$	df	t^*	Confidence interval for SATV $\mu_M - \mu_F$
162.3	1.9747	23.7402 to 69.7538	167.9	1.9742	-12.9981 to 37.3381
78	1.9908	23.5521 to 69.9419	78	1.9908	-13.2104 to 37.5504
70	1.994	23.5154 to 69.9786	70	1.994	-13.2506 to 37.5906
222	1.9707	23.6978 to 69.7962	222	1.9707	-13.3584 to 37.6984
100	1.984	23.5423 to 69.9517	100	1.984	-13.5306 to 37.8706

Men's SATM		Women's SATM
	3	0
	3	5
400	4	1334
99999888776	4	56777888999
44444333322222111000	5	0111123334
9999998888887776655555555555	5	5555555666777778889999
444444444433333332222222211100000000	6	00011222233334444
99999998777776666655555	6	55555789
3222211100000	7	1124
77766655555	7	
0	8	

Men's SATV		Women's SATV
98	2	9
4322	3	33
9999988766	3	55669
44444444433211111100000	4	0122223333444
9999988888888887777766666555	4	5666666777777888888899999
4444333332222111000000000000	5	01111122334
99888877777766666555	5	566777777889
43333332111100000	6	0000
9987775	6	668
420	7	00
6	7	5

7.133. When taking the sample, note that the number of men and women within the sample will vary, although we expect that the proportions of men and women will be the same as in the population—that is, an "average" sample will contain 72.5 men and 39.5 women. In general, the means and standard deviations within a sample should be similar to those found for the whole data set, so that conclusions drawn from the sample and those drawn from the whole data set would differ mostly because standard errors from the sample would be larger by a factor of about $\sqrt{2}$. For example, confidence intervals from the sample would be *wider* by a factor of about $\sqrt{2}$, while t statistics would be *smaller* by a factor of $1/\sqrt{2}$.

7.134. For testing $\mu_1 = \mu_2$ against a two-sided alternative, we would reject H_0 if $t = \frac{\bar{x}_1 - \bar{x}_2}{\text{SE}_D}$ is greater (in absolute value) than t^*, where $\text{SE}_D = 2.5\sqrt{2/n}$. (Rather than determining t^* for each considered sample size, we might use $t^* \doteq 2$.) We therefore want to choose n so that

$$P\left(\left|\frac{\bar{x}_1 - \bar{x}_2}{\text{SE}_D}\right| > t^*\right) = 1 - P\left(-t^* < \frac{\bar{x}_1 - \bar{x}_2}{\text{SE}_D} < t^*\right) = 0.90$$

when $\mu_1 - \mu_2 = 0.4$ inch. With $\delta = 0.4/\text{SE}_D \doteq 0.1131\sqrt{n}$, this means that

$$P\left(-t^* - \delta < Z < t^* - \delta\right) = 0.10$$

where Z has a $N(0, 1)$ distribution. By trial and error, we find that two samples of size 822 will do this. (This answer will vary slightly depending on what students do with t^* in the formula above.)

    Note: *Determining the necessary sample size can be made a bit easier with some software, or a web site like* `http://calculators.stat.ucla.edu/powercalc/`. *The output of the G•Power program below gives the total sample size as 1644 (that is, two samples of size 822). The web site tells us that "The equal sample size for both groups is calculated to be 821.854."*

G•Power output

```
A priori analysis for "t-Test (means)", two-tailed:
Alpha: 0.0500
Power (1-beta): 0.9000
Effect size "d": 0.1600
Total sample size: 1644
Actual power: 0.9001
Critical value: t(1642) = 1.9614
Delta: 3.2437
```

7.135. Using a one-sided alternative as before, we reject H_0 if $t > t^*$, where $t^* = 1.6606$ for df $= 98$. (If using Table D, $t^* = 1.664$ for df $= 80$.) The noncentrality parameter for a difference of d grams is $\delta = \dfrac{d}{650\sqrt{2/50}} = d/130$. The normal approximation for the power is $P(Z > t^* - \delta)$; the table and plot below show both the normal approximation ("Power-1") and software-computed power ("Power-2") for a variety of alternatives. We can see, for example, that samples of size 50 would do a fairly good job of detecting differences of 300 g or more.

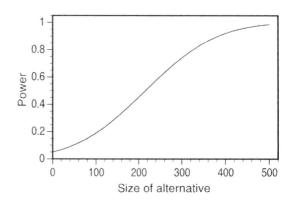

d	δ	Power-1	Power-2
50	0.3846	0.1010	0.1033
100	0.7692	0.1864	0.1892
150	1.1538	0.3062	0.3089
200	1.5385	0.4514	0.4534
250	1.9231	0.6035	0.6045
300	2.3077	0.7412	0.7411
350	2.6923	0.8489	0.8482
400	3.0769	0.9217	0.9208
450	3.4615	0.9641	0.9635
500	3.8462	0.9856	0.9852

7.136. See also the graph and table in the solution to Exercise 7.19. The plot (below, left) shows that t^* approaches 1.96 as df increases, at first very rapidly, and then more slowly.

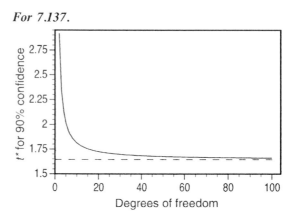

For 7.136.   *For 7.137.*

7.137. See also the graph and table in the solution to Exercise 7.19. The plot (above, right) shows that t^* approaches 1.645 as df increases, at first very rapidly, and then more slowly.

7.138. The margin of error is $t^*/\sqrt{n}$, using t^* for df $= n - 1$ and 95% confidence. For example, when $n = 5$, the margin of error is 1.2417, and when $n = 10$, it is 0.7154, and for $n = 100$, it is 0.1984. As the plot (below, left) shows, as sample size increases, margin of error decreases (toward 0, although it gets there very slowly).

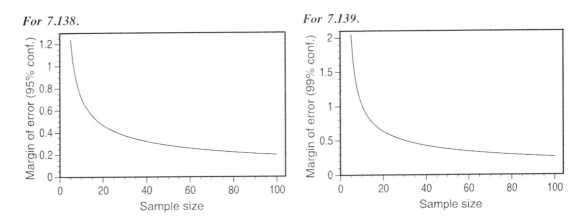

For 7.138.

For 7.139.

7.139. The margin of error is $t^*/\sqrt{n}$, using t^* for df $= n - 1$ and 99% confidence. For example, when $n = 5$, the margin of error is 2.0590, and when $n = 10$, it is 1.0277, and for $n = 100$, it is 0.2626. As the plot (above, right) shows, as sample size increases, margin of error decreases (toward 0, although it gets there very slowly).

7.140. **(a)** The distributions can be compared using a back-to-back stemplot (shown), or two histograms, or side-by-side boxplots. Both distributions are right-skewed; four-bedroom homes are generally more expensive. The top three prices from the three-bedroom distribution qualify as outliers using the $1.5 \times IQR$ criterion. Boxplots are probably a poor choice for displaying the distributions, because they leave out so much detail, but five-number summaries do illustrate that four-bedroom prices are higher at every level. Summary statistics are given in the table below. **(b)** For testing $H_0\colon \mu_3 = \mu_4$ vs. $H_a\colon$ $\mu_3 \ne \mu_4$, we have $t \doteq -3.08$ with either df $= 12.1$ ($P = 0.0095$) or df $= 8$ ($P = 0.0151$). We reject H_0 and conclude that the mean prices are different (specifically, that 4BR houses are more expensive). **(c)** The one-sided alternative $\mu_3 < \mu_4$ could have been justified, because it would be reasonable to expect that four-bedroom homes would be more expensive. **(d)** The 95% confidence interval for the difference $\mu_4 - \mu_3$ is about \$19,182 to \$111,614 (df $= 12.1$) or \$16,452 to \$114,344 (df $= 8$). **(e)** While the data were not gathered from an SRS, it seems that they should be a fair representation of three- and four-bedroom houses in West Lafayette. (Even so, the small sample size for four-bedroom houses, the skewness of the data, and the outliers in the three-bedroom data should make us cautious about the t procedures. Additionally, we might question independence in these data: When setting the asking price for a home, sellers are almost certainly influenced by the asking prices for similar homes on the market in the area.)

3BR		4BR
7776	0	
9988	0	
11110	1	
32222222	1	23
544	1	55
	1	7
9	1	
0	2	
	2	23
5	2	4
6	2	
	2	9

	n	$\bar{x}$	s	Min	Q_1	M	Q_3	Max
3BR	28	\$129,546	\$49,336	\$65,500	\$95,750	\$123,450	\$138,950	\$265,000
4BR	9	\$194,944	\$57,204	\$121,900	\$148,450	\$176,900	\$240,000	\$294,000

Chapter 8 Solutions

8.1. Recall the text's guidelines: Plus four confidence intervals can be used whenever $n \geq 10$. Large-sample intervals can be used when the number of successes and the number of failures are both at least 15. **(a)** Use a plus four interval (the number of failures is five—too small for the large-sample procedure). **(b)** With 15 successes and 85 failures, a large-sample (or plus four) interval can be used. **(c)** Use a plus four interval (we have only two successes and eight failures). **(d)** Neither approach is appropriate, as the sample size is too small. **(e)** With 20 successes and 30 failures, a large-sample (or plus four) interval can be used.

8.2. The guidelines are summarized in the previous solution. **(a)** Neither approach is appropriate, as the sample size is too small. **(b)** Use a plus four interval (12 successes is too small for the large-sample procedure). **(c)** With 18 successes and 22 failures, a large-sample (or plus four) interval can be used. **(d)** Use a plus four interval (we have only two successes and 13 failures). **(e)** With 225 successes and 275 failures, a large-sample (or plus four) interval can be used.

8.3. (a) The margin of error equals z^* times standard error; for 95% confidence, we would have $z^* = 1.96$. **(b)** H_0 should refer to p (the population proportion), not $\hat{p}$ (the sample proportion). **(c)** Use normal distributions (and a z test statistic) for significance tests involving proportions.

8.4. (a) The mean is $\mu = p = 0.4$ and the standard deviation is $\sigma = \sqrt{p(1-p)/n} = \sqrt{0.004} \doteq 0.06325$. **(b)** Normal curve on the right. **(c)** p^* should be either $1.96\sigma \doteq 0.1240$ or $2\sigma \doteq 0.1265$, so the points marked on the curve should be either 0.276 and 0.524, or 0.2735 and 0.5265.

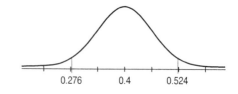

8.5. (a) $\hat{p} = \frac{3547}{5594} \doteq 0.6341$. The standard error is $\text{SE}_{\hat{p}} = \sqrt{\hat{p}(1-\hat{p})/5594} \doteq 0.006440$, so the margin of error for 95% confidence is $1.96\,\text{SE}_{\hat{p}} \doteq 0.01262$, and the interval is 0.6214 to 0.6467. This interval was found using a procedure that includes the correct proportion 95% of the time. **(b)** We do not know if those who *did* respond can reliably represent those who did not.

8.6. (a) $\hat{p} = \frac{1447}{3469} \doteq 0.4171$. The standard error is $\text{SE}_{\hat{p}} = \sqrt{\hat{p}(1-\hat{p})/5594} \doteq 0.008372$, so the margin of error for 95% confidence is $1.96\,\text{SE}_{\hat{p}} \doteq 0.01641$, and the interval is 0.4007 to 0.4335. **(b)** The margin of error depends on the confidence level (95% in both cases) and on $\text{SE}_{\hat{p}}$. The sample size for male athletes was 1.6 times larger than the sample for female athletes, making the males' $\text{SE}_{\hat{p}}$ smaller, resulting in a smaller margin of error for men. (Another contributing factor to the smaller $\text{SE}_{\hat{p}}$ for males was that $\hat{p}(1-\hat{p})$ was slightly smaller for men: 0.2320 compared to 0.2431 for women.)

8.7. (a) $\text{SE}_{\hat{p}} = \sqrt{(0.87)(0.13)/430,000} \doteq 0.0005129$. For 99% confidence, the margin of error is $2.576\,\text{SE}_{\hat{p}} \doteq 0.001321$. **(b)** One source of error is indicated by the wide variation in response rates: We cannot assume that the statements of respondents represent the opinions of nonrespondents. The effect of the participation fee is harder to predict, but one possible impact is on the types of institutions that participate in the survey: Even though the fee is scaled for institution size, larger institutions can more easily absorb it. These other sources of error are much more significant than sampling error, which is the only error accounted for in the margin of error from part (a).

8.8. If p_i represents the success rate of rat i, for $1 \leq i \leq 6$, then $\hat{p}_i$ and $\tilde{p}_i$ (the large-sample and plus four estimates of p_i) are:

i	1,2,4,6	3	5
$\hat{p}_i$	1	0.9125	0.9250
m.e.	0	0.081375	0.075853
CI	1 to 1	0.8311 to 0.9939	0.8491 to 1.0009
$\tilde{p}_i$	0.9762	0.8929	0.9048
m.e.	0.04285	0.08693	0.0825
CI	0.9333 to 1.0190	0.8059 to 0.9798	0.8223 to 0.9873

Note that two of the confidence interval upper limits should be reported as "1." The large-sample estimates are not really appropriate for these results—recall that the text's guidelines say that both the success count and the failure count should be at least 15. For the four rats with perfect scores in the 80 trials, the plus four intervals allow for the possibility that they might not always be perfect, but do indicate that their probability of success is almost certainly quite high (93% or better).

8.9. **(a)** $\hat{p} = \frac{390}{1191} \doteq 0.3275$. The standard error is $SE_{\hat{p}} = \sqrt{\hat{p}(1-\hat{p})/1191} \doteq 0.01360$, so the margin of error for 95% confidence is $1.96\,SE_{\hat{p}} \doteq 0.02665$, and the interval is 0.3008 to 0.3541. **(b)** $\tilde{p} = \frac{392}{1195} \doteq 0.3280$. The standard error is $SE_{\tilde{p}} = \sqrt{\tilde{p}(1-\tilde{p})/1195} \doteq 0.01358$, so the margin of error for 95% confidence is $1.96\,SE_{\tilde{p}} \doteq 0.02662$, and the interval is 0.3014 to 0.3547. With large samples, the two methods give similar results. **(c)** The nonresponse rate ($\frac{45}{1236} \doteq 3.6\%$) is quite small, which suggests that the results should be reliable: If we had information for the few congregations which failed to respond, our conclusions would probably not change very much. **(d)** Speakers and listeners probably perceive sermon length differently (just as, say, students and lecturers have different perceptions of the length of a class period).

8.10. **(a)** $\hat{p} = \frac{707}{1191} \doteq 0.5936$. The standard error is $SE_{\hat{p}} = \sqrt{\hat{p}(1-\hat{p})/1191} \doteq 0.01423$, so the margin of error for 95% confidence is $1.96\,SE_{\hat{p}} \doteq 0.02789$, and the interval is 0.5657 to 0.6215. **(b)** $\tilde{p} = \frac{392}{1195} \doteq 0.5933$. The standard error is $SE_{\tilde{p}} = \sqrt{\tilde{p}(1-\tilde{p})/1195} \doteq 0.01421$, so the margin of error for 95% confidence is $1.96\,SE_{\tilde{p}} \doteq 0.02785$, and the interval is 0.5655 to 0.6212. As in the previous exercise, we see similar results from the two methods. **(c)** As before, the low nonresponse rate suggests that the results should be reliable. **(d)** It might be reasonable to expect that congregational leaders and members have similar impressions of the congregation's theological orientation, although one can imagine situations where that might not be the case.

8.11. We estimate $\hat{p} = \frac{448}{1280} = 0.35$, $SE_{\hat{p}} \doteq 0.01333$, and the 95% confidence interval is 0.3239 to 0.3761. (The plus four method gives similar results: $\tilde{p} \doteq 0.3505$, $SE_{\tilde{p}} \doteq 0.01332$, and the 95% confidence interval is 0.3244 to 0.3766.)

8.12. We estimate $\hat{p} = \frac{192}{1050} \doteq 0.1829$, $SE_{\hat{p}} \doteq 0.01193$, and the 95% confidence interval is 0.1595 to 0.2062. (The plus four method gives similar results: $\tilde{p} \doteq 0.1841$, $SE_{\tilde{p}} \doteq 0.01194$, and the 95% confidence interval is 0.1607 to 0.2075.)

8.13. A 99% confidence interval would be wider: We need a larger margin of error (by a factor of 2.576/1.96) in order to be more confident that we have included p. The large-sample 99% confidence interval is 0.3157 to 0.3843; the plus four interval is 0.3162 to 0.3848.

8.14. A 90% confidence interval would be narrower: The margin of error will be smaller (by a factor of 1.645/1.96) if we are willing to be less confident that we have included p. The large-sample 99% confidence interval is 0.1632 to 0.2025; the plus four interval is 0.1644 to 0.2037.

8.15. With $\hat{p} = 0.69$, $SE_{\hat{p}} \doteq 0.02830$, and the 95% confidence interval is 0.6345 to 0.7455. (If we assume that 184 of the 267 women had been on a diet, we could find the plus four interval: $\tilde{p} \doteq 0.6863$, $SE_{\tilde{p}} \doteq 0.02818$, and the interval is 0.6311 to 0.7416.)

8.16. With $\hat{p} = 0.583$, $SE_{\hat{p}} \doteq 0.03023$, and the 95% confidence interval is 0.5237 to 0.6423. (If we assume that 155 of the 266 high school students had been on a diet, we could find the plus four interval: $\tilde{p} \doteq 0.5815$, $SE_{\tilde{p}} \doteq 0.03002$, and the interval is 0.5226 to 0.6403.)

8.17. We estimate $\hat{p} = \frac{594}{2533} \doteq 0.2345$, $SE_{\hat{p}} \doteq 0.00842$, and the 95% confidence interval is 0.2180 to 0.2510. (The plus four method gives similar results: $\tilde{p} \doteq 0.2349$, $SE_{\tilde{p}} \doteq 0.00842$, and the 95% confidence interval is 0.2184 to 0.2514.)

8.18. (a) We estimate $\hat{p} = \frac{1434}{2533} \doteq 0.5661$, $SE_{\hat{p}} \doteq 0.00985$, and the 95% confidence interval is 0.5468 to 0.5854. (The plus four method gives similar results: $\tilde{p} \doteq 0.5660$, $SE_{\tilde{p}} \doteq 0.00984$, and the 95% confidence interval is 0.5467 to 0.5853.) **(b)** Pride or embarrassment might lead respondents to claim that their income was above $25,000 even if it were not. Consequently, it would not be surprising if the true proportion p were lower than the estimate $\hat{p}$. (There may also be some who would understate their income, out of humility or mistrust of the interviewer. While this would seem to have less of an impact, it makes it difficult to anticipate the overall effect of untruthful responses.) **(c)** Respondents would have little reason to lie about pet ownership; the few that might lie about it would have little impact on our conclusions. The number of untruthful responses about income is likely to be much larger and have a greater impact.

8.19. (a) $\tilde{p} = \frac{12}{14} \doteq 0.8571$. **(b)** $SE_{\tilde{p}} \doteq 0.09352$, so the margin of error is $1.96\,SE_{\tilde{p}} \doteq 0.1833$. The interval is therefore 0.6738 to 1.0404; the upper limit should be taken to be 1. **(c)** No; we would not expect everyone to match the performance of the top salesperson.

8.20. (a) $\hat{p} = \frac{542}{1711} \doteq 0.3168$; about 31.7% of bicyclists aged 15 or older killed between 1987 and 1991 had alcohol in their systems at the time of the accident. (b) $\text{SE}_{\hat{p}} = \sqrt{\hat{p}(1-\hat{p})/1711} \doteq 0.01125$; the 99% confidence interval is $\hat{p} \pm 2.576\,\text{SE}_{\hat{p}} = 0.2878$ to 0.3457. (The plus four method gives similar results: $\tilde{p} \doteq 0.3172$, $\text{SE}_{\tilde{p}} \doteq 0.01124$, and the interval is 0.2883 to 0.3461.) (c) No: We do not know, for example, what percentage of cyclists who were *not* involved in fatal accidents had alcohol in their systems. (d) $\hat{p} = \frac{386}{1711} \doteq 0.2256$, $\text{SE}_{\hat{p}} \doteq 0.01010$, and the 99% confidence interval is 0.1996 to 0.2516. (The plus four method gives similar results: $\tilde{p} \doteq 0.2262$, $\text{SE}_{\tilde{p}} \doteq 0.01010$, and the interval is 0.2002 to 0.2523.)

8.21. Recall the rule of thumb from Chapter 5: use the normal approximation if $np \geq 10$ and $n(1-p) \geq 10$. We use p_0 (the value specified in H_0) to make our decision.
(a) No: $np_0 = 9$. (b) Yes: $np_0 = 18$ and $n(1 - p_0) = 12$. (c) Yes: $np_0 = n(1 - p_0) = 500$.
(d) No: $np_0 = 5$.

8.22. (a) Because we have defined p as the proportion who prefer fresh-brewed coffee, we should compute $\hat{p} = \frac{28}{40} = 0.7$. To test H_0: $p = 0.5$ vs. H_a: $p > 0.5$, the standard error is $\sigma_{\hat{p}} = \sqrt{(0.5)(0.5)/40} \doteq 0.07906$, and the test statistic is $z = \frac{0.7-0.5}{0.07906} \doteq 2.53$. The P-value 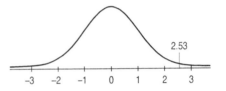 is 0.0057. (b) Curve on the right. (c) The result is significant at the 5% level, so we reject H_0 and conclude that a majority of people prefer fresh-brewed coffee. (d) The appropriate standard error for a confidence interval is $\text{SE}_{\hat{p}} = \sqrt{(0.7)(0.3)/40} \doteq 0.07246$. The margin of error for 95% confidence is $1.96\,\text{SE}_{\hat{p}} \doteq 0.1420$, and the confidence interval is 0.5580 to 0.8420.

8.23. (a) Testing H_0: $p = 0.5$ vs. H_a: $p \neq 0.5$, we have $\hat{p} = \frac{5067}{10000} = 0.5067$, and $\sigma_{\hat{p}} = \sqrt{(0.5)(0.5)/10000} = 0.005$, so $z = \frac{0.0067}{0.005} = 1.34$, for which $P = 0.1802$. This is not significant at $\alpha = 0.05$ (or even $\alpha = 0.10$).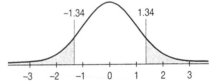
(b) $\text{SE}_{\hat{p}} = \sqrt{\hat{p}(1-\hat{p})/10000} \doteq 0.005$, so the 95% confidence interval is $0.5067 \pm (1.96)(0.005)$, or 0.4969 to 0.5165.

8.24. With no prior knowledge of the value of p (the proportion of "Yes" responses), take $p^* = 0.5$: $n = \left(\frac{1.96}{2(0.15)}\right)^2 \doteq 42.7$—use $n = 43$.

8.25. As a quick estimate, we can observe that to cut the margin of error in half, we must quadruple the sample size, from 43 to 172. Using the sample-size formula, we find $n = \left(\frac{1.96}{2(0.075)}\right)^2 \doteq 170.7$—use $n = 171$. (The difference in the two answers is due to rounding.)

8.26. $n = \left(\frac{1.96}{0.1}\right)^2 (0.3)(0.7) \doteq 80.7$—use $n = 81$.

8.27. The required sample sizes are found by computing $\left(\frac{1.96}{0.1}\right)^2 p^*(1-p^*) = 384.16 p^*(1-p^*)$: To be sure that we meet our target margin of error, we should take the largest sample indicated: $n = 97$ or larger.

p^*	n	Rounded up
0.1	34.57	35
0.2	61.47	62
0.3	80.67	81
0.4	92.20	93
0.5	96.04	97
0.6	92.20	93
0.7	80.67	81
0.8	61.47	62
0.9	34.57	35

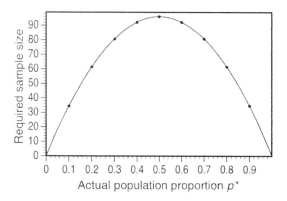

8.28. $n = \left(\frac{1.96}{0.02}\right)^2 (0.25)(0.75) = 1800.75$ — use $n = 1801$. If the sample finds $\hat{p} = 0.15$, then $\mathrm{SE}_{\hat{p}} \doteq 0.008414$ and the actual margin of error is 0.01649.

8.29. The margins of error using large-sample methods (m.e.1) are $1.96\sqrt{\hat{p}(1-\hat{p})/10}$. Also given are the plus four margins m.e.2 $= 1.96\sqrt{\tilde{p}(1-\tilde{p})/14}$.

$\hat{p}$	0.1	0.2	0.3	0.4	0.5	0.6	0.7	0.8	0.9
m.e.1	0.1859	0.2479	0.2840	0.3036	0.3099	0.3036	0.2840	0.2479	0.1859
m.e.2	0.2149	0.2366	0.2510	0.2592	0.2619	0.2592	0.2510	0.2366	0.2149

8.30. With $n = 400$, the margins of error are m.e.1 $= 1.96\sqrt{\hat{p}(1-\hat{p})/400}$. (The plus four margins are m.e.2 $= 1.96\sqrt{\tilde{p}(1-\tilde{p})/404}$.) The new margins of error are much less than with the smaller sample (in fact, they have decreased by a factor of $\frac{1}{\sqrt{40}} \doteq 0.158$). Even in the worst case, the margin of error is less than 0.05.

$\hat{p}$	0.1	0.2	0.3	0.4	0.5	0.6	0.7	0.8	0.9
m.e.1	0.0294	0.0392	0.0449	0.0480	0.0490	0.0480	0.0449	0.0392	0.0294
m.e.2	0.0298	0.0392	0.0448	0.0478	0.0488	0.0478	0.0448	0.0392	0.0298

8.31. The text recommends using the large-sample interval when the number of successes and the number of failures in both samples are all at least 10. The plus four interval is recommended when both sample sizes are at least 5. **(a)** All counts are 10 or more, so a large-sample (or plus four) interval can be used. **(b)** Use a plus four interval (both sample sizes are 5). **(c)** Use a plus four interval (the count of successes in the first sample is 8, and the count of failures in the second sample is 5). **(d)** Neither approach is appropriate, as the first sample size is too small. **(e)** Use a plus four interval (the second sample has 8 successes and 2 failures).

8.32. The guidelines are summarized in the previous solution. **(a)** Neither approach is appropriate, as the first sample size is too small. **(b)** All counts are at least 92, so a large-sample (or plus four) interval can be used. **(c)** Use a plus four interval (the first sample sizes is 6). **(d)** All counts are at least 18, so a large-sample (or plus four) interval can be used. **(e)** Use a plus four interval (the failure count in the second sample is 6).

8.33. (a) H_0 should refer to p_1 and p_2 (population proportions) rather than $\hat{p}_1$ and $\hat{p}_2$ (sample proportions). **(b)** Knowing $\hat{p}_1 = \hat{p}_2$ does not tell us that the success counts are equal $(X_1 = X_2)$ *unless* the sample sizes are equal $(n_1 = n_2)$. **(c)** Confidence intervals only account for random sampling error.

8.34. (a) The mean is $\mu_D = p_1 - p_2 = 0.4 - 0.5 = -0.1$, and the standard deviation is $\sigma_D = \sqrt{\frac{p_1(1-p_1)}{50} + \frac{p_2(1-p_2)}{60}} \doteq 0.09469$. **(b)** Normal curve on the right. **(c)** d should be either $1.96\sigma_D \doteq 0.1856$ or $2\sigma_D \doteq 0.1894$, so the points marked on the curve should be either -0.2856 and 0.0856, or -0.2894 and 0.0894.

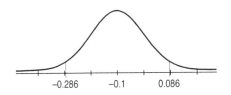

    Note: *Because this problem told us which population was "first" and which was "second," we did not follow the suggestion in the text to arrange them so that the population 1 had the larger proportion. Where necessary, we do so in the remaining exercises.*

8.35. We have $\hat{p}_m = \frac{3547}{5594} \doteq 0.6341$, $\hat{p}_f = \frac{1447}{3469} \doteq 0.4171$, and pooled proportion $\hat{p} = \frac{3547+1447}{5594+3469} \doteq 0.5510$. For the test of H_0: $p_m = p_f$ vs. H_a: $p_m \neq p_f$, the appropriate standard error is $SE_{D_p} = \sqrt{\hat{p}(1-\hat{p})\left(\frac{1}{5594} + \frac{1}{3469}\right)} \doteq 0.01075$ and the test statistic is $z = (\hat{p}_m - \hat{p}_f)/SE_{D_p} \doteq 20.18$—overwhelming evidence that the two proportions are different. The standard error for a confidence interval is $SE_D = \sqrt{\hat{p}_1(1-\hat{p}_1)/n_1 + \hat{p}_2(1-\hat{p}_2)/n_2} \doteq 0.01056$, and the 95% confidence interval is 0.1962 to 0.2377. (The plus four interval is nearly identical: 0.1962 to 0.2376.) This interval and the significance test are only designed to deal with random sampling error; other sources of error such as nonresponse could throw all conclusions into doubt.

8.36. (a) $\hat{p}_1 = \frac{35}{165} \doteq 0.2121$ and $\hat{p}_2 = \frac{17}{283} \doteq 0.0601$ (arranged so that population 1 has the larger proportion). **(b)** $\hat{p}_1 - \hat{p}_2 \doteq 0.1521$ and the standard error (for constructing a confidence interval) is $SE_D \doteq 0.03482$. **(c)** The hypotheses are H_0: $p_1 = p_2$ vs. H_a: $p_1 > p_2$. The alternative reflects the reasonable expectation that reducing pollution might decrease wheezing. **(d)** The pooled estimate of the proportion is $\hat{p} = \frac{17+35}{283+165} \doteq 0.1161$, and $SE_{D_p} \doteq 0.03137$, so $z = (\hat{p}_1 - \hat{p}_2)/SE_{D_p} \doteq 4.85$. The P-value is very small ($P < 0.0001$). **(e)** The 95% confidence interval, using the standard error from part (b), has margin of error $1.96\,SE_D \doteq 0.06824$: 0.0838 to 0.2203. (The plus four interval is 0.0839 to 0.2209.) The percentage reporting improvement was between 8% and 22% higher for bypass residents. **(f)** There may be geographic factors (e.g., weather) or cultural factors (e.g., diet) that limit how much we can generalize the conclusions.

8.37. Pet owners had the lower proportion of women, so we call them "population 2":
$\hat{p}_2 = \frac{285}{595} \doteq 0.4790$. For non-pet owners, $\hat{p}_1 = \frac{1024}{1939} \doteq 0.5281$. $SE_D \doteq 0.02341$, so the 95% confidence interval is 0.0032 to 0.0950. (The plus four interval is 0.0032 to 0.0948.)

8.38. Population 1 is non-pet owners: $\hat{p}_1 = 0.577$ and $\hat{p}_2 = 0.533$, so $SE_D \doteq 0.02333$ and the 95% confidence interval is -0.0017 to 0.0897. (If we assume that 1119 non-pet owners and 317 pet owners were married, then the plus four interval is -0.0013 to 0.0900.) The proportion of non-pet owners who are married is 0% to 9% higher than that proportion for pet owners.

8.39. This time, pet owners are "population 1": $\hat{p}_1 = \frac{310}{595} \doteq 0.5210$. For non-pet owners,

$\hat{p}_2 = \frac{915}{1939} \doteq 0.4719$. These could be found by subtracting from 1 the proportions of Exercise 8.37. The standard error (0.02341) and the confidence interval (0.0032 to 0.0950) are the same as in the solution to Exercise 8.37. (The plus four interval is also unchanged.)

8.40. This time, pet owners are "population 1": $\hat{p}_1 = 1 - 0.533 = 0.467$ and $\hat{p}_2 = 1 - 0.577 = 0.423$. The standard error (0.02333) and the confidence interval (-0.0017 to 0.0897) are the same as in the solution to Exercise 8.38. (The plus four interval is also unchanged.)

8.41. With equal sample sizes, the pooled estimate of the proportion is $\hat{p} = 0.235$, the average of $\hat{p}_1 = 0.29$ and $\hat{p}_2 = 0.18$. This can also be computed by taking $X_1 = (0.29)(1370) = 397.3$ and $X_2 = (0.18)(1370) = 246.6$, so $\hat{p} = (X_1 + X_2)/(1370 + 1370)$. The standard error for a significance test is $SE_{D_p} \doteq 0.01620$, and the test statistic is $z \doteq 6.79$ ($P < 0.0001$); we conclude that the proportions are different. The standard error for a confidence interval is $SE_D \doteq 0.01606$, and the 95% confidence interval is 0.0785 to 0.1415. The interval gives us an idea of how large the difference is: Music downloads dropped 8% to 14%.

8.42. The table below shows the results from the previous exercise, and those with different sample sizes. For part (iii), two answers are given, corresponding to the two ways one could interpret which is the "first sample size."

	n_1	n_2	$\hat{p}$	SE_{D_p}	z	SE_D	Confidence interval
8.41	1370	1370	0.2350	0.01620	6.79	0.01606	0.0785 to 0.1415
(i)	1200	1200	0.2350	0.01731	6.35	0.01716	0.0764 to 0.1436
(ii)	1600	1600	0.2350	0.01499	7.34	0.01486	0.0809 to 0.1391
(iii)	1200	1600	0.2271	0.01600	6.87	0.01624	0.0782 to 0.1418
	1600	1200	0.2429	0.01638	6.72	0.01586	0.0789 to 0.1411

As one would expect, we see in (i) and (ii) that smaller samples result in smaller z (weaker evidence) and wider intervals, while larger samples have the reverse effect. The results of (iii) show that the effect of varying unequal sample sizes is more complicated.

8.43. We find $\hat{p}_1 = \frac{73}{91} \doteq 0.8022$ and $\hat{p}_2 = \frac{75}{109} \doteq 0.6881$. For a confidence interval, $\text{SE}_D \doteq 0.06093$, so the 95% confidence interval for $p_1 - p_2$ is $(0.8022 - 0.6881) \pm (1.96)(0.06093) = -0.0053$ to 0.2335. (The plus four interval is -0.0081 to 0.2301.)

8.44. The question posed in Exercise 8.43 is, "Do high-tech companies tend to offer stock options more often than other companies?" Therefore, we test H_0: $p_1 = p_2$ vs. H_a: $p_1 > p_2$. With $\hat{p}_1 \doteq 0.8022$, $\hat{p}_2 \doteq 0.6881$, and $\hat{p} = \frac{73+75}{91+109} = 0.74$, we find $\text{SE}_{D_p} \doteq 0.06229$, so $z = (\hat{p}_1 - \hat{p}_2)/\text{SE}_{D_p} \doteq 1.83$. This gives $P = 0.0336$—fairly strong evidence that high-tech companies are more likely to offer stock options.

8.45. We find $\hat{p}_1 = \frac{54}{639} \doteq 0.0845$ and $\hat{p}_2 = \frac{22}{743} \doteq 0.0296$. For a confidence interval, $\text{SE}_D \doteq 0.01264$, so the 95% confidence interval for $p_1 - p_2$ is 0.0301 to 0.0797. (The plus four interval is 0.0299 to 0.0799.)

8.46. We test H_0: $p_1 = p_2$ vs. H_a: $p_1 > p_2$. With $\hat{p}_1 \doteq 0.0845$, $\hat{p}_2 \doteq 0.0296$, and $\hat{p} = \frac{54+22}{639+743} \doteq 0.0550$, we find $\text{SE}_{D_p} \doteq 0.01230$, so $z = (\hat{p}_1 - \hat{p}_2)/\text{SE}_{D_p} \doteq 4.46$. This gives $P < 0.0001$—strong evidence that complainers are more likely to leave the HMO.

8.47. (a) $\hat{p}_f = \frac{48}{60} = 0.8$, so $\text{SE}_{\hat{p}} \doteq 0.05164$ for females. $\hat{p}_m = \frac{52}{132} = 0.3\overline{9}$, so $\text{SE}_{\hat{p}} \doteq 0.04253$ for males. (b) $\text{SE}_D = \sqrt{0.05164^2 + 0.04253^2} \doteq 0.06690$, so the interval is $(\hat{p}_f - \hat{p}_m) \pm 1.645\,\text{SE}_D$, or 0.2960 to 0.5161. There is (with high confidence) a considerably higher percentage of juvenile references to females than to males.

8.48. (a) $\hat{p}_1 = \frac{515}{1520} \doteq 0.3388$ for men, and $\hat{p}_2 = \frac{27}{191} \doteq 0.1414$ for women. $\text{SE}_D \doteq 0.02798$, so the 95% confidence interval for $p_1 - p_2$ is 0.1426 to 0.2523. (The plus four interval is 0.1389 to 0.2490.) (b) The female contribution is larger, because the sample size for women is much smaller. (Specifically, $\hat{p}_1(1 - \hat{p}_1)/n_1 \doteq 0.0001474$, while $\hat{p}_2(1 - \hat{p}_2)/n_2 \doteq 0.0006355$.) Note that if the sample sizes had been similar, the male contribution would have been larger (assuming the proportions remained the same), because the numerator term $p_i(1 - p_i)$ is greater for men than women.

8.49. We test H_0: $p_1 = p_2$ vs. H_a: $p_1 \neq p_2$. With $\hat{p}_1 \doteq 0.5281$, $\hat{p}_2 \doteq 0.4790$, and $\hat{p} = \frac{1024+285}{1939+595} \doteq 0.5166$, we find $\text{SE}_{D_p} \doteq 0.02342$, so $z = (\hat{p}_1 - \hat{p}_2)/\text{SE}_{D_p} \doteq 2.10$. This gives $P = 0.0360$—significant evidence (at the 5% level) that a higher proportion of non-pet owners are women.

8.50. We test H_0: $p_1 = p_2$ vs. H_a: $p_1 \neq p_2$. We were given $\hat{p}_1 = 0.577$ and $\hat{p}_2 = 0.533$, which correspond to $X_1 \doteq 1119^*$ and $X_2 = 317$. Then $\hat{p} = \frac{1119+317}{1939+595} \doteq 0.5667$, $\text{SE}_{D_p} \doteq 0.02322$, $z = (\hat{p}_1 - \hat{p}_2)/\text{SE}_{D_p} \doteq 1.91$, and $P = 0.0563$. Although the proportions suggest that pet owners are more likely to be married, the difference is not quite significant.
    *In fact, either $X_1 = 1118$ or 1119 would result in $\hat{p}_1 = 0.577$ when rounded to three decimal places. The impact of choosing $X_1 = 1118$, or of using $X_1 = (1939)(0.577) = 1118.803$ and $X_2 = (595)(0.533) = 317.135$, is minimal; either approach results in $z \doteq 1.89$ instead of 1.91, and a very similar P-value.

8.51. We test H_0: $p_f = p_m$ vs. H_a: $p_f \neq p_m$. With $\hat{p}_f = 0.8$, $\hat{p}_m = 0.\overline{39}$, and $\hat{p} = \frac{48+52}{60+132} \doteq 0.5208$, we find $\mathrm{SE}_{D_p} \doteq 0.07778$, so $z = (\hat{p}_f - \hat{p}_m)/\mathrm{SE}_{D_p} \doteq 5.22$. This gives a very small P-value—significant evidence (for any reasonable choice of α) that juvenile references occur more often for females than for males.

8.52. We test H_0: $p_m = p_f$ vs. H_a: $p_m \neq p_f$. With $\hat{p}_m \doteq 0.3388$, $\hat{p}_f \doteq 0.1414$, and $\hat{p} = \frac{515+27}{1520+191} \doteq 0.3168$, we find $\mathrm{SE}_{D_p} \doteq 0.03571$, so $z = (\hat{p}_m - \hat{p}_f)/\mathrm{SE}_{D_p} \doteq 5.53$. This gives a very small P-value—significant evidence (for any reasonable choice of α) that males killed in bicycle accidents were more likely to test positive for alcohol.

8.53. We must assume that we can treat the births recorded during these two times as independent SRSs. Note that the rules of thumb for the normal approximation are not satisfied here; specifically, three birth defects are less than ten. Additionally, one might call into question the assumption of independence, because there may have been multiple births to the same set of parents included in these counts (either twins/triplets/etc., or "ordinary" siblings).

If we carry out the analysis in spite of these issues, we find $\hat{p}_1 = \frac{16}{414} \doteq 0.03865$ and $\hat{p}_2 = \frac{3}{228} \doteq 0.01316$. We might then find a 95% confidence interval: $\mathrm{SE}_D \doteq 0.01211$, so the interval is $\hat{p}_1 - \hat{p}_2 \pm (1.96)(0.01211) = 0.00175$ to 0.04923. (Note that this does not take into account the presumed direction of the difference.)

This setting does meet our requirements for the plus four method, for which $\tilde{p}_1 = 0.04086$ and $\tilde{p}_2 = 0.01739$, $\mathrm{SE}_D = 0.01298$, and the 95% confidence interval is -0.0020 to 0.0489.

We could also perform a significance test of H_0: $p_1 = p_2$ vs. H_a: $p_1 > p_2$: $\hat{p} = \frac{19}{642} \doteq 0.02960$, $\mathrm{SE}_{D_p} \doteq 0.01398$, $z \doteq 1.82$, $P = 0.0344$.

Both the large-sample interval and the significance test suggest that the two proportions are different (but not much); the plus four interval does not establish that $p_1 \neq p_2$. Also, we must recognize that the issues noted above make this conclusion questionable.

8.54. (a) The table below summarizes the margins of error m.e.$= 1.96\sqrt{\hat{p}(1-\hat{p})/n}$:

	$\hat{p}$	m.e.	95% confidence interval
Current downloaders ($n = 247$):			
Downloading less	38%	6.05%	31.95% to 44.05%
Use P2P networks	33.33%	5.88%	27.45% to 39.21%
Use e-mail/IM	24%	5.33%	18.67% to 29.33%
Use music-related sites	20%	4.99%	15.01% to 24.99%
Use paid services	17%	4.68%	12.32% to 21.68%
All users ($n = 1371$):			
Have used paid services	7%	1.35%	5.65% to 8.35%
Currently use paid services	3%	0.90%	2.10% to 3.90%

(b) Obviously, students' renditions of the above information in a paragraph will vary.
(c) Student opinions may vary on this. Personally, I lean toward (B), although I would be inclined to report two margins of error: "no more than 6%" for the current downloaders, and "no more than 1.4%" for all users.

8.55. We compute $\hat{p} = \frac{152}{248} \doteq 0.6129$. To test H_0: $p = 0.485$ vs. H_a: $p \neq 0.485$, the standard error is $\sigma_{\hat{p}} = \sqrt{(0.485)(0.515)/248} \doteq 0.03174$, the test statistic is $z = (\hat{p} - 0.485)/\sigma_{\hat{p}} \doteq 4.03$, and $P < 0.0001$. For constructing a confidence interval, the appropriate standard error is $\text{SE}_{\hat{p}} = \sqrt{\hat{p}(1-\hat{p})/248} \doteq 0.03093$, so the 95% confidence interval is 0.5523 to 0.6735. (The plus four method gives similar results: $\tilde{p} \doteq 0.6111$, $\text{SE}_{\tilde{p}} \doteq 0.03071$, and the interval is 0.5509 to 0.6713.) The significance test revealed strong evidence that heavy lottery players are more likely to be men; the confidence interval further tells us that between 55% and 67% of heavy lottery players are men.

8.56. See the solutions to Exercises 8.43 and 8.44 for the confidence interval and test.

8.57. (a) People have different symptoms; for example, not all who wheeze consult a doctor. (b) In the table (below), we find for "sleep" that $\hat{p}_1 = \frac{45}{282} \doteq 0.1596$ and $\hat{p}_2 = \frac{12}{164} \doteq 0.0732$, so the difference is $\hat{p}_1 - \hat{p}_2 \doteq 0.0864$. Therefore, $\text{SE}_D \doteq 0.02982$ and the margin of error for 95% confidence is 0.05844. Other computations are performed in like manner. (Plus four intervals are no shown, but are similar.) (c) It is reasonable to expect that the bypass proportions would be higher—that is, we expect more improvement where the pollution decreased—so we could use the alternative $p_1 > p_2$. (d) For "sleep," we find $\hat{p} = \frac{45+12}{282+164} \doteq 0.1278$ and $\text{SE}_{D_p} \doteq 0.03279$. Therefore, $z \doteq (0.1596 - 0.0732)/\text{SE}_{D_p} \doteq 2.64$. Other computations are similar. Only the "sleep" difference is significant. (e) 95% confidence intervals are shown below. Part (b) showed improvement relative to control group, which is a better measure of the effect of the bypass, because it allows us to account for the improvement reported over time even when no change was made.

Complaint	Bypass minus congested				Bypass	
	$\hat{p}_1 - \hat{p}_2$	95% CI	z	P	$\hat{p}$	95% CI
Sleep	0.0864	0.0280 to 0.1448	2.64	0.0042	0.1596	0.1168 to 0.2023
Number	0.0307	−0.0361 to 0.0976	0.88	0.1897	0.1596	0.1168 to 0.2023
Speech	0.0182	−0.0152 to 0.0515	0.99	0.1600	0.0426	0.0190 to 0.0661
Activities	0.0137	−0.0395 to 0.0670	0.50	0.3100	0.0925	0.0586 to 0.1264
Doctor	−0.0112	−0.0796 to 0.0573	−0.32	0.6267	0.1174	0.0773 to 0.1576
Phlegm	−0.0220	−0.0711 to 0.0271	−0.92	0.8217	0.0474	0.0212 to 0.0736
Cough	−0.0323	−0.0853 to 0.0207	−1.25	0.8950	0.0575	0.0292 to 0.0857

8.58. (a) $\hat{p}_f = \frac{63}{296} \doteq 0.2128$ and $\hat{p}_m = \frac{27}{251} \doteq 0.1076$, so $\text{SE}_D \doteq 0.03080$ and the interval is 0.0449 to 0.1656. (The plus four interval is 0.0435 to 0.1647.) (b) For testing H_0: $p_f = p_m$ vs. H_a: $p_f \neq p_m$, we find $\hat{p} = \frac{63+27}{296+251} \doteq 0.1645$, we find $\text{SE}_{D_p} \doteq 0.03181$, so $z = (\hat{p}_f - \hat{p}_m)/\text{SE}_{D_p} \doteq 3.31$. This gives $P = 0.0009$—significant evidence that women are more likely than men to be label users.

8.59. (a) For testing H_0: $p_1 = p_2$ vs. H_a: $p_1 \neq p_2$, we find $\hat{p}_1 = \frac{643}{1132} \doteq 0.5680$, $\hat{p}_2 = \frac{349}{852} \doteq 0.4096$, and $\hat{p} = \frac{643+349}{1132+852} = 0.5$. Then $\text{SE}_{D_p} \doteq 0.02268$, so $z = (\hat{p}_1 - \hat{p}_2)/\text{SE}_{D_p} \doteq 6.98$. This gives a tiny P-value, and very strong evidence that those who arrange travel on the Internet are more likely to have completed college. (b) $\text{SE}_D \doteq 0.02237$ and the 95% confidence interval is 0.1145 to 0.2022. (The plus four interval is 0.1143 to 0.2019.)

8.60. We choose to look at the proportions with income over $50,000; the results are essentially the same if we work with the complementary proportions. The sample proportions are $\hat{p}_1 = \frac{378}{871} \doteq 0.4340$ and $\hat{p}_2 = \frac{200}{677} \doteq 0.2954$; the pooled proportion for testing H_0: $p_1 = p_2$ vs. H_a: $p_1 \neq p_2$ is $\hat{p} = \frac{378+200}{871+677} \doteq 0.3734$. This leads to $SE_{D_p} \doteq 0.02478$, $z \doteq 5.59$, and $P < 0.0001$. For the 95% confidence interval for $p_1 - p_2$, $SE_D \doteq 0.02428$, so the interval is 0.0910 to 0.1861 (the plus four interval is 0.0906 to 0.1857).

8.61. For the education question, there were 1132 users and 852 nonusers. Only 871 users and 677 nonusers responded to the income question, so the proportions not responding to the income question were (for users) $\hat{p}_1 = \frac{1132-871}{1132} \doteq 0.2306$ and (for nonusers) $\hat{p}_2 = \frac{852-677}{852} \doteq 0.2054$. Therefore, $\hat{p} \doteq 0.2198$, $SE_{D_p} \doteq 0.01878$, and $z \doteq 1.34$. For a two-sided alternative, $P = 0.1802$, so we have little reason to suspect a difference in nonresponse rates between users and nonusers. For a 95% confidence interval, $SE_D \doteq 0.01866$ and the interval is −0.0114 to 0.0617 (the plus four interval is −0.0116 to 0.0615).

    More than 20% did not respond to the income question; this lack of response makes the conclusions for Exercise 8.60 suspect.

8.62. (a) The number of orders completed in five days or less before the changes was $X_1 = (0.16)(200) = 32$. With $\hat{p}_1 = 0.16$, $SE_{\hat{p}} \doteq 0.02592$, and the 95% confidence interval for p_1 is 0.1092 to 0.2108. (The plus four interval is 0.1155 to 0.2178.) **(b)** After the changes, $X_2 = (0.9)(200) = 180$. With $\hat{p}_2 = 0.9$, $SE_{\hat{p}} \doteq 0.02121$, and the 95% confidence interval for p_2 is 0.8584 to 0.9416. (The plus four interval is 0.8496 to 0.9347.) **(c)** $SE_D \doteq 0.03350$ and the 95% confidence interval for $p_2 - p_1$ is 0.6743 to 0.8057, or about 67.4% to 80.6%. (The plus four interval is 0.6666 to 0.7988.)

8.63. The standard error is $SE_{\hat{p}} \doteq \sqrt{(0.38)(0.62)/1006} \doteq 0.01530$, so the margin of error for 95% confidence is $1.96\,SE_{\hat{p}} \doteq 0.02999$, or about ±0.03.

8.64. (a) $X_1 = 121 \doteq (0.903)(134)$ die-hard fans and $X_2 = 161 \doteq (0.679)(237)$ less loyal fans watched or listened as children. **(b)** $\hat{p} = \frac{121+161}{134+237} \doteq 0.7601$ and $SE_{D_p} \doteq 0.04615$, so we find $z \doteq 4.85$ ($P < 0.0001$)—strong evidence of a difference in childhood experience. **(c)** For a 95% confidence interval, $SE_D \doteq 0.03966$ and the interval is 0.1459 to 0.3014. (The plus four interval is 0.1410 to 0.2975.) If students work with the rounded proportions (0.903 and 0.679), the 95% confidence interval is 0.1463 to 0.3017.

8.65. With $\hat{p}_1 = \frac{2}{3}$ and $\hat{p}_2 = 0.2$, we have $\hat{p} = \frac{134\hat{p}_1 + 237\hat{p}_2}{134+237} \doteq 0.3686$, $SE_{D_p} \doteq 0.05214$, and $z = 8.95$—very strong evidence of a difference. (If we assume that "two-thirds of the die-hard fans" and "20% of the less loyal fans" mean 89 and 47 fans respectively, then $\hat{p} \doteq 0.3666$ and $z \doteq 8.94$; the conclusion is the same.) For a 95% confidence interval, $SE_D \doteq 0.04831$ and the interval is 0.3720 to 0.5613. (With $X_1 = 89$ and $X_2 = 47$, the interval is 0.3712 to 0.5606; the plus four interval is 0.3666 to 0.5553.)

8.66. We test H_0: $p_f = p_m$ vs. H_a: $p_f \neq$ p_m for each text, where, e.g., p_f is the proportion of juvenile female references. We can reject H_0 for texts 2, 3, 6, and 10. The last three texts do not stand out as different from the first seven. Texts 7 and 9 are notable as the only two with a majority of juvenile male references, while six of the ten texts had juvenile female references a majority of the time.

Text	$\hat{p}_f$	$\hat{p}_m$	$\hat{p}$	z	P
1	.4000	.2059	.2308	0.96	.3361
2	.7143	.2857	.3286	2.29	.0220
3	.4464	.2154	.3223	2.71	.0067
4	.1447	.1210	.1288	0.51	.6123
5	.6667	.2791	.3043	1.41	.1584
6	.8000	.3939	.5208	5.22	.0000
7	.9500	.9722	.9643	−0.61	.5437
8	.2778	.1818	.2157	0.80	.4259
9	.6667	.7273	.7097	−0.95	.3399
10	.7222	.2520	.3103	4.04	.0001

8.67. The proportions, z-values, and P-values are

Text	1	2	3	4	5	6	7	8	9	10
$\hat{p}$	.8718	.9000	.5372	.6738	.9348	.6875	.6429	.6471	.7097	.8759
z	4.64	6.69	0.82	5.31	5.90	5.20	3.02	2.10	6.60	9.05
P	≈ 0	≈ 0	.4133	≈ 0	≈ 0	≈ 0	.0025	.0357	≈ 0	≈ 0

We reject H_0: $p = 0.5$ for all texts except Text 3 and (perhaps) Text 8. If we are using a "multiple comparisons" procedure such as Bonferroni (see Chapter 6), we also might fail to reject H_0 for Text 7.

The last three texts do not seem to be any different from the first seven; the gender of the author does not seem to affect the proportion.

8.68. We have $\hat{p}_1 = \frac{28}{53} \doteq 0.5283$, $\hat{p}_2 = \frac{10}{50} = 0.2$, and $\hat{p} = \frac{38}{103} \doteq 0.3689$, so $\text{SE}_{D_p} \doteq 0.09513$ and $z = 3.45$. It is reasonable to expect that older children would be better at sorting, so we use the one-sided alternative $p_1 > p_2$, for which $P = 0.0006$. (Of course, this test statistic is significant even with a two-sided alternative.) For a 90% confidence interval, $\text{SE}_D \doteq 0.08889$ and the interval is 0.1821 to 0.4745. (The plus four interval is 0.1710 to 0.4604.)

8.69. The standard error is $\text{SE}_{\hat{p}} \doteq \sqrt{(0.43)(0.57)/1006} \doteq 0.01561$, so the margin of error for 95% confidence is $1.96\,\text{SE}_{\hat{p}} \doteq 0.03059$, or about ± 0.0306.

Because the sample sizes are equal, $\hat{p} = 0.405$, the average of the two proportions. (Alternatively, take $X_1 \doteq (0.38)(1006) = 382.28$ and $X_2 \doteq (0.43)(1006) = 432.58$.) Then $\text{SE}_{D_p} \doteq 0.02189$ and $z = -2.28$, for which $P = 0.0223$ (with a two-sided alternative). For a 95% confidence interval, $\text{SE}_D \doteq 0.02186$ and the interval is -0.0928 to -0.0072.

8.70. (a) $\hat{p} = \frac{411}{875} \doteq 0.4697$, $\text{SE}_D \doteq 0.01687$, and the 95% confidence interval is 0.4366 to 0.5028. (The plus four interval is 0.4369 to 0.5028.) (b) Expressed as percents, the confidence interval is 43.66% to 50.28% (plus four: 43.69% to 50.28%). (c) Multiply the upper and lower limits of the confidence interval by 37,000: about 16,156 to 18,603 students (plus four: 16,159 to 18,600 students).

8.72. (a) H_0: $p_1 = p_2$; H_a: $p_1 \neq p_2$. $\hat{p}_1 = \frac{28}{82} \doteq 0.3415$, $\hat{p}_2 = \frac{30}{78} \doteq 0.3846$, and

$\hat{p} = \frac{58}{160} \doteq 0.3625$, so $SE_D \doteq 0.07603$ and $z \doteq -0.57$. For the two-sided alternative, this gives $P = 0.5687$. **(b)** Gastric freezing is not significantly more (or less) effective than a placebo treatment.

8.73. The difference becomes more significant (i.e., the P-value decreases) as the sample size increases. For small sample sizes, the difference between $\hat{p}_1 = 0.6$ and $\hat{p}_2 = 0.5$ is not significant, but with larger sample sizes, we expect that the sample proportions should be better estimates of their respective population proportions, so $\hat{p}_1 - \hat{p}_2 = 0.1$ suggests that $p_1 \neq p_2$.

n	z	P
10	0.45	0.6527
20	0.64	0.5222
40	0.90	0.3681
50	1.01	0.3125
80	1.27	0.2041
100	1.42	0.1556
500	3.18	0.0015
1000	4.49	0.0000

8.74. Shown are both the large sample (m.e.$_{.large}$, "●" in the graph) and plus four (m.e.$_{.+4}$, "○" in the graph) margins of error. The plus four method is better for $n = 10$ and $n = 20$, which do not meet the text's recommendations for the large sample method; for larger n, either method can be used. The graph illustrates how the two methods give very similar answers for $n \geq 50$.

n	m.e.$_{.large}$	m.e.$_{.+4}$
10	0.4339	0.3973
20	0.3068	0.2930
40	0.2169	0.2119
50	0.1940	0.1904
80	0.1534	0.1516
100	0.1372	0.1359
500	0.0614	0.0612
1000	0.0434	0.0433

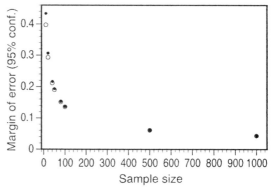

8.75. Shown are both the large sample (m.e.$_{.large}$, "●" in the graph) and plus four (m.e.$_{.+4}$, "○" in the graph) margins of error. The plus four method is better for $n = 10$, which does not meet the text's recommendations for the large sample method; for larger n, either method can be used. The graph illustrates how the two methods give very similar answers for $n \geq 50$. Also note that the margins of error in this "worst case" are not very different from those for the case $\hat{p}_1 = 0.6$ and $\hat{p}_2 = 0.5$ in the previous exercise.

n	m.e.$_{.large}$	m.e.$_{.+4}$
10	0.4383	0.4001
20	0.3099	0.2955
40	0.2191	0.2138
50	0.1960	0.1922
80	0.1549	0.1530
100	0.1386	0.1372
500	0.0620	0.0619
1000	0.0438	0.0438

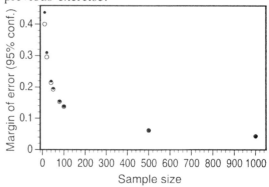

8.76. (a) From the previous exercise, we see that n is between 100 and 500. Using either trial and error, or the formula derived in part (b), we find that $n \geq 193$ is needed.

(b) Generally, the margin of error is $m = z^* \sqrt{\dfrac{\hat{p}_1(1-\hat{p}_1)}{n} + \dfrac{\hat{p}_2(1-\hat{p}_2)}{n}}$; with $\hat{p}_1 = \hat{p}_2 = 0.5$, this is $m = z^* \sqrt{0.5/n}$. Solving for n, we find $n = (z^*/m)^2/2$.

8.77. (a) $p_0 = \dfrac{143.611}{181.535} \doteq 0.7911$. **(b)** $\hat{p} = \dfrac{339}{870} \doteq 0.3897$, $\sigma_{\hat{p}} \doteq 0.0138$, and $z = (\hat{p} - p_0)/\sigma_{\hat{p}} \doteq -29.1$, so $P \doteq 0$ (regardless of whether H_a is $p > p_0$ or $p \neq p_0$). This is very strong evidence against H_0; we conclude that Mexican Americans are underrepresented on juries. **(c)** $\hat{p}_1 = \dfrac{339}{870} \doteq 0.3897$, while $\hat{p}_2 = \dfrac{143.611 - 339}{181.535 - 870} \doteq 0.7930$. Then $\hat{p} \doteq 0.7911$ (the value of p_0 from part (a)), $\mathrm{SE}_{D_p} \doteq 0.01382$, and $z \doteq -29.2$—and again, we have a tiny P-value and reject H_0.

8.79. In each case, the standard error is $\sqrt{\hat{p}(1 - \hat{p})/1280}$. One observation is that, while many feel that loans are a burden and wish they had borrowed less, a majority are satisfied with the benefits they receive from their education.

	$\hat{p}$	$\mathrm{SE}_{\hat{p}}$	95% confidence interval
Burdened by debt	0.555	0.01389	0.5278 to 0.5822
Would borrow less	0.544	0.01392	0.5167 to 0.5713
More hardship	0.343	0.01327	0.3170 to 0.3690
Loans worth it	0.589	0.01375	0.5620 to 0.6160
Career opportunities	0.589	0.01375	0.5620 to 0.6160
Personal growth	0.715	0.01262	0.6903 to 0.7397

Chapter 9 Solutions

9.1. (a) There are about 3,388,000 full-time college students aged 15 to 19. (Note that numbers are in thousands.) **(b)** The joint distribution is found by dividing each number in the table by 16,388 (the total of all the numbers). These proportions are given in italics on the right. For example, $\frac{3388}{16388} \doteq 0.2067$, meaning that about 20.7% of all college students are full-time and aged 15 to 19. **(c)** The marginal distribution of age is found by dividing the *row* totals by 16,388; they are in the right margin of the table,

	FT	PT	
15–19	3388	389	3777
	0.2067	*0.0237*	*0.2305*
20–24	5238	1164	6402
	0.3196	*0.0710*	*0.3907*
25–34	1703	1699	3402
	0.1039	*0.1037*	*0.2076*
35+	762	2045	2807
	0.0465	*0.1248*	*0.1713*
	11091	5297	16388
	0.6768	0.3232	

and the graph on the left below. For example, $\frac{3777}{16388} \doteq 0.2305$, meaning that about 23% of all college students are aged 15 to 19. **(d)** The marginal distribution of status is found by dividing the *column* totals by 16,388; they are in the bottom margin of the table, and the graph on the right below. For example, $\frac{11091}{16388} \doteq 0.6768$, meaning that about 67.7% of all college students are full-time.

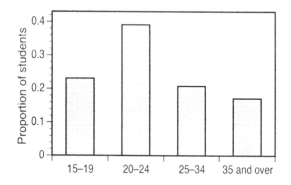
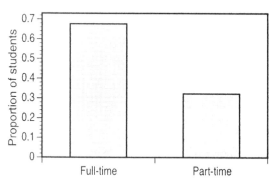

9.2. Refer to the counts in the solution to Exercise 9.1. For each age category, the conditional distribution of status is found by dividing the counts in that row by that row total. For example, $\frac{3388}{3777} \doteq 0.8970$ and $\frac{389}{3777} \doteq 0.1030$, meaning that of all college students in the 15–19 age range, about 89.7% are full-time, and the rest (10.3%) are part-time. Note that each pair of numbers should add to 1 (except for rounding error, but with only two numbers, that rarely happens). Graphical presentations may vary; one possibility is shown below. We see that the older the students are, the more likely they are to be part-time.

	FT	PT
15–19	0.8970	0.1030
20–24	0.8182	0.1818
25–34	0.5006	0.4994
35+	0.2715	0.7285

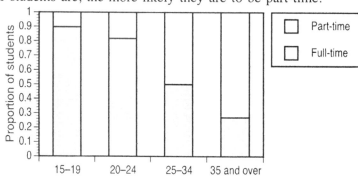

9.3. Refer to the counts in the solution to Exercise 9.1. For each status category, the conditional distribution of age is found by dividing the counts in that column by that column total. For example, $\frac{3388}{11091} \doteq 0.3055$, $\frac{5238}{11091} \doteq 0.4723$, etc., meaning that of all full-time college students, about 30.55% are aged 15 to 19, 47.23% are 20 to 24, and so on. Note that each set of four numbers should add to 1 (except for rounding error). Graphical presentations may vary; one possibility is shown below. We see that full-time students are dominated by younger ages, while part-time students are more likely to be older. (This is essentially the same observation made in the previous exercise, seen from a different viewpoint.)

	FT	PT
15–19	0.3055	0.0734
20–24	0.4723	0.2197
25–34	0.1535	0.3207
35+	0.0687	0.3861

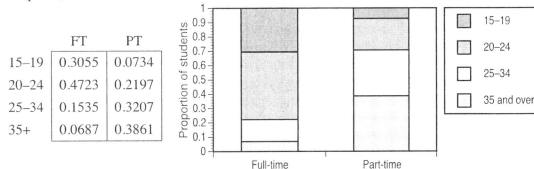

9.4. **(a)** There are about 890,000 male recent high school graduates aged 16 to 24 years enrolled full-time in two-year colleges. **(b)** The marginal distribution of gender is found by dividing the *column* totals by 10,421 (the grand total for the table); they are in the bottom margin of the table, and the graph on the left below. For example, $\frac{4842}{10421} \doteq 0.4646$, meaning that about 46.5% of all these students are men. **(c)** The marginal distribution of status is found by dividing the *row* totals by 10,421; they are in the right margin of the table, and the graph on the right below. For example, $\frac{1859}{10421} \doteq 0.1784$, meaning that about 17.8% of these students are enrolled full-time in two-year colleges.

	Men	Women	
2yr FT	890	969	1859
			0.1784
2yr PT	340	403	743
			0.0713
4yr FT	2897	3321	6218
			0.5967
4yr PT	249	383	632
			0.0606
Grad	306	366	672
			0.0645
Voc	160	137	297
			0.0285
	4842	5579	10421
	0.4646	0.5354	

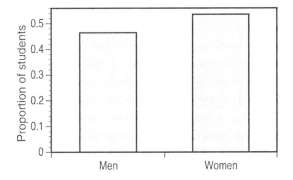

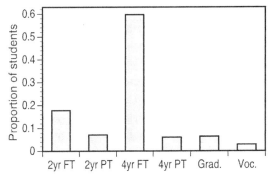

9.5. Refer to the counts in the solution to Exercise 9.4. For each status, the conditional distribution of gender is found by dividing the counts in that row by that row total. For example, $\frac{890}{1859} \doteq 0.4788$ and $\frac{969}{1859} \doteq 0.5212$, meaning that of all full-time students at two-year colleges, about 47.9% are men, and the rest (52.1%) are women. Note that each pair of numbers should add to 1 (except for rounding error, but with only two numbers, that rarely happens). Graphical presentations may vary; one possibility is shown below. We see that women make up the majority of all groups except for vocational school students.

	Men	Women
2-yr FT	0.4788	0.5212
2-yr PT	0.4576	0.5424
4-yr FT	0.4659	0.5341
4-yr PT	0.3940	0.6060
Grad.	0.4554	0.5446
Voc.	0.5387	0.4613

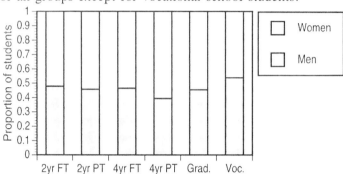

9.6. Refer to the counts in the solution to Exercise 9.4. For each gender, the conditional distribution of status is found by dividing the counts in that column by that column total. For example, $\frac{890}{4842} \doteq 0.1838$, $\frac{340}{4842} \doteq 0.0702$, etc., meaning that of all male college students, about 18.38% are enrolled full-time in two-year colleges, 7.02% are attending a two-year college part-time, and so on. Note that each set of six numbers should add to 1 (except for rounding error). Graphical presentations may vary; one possibility is shown below. We see that there is little difference between genders in the distribution of status: The percentages of men and women in each status category are quite similar.

	Men	Women
2-yr FT	0.1838	0.1737
2-yr PT	0.0702	0.0722
4-yr FT	0.5983	0.5953
4-yr PT	0.0514	0.0687
Grad.	0.0632	0.0656
Voc.	0.0330	0.0246

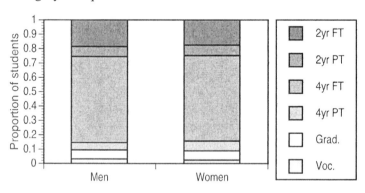

9.7. Two examples are shown on the right. In general, choose a to be any number from 0 to 200, and then all the other entries can be determined.

50	150
150	50

175	25
25	175

   Note: *This is why we say that such a table has "one degree of freedom": We can make one (nearly) arbitrary choice for the value of a, and then have no more decisions to make.*

9.8. To construct such a table, we can start by choosing values for the row and column sums $r1, r2, r3, c1, c2, c3$, as well as the grand total N. Note that the $N = r1 + r2 + r3 = c1 + c2 + c3$, so we only have five choices to make. Then find each count $a, b, c, d, e, f, g, h, i$ by taking the corresponding *row* total, times the corresponding *column* total, divided by the *grand* total. For example, $a = r1 \times c1/N$ and $f = r2 \times c3/N$. Of course, these counts should be whole numbers, so it may be necessary to make adjustments in the row and column totals to meet this requirement.

a	b	c	r1
d	e	f	r2
g	h	i	r3
c1	c2	c3	N

The simplest such table would have all nine counts $a, b, c, d, e, f, g, h, i$ equal to one another.

9.9. (a) $\frac{125+155+180}{900} = 51.1\%$ did not respond.

(b) $\frac{125}{300} \doteq 41.7\%$ of small businesses, $\frac{155}{300} \doteq$ 51.7% of medium-sized businesses, and $\frac{180}{300} = 60.0\%$ of large businesses did not respond. Generally, the larger the business, the less likely it is to respond. **(c)** At right. **(d)** Of the 440 total responses, $\frac{175}{440} \doteq 39.8\%$ came from small businesses, $\frac{145}{440} \doteq 33.0\%$ from medium-sized businesses, and $\frac{120}{440} \doteq$ 27.3% from large businesses. **(e)** No: Almost 40% of respondents were small businesses, while just over a quarter of all responses come from large businesses.

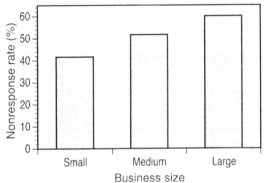

9.10. (a) Use column percents, e.g., $\frac{68}{225} \doteq 30.22\%$ of females are in administration. See table and graph below. The biggest difference between women and men is in Administration: a higher percentage of women chose this major. Meanwhile, a greater proportion of men chose other fields, especially Finance. **(b)** There were 386 responses; $\frac{336}{722} \doteq 46.5\%$ did not respond.

	Female	Male	Overall
Accting.	30.22%	34.78%	32.12%
Admin.	40.44%	24.843%	33.94%
Econ.	2.22%	3.7%	2.85%
Fin.	27.11%	36.65%	31.09%

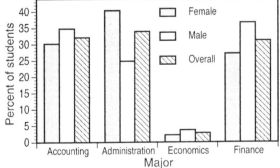

9.11. $\frac{14}{24} \doteq 58.33\%$ of desipramine users did
not have a relapse, while $\frac{6}{24} = 25\%$ of
lithium users and $\frac{4}{24} \doteq 16.67\%$ of those
who received placebos succeeded in breaking
their addictions. Desipramine seems to be
effective. Note that use of percentages is not
as crucial here as in other cases because each
drug was given to 24 addicts.

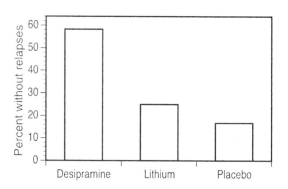

9.12. Compute column percents, e.g.,
$\frac{61,941}{355,265} \doteq 17.44\%$ of those U.S. degrees
considered in this table are in engineer-
ing. See table and graph at right. We
observe that there are considerably more
social science degrees, and fewer engineering degrees, in the U.S. The Western
Europe and Asia distributions are similar.

Field	United States	Western Europe	Asia	Overall
Eng.	17.44%	38.26%	36.96%	32.78%
Nat. sci.	31.29%	33.73%	31.97%	32.29%
Soc. sci.	51.28%	28.01%	31.07%	34.93%

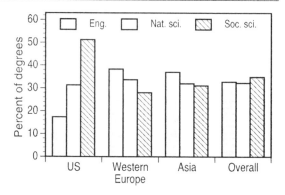

9.13. (a) Different graphical presentations are possible; one is shown below. More women
perform volunteer work; the notably higher percentage of women who are "strictly
voluntary" participants accounts for the difference. (The "court-ordered" and "other"
percentages are similar for men and women.) **(b)** Either by adding the three "participant"
categories, or by subtracting from 100% the non-participant percentage, we find that 40.3%
of men and 51.3% of women are participants. The relative risk of being a volunteer is
therefore $\frac{51.3\%}{40.3\%} \doteq 1.27$.

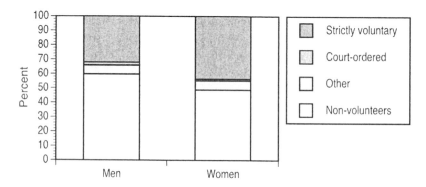

9.14. Table shown on the right; for example, $\frac{31.9\%}{40.3\%} \doteq$
79.16%. The percents in each row sum to 100%,
with no rounding error for up to four places after
the decimal. Both this graph and the graph in the

Gender	Strictly voluntary	Court-ordered	Other
Men	79.16%	5.21%	15.63%
Women	85.19%	2.14%	12.67%

previous exercise show that women are more likely to volunteer, but in this view we cannot
see the difference in the rate of non-participation.

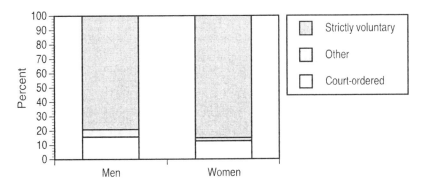

9.15. **(a)** At right. **(b)** $\frac{490}{800} = 61.25\%$ of male applicants are admitted, while only $\frac{400}{700} \doteq 57.14\%$ of females are admitted.

	Admit	Deny
Male	490	310
Female	400	300

(c) $\frac{400}{600} \doteq 66.67\%$ of male business school applicants are admit-
ted; for females, this rate is the same: $\frac{200}{300} \doteq 66.67\%$. In the law school, $\frac{90}{200} = 45\%$ of males
are admitted, compared with $\frac{200}{400} = 50\%$ of females. **(d)** A majority (6/7) of male applicants
apply to the business school, which admits $\frac{400+200}{600+300} \doteq 66.67\%$ of all applicants. Meanwhile,
a majority (3/5) of women apply to the law school, which admits only $\frac{90+200}{200+400} \doteq 48.33\%$ of
its applicants.

9.16. Tables will vary, of course. The key idea is that one gender should be more likely to
apply to the schools that are easier to get into. For example, if the four schools admit 50%,
60%, 70%, and 80% of applicants, and men are more likely to apply to the first two, while
women apply to the latter two, women will be admitted more often.

A nice variation on this exercise is to describe two basketball teams practicing. You
observe that one team makes 50% of their shots, while the other makes only 40%. Does that
mean the first team is more accurate? Not necessarily; perhaps they attempted more lay-ups
while the other team spent more time shooting three-pointers. (Some students will latch onto
this kind of example much more quickly than discussions of male/female admission rates.)

9.17. If we ignore the "year" classification, we see that Department A teaches 32 small classes out of 52, or about 61.54%, while Department B teaches 42 small classes out of 106, or about 39.62%. (These agree with the dean's numbers.)

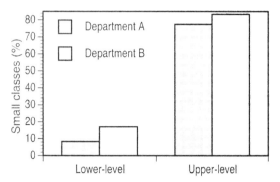

For the report to the dean, students may analyze the numbers in a variety of ways, some valid and some not. The key observations are: (i) When considering only first- and second-year classes, A has fewer small classes ($\frac{1}{12} \doteq 8.33\%$) than B ($\frac{12}{70} \doteq 17.14\%$). Likewise, when considering only upper-level classes, A has $\frac{31}{40} = 77.5\%$ and B has $\frac{30}{36} \doteq 83.33\%$ small classes. The graph on the right illustrates this. These numbers are given in the back of the text, so most students should include this in their analysis! (ii) $\frac{40}{52} \doteq 77.78\%$ of A's classes are upper-level courses, compared to $\frac{36}{106} \doteq 33.96\%$ of B's classes.

9.18. (a) df $= (r-1)(c-1) = (3)(4) = 12$, and $0.005 < P < 0.01$ ($P = 0.00996$).
(b) df $= (r-1)(c-1) = (3)(2) = 6$, and $P < 0.0005$ ($P = 0.0002$).
(c) df $= (r-1)(c-1) = (4)(3) = 12$, and $0.005 < P < 0.01$ ($P = 0.00996$).
(d) df $= (r-1)(c-1) = (6)(5) = 30$, and $P > 0.25$ ($P = 0.6633$).

9.19. (a) df $= (r-1)(c-1) = (1)(1) = 1$, and $P > 0.25$ ($P = 0.2524$).
(b) df $= (r-1)(c-1) = (3)(3) = 9$, and $0.025 < P < 0.05$ ($P = 0.0409$).
(c) df $= (r-1)(c-1) = (1)(7) = 7$, and $0.001 < P < 0.0025$ ($P = 0.0024$).
(d) df $= (r-1)(c-1) = (4)(2) = 8$, and $0.10 < P < 0.15$ ($P = 0.1260$).

9.20. (a) The best numerical summary would note that we view target audience ("magazine readership") as explanatory, so we should compute the conditional distribution of model dress for each audience. This table and graph are shown below.
(b) Minitab output is shown on the right: $X^2 \doteq 80.9$, df $= 2$, and P is very small. We have very strong evidence that target audience affects model dress. **(c)** The sample is not an SRS: A set of magazines were chosen, and then all

Minitab output

	Women	Men	Genl	Total
1	351	514	248	1113
	424.84	456.56	231.60	
2	225	105	66	396
	151.16	162.44	82.40	
Total	576	619	314	1509

```
ChiSq = 12.835 +  7.227 +  1.162 +
        36.074 + 20.312 +  3.265 = 80.874
df = 2,  p = 0.000
```

ads in three issues of those magazines were examined. It is not clear how this sampling approach might invalidate our conclusions, but it does make them suspect.

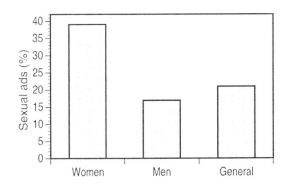

Model dress	Magazine readership		
	Women	Men	General
Not sexual	60.94%	83.04%	78.98%
Sexual	39.06%	16.96%	21.02%

9.21. (a) As the conditional distribution of model dress for each age group has been given to us, it only remains to display this distribution graphically. One such presentation is shown below. **(b)** In order to perform the significance test, we must first recover the counts from the percents. For example, there were $(0.723)(1006) \doteq 727$ non-sexual ads in young adult magazines. The remainder of these counts can be seen in the Minitab output below, where we see $X^2 \doteq 2.59$, df $= 1$, and $P \doteq 0.108$—not enough evidence to conclude that age group affects model dress.

Minitab output

```
          Young    Mature    Total
     1      727       383     1110
          740.00    370.00

     2      279       120      399
          266.00    133.00

 Total     1006       503     1509

ChiSq =  0.228 +  0.457 +
         0.635 +  1.271 = 2.591
 df = 1, p = 0.108
```

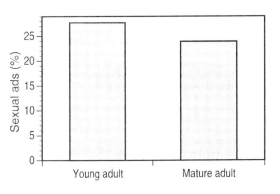

9.22. (a) Subtract the "agreed" counts from the sample sizes to get the "disagreed" counts. The table is in the Minitab output on the right. (The output has been slightly altered to have more descriptive row and column headings.) We find $X^2 \doteq 2.67$, df $= 1$, $P = 0.103$, so we cannot conclude that students and non-students differ in the response to this question. **(b)** For testing $H_0: p_1 = p_2$ vs. $H_a: p_1 \neq p_2$, we have $\hat{p}_1 \doteq 0.3607$, $\hat{p}_2 \doteq 0.5085$, $\hat{p} \doteq 0.4333$, $SE_{D_p} \doteq 0.09048$, and $z = -1.63$. Up to rounding,

Minitab output

```
           Students   Non-st    Total
  Agr          22        30        52
             26.43     25.57

  Dis          39        29        68
             34.57     33.43

 Total         61        59       120

ChiSq =  0.744 +  0.769 +
         0.569 +  0.588 = 2.669
 df = 1, p = 0.103
```

$z^2 = X^2$, and the P-values are the same. **(c)** The statistical tests in (a) and (b) assume that we have two SRSs, which we clearly do not have here. Furthermore, the two groups differed in geography (northeast/West Coast) in addition to student/non-student classification. These issues mean we should not place too much confidence in the conclusions of our significance test—or, at least, we should not generalize our conclusions too far beyond the populations "upper level northeastern college students taking a course in Internet marketing" and "West Coast residents willing to participate in commercial focus groups."

9.23. (a) First we must find the counts in each cell of the two-way table. For example, there were about $(0.172)(5619) \doteq 966$ Division I athletes who admitted to wagering. These counts are shown in the Minitab output on the right, where we see that $X^2 \doteq 76.7$, df $= 2$, and $P < 0.0001$. There is very strong evidence that the percentage of athletes who admit to wagering

Minitab output

	Div1	Div2	Div3	Total
1	966	621	998	2585
	1146.87	603.54	834.59	
2	4653	2336	3091	10080
	4472.13	2353.46	3254.41	
Total	5619	2957	4089	12665

ChiSq = 28.525 + 0.505 + 31.996 +
            7.315 + 0.130 + 8.205 = 76.675
df = 2, p = 0.000

differs by division. **(b)** Even with much smaller numbers of students (say, 1000 from each division), P is still very small. Presumably the estimated numbers are reliable enough that we would not expect the true counts to be less than 1000, so we need not be concerned about the fact that we had to estimate the sample sizes. **(c)** If the reported proportions are wrong, then our conclusions may be suspect—especially if it is the case that athletes in some division were more likely to say they had not wagered when they had. **(d)** It is difficult to predict exactly how this might affect the results: Lack of independence could cause the estimated percents to be too large, or too small, if our sample included several athletes from teams which have (or do not have) a "gambling culture."

9.24. (a) The missing entries (shown shaded on the right) are found by subtracting the mutation counts from the total. **(b)** $\frac{30}{96} = 31.25\%$ of steel-mill rats and $\frac{23}{150} \doteq 15.33\%$ of rural rats showed mutation at the *Hm-2* gene locus. **(c)** The Minitab output below

	Location	
Mutation	Steel-mill air	Rural air
Yes	30	23
No	66	127
Total	96	150

shows $X^2 \doteq 8.773$, df $= 1$, $P \doteq 0.003$—strong evidence that location and mutation occurrence are related.

Minitab output

	Mill	Rural	Total
1	30	23	53
	20.68	32.32	
2	66	127	193
	75.32	117.68	
Total	96	150	246

ChiSq = 4.197 + 2.686 +
            1.153 + 0.738 = 8.773
df = 1, p = 0.003

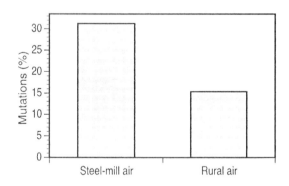

9.25. The Minitab output on the right shows both the two-way table (column and row headings have been changed to be more descriptive) and the results for the significance test: $X^2 \doteq 12.0$, df $= 1$, $P = 0.001$, so we conclude that gender and flower choice are related. The count of 0 does not invalidate the test: Our smallest expected count is 6, while the text says that "for 2×2 tables, we require that all four expected cell counts be 5 or more."

Minitab output

	Female	Male	Total
bihai	20	0	20
	14.00	6.00	
no	29	21	50
	35.00	15.00	
Total	49	21	70

ChiSq = 2.571 + 6.000 +
        1.029 + 2.400 = 12.000
df = 1, p = 0.001

9.26. The graph on the right depicts the conditional distribution of domain type for each journal; for example, in *NEJM*, $\frac{41}{97} \doteq 42.27\%$ of Internet references were to .gov domains, $\frac{37}{97} \doteq 38.14\%$ were to .org domains, and so on. The (slightly altered) Minitab output shows the expected counts, which tell a story similar to the bar graph, and show that the relationship between journal and domain type is significant ($X^2 \doteq 56.12$, df $= 8$, $P < 0.0005$).

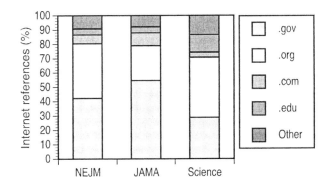

Minitab output

	NEJM	JAMA	Science	Total
.gov	41	103	111	255
	36.81	71.72	146.47	
.org	37	46	162	245
	35.36	68.91	140.73	
.com	6	17	14	37
	5.34	10.41	21.25	
.edu	4	8	47	59
	8.52	16.59	33.89	
other	9	15	52	76
	10.97	21.37	43.65	
Total	97	189	386	672

ChiSq = 0.477 + 13.644 + 8.591 +
        0.076 + 7.615 + 3.215 +
        0.081 + 4.178 + 2.475 +
        2.395 + 4.451 + 5.072 +
        0.354 + 1.901 + 1.595 = 56.120
df = 8, p = 0.000

9.27. The graph on the right depicts the conditional distribution of pet ownership for each education level; for example, among those who did not finish high school, $\frac{421}{542} \doteq 77.68\%$ owned no pets, $\frac{93}{542} \doteq 17.16\%$ owned dogs, and $\frac{28}{542} \doteq 5.17\%$ (the rest) owned cats. (One could instead compute column percents—the conditional distribution of education for each pet-ownership group—but education level makes more sense as the explanatory variable here.) The (slightly altered) Minitab output shows that the relationship between education level and pet ownership is significant ($X^2 \doteq 23.15$, df = 4, $P < 0.0005$). Specifically, dog owners have less education, and cat owners more, than we would expect if there were no relationship between pet ownership and educational level.

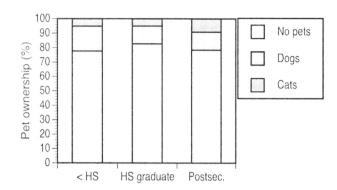

Minitab output

	None	Dogs	Cats	Total
<HS	421	93	28	542
	431.46	73.25	37.29	
HS	666	100	40	806
	641.61	108.93	55.46	
>HS	845	135	99	1079
	858.93	145.82	74.25	
Total	1932	328	167	2427

ChiSq = 0.253 + 5.326 + 2.316 +
        0.927 + 0.732 + 4.310 +
        0.226 + 0.803 + 8.254 = 23.147
df = 4, p = 0.000

9.28. The graph on the right depicts the conditional distribution of pet ownership for each gender; for example, among females, $\frac{1024}{1266} \doteq 80.88\%$ owned no pets, $\frac{157}{1266} \doteq 12.40\%$ owned dogs, and $\frac{85}{1266} \doteq 6.71\%$ (the rest) owned cats. (One could instead compute column percents—the conditional distribution of gender for each pet-ownership group—but gender makes more sense as the explanatory variable here.) The (slightly altered) Minitab output shows that the relationship between education level and pet ownership is *not* significant ($X^2 \doteq 2.838$, df = 2, $P = 0.242$).

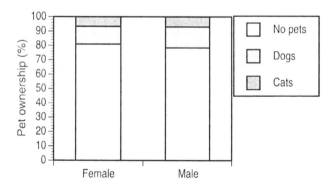

Minitab output

	None	Dogs	Cats	Total
Female	1024	157	85	1266
	1008.53	170.60	86.86	
Male	915	171	82	1168
	930.47	157.40	80.14	
Total	1939	328	167	2434

ChiSq = 0.237 + 1.085 + 0.040 +
        0.257 + 1.176 + 0.043 = 2.838
df = 2, p = 0.242

9.29. The missing entries can be seen in the "Other" column of the Minitab output below; they are found by subtracting the engineering, management, and liberal arts counts from each row total. The graph on the right shows the conditional distribution of transfer area for each initial major; for example, of those initially majoring in biology, $\frac{13}{398} \doteq 3.27\%$ transferred to engineering, $\frac{25}{398} \doteq 6.28\%$ transferred to management, and so on. The relationship is significant ($X^2 \doteq 50.53$, df = 9, $P < 0.0005$). The largest contributions to X^2 come from chemistry or physics to engineering and biology to liberal arts (more transfers than expected), and biology to engineering and chemistry to liberal arts (fewer transfers than expected).

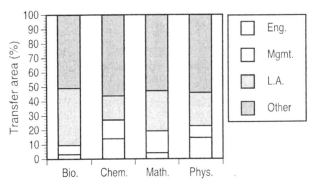

Minitab output

	Eng	Mgmt	LA	Other	Total
Bio	13	25	158	202	398
	25.30	34.56	130.20	207.95	
Chem	16	15	19	64	114
	7.25	9.90	37.29	59.56	
Math	3	11	20	38	72
	4.58	6.25	23.55	37.62	
Phys	9	5	14	33	61
	3.88	5.30	19.96	31.87	
Total	41	56	211	337	645

ChiSq = 5.979 + 2.642 + 5.937 + 0.170 +
        10.574 + 2.630 + 8.973 + 0.331 +
        0.543 + 3.608 + 0.536 + 0.004 +
        6.767 + 0.017 + 1.777 + 0.040 = 50.527
df = 9, p = 0.000

9.30. (a) At right. The entries on the first line are computed as $\hat{p} = \frac{16}{601} \doteq 0.0266$ and $\sigma_{\hat{p}} = \sqrt{\hat{p}(1 - \hat{p})/601} \doteq 0.00657$, and the second line is found in a similar way. **(b)** The expected counts are in the Minitab output on the right. There we see $X^2 \doteq 27.10$, df = 1, and $P < 0.0005$, so we conclude that there is an association between age and whether or not the employee was terminated—specifically, older employees were more likely to be terminated.

Over 40?	n	Proportion terminated	Standard error
No	601	0.0266	0.00657
Yes	853	0.0961	0.01009

Minitab output

	Under40	Over40	Total
Term	16	82	98
	40.51	57.49	
Not	585	771	1356
	560.49	795.51	
Total	601	853	1454

ChiSq = 14.827 + 10.447 +
        1.072 + 0.755 = 27.101
df = 1, p = 0.000

9.31. The analysis might include, for example, expected counts and column percents (shown in the table). We note that older employees are almost twice as likely as under-40 employees to fall into the two lowest performance appraisal categories (partially/fully meets expectations), and are only about one-third as likely to have the highest appraisal. The differences in the percentages are significant:

	Under 40	Over 40	
Partially/ fully meets expectations	82 126.79 16.33%	237 192.21 31.14%	319 25.26%
Usually exceeds expectations	357 337.45 71.12%	492 511.55 64.65%	849 67.22%
Continually exceeds expectations	63 37.76 12.55%	32 57.24 4.20%	95 7.52%
	502	761	1263

$X^2 = 15.824 + 10.438 + 1.133 + 0.747 + 16.872 + 11.130 = 56.144$ (df = 2) has $P < 0.0005$.

9.32. (a) The null hypothesis is $H_0: p_1 = p_2$, where p_1 and p_2 are the proportions of women customers in each city. $\hat{p}_1 = \frac{203}{241} \doteq 0.8423$, $\hat{p}_2 = \frac{150}{218} \doteq 0.6881$, and $\hat{p} = \frac{203+150}{241+218} \doteq 0.7691$, so $SE_{D_p} \doteq 0.03939$, $z = 3.92$, and $P = 0.0001$.
(b) $X^2 \doteq 15.334$, which equals z^2. With df = 1, Table F tells us that $P < 0.0005$. **(c)** For a confidence interval, we compute $SE_D \doteq 0.03919$, and the 95% confidence interval is $0.1543 \pm 0.0768 \doteq 0.0774$ to 0.2311. Using the plus four method: $\tilde{p}_1 \doteq 0.8395$ and $\tilde{p}_2 \doteq 0.6864$, $SE_D \doteq 0.03915$, and the interval is $0.1531 \pm 0.0767 \doteq 0.0764$ to 0.2299.

Minitab output

	City1	City2	Total
M	38 55.66	68 50.34	106
W	203 185.34	150 167.66	353
Total	241	218	459

ChiSq = 5.601 + 6.192 +
        1.682 + 1.859 = 15.334
df = 1, p = 0.000

9.33. With $X^2 = 3.955$ and df $= (5-1)(2-1) = 4$, Table F tells us that $P > 0.25$ (or, with software, we find that $P = 0.413$). There is little evidence to make us believe that there is a relationship between city and income.

9.34. Note that the given counts actually form a three-way table (classified by adhesive, side, and checks). Therefore, this analysis should *not* be done as if the counts come from a 2×4 two-way table; for one thing, no conditional distribution will answer the question of interest (how to avoid face checks). Nonetheless, many students may do this analysis, for which they will find $X^2 = 6.798$, df $= 3$, and $P = 0.079$.

	Face checks	
	No	Yes
PVA/loose	10	54
PVA/tight	44	20
UF/loose	21	43
UF/tight	37	27

A better approach is to rearrange the table as shown on the right. The conditional distributions across the rows will then give us information about avoiding face checks; the graph below illustrates this. We find $X^2 \doteq 45.08$, df $= 3$, and $P < 0.0005$, so we conclude that the appearance of face checks is related to the adhesive/side combination—specifically, we recommend the PVA/tight combination.

Another approach (not quite as good as the previous one) is to perform two separate analyses—say, one for loose side, and one for tight side. These computations show that UF is better than PVA for loose side ($X^2 \doteq 5.151$, df $= 1$, $P = 0.023$), but there is no significant difference for tight side ($X^2 \doteq 1.647$, df $= 1$, $P = 0.200$). We could also do separate analyses for PVA ($X^2 \doteq 37.029$, df $= 1$, $P < 0.0005$) and UF ($X^2 \doteq 8.071$, df $= 1$, $P = 0.005$), from which we conclude that for either adhesive, the tight side has fewer face checks.

Minitab output

	NoChk	Chk	Total
PVA-L	10	54	64
	28.00	36.00	
PVA-T	44	20	64
	28.00	36.00	
UF-L	21	43	64
	28.00	36.00	
UF-T	37	27	64
	28.00	36.00	
Total	112	144	256

ChiSq = 11.571 + 9.000 +
        9.143 + 7.111 +
        1.750 + 1.361 +
        2.893 + 2.250 = 45.079
df = 3, p = 0.000

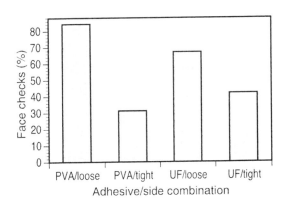

Minitab output

```
- - - - - - Loose side  - - - - - - -
          NoChk   Chk   Total
PVA        10      54     64
          15.50   48.50

UF         21      43     64
          15.50   48.50

Total      31      97    128

ChiSq =  1.952 +  0.624 +
         1.952 +  0.624 = 5.151
df = 1, p = 0.023
- - - - - - Tight side  - - - - - - -
          NoChk   Chk   Total
PVA        44      20     64
          40.50   23.50

UF         37      27     64
          40.50   23.50

Total      81      47    128

ChiSq =  0.302 +  0.521 +
         0.302 +  0.521 = 1.647
df = 1, p = 0.200
```

Minitab output

```
- - - - - - - PVA  - - - - - - - -
          NoChk   Chk   Total
Loose      10      54     64
          27.00   37.00

Tight      44      20     64
          27.00   37.00

Total      54      74    128

ChiSq = 10.704 +  7.811 +
        10.704 +  7.811 = 37.029
df = 1, p = 0.000
- - - - - - - UF  - - - - - - - -
          NoChk   Chk   Total
Loose      21      43     64
          29.00   35.00

Tight      37      27     64
          29.00   35.00

Total      58      70    128

ChiSq =  2.207 +  1.829 +
         2.207 +  1.829 = 8.071
df = 1, p = 0.005
```

9.35. (a) We should examine column percents, because we suspect that "source" is explanatory. These are given in the table (along with expected counts for the chi-square test). The test statistic for cats is

$$X^2 = 1.305 + 0.666 + 2.483$$
$$+ 0.632 + 0.323 + 1.202 = 6.611,$$

(df = 2, $P = 0.037$). For dogs,

$$X^2 = 0.569 + 9.423 + 9.369$$
$$+ 0.223 + 3.689 + 3.668 = 26.939,$$

(df = 2, $P < 0.0005$). The test is certainly significant for dogs, and is

Cats	Private	Pet store	Other	
Cases	124	16	76	216
	111.92	13.05	91.03	
	36.15%	40.00%	27.24%	32.63%
Control	219	24	203	446
	231.08	26.95	187.97	
	63.85%	60.00%	72.76%	67.37%
	343	40	279	662

Dogs	Private	Pet store	Other	
Cases	188	7	90	285
	198.63	21.10	65.27	
	26.63%	9.33%	38.79%	28.13%
Control	518	68	142	728
	507.37	53.90	166.73	
	73.37%	90.67%	61.21%	71.87%
	706	75	232	1013

significant at $\alpha = 0.05$ for cats. **(b)** Dogs from pet stores are less likely to go to a shelter, while "other source" dogs are more likely to go. Private-source cats were slightly more likely, and other-source cats slightly less likely, to be taken to the shelter. **(c)** The control group data should be reasonably like an SRS, because the sample was taken using a random-digit dialer. The cases data may be less like an SRS; this is difficult to judge. (For example, we would like to know, was this a sample of people who brought their pets to the shelter during a specific time period?)

9.36. (a) We view intervention (or prenotification) as explanatory, so we compute column percentages—that is, the conditional response distribution for each column. These are given in the tables, and shown in the graphs, below. **(b)** For intervention, $X^2 = 4.906 + 56.765 + 41.398 + 2.872 + 33.234 + 24.237 = 163.413$, df = 2, $P < 0.0005$. For prenotification, $X^2 = 0.461 + 0.460 + 0.497 + 0.496 = 1.914$, df = 1, $P = 0.167$. Intervention has a significant effect on response rates—specifically, letters and phone calls both increase the response rate, with the latter being more effective. Prenotification is not effective. **(c)** We might not be able to generalize these conclusions too widely; for example, the intervention result might not apply to non-students, or to students from other areas.

	Letter	Phone call	None	
Yes	171	146	118	435
	144.38	79.02	211.59	
	43.73%	68.22%	20.59%	36.93%
No	220	68	455	743
	246.62	134.98	361.41	
	56.27%	31.78%	79.41%	63.07%
	391	214	573	1178

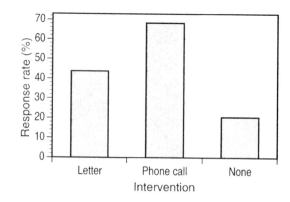

	Letter	No letter	
Yes	2570 2604.65 51.22%	2645 2610.35 52.59%	5215 51.91%
No	2448 2413.35 48.78%	2384 2418.65 47.41%	4832 48.09%
	5018	5029	10047

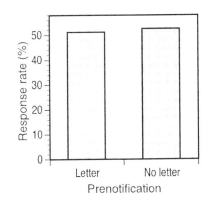

9.37. (a) For testing H_0: $p_1 = p_2$ vs. H_a: $p_1 \neq p_2$, we find $\hat{p}_1 = \frac{28}{82} \doteq 0.3415$, $\hat{p}_2 = \frac{30}{78} \doteq 0.3846$, and $\hat{p} = \frac{58}{160} = 0.3625$. Then $SE_{D_p} \doteq 0.07603$ and $z \doteq -0.5675$, so that $P = 0.5703$; there is no reason to believe that the proportions are different. **(b)** Table at right (with expected counts and column percents). To test H_0: There is no relationship between treatment and relief vs. H_a: There is a relationship, we find $X^2 = 0.322$ (which does equal z^2, up to rounding error), df $= 1$, $P = 0.570$. **(c)** Gastric freezing is not effective (or "is no more effective than a placebo").

	Gastric Freezing	Control	
Relief	28 29.73 34.15%	30 28.27 38.46%	58 36.25%
No relief	54 52.28 65.85%	48 49.72 61.54%	102 63.75%
	82	78	160

9.38. Since we suspect that student loans may explain career choice, we examine column percents (in the table below, left). We observe that those with loans are *slightly* more likely to be in Agriculture, Science, and Technology fields, and less likely to be in Management. However, the differences in the table are not significant: $X^2 = 6.525$, df $= 6$, $P = 0.368$.

For 9.38.

	Loan	No loan	
Agric.	32 8.7%	35 7.0%	67 7.7%
CDFS	37 10.1%	50 10.1%	87 10.1%
Eng.	98 26.6%	137 27.6%	235 27.2%
LA/Educ.	89 24.2%	124 24.9%	213 24.6%
Mgmt.	24 6.5%	51 10.3%	75 8.7%
Science	31 8.4%	29 5.8%	60 6.9%
Tech.	57 15.5%	71 14.3%	128 14.8%
	368	497	865

For 9.39.

	Low	Medium	High	
Agric.	5 13.5%	27 6.8%	35 8.2%	67 7.7%
CDFS	1 2.7%	32 8.0%	54 12.6%	87 10.1%
Eng.	12 32.4%	129 32.3%	94 22.0%	235 27.2%
LA/Educ.	7 18.9%	77 19.3%	129 30.1%	213 24.6%
Mgmt.	3 8.1%	44 11.0%	28 6.5%	75 8.7%
Science	7 18.9%	29 7.3%	24 5.6%	60 6.9%
Tech.	2 5.4%	62 15.5%	64 15.0%	128 14.8%
	37	400	428	865

9.39. For the table (above, right), $X^2 = 43.487$ (df $= 12$), so $P < 0.0005$, indicating that there is a relationship between PEOPLE score and field of study.

Science has a large proportion of low-scoring students, while liberal arts/education has a large percentage of high-scoring students. (These two table entries make the largest contributions to the value of X^2.)

9.40. **(a)** The 2×2 table is included in the Minitab output (below, left). **(b)** We find $X^2 \doteq 10.95$, df $= 1$, and $P = 0.001$, so we conclude that there is a relationship between gender and label use—specifically, women are more likely to be label users. **(c)** In Exercise 8.58, we found $z \doteq 3.31$, and (up to rounding) $z^2 = X^2$.

For 9.40.   *For 9.41.*

Minitab output   **Minitab output**

	Women	Men	Total
User	63	27	90
	48.70	41.30	
Non	233	224	457
	247.30	209.70	
Total	296	251	547

ChiSq = 4.198 + 4.950 +
         0.827 + 0.975 = 10.949
df = 1, p = 0.001

	Mex-Am	Other	Total
Juror	339	531	870
	688.25	181.75	
Not	143272	37393	180665
	142922.75	37742.25	
Total	143611	37924	181535

ChiSq =177.226 +671.122 +
          0.853 + 3.232 = 852.433
df = 1, p = 0.000

9.41. The Minitab output (above, right) shows the 2×2 table and significance test details: $X^2 = 852.433$, df $= 1$, $P < 0.0005$. Using $z = -29.2$, computed in the solution to Exercise 8.77(c), this equals z^2 (up to rounding).

9.42. Minitab outputs for both analyses are given below. For cats, $X^2 = 8.460$ (df $= 4$), which gives $P = 0.077$. We do not reject H_0 this time; with the 2×3 table, we had $P = 0.037$, so having more cells has "weakened" the evidence. For dogs: $X^2 = 33.208$ (df $= 4$), which gives $P < 0.0005$. The conclusion is the same as before: We reject H_0.

Minitab output

```
- - - - - - - - - - - - - - - - - - -  Cats  - - - - - - - - - - - - - - - - - - -
             Private    Store     Home    Stray   Shelter    Total
    Cases        124       16       20       38        18      216
              111.92    13.05    18.92    50.25     21.86

     Ctrl        219       24       38      116        49      446
              231.08    26.95    39.08   103.75     45.14

    Total        343       40       58      154        67      662
```

ChiSq = 1.305 + 0.666 + 0.061 + 2.985 + 0.682 +
        0.632 + 0.323 + 0.030 + 1.446 + 0.330 = 8.460
df = 4, p = 0.077

```
- - - - - - - - - - - - - - - - - - -  Dogs  - - - - - - - - - - - - - - - - - - -
             Private    Store     Home    Stray   Shelter    Total
    Cases        188        7       11       23        56      285
              198.63    21.10     8.72    21.94     34.61

     Ctrl        518       68       20       55        67      728
              507.37    53.90    22.28    56.06     88.39

    Total        706       75       31       78       123     1013
```

ChiSq = 0.569 + 9.423 + 0.595 + 0.051 + 13.228 +
        0.223 + 3.689 + 0.233 + 0.020 + 5.178 = 33.208
df = 4, p = 0.000

9.43. (a) The bar graph on the right shows how parental assessment of URIs compares for the two treatments. Note that parental assessment data were apparently not available for all URIs: We have assessments for 329 echinacea URIs and 367 placebo URIs. Minitab output gives $X^2 = 2.506$, df = 2, $P = 0.286$, so treatment is not significantly associated with parental assessment. **(b)** If we divide each echinacea count by 337 and each placebo count by 370, we obtain the table of proportions (below, left), and illustrated in the bar graph (below, right). **(c)** The only significant results are for rash ($z = 2.74$, $P = 0.0061$), drowsiness ($z = 2.09$, $P = 0.0366$), and other ($z = 2.09$, $P = 0.0366$). A 10×2 table would not be appropriate, because each URI could have multiple adverse events. **(d)** All results are unfavorable to echinacea, so in this situation we are not concerned that we have falsely concluded that there are differences. In general, when we perform a large number of significance tests and find a few to be significant, we should be concerned that the significant results may simply be due to chance.

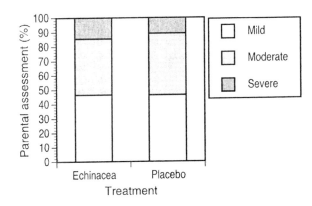

Minitab output

	Echin	Placebo	Total
Mild	153	170	323
	152.68	170.32	
Mod	128	157	285
	134.72	150.28	
Sev	48	40	88
	41.60	46.40	
Total	329	367	696

ChiSq = 0.001 + 0.001 +
        0.335 + 0.300 +
        0.985 + 0.883 = 2.506
df = 2, p = 0.286

Event	$\hat{p}_1$	$\hat{p}_2$	z	P
Itchiness	0.0386	0.0189	1.57	0.1154
Rash	0.0712	0.0270	2.74	0.0061
"Hyper"	0.0890	0.0622	1.35	0.1756
Diarrhea	0.1128	0.0919	0.92	0.3595
Vomiting	0.0653	0.0568	0.47	0.6357
Headache	0.0979	0.0649	1.61	0.1068
Stomachache	0.1543	0.1108	1.71	0.0875
Drowsiness	0.1869	0.1297	2.09	0.0367
Other	0.1869	0.1297	2.09	0.0367
Any event	0.4510	0.3946	1.52	0.1290

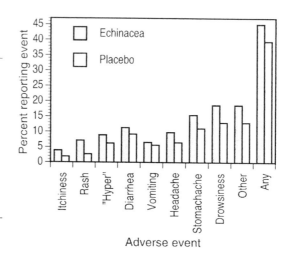

(e) We would expect multiple observations on the same child to be dependent, so the assumptions for our analysis are not satisfied. Examination of the data reveals that the results for both groups are quite similar, so we are inclined to agree with the authors that there are no statistically significant differences. **(f)** Student opinions about the criticisms of this study will vary. The third criticism might be dismissed as sounding like conspiracy-theory paranoia, but the other three address the way that echinacea was administered; certainly we cannot place too much faith in a clinical trial if it turns out that the treatments were not given properly!

9.45. In Exercise 9.11, we are comparing three populations (model 1). Specifically, we compare nonrelapse rates among the populations of desipramine users, lithium users, and placebo users. In Exercise 9.23: One could argue for either answer. If we chose three separate random samples from each division, then we are comparing three populations (model 1). If a single random sample of student athletes was chosen, and then we classified each student by division and by gambling response, this is a test for independence (model 2). In Exercise 9.24, we are comparing two populations (model 1): mice exposed to steel-mill air, and those exposed to rural air. In Exercise 9.27, we test for independence (model 2) between education level and pet ownership.

   Note: *For some of these problems, either answer may be acceptable, provided a reasonable explanation is given. The distinctions between the models can be quite difficult to make, since the difference between several populations might, in fact, involve classification by a categorical variable. In many ways, it comes down to how the data were collected. Of course, the difficulty is that the method of collecting data may not always be apparent, in which case we have to make an educated guess. One question we can ask to educate our guess is whether we have data that can be used to estimate the (population) marginal distributions.*

9.46. (a) Each quadrant accounts for one-fourth of the area, so we expect it to contain one-fourth of the 100 trees. **(b)** Some random variation would not surprise us; we no more expect exactly 25 trees per quadrant than we would expect to see exactly 50 heads when flipping a fair coin 100 times. **(c)** The table on the right shows the individual computations, from which we obtain $X^2 = 10.8$, df $= 3$, and $P = 0.0129$. We conclude that the distribution is not random.

Observed	Expected	$(o-e)^2/e$
18	25	1.96
22	25	0.36
39	25	7.84
21	25	0.64
100		10.8

9.47. The table on the right shows the individual computations, from which we obtain $X^2 = 5.016$, df $= 3$, and $P = 0.1706$. We have little reason to doubt that our survey responses match the college population.

Observed	Expected	$(o-e)^2/e$
154	59.74	0.5515
66	55.62	1.9372
56	51.5	0.3932
30	39.14	2.1344
206		5.0163

9.48. Shown in the column labeled "p" are the probabilities from Table A. For the goodness of fit test, $X^2 = 1.9023$, df $= 4$, and $P = 0.7537$—no reason to doubt that the numbers come from a standard normal distribution.

Observed	p	Expected	$(o-e)^2/e$
98	0.2119	105.95	0.5965
112	0.2088	104.40	0.5533
79	0.1586	79.30	0.0011
111	0.2088	104.40	0.4172
100	0.2119	105.95	0.3341
500			1.9023

9.50. Because we have divided the interval from 0 to 1 into five equal-sized pieces, each interval has probability $\frac{1}{5}$, so we expect $100 = (500)\left(\frac{1}{5}\right)$ numbers per interval. The table on the right shows the individual computations, from which we obtain $X^2 = 4.84$, df $= 4$, and $P = 0.3041$. We have little reason to doubt that these numbers came from a uniform distribution.

Observed	Expected	$(o-e)^2/e$
113	100	1.69
95	100	0.25
108	100	0.64
99	100	0.01
85	100	2.25
500		4.84

9.52. A *P*-value of 0.999 is suspicious because it means that there was an almost-perfect match between the observed and expected counts. (The table on the right shows how small X^2 must be in order to have a *P*-value of 0.999; recall that X^2 is small when the observed and expected counts are close.) We expect a certain amount of difference between these counts due to chance, and become suspicious if the difference is too small. In particular, when H_0 is true, a match like this would occur only once in 1000 attempts; if there were 1000 students in the class, that might not be too surprising.

df	X^2
1	2×10^{-6}
2	0.0020
3	0.0243
4	0.0908
5	0.2102
6	0.3810
7	0.5985
8	0.8571
9	1.1519
10	1.4787

Chapter 10 Solutions

10.1. The table below gives two sets of answers: those found with critical values from Table D, and those found with software. In each case, the margin of error is $t^*\text{SE}_{b_1} = 8.05t^*$, with df $= n - 3$.

	df	b_1	t^*	Interval	t^*	Interval
(a)	23	16.1	2.069	-0.5555 to 32.7555	2.0687	-0.5527 to 32.7527
(b)	23	6.1	2.069	-10.5555 to 22.7555	2.0687	-10.5527 to 22.7527
(c)	123	16.1	1.984*	0.1288 to 32.0712	1.9794	0.1655 to 32.0345

*Note that for (c), if we use Table D, we take df $= 100$.

10.2. The test statistic is $t = b_1/\text{SE}_{b_1} = b_1/8.05$, with df $= n - 2$. We have significant evidence against H_0 only in (c); this is consistent with the confidence intervals from the previous exercise.

	df	b_1	t	P (Table D)	P (software)
(a)	23	16.1	2.00	$0.05 < P < 0.10$	0.0574
(b)	23	6.1	0.76	$0.40 < P < 0.50$	0.4563
(c)	123	16.1	2.00	$0.04 < P < 0.05*$	0.0477

*Note that for (c), if we use Table D, we take df $= 100$.

10.3. (a) The parameters are β_0, β_1, and σ; b_0, b_1, and s are the *estimates* of those parameters. **(b)** H_0 should refer to β_1 (the population slope) rather than b_1 (the estimated slope). **(c)** The confidence interval will be narrower than the prediction interval, because the confidence interval accounts only for the uncertainty in our estimate of the mean response, while the prediction interval must also account for the random error of an individual response.

10.4. (a) Stemplots are shown on the right. x (watershed area) is right-skewed; $\bar{x} \doteq 28.2857$ km^2, $s_x \doteq 17.7142$ km^2. y (IBI) is left-skewed; $\bar{y} \doteq 65.9388$, $s_y \doteq 18.2796$. **(b)** The scatterplot (below, left) shows a weak positive association, with more scatter in y for small x. **(c)** $y_i = \beta_0 + \beta_1 x_i + \epsilon_i$, $i = 1, 2, ..., 49$; ϵ_i are independent $N(0, \sigma)$ variables. **(d)** The hypotheses are H_0: $\beta_1 = 0$ vs. H_a: $\beta_1 \neq 0$. **(e)** See the Minitab output below. The regression equation is $\widehat{\text{IBI}} = 52.92 + 0.4602$ Area, and the estimated standard deviation is $s \doteq 16.53$. For testing the hypotheses in (d), $t = 3.42$ and $P = 0.001$. **(f)** The residual plot (below, right) again shows that there is more variation for small

Area	IBI
0 | 2	2 | 99
0 | 5688999	3 | 233
1 | 0024	3 | 9
1 | 66889	4 | 13
2 | 111133	4 | 67
2 | 66667889	5 | 34
3 | 112244	5 | 556899
3 | 9	6 | 0124
4 |	6 | 7
4 | 799	7 | 11124
5 | 244	7 | 56889
5 | 789	8 | 001222344
6 |	8 | 556899
6 | 9	9 | 1
7 | 0	

x. **(g)** As we can see from a stemplot and/or a normal quantile plot (both below), the residuals are somewhat left-skewed but otherwise seem reasonably close to normal. **(h)** Student opinions may vary. The two apparent deviations from the model are (i) a possible change in standard deviation as x changes and (ii) possible nonnormality of error terms.

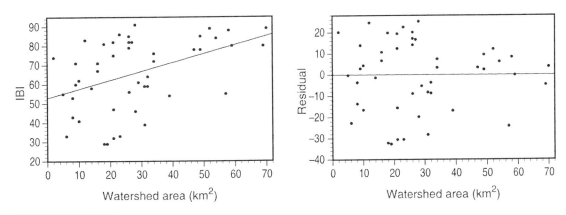

Minitab output

```
The regression equation is IBI = 52.9 + 0.460 Area

Predictor      Coef      Stdev    t-ratio       p
Constant     52.923      4.484      11.80   0.000
Area         0.4602     0.1347       3.42   0.001

s = 16.53       R-sq = 19.9%     R-sq(adj) = 18.2%
```

```
-3 | 2200
-2 | 8
-2 | 42
-1 | 9665
-1 | 3
-0 | 8885
-0 | 433100
 0 | 223334
 0 | 666789
 1 | 022334
 1 | 6799
 2 | 0024
 2 | 5
```

10.5. (a) The stemplot of percent forested is shown on the right; see the solution to the previous exercise for the stemplot of IBI. x (percent forested) is right-skewed; $\bar{x} = 39.3878\%$, $s_x = 32.2043\%$. y (IBI) is left-skewed; $\bar{y} = 65.9388$, $s_y = 18.2796$. **(b)** The scatterplot (below, left) shows a weak positive association, with more scatter in y for small x. **(c)** $y_i = \beta_0 + \beta_1 x_i + \epsilon_i$, $i = 1, 2, ..., 49$; ϵ_i are independent $N(0, \sigma)$ variables. **(d)** The hypotheses are H_0: $\beta_1 = 0$ vs. H_a: $\beta_1 \neq 0$. **(e)** See the Minitab output below. The regression equation is $\widehat{IBI} = 59.91 + 0.1531$ Forest, and the estimated standard deviation is $s \doteq 17.79$. For testing the hypotheses in (d), $t = 1.92$ and $P = 0.061$. **(f)** The residual plot (below, right) shows a slight curve—the residuals seem to be (very) slightly lower in the middle and higher on the ends. **(g)** As we can see from a stemplot and/or a normal quantile plot (both below), the residuals are left-skewed. **(h)** Student opinions may vary. The three apparent deviations from the model are (i) a possible change in standard deviation as x changes, (ii) possible curvature of residuals, and (iii) possible nonnormality of error terms.

Percent forested

```
 0 | 00000033789
 1 | 0014778
 2 | 125
 3 | 123339
 4 | 133799
 5 | 229
 6 | 38
 7 | 599
 8 | 069
 9 | 055
10 | 00
```

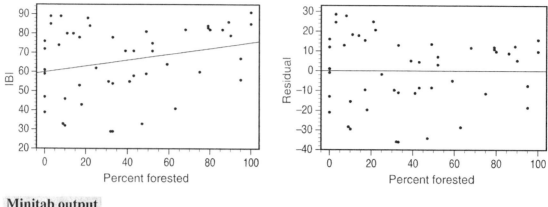

Minitab output

```
The regression equation is IBI = 59.9 + 0.153 Forest

Predictor       Coef        Stdev      t-ratio         p
Constant       59.907        4.040       14.83     0.000
Forest        0.15313       0.07972       1.92     0.061

s = 17.79       R-sq = 7.3%       R-sq(adj) = 5.3%
```

```
-3 | 55
-3 | 4
-2 | 988
-2 | 0
-1 | 985
-1 | 2110
-0 | 99887
-0 | 410
 0 | 134
 0 | 557899
 1 | 01122333
 1 | 55678
 2 | 044
 2 | 78
```

10.6. With the regression equation $\widehat{\text{IBI}} = 52.92 + 0.4602$ Area, the predicted mean response when $x =$ Area $= 30$ km^2 is $\hat{\mu}_y = \widehat{\text{IBI}} \doteq 66.73$. While it is possible to find SE$_{\hat{\mu}}$ and SE$_{\hat{y}}$ using the formulas from Section 10.2, we rely on the software output shown below. (SE$_{\hat{\mu}}$ is reported by Minitab as "Stdev.fit." Note that SE$_{\hat{y}} = \sqrt{s^2 + \text{SE}_{\hat{\mu}}^2}$, where $s \doteq 16.53$.) **(a)** The 95% confidence interval for μ_y is 61.95 to 71.50. **(b)** The 95% prediction interval for a future response is 33.12 to 100.34. **(c)** Among *many* streams with watershed area 30 km^2, we estimate the mean IBI to be between about 61.95 and 71.50. For an *individual* stream with watershed area 30 km^2, we expect its IBI to be between about 33.12 and 100.34. **(d)** We probably cannot reliably apply these results elsewhere; it is likely that the particular characteristics of the Ozark Highland region play some role in determining the regression coefficients.

Minitab output

```
  Fit  Stdev.Fit     95.0% C.I.          95.0% P.I.
66.73       2.37   (  61.95,   71.50)  (  33.12,   100.34)
```

10.7. (a) The stemplots (below. left) are fairly symmetric. For x (MOE). $\bar{x} \doteq 1,799,180$ and $s_x \doteq 329,253$; for y (MOR), $\bar{y} \doteq 11,185$ and $s_y \doteq 1980$. **(b)** The plot (below, right) shows a moderately strong, positive, linear relationship. Because we would like to predict MOR from MOE, we should put MOE on the x axis. **(c)** The model is $y_i = \beta_0 + \beta_1 x_i + \epsilon_i$, $i = 1, 2, \dots, 32$; ϵ_i are independent $N(0, \sigma)$ variables. The regression equation is $\widehat{MOR} = 2653 + 0.004742\,MOE$, $s \doteq 1238$. The slope is significantly different from 0: $t = 7.02$ (df $= 30$), $P < 0.0001$. **(d)** Assumptions appear to be met: A stemplot of the residuals shows one slightly low (not quite an outlier), but acceptable, and the plot of residuals against MOE (not shown) does not suggest any particular pattern.

MOE | MOR | Residuals

MOE		MOR		Residuals	
11	6	6	3	−3	3
12		7		−2	
13	55	8	3588	−2	
14	1578	9	222	−1	6
15	5589	10	22356	−1	31110
16	14	11	223455799	−0	76555
17	2479	12	00777	−0	43221
18	447	13	469	0	00223
19	358	14	5	0	78
20	0348	15	3	1	1334
21	8			1	599
22	1			2	1
23	47				
24					
25	3				

10.8. (a) The 95% confidence interval gives a range of values for the mean MOR of *many* pieces of wood with MOE equal to 2,000,000. The prediction interval gives a range of values for the MOR of *one* piece of wood with MOE equal to 2,000,000. **(b)** The prediction interval will include more values, because the confidence interval accounts only for the uncertainty in our estimate of the mean response, while the prediction interval must also account for the random error of an individual response. **(c)** With the regression equation $\widehat{MOR} = 2653 + 0.004742\,MOE$, the predicted mean response when $x = MOE = 2,000,000$ is $\hat{\mu}_y = \widehat{MOE} \doteq 12,137$. The Minitab output below gives the two intervals, along with $SE_{\hat{\mu}}$ ("Stdev.fit").

Minitab output

```
    Fit  Stdev.Fit     95.0% C.I.         95.0% P.I.
  12137        257  ( 11611,  12663)  (  9554,  14720)
```

10.9. (a) x (CRP) is sharply right-skewed with high outliers; $\bar{x} = 10.0323$ and $s_x = 16.5632$. y (retinol) is slightly right-skewed; $\bar{y} = 0.7648$ and $s_y = 0.3949$. **(b)** No; no assumption is made about the distribution of x values. Note that this does not mean that we do not care about the distribution of the x values; the outliers cause trouble, as we see in (d). **(c)** The regression equation is $\widehat{RETINOL} = 0.8430 - 0.007800\ CRP$, $s = 0.3781$. With $\alpha = 0.05$, the slope is significantly different from 0: $t = -2.13$ (df $= 38$), $P = 0.039$.

CRP	
0	00000000000000003334
0	55555677899
1	2
1	5
2	02
2	6
3	0
3	
4	
4	6
5	
5	9
6	
6	
7	3

Retinol	
0	2333333333333
0	455
0	6667
0	88889999
1	00011111
1	23
1	4
1	
1	9

(d) The high outliers in CRP are influential, as we can see from the small residuals on the right end of the plot below. Additionally, a stemplot or quantile plot of the residuals (not shown) shows that the distribution is right-skewed rather than normal.

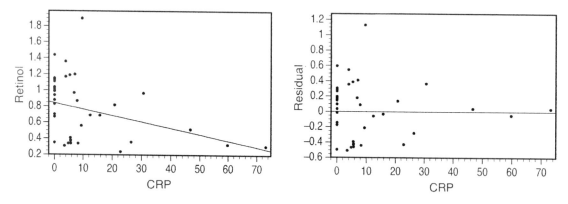

10.10. (a) Both distributions are right-skewed. OC has $\bar{x} = 33.4161$ and $s_x = 19.6097$; VO+ has $\bar{y} = 985.8065$ and $s_y = 579.8581$. **(b)** Put OC on the x axis, because we hope to use it as the explanatory variable. We see a positive association, but one point is an outlier (it is far above the pattern of the rest of the points) and there appears to be more scatter about the line for large values of OC. **(c)** The regression equation is $\hat{y} = 334.0 + 19.505x$, $s = 443.3$. The slope is significantly different from 0: $t = 4.73$, $P < 0.0005$. The residuals appear to be somewhat right-skewed, and the unusual point noted in (b) corresponds to a high outlier in the distribution of residuals.

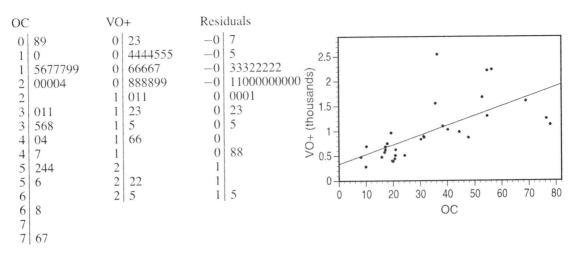

```
OC                VO+              Residuals
0 | 89            0 | 23           -0 | 7
1 | 0             0 | 4444555      -0 | 5
1 | 5677799       0 | 66667        -0 | 33322222
2 | 00004         0 | 888899       -0 | 11000000000
2 |               1 | 011           0 | 0001
3 | 011           1 | 23            0 | 23
3 | 568           1 | 5             0 | 5
4 | 04            1 | 66            0 |
4 | 7             1 |               0 | 88
5 | 244           2 |               1 |
5 | 6             2 | 22            1 |
6 |               2 | 5             1 | 5
6 | 8
7 |
7 | 67
```

10.11. **(a)** Both distributions are right-skewed (TRAP more than VO–). TRAP has $\bar{x} = 13.2484$ and $s_x = 6.5282$; VO– has $\bar{y} = 889.1935$ and $s_y = 427.6161$. **(b)** Put TRAP on the x axis, because we hope to use it as the explanatory variable. We see a positive association, but one point is an outlier (it is far above the pattern of the rest of the points). **(c)** The regression equation is $\hat{y} = 300.9 + 44.406x$, $s = 319.7$. The slope is significantly different from 0: $t = 4.97$, $P < 0.0005$. The unusual point noted in (b) corresponds to a high outlier among the residuals; otherwise the distribution of residuals seems reasonably normal.

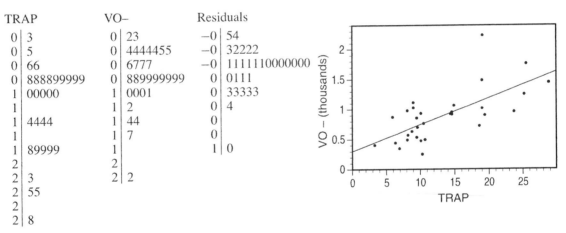

```
TRAP              VO-              Residuals
0 | 3             0 | 23           -0 | 54
0 | 5             0 | 4444455      -0 | 32222
0 | 66            0 | 6777         -0 | 1111110000000
0 | 888899999     0 | 889999999     0 | 0111
1 | 00000         1 | 0001          0 | 33333
1 |               1 | 2             0 | 4
1 | 4444          1 | 44            0 |
1 |               1 | 7             0 |
1 | 89999         1 |               1 | 0
2 |               2 |
2 | 3             2 | 2
2 | 55
2 |
2 | 8
```

10.12. After taking (natural) logarithms, both distributions are considerably less skewed; logOC is irregular, while logVO+ is quite symmetric. logOC has $\bar{x} = 3.3379$ and $s_x = 0.6085$; logVO+ has $\bar{y} = 6.7419$ and $s_y = 0.5554$. (If common logarithms are used, multiply these results by about 2.3026.) The scatterplot shows a positive association, stronger than that seen in Exercise 10.10. The regression equation is $\hat{y} = 4.3852 + 0.7060x$, $s = 0.3580$. The slope is significantly different from 0: $t = 6.57$, $P < 0.0005$. The distribution of the residuals appears to be much more normal than in Exercise 10.10.

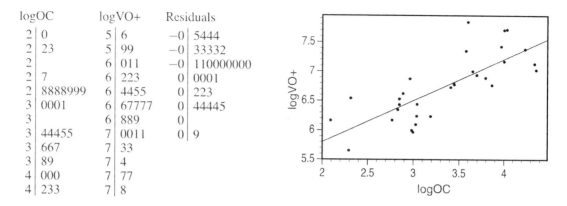

10.13. After taking (natural) logarithms, both distributions are somewhat irregular, but slightly more symmetric. logTRAP has $\bar{x} = 2.4674$ and $s_x = 0.4979$; logVO– has $\bar{y} = 6.6815$ and $s_y = 0.4832$. (If common logarithms are used, multiply these results by about 2.3026.) The scatterplot shows a positive association; the outlier visible in Exercise 10.11 has moved closer to the other points. The regression equation is $\hat{y} = 5.0910 + 0.6446x$, $s = 0.3674$. The slope is significantly different from 0: $t = 4.78$, $P < 0.0005$. The distribution of the residuals appears to be reasonably normal, apart from a low outlier.

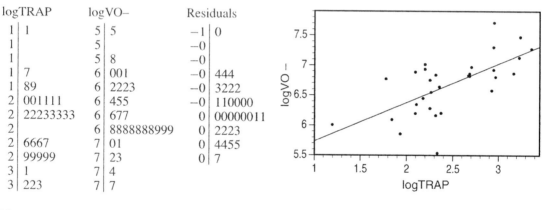

10.14. (a) With all 60 points, the regression equation is $\hat{y} = -34.55 + 0.8605x$, $s \doteq 20.17$. (This is the solid line in the scatterplot on the right.) The slope is significantly different from 0: $t = 4.82$, $P < 0.0005$. **(b)** Without the four points from the bottom of the scatterplot, the regression equation is $\hat{y} = -33.40 + 0.8818x$, $s \doteq 15.18$. (This is the dashed line in the scatterplot.) The slope is again significantly different from 0: $t = 6.57$, $P < 0.0005$.

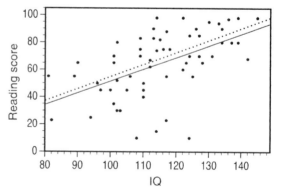

With the outliers removed, the line changes slightly; the most significant change is the decrease in the estimated standard deviation s. This correspondingly makes t larger (i.e., b_1 is *more* significantly different from 0), and makes the regression line more useful for prediction (r^2 increases from 28.9% to 44.4%). Of course, we should not arbitrarily remove data points; more investigation is needed to determine why these students' reading scores were so much lower than we would expect based on their IQs.

10.15. (a) Both variables are right-skewed. For pure tones, $\bar{x} \doteq 106.20$ and $s \doteq 91.76$ spikes/second, and for monkey calls, $\bar{y} = 176.57$ and $s_y = 111.85$ spikes/second. (b) There is a moderate positive association; the third point (circled) has the largest residual; the first point (marked with a square) is an outlier for tone response. (c) With all 37 points, $\widehat{\text{CALL}} = 93.9 + 0.778 \text{ TONE}$ and $s = 87.30$; the test of $\beta_1 = 0$ gives $t = 4.91$, $P < 0.0001$. (d) Without the first point, $\hat{y} = 101 + 0.693x$, $s = 88.14$, $t = 3.18$. Without the third point, $\hat{y} = 98.4 + 0.679x$, $s = 80.69$, $t = 4.49$. With neither, $\hat{y} = 116 + 0.466x$, $s = 79.46$, $t = 2.21$. The line changes a bit, but always has a slope significantly different from 0.

Tone		Call		Residual	
0	122222233444	0	4	−1	65
0	55556777	0	566667889	−1	3
1	0011244	1	011223334	−0	8876555
1	566778	1	5889999	−0	44444331100
2	24	2	0004	0	012334
2	5	2	7	0	667888
3		3	0134	1	14
3		3		1	7
4		4		2	0
4	7	4	8		
		5	0		

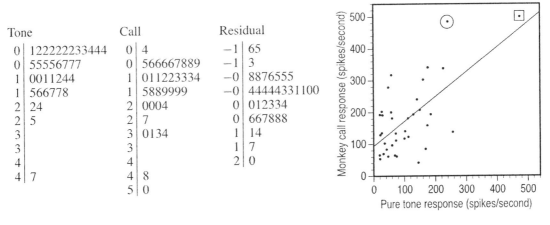

10.16. The model is $y_i = \beta_0 + \beta_1 x_i + \epsilon_i$; ϵ_i are independent $N(0, \sigma)$ variables. (a) β_0 represents the fixed costs. (b) β_1 represents how costs change as the number of students changes. This should be positive, because more students mean more expenses. (c) The error term (ϵ_i) allows for variation among equal-sized schools.

10.17. (a) The scatterplot shows a weak negative association; the regression equation is $\widehat{\text{BONDS}} = 53.41 - 0.1962 \text{ STOCKS}$ with $s \doteq 59.88$. (b) For testing H_0: $\beta_1 = 0$ vs. H_a: $\beta_1 \neq 0$, we have $t = -1.27$ (df $= 14$) and $P = 0.226$. The slope is *not* significantly different from 0. (c) The scatterplot shows a lot of variation, so s is large and t is small.

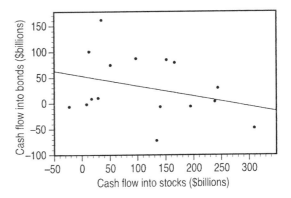

10.18. (a) The t statistic for testing H_0: $\beta_1 = 0$ vs. H_a: $\beta_1 \neq 0$ is $t = b_1 / \text{SE}_{b_1} = 0.76 / 0.44 \doteq 1.73$ with df $= 80$. This has $P = 0.0880$, so we do not reject H_0. (b) For the one-sided alternative $\beta_1 > 0$, we would have $P = 0.0440$, so we could reject H_0 at the 5% significance level.

10.19. See also the solutions to Exercises 2.12 and 2.48.
(a) MA angle is the explanatory variable, so it should be on the horizontal axis of the scatterplot. (This scatterplot has the same scale on both axes because both variables are measured in degrees.) (b) The scatterplot shows a moderate-to-weak positive linear association, with one clear outlier (the patient with HAV angle 50˚). (c) The model is $y_i = \beta_0 + \beta_1 x_i + \epsilon_i$, $i = 1, 2, \ldots, 38$; ϵ_i are independent $N(0, \sigma)$ variables. (d) Because doctors expect there to be a positive association, we use a one-sided alternative: H_0: $\beta_1 = 0$ vs. H_a: $\beta_1 > 0$. (e) For the estimated slope $b_1 \doteq 0.3388$, we have $t = 1.90$ (df $= 36$) and $P = 0.033$ (half of Minitab's two-sided P-value); this is significant evidence (at $\alpha = 0.05$) to support the doctors' belief.

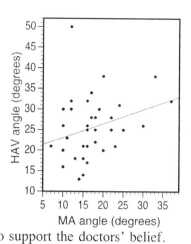

Minitab output

```
The regression equation is HAV = 19.7 + 0.339 MA

Predictor      Coef       Stdev     t-ratio        p
Constant     19.723       3.217        6.13    0.000
MA            0.3388      0.1782        1.90    0.065

s = 7.224      R-sq = 9.1%      R-sq(adj) = 6.6%
```

10.20. Software (Minitab output above) reports $b_1 \doteq 0.3388$ and $SE_{b_1} \doteq 0.1782$. For a t distribution with df $= 36$, $t^* \doteq 2.0281$ for a 95% confidence interval, so the interval is -0.0226 to 0.7002. The slope was significantly different from 0 using a one-sided alternative, but this interval tells us that it could be 0 (or even slightly negative); we would not reject $\beta_1 = 0$ in favor of a two-sided alternative.

10.21. (a) Aside from the one high point (70 months of service, and wages 97.6801), there is a moderate positive association—fairly clear, but with quite a bit of scatter. (b) The regression equation is $\widehat{WAGES} = 43.383 + 0.07325$ LOS, with $s \doteq 10.21$ (Minitab output below). The slope is significantly different from 0: $t = 2.85$ (df $= 57$), $P = 0.006$. (c) Wages rise an average of 0.07325 wage units per week of service. (d) We have $b_1 \doteq 0.07325$ and $SE_{b_1} \doteq 0.02571$. For a t distribution with df $= 57$, $t^* \doteq 2.0025$ for a 95% confidence interval, so the interval is 0.0218 to 0.1247.

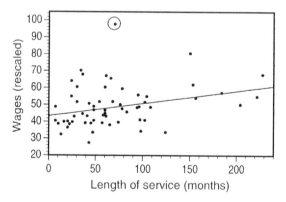

Minitab output

```
The regression equation is wages = 43.4 + 0.0733 los

Predictor      Coef       Stdev     t-ratio        p
Constant     43.383       2.248       19.30    0.000
los          0.07325     0.02571       2.85    0.006

s = 10.21      R-sq = 12.5%      R-sq(adj) = 10.9%
```

10.22. The table below summarizes the regression results with the outlier excluded, and those with all points. **(a)** The intercept and slope estimates change very little, but the estimate of σ increases from 10.21 to 11.98. **(b)** With the outlier, the t statistic decreases (because s has increased), and the P-value increases slightly—although it is still significant at the 5% level. **(c)** The interval width $2t^*SE_{b_1}$ increases from 0.1030 to 0.1207—roughly the same factor by which s increased. (Because the degrees of freedom change from 57 to 58, t^* decreases from 2.0025 to 2.0017, but the change in s has a much greater impact.)

	b_0	b_1	s	t	P	Interval width
Outlier excluded	43.383	0.07325	10.21	2.85	0.006	0.1030
All points	44.213	0.07310	11.98	2.42	0.018	0.1207

Minitab output

```
The regression equation is wages = 44.2 + 0.0731 los

Predictor      Coef       Stdev      t-ratio        p
Constant      44.213      2.628        16.82    0.000
los          0.07310     0.03015         2.42    0.018

s = 11.98      R-sq = 9.2%       R-sq(adj) = 7.6%
```

10.23. (a) The trend appears to be quite linear. **(b)** The regression equation is $\widehat{LEAN} = -61.12 + 9.3187\ YEAR$ with $s \doteq 4.181$. The regression explains $r^2 = 98.8\%$ of the variation in lean. **(c)** The rate we seek is the slope. For df $= 11$ and 99% confidence, $t^* = 3.1058$, so the interval is $9.3187 \pm (3.1058)(0.3099) = 8.3562$ to 10.2812 tenths of a millimeter/year.

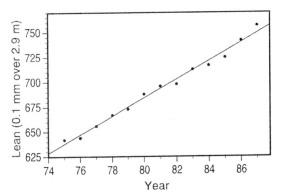

Minitab output

```
The regression equation is Lean = -61.1 + 9.32 Year

Predictor      Coef       Stdev      t-ratio        p
Constant      -61.12      25.13        -2.43    0.033
Year         9.3187      0.3099        30.07    0.000

s = 4.181      R-sq = 98.8%      R-sq(adj) = 98.7%
```

10.24. (a) $\hat{y} = -61.12 + 9.3187(18) \doteq 107$, for a prediction of 2.9107 m. **(b)** This is an example of extrapolation—trying to make a prediction outside the range of given x values. Minitab reports $SE_{\hat{y}} = 19.56$, so a 95% prediction interval for $\hat{y}$ when $x^* = 18$ is about 62.6 to 150.7. The width of the interval is an indication of how unreliable the prediction is.

Minitab output

```
    Fit   Stdev.Fit        95.0% C.I.            95.0% P.I.
 106.62       19.56   (  63.56, 149.68)   (  62.58, 150.65) XX
    XX denotes a row with very extreme X values
```

10.25. (a) Use $x = 107$ (the number of years after 1900). (b) $\hat{y} = -61.12 + 9.3187(107) \doteq 936$, for a prediction of 2.9936 m. (c) A prediction interval is appropriate, because we are interested in one future observation, not the mean of all future observations; in this situation, it does not make sense to talk of more than one future observation. In the output below, note that Minitab warns us of the risk of extrapolation.

Minitab output

```
    Fit  Stdev.Fit       95.0% C.I.           95.0% P.I.
  935.98       8.14  ( 918.06,  953.90)  ( 915.83,  956.13) XX
    XX denotes a row with very extreme X values
```

10.26. (a) Scatterplot below, left. (b) Scatterplot below, right. (c) The regression equation is $\hat{y} = -872.93 + 0.4464x$ with $s \doteq 0.1739$. For 95% confidence with df $= 4$, $t^* = 2.7765$, so with $b_1 \doteq 0.4464$ and $SE_{b_1} \doteq 0.006856$, the confidence interval is 0.4274 to 0.4654.

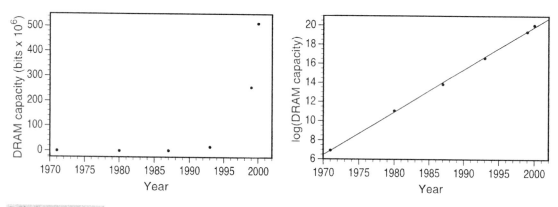

Minitab output

The regression equation is logBits = - 873 + 0.446 year

```
Predictor       Coef        Stdev     t-ratio         p
Constant     -872.93        13.63      -64.03     0.000
year        0.446390     0.006856       65.11     0.000

s = 0.1739      R-sq = 99.9%      R-sq(adj) = 99.9%
```

10.27. Recall that testing H_0: $\rho = 0$ vs. H_a: $\rho \neq 0$ is the same as testing H_0: $\beta_1 = 0$ vs. H_a: $\beta_1 \neq 0$. In the solution to Exercise 10.17, we had $t = -1.27$ (df $= 14$) and $P = 0.226$, so we cannot reject H_0.

10.28. (a) With $r = -0.19$ and $n = 713$, we have $t = \frac{r\sqrt{n-2}}{\sqrt{1-r^2}} \doteq -5.16$. (b) Comparing to a t distribution with df $= 711$ (or anything reasonably close), the P-value is less than 0.0001, so we conclude that $\rho \neq 0$.

10.29. Because DFT $=$ DFM $+$ DFE and SST $=$ SSM $+$ SSE, we can find the missing degrees of freedom (DF) and sum of squares (SS) entries by subtraction: df $=$ DFE $= 28$ and SSE $= 10152.4$. The missing entry in the mean square (MS) column is MSE $=$ SSE/DFE $\doteq 362.6$. (We can also compute MSE $=$ MSM/F $\doteq 362.7$—the same answer, up to rounding.)

10.30. $s = \sqrt{\text{MSE}} \doteq 19.0416$ and $r^2 = \frac{\text{SSM}}{\text{SST}} = \frac{3445.9}{13598.3} \doteq 0.2534$.

10.31. As $s_x = \sqrt{\frac{1}{29} \sum (x_i - \bar{x})^2} = 16.45\%$, we have $\sqrt{\sum (x_i - \bar{x})^2} = s_x \sqrt{29} \doteq 88.5860\%$, so

$$\text{SE}_{b_1} = \frac{s}{\sqrt{\sum (x_i - \bar{x})^2}} \doteq \frac{19.0420}{88.5860} \doteq 0.2150.$$

Alternatively, note that we have $F = 9.50$ and $b_1 = 0.663$. Because $t^2 = F$, we know that $t = 3.0822$ (take the positive square root, because $t = b_1 / \text{SE}_{b_1}$, and b_1 is positive). Then $\text{SE}_{b_1} = b_1 / t = 0.2151$—the same answer, up to rounding. (Note that with this approach, we do not need to know that $s_x = 16.45\%$.)

With df $= 28$, $t^* = 2.0484$ for 95% confidence, so the 95% confidence interval is $0.663 \pm 0.4403 = 0.2227$ to 1.1033.

10.32. (a) With $\bar{x} \doteq 80.9$, $s_x \doteq 17.2$, $\bar{y} \doteq 43.5$, $s_y \doteq 20.3$, and $r \doteq 0.68$, we find

$$b_1 = (0.68) \left(\frac{20.3}{17.2} \right) \doteq 0.8026$$

$$b_0 = 43.5 - (0.8026)(80.9) \doteq -21.4270$$

(Answers may vary slightly due to rounding.) The regression equation is therefore $\widehat{\text{GHP}} = -21.4270 + 0.8026\,\text{FVC}$. **(b)** Testing $\beta_1 = 0$ is equivalent to testing $\rho = 0$, so the test statistic is $t = \frac{r\sqrt{n-2}}{\sqrt{1-r^2}} \doteq 6.43$ (df $= 48$), for which $P < 0.0005$. The slope (correlation) is significantly different from 0.

10.33. Use the formula $t = \frac{r\sqrt{n-2}}{\sqrt{1-r^2}}$ with $r = 0.5$. For $n = 20$, $t = 2.45$ with df $= 18$, for which the two sided P-value is $P = 0.0248$. For $n = 10$, $t = 1.63$ with df $= 8$, for which the two sided P-value is $P = 0.1411$. With the larger sample size, r should be a better estimate of ρ, so we are less likely to get $r = 0.5$ unless ρ is really not 0.

10.34. Most of the small banks have negative residuals, while most large-bank residuals are positive. This means that, generally, wages at large banks are higher, and small bank wages are lower, than we would predict from the regression.

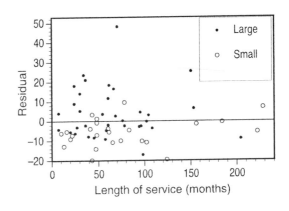

10.35. (a) Not surprisingly, there is a positive association between scores. The 47th pair of scores (circled) is an outlier—the ACT score (21) is higher than one would expect for the SAT score (420). Since this SAT score is so low, this point may be influential. No other points fall outside the pattern. **(b)** The regression equation is $\hat{y} = 1.626 + 0.02137x$. The slope is significantly different from 0: $t = 10.78$ (df $= 58$) for which $P < 0.0005$. **(c)** $r = 0.8167$.

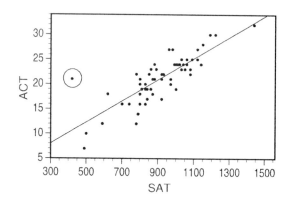

Minitab output

The regression equation is ACT = 1.63 + 0.0214 SAT

```
Predictor        Coef       Stdev     t-ratio         p
Constant        1.626       1.844        0.88     0.382
SAT          0.021374    0.001983       10.78     0.000

s = 2.744      R-sq = 66.7%      R-sq(adj) = 66.1%
```

10.36. (a) The means are identical (21.133). **(b)** For the observed ACT scores, $s_y = 4.714$; for the fitted values, $s_{\hat{y}} = 3.850$. **(c)** For $z = 1$, the SAT score is $\bar{x} + s_x = 912.7 + 180.1 = 1092.8$. The predicted ACT score is $\hat{y} \doteq 25$ (Minitab reports 24.983), which gives a standard score of about 1 (using the standard deviation of the *predicted* ACT scores. **(d)** For $z = -1$, the SAT score is $\bar{x} - s_x = 912.7 - 180.1 = 732.6$. The predicted ACT score is $\hat{y} \doteq 17.3$ (Minitab reports 17.285), which gives a standard score of about -1. **(e)** It appears that the standard score of the predicted value is the same as the explanatory variable's standard score. (See note below.)

    Notes: **(a)** This will always be true, because $\sum_i \hat{y}_i = \sum_i (b_0 + b_1 x_i) = n b_0 + b_1 \sum_i x_i = n(\bar{y} - b_1 \bar{x}) + b_1 n \bar{x} = n \bar{y}$. **(b)** The standard deviation of the predicted values will be $s_{\hat{y}} = |r| s_y$; in this case, $s_{\hat{y}} = (0.8167)(4.714)$. To see this, note that the variance of the predicted values is $\frac{1}{n-1} \sum_i (\hat{y}_i - \bar{y})^2 = \frac{1}{n-1} \sum_i (b_1 x_i - b_1 \bar{x})^2 = b_1^2 s_x^2 = r^2 s_y^2$. **(e)** For a given standard score z, note that $\hat{y} = b_0 + b_1(\bar{x} + z s_x) = \bar{y} - b_1 \bar{x} + b_1 \bar{x} + b_1 z s_x = \bar{y} + z r s_y$. If $r > 0$, the standard score for $\hat{y}$ equals z; if $r < 0$, the standard score is $-z$.

10.37. (a) For SAT: $\bar{x} = 912.\overline{6}$ and $s_x = 180.1117$. For ACT: $\bar{y} = 21.1\overline{3}$ and $s_y = 4.7137$. Therefore, the slope is $a_1 \doteq 0.02617$ and the intercept is $a_0 \doteq -2.7522$. (b) The new line is dashed. (c) For example, the first prediction is $-2.7522 + (0.02617)(1000) \doteq 23.42$. Up to rounding error, the mean and standard deviation of the predicted scores are the same as those of the ACT scores: $\bar{y} = 21.1\overline{3}$ and $s_y = 4.7137$.

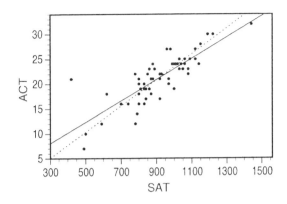

Note: *The usual least-squares line minimizes the total squared vertical distance from the points to the line. If instead we seek to minimize the total of $\sum_i |h_i v_i|$, where h_i is the horizontal distance and v_i is the vertical distance, we obtain the line $\hat{y} = a_0 + a_1 x$—except that we must choose the sign of a_1 to be the same as the sign of r. (It would hardly be the "best line" if we had a positive slope with a negative association.) If $r = 0$, either sign will do.*

10.38. (a) The regression equations are:

$\widehat{WEIGHT} = -468.91 + 28.462$ LENGTH with $s \doteq 109.4$ and $r^2 \doteq 0.902$

$\widehat{WEIGHT} = -449.44 + 174.63$ WIDTH with $s \doteq 107.9$ and $r^2 \doteq 0.905$

(b) Both scatterplots suggest that the relationships are curved rather than linear. (Points to the left and right lie above the line; those in the middle are generally below the line.)

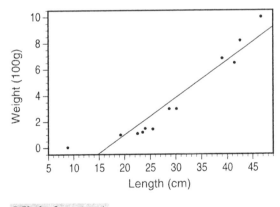 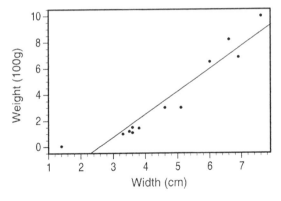

Minitab output

```
 – – – – – – – – –     MODEL 1: LENGTH & WEIGHT   – – – – – – – – –
The regression equation is weight = -469 + 28.5 length

Predictor      Coef       Stdev      t-ratio       p
Constant     -468.91      92.55       -5.07      0.000
length        28.462       2.967       9.59      0.000

s = 109.4        R-sq = 90.2%     R-sq(adj) = 89.2%
 – – – – – – – – –     MODEL 2: WIDTH & WEIGHT   – – – – – – – – –
The regression equation is weight = -449 + 175 width

Predictor      Coef       Stdev      t-ratio       p
Constant     -449.44      89.27       -5.03      0.000
width         174.63      17.93        9.74      0.000

s = 107.9        R-sq = 90.5%     R-sq(adj) = 89.5%
```

10.39. (a) For squared length: $\widehat{\text{WEIGHT}} = -117.99 + 0.4970 \text{ SQLEN}$, $s \doteq 52.76$, $r^2 = 0.977$.
(b) For squared width: $\widehat{\text{WEIGHT}} = -98.99 + 18.732 \text{ SQWID}$, $s \doteq 65.24$, $r^2 = 0.965$.
Both scatterplots look more linear.

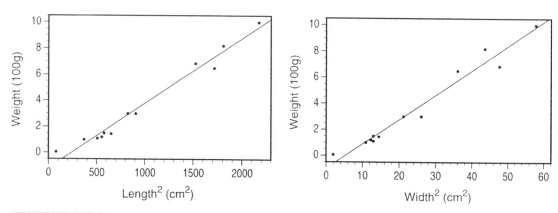

Minitab output

```
- - - - - - - -     MODEL 1: SQUARED LENGTH & WEIGHT     - - - - - - - -
The regression equation is weight = -118 + 0.497 sqlen

Predictor       Coef        Stdev      t-ratio        p
Constant      -117.99       27.88       -4.23      0.002
sqlen          0.49701      0.02400     20.71      0.000

s = 52.76        R-sq = 97.7%      R-sq(adj) = 97.5%
- - - - - - - -     MODEL 2: SQUARED LENGTH & WEIGHT     - - - - - - - -
The regression equation is weight = -99.0 + 18.7 sqwid

Predictor       Coef        Stdev      t-ratio        p
Constant       -98.99       33.67       -2.94      0.015
sqwid          18.732        1.126      16.64      0.000

s = 65.24        R-sq = 96.5%      R-sq(adj) = 96.2%
```

10.40. (a) The regression line is $\widehat{\text{WEIGHT}} = -115.10 + 3.1019(\text{LENGTH})(\text{WIDTH})$, $s \doteq 41.69$, $r^2 = 0.986$. **(b)** As measured by r^2, this last model is (by a slim margin) the best. (However, this scatterplot again gives some suggestion of curvature, indicating that some other model might do better still.)

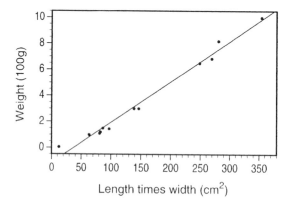

Minitab output

```
The regression equation is weight = -115 + 3.10 lenwid

Predictor       Coef        Stdev      t-ratio        p
Constant      -115.10       21.87       -5.26      0.000
lenwid          3.1019       0.1179     26.32      0.000

s = 41.69        R-sq = 98.6%      R-sq(adj) = 98.4%
```

10.41. The table on the right shows the correlations and the corresponding test statistics. The first two results agree with the results of (respectively) Exercises 10.4 and 10.5.

	r	*t*	*P*
IBI/area	0.4459	3.42	0.0013
IBI/forest	0.2698	1.92	0.0608
area/forest	−0.2571	−1.82	0.0745

10.42. The correlation was significant for vegetables, fruit, and meat, and nearly significant for eggs. All the significant correlations are negative, meaning (for example) that children with *high* neophobia tend to eat these foods *less* frequently.

	r	*t*	*P*
Vegetables	−0.27	−6.65	0.0000
Fruit	−0.16	−3.84	0.0001
Meat	−0.15	−3.60	0.0004
Eggs	−0.08	−1.90	0.0576
Sweet/fatty snacks	0.04	0.95	0.3430
Starchy staples	−0.02	−0.47	0.6355

10.43. Quickness and creativity are both (significantly) positively correlated with all GRE scores, so creative people are *not* penalized (contradicting the critics), while quick workers do better (as some have suggested). Depth is positively associated with verbal scores (refuting the opinion that deep thinkers are penalized). The only other significant correlations are those for conscientious workers, who apparently tend to score *lower* on all parts of the GRE. Depending on what "conscientiousness" measures, this might simply be the flip side of the positive correlation with quickness; perhaps "conscientious" means (in part) that these people work more slowly.

	Analytical	Quantitative	Verbal
Conscientiousness	−0.17**	−0.14**	−0.12*
Rationality	−0.06	−0.03	−0.08
Ingenuity	−0.06	−0.08	−0.02
Quickness	0.21***	0.15**	0.26***
Creativity	0.24***	0.26***	0.29***
Depth	0.06	0.08	0.15**

10.44. See also the solution to Exercise 2.13. **(a)** The association is linear and positive; the women's points show a stronger association. As a group, males typically have larger values for both variables. **(b)** The women's regression line (the solid line in the graph) is $\hat{y} = 201.2 + 24.026x$, with $s \doteq 95.08$ and $r^2 = 0.768$. The men's line (the dashed line) is $\hat{y} = 710.5 + 16.75x$, with $s \doteq 167.1$ and $r^2 = 0.351$. The women's slope is significantly different from 0 ($t = 5.76$, df = 10, $P < 0.0005$), but the men's is not ($t = 1.64$, df = 5, $P = 0.161$). These test results, and the values of s and r^2, confirm the observation that the women's association is stronger—however, see the solution to the next exercise.

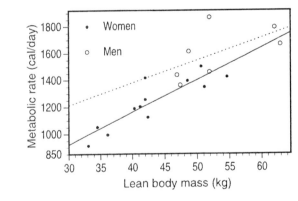

10.45. (a) These intervals (in the table below) overlap quite a bit. **(b)** These quantities can be computed from the data, but it is somewhat simpler to recall that they can be found from the sample standard deviations $s_{x,w}$ and $s_{x,m}$:

$$s_{x,w}\sqrt{11} \doteq 6.8684\sqrt{11} \doteq 22.78 \quad \text{and} \quad s_{x,m}\sqrt{6} \doteq 6.6885\sqrt{6} \doteq 16.38.$$

The women's SE_{b_1} is smaller in part because it is divided by a large number. **(c)** In order to reduce SE_{b_1} for men, we should choose our new sample to include men with a wider variety of lean body masses. (Note that just taking a larger sample will reduce SE_{b_1}; it is reduced even *more* if we choose subjects who will increase $s_{x,m}$.)

	b_1	SE_{b_1}	df	t^*	Interval
Women	24.026	4.174	10	2.2281	14.7257 to 33.3263
Men	16.75	10.20	5	2.5706	−9.4699 to 42.9699

10.46. Scatterplots, and portions of the Minitab outputs, are shown below. The equations are: For all points, $\widehat{\text{MPG}} = -7.796 + 7.8742$ LOGMPH; for speed ≤ 30 MPH, $\widehat{\text{MPG}} = -9.786 + 8.5343$ LOGMPH; and for fuel efficiency ≤ 20 MPG, $\widehat{\text{MPG}} = -5.264 + 7.0142$ LOGMPH. Students might make a number of observations about the effects of the restrictions; e.g., the estimated coefficients (and their standard errors) change quite a bit.

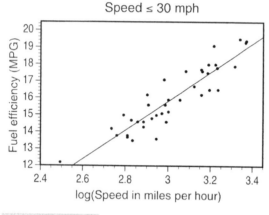
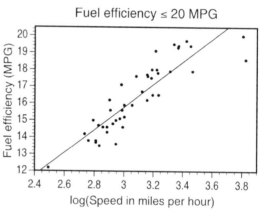

Minitab output

```
— — — — — — — — — — — —  All points  — — — — — — — — — — — — — — —
Predictor     Coef       Stdev     t-ratio       p
Constant     -7.796      1.155      -6.75      0.000
logMPH        7.8742     0.3541     22.24      0.000

s = 0.9995      R-sq = 89.5%     R-sq(adj) = 89.3%
— — — — — — — — — — —  Speed 30 MPH or less  — — — — — — — — — — — —
Predictor     Coef       Stdev     t-ratio       p
Constant     -9.786      1.862      -5.26      0.000
logMPH        8.5343     0.6154     13.87      0.000

s = 0.7600      R-sq = 83.5%     R-sq(adj) = 83.1%
— — — — — — — — —  Fuel efficiency 20 MPG or less  — — — — — — — — —
Predictor     Coef       Stdev     t-ratio       p
Constant     -5.264      1.778      -2.96      0.005
logMPH        7.0142     0.5779     12.14      0.000

s = 0.9363      R-sq = 77.8%     R-sq(adj) = 77.3%
```

Chapter 11 Solutions

11.1. The table below gives two sets of answers: those found with critical values from Table D, and those found with software. In each case, the margin of error is $t^* \mathrm{SE}_{b_k}$, with $\mathrm{df} = n - 3$.

	df	Coeff.	SE	t^*	Interval	t^*	Interval
(a)	22	$b_1 = 12.1$	7.2	2.074	-2.8328 to 27.0328	2.0739	-2.8319 to 27.0319
	22	$b_2 = 17.3$	4.1	2.074	8.7966 to 25.8034	2.0739	8.7971 to 25.8029
(b)	100	$b_1 = 12.1$	7.2	1.984	-2.1848 to 26.3848	1.9840	-2.1846 to 26.3846
	100	$b_2 = 7.3$	4.1	1.984	-0.8344 to 15.4344	1.9840	-0.8343 to 15.4343

11.2. The test statistic is $t = b_k / \mathrm{SE}_{b_k}$, with $\mathrm{df} = n - 3$. Only b_2 in part (a) is significantly different from 0. (This is consistent with the confidence intervals from the previous exercise.)

	df	Coeff.	SE	t	P (Table D)	P (software)
(a)	22	$b_1 = 12.1$	7.2	1.68	$0.10 < P < 0.20$	0.1070
	22	$b_2 = 17.3$	4.1	4.22	$P < 0.001$	0.0004
(b)	100	$b_1 = 12.1$	7.2	1.68	$0.05 < P < 0.10$	0.0960
	100	$b_2 = 7.3$	4.1	1.78	$0.05 < P < 0.10$	0.0780

11.3. **(a)** This sentence should refer to the *squared* multiple correlation. **(b)** H_0 should refer to β_2 (the population coefficient) rather than b_2 (the estimated coefficient). **(c)** Only the errors (ϵ_i) are assumed to be normal.

11.4. **(a)** $\hat{y} = -2.6 + 4.1(5) - 3.2(3) = 8.3$. **(b)** No: We can compute predicted values for any values of x_1 and x_2 (although of course it helps if they are close to those in the data set). **(c)** This is determined by the coefficient of x_2: An increase of one unit in x_2 results in a *decrease* of 3.2 units in $\hat{y}$.

11.5. **(a)** The hypotheses and test results are:

Hypotheses	t	P	Conclusion
$H_0: \beta_1 = 0$ vs. $H_a: \beta_1 \neq 0$	4.55	$P < 0.001$	Reject H_0; GPA is significant
$H_0: \beta_2 = 0$ vs. $H_a: \beta_2 \neq 0$	2.69	$P < 0.01$	Reject H_0; popularity is significant
$H_0: \beta_3 = 0$ vs. $H_a: \beta_3 \neq 0$	2.69	$P < 0.01$	Reject H_0; depression is significant

(b) $b_1 < 0$, so marijuana use decreases with increasing GPA; b_2 and b_3 are positive, so marijuana use increases with popularity and depression. **(c)** The numbers 3 and 85 are the degrees of freedom of the F statistic ($p = 3$ explanatory variables and $n - p - 1 = 85$ degrees of freedom left over after estimating the four regression coefficients). **(d)** $H_0: \beta_1 = \beta_2 = \beta_3 = 0$ is rejected in favor of H_a: at least one β_i is nonzero. **(e)** Students may have lied (or erred) in their responses, which may make our conclusions unreliable. This risk is especially great because all four variables were measured with questionnaire responses. **(f)** We cannot assume that students are the same everywhere; for example, these conclusions might not hold for nonsuburban students, or those who live in other states.

11.6. The hypotheses are essentially the same as in the previous exercise, so they are not restated here. We see from the test results that, as for marijuana, cigarette and alcohol use decreases with increasing GPA, and increases with increasing popularity and depression. Cocaine use also decreases as GPA increases, but it also drops when popularity increases, and is not significantly affected by depression. The sizes of the coefficients also tell us the relative impact of the explanatory variables; for example, the effect of increasing GPA is similar for marijuana and cocaine, but considerably less for cigarettes and alcohol. Similarly, the sizes of R^2 and F give some indication of the predictive usefulness of these regression formulas.

   Note: *The problem of doing several significance tests deserves mention here. A procedure such as the Bonferroni method (first mentioned in Chapter 6, and discussed further in Chapter 12) would say that, as we are performing 12 t tests, we should have $P < 0.05/12 \doteq 0.0042$ before we declare a result significant at the 5% level. By this standard, considerably fewer of the individual coefficients would be significantly different from 0.*

11.7. **(a)** Because this coefficient is negative, U.S. subjects are *less* willing to pay more. (Specifically, for a U.S. and U.K. subject for which all other characteristics are the same, we predict that the U.K. subject would be willing to pay about 0.2304 units more than the U.S. subject.) **(b)** We have $t = -4.196$ and df ≈ 1800 (the question does not clearly state how many explanatory variables are being used). For testing $H_0: \beta_1 = 0$ vs. $H_a: \beta_1 \neq 0$, Table D tells us that $P < 0.001$. (In fact, it is much smaller than that—software gives $P \doteq 0.00003$.) **(c)** The U.K. response rate is much lower than the U.S. rate, so we might have missed a significant portion of U.K. opinion. Also, "don't know" responses are not much better than no response at all.

11.8. **(a)** No—at least, not entirely. Assuming that we had a standard regression model, we know that the fitted regression equation is $\hat{y} = b_0 + 1.02x_1 + 0.96x_2 + 0.30x_3$; the constant b_0 is not given. **(b)** No: With a multiple regression model, it can happen that some individual coefficients are not significantly different from 0, because those tests "assess the significance of each predictor variable assuming that all other predictors are included in the regression equation." **(c)** With $n = 282$ and $p = 3$, the degrees of freedom for the F statistic are 3 and 278. The P-value for this F statistic is very small; 45.64 is much larger than 5.63, the largest critical value listed for an $F(3, 200)$ distribution in Table E. **(d)** The regression explains $R^2 = 33\%$ of the variation in exercise enjoyment. **(e)** It seems likely that men and women differ in how they respond to exercise in general (and aerobic dance in particular), so we should be reluctant to extend these results to men.

11.9. **(a)** $y_i = \beta_0 + \beta_1 x_{i1} + \beta_2 x_{i2} + \cdots + \beta_6 x_{i6} + \epsilon_i$, where $i = 1, 2, \ldots, 200$, and ϵ_i are independent $N(0, \sigma)$ random variables. **(b)** The sources of variation are model (df $= p = 6$), error (df $= n - p - 1 = 193$), and total (df $= n - 1 = 199$).

11.10. **(a)** With $n = 54$ and $p = 3$, the degrees of freedom in the ANOVA table are DFM $= p = 3$, DFE $= n - p - 1 = 50$, and DFT $= n - 1 = 53$. With the first two degrees of freedom, we can find MSM = SSM/DFM = 6 and MSE = SSE/DFE = 2, and then compute $F = $ MSM/MSE $= 3$. (b) The degrees of freedom for the F statistic are DFM $= 3$ and DFE $= 50$. (c) Because $2.79 < F < 3.39$, $0.025 < P < 0.050$. (Software gives $P = 0.039$.)

For reference, the whole ANOVA table looks like this:

SOURCE	DF	SS	MS	F	p
Model	3	18	6	3	0.039
Error	50	100	2		
Total	53	118			

11.11. $R^2 = \dfrac{\text{SSM}}{\text{SST}} = \dfrac{18}{118} \doteq 0.1525$.

11.12. No (or at least, not necessarily). It is possible that, although no individual coefficient is significant, the whole group (or some subset) is. Recall that the t tests "assess the significance of each predictor variable assuming that all other predictors are included in the regression equation." If one variable is removed from the model (because its t statistic is not significant), we can no longer use the other t statistics to draw conclusions about the remaining coefficients.

11.13. (a) The regression equation is $\widehat{\text{SCORE}} = 3.33 + 0.82\,\text{UNFAV} + 0.57\,\text{FAV}$. (b) Because $P < 0.01$, we reject H_0: $\beta_1 = \beta_2 = 0$ in favor of H_a: at least one of β_1 and β_2 is nonzero. (c) The estimates of β_0, β_1, and β_2 are all significantly different from 0 (all have $P < 0.01$). (d) The t statistics have df $= n - p - 1 = 152 - 2 - 1 = 149$.

11.14. (a) The regression equation is $\widehat{\text{SCORE}} = 3.96 + 0.86\,\text{UNFAV} + 0.66\,\text{FAV}$. (b) Because $P < 0.01$, we reject H_0: $\beta_1 = \beta_2 = 0$ in favor of H_a: at least one of β_1 and β_2 is nonzero. (c) The estimates of β_0, β_1, and β_2 are all significantly different from 0 (all have $P < 0.01$). (d) The t statistics have df $= n - p - 1 = 162 - 2 - 1 = 159$.

11.15. All coefficients are positive, so the associations are positive, as expected. The unfavorable coefficients are larger than (and their t statistics at least as large as) those for favorable nutrients, so unfavorable nutrients do have a stronger effect.

11.16. (a) The scatterplot (below, left) suggests a positive association with a slight curve. (b) The regression equation is $\widehat{\text{ASSETS}} = -17.121 + 0.0832\,\text{ACCTS}$, with $s \doteq 20.19$ and $R^2 = 0.938$. The slope is significantly different from 0: $t = 10.96$ (df $= 8$) for which $P < 0.0005$. (c) The residual scatterplot (below, right) also suggests a curved relationship: The residuals are negative in the middle, and positive on the left and right ends. (d) The regression equation is $\widehat{\text{ASSETS}} = 7.608 - 0.00457\,\text{ACCTS} + 0.00003361\,\text{ACCTS}^2$, with $s = 12.41$ and $R^2 = 0.979$. The coefficient of ACCTS is *not* significantly different from 0 ($t = -0.19$, $P = 0.853$), but the coefficient of ACCTS^2 is ($t = 3.76$, $P = 0.007$). (The constant b_0 is also not significantly different from 0.) The plot of residuals against accounts (or squared accounts) is not shown, but reveals no obvious pattern.

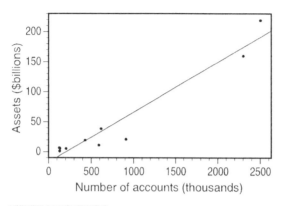 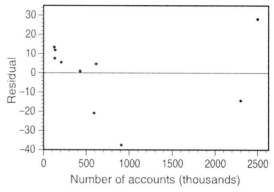

Minitab output

```
– – – – – – – – – – – – – – –  Linear model   – – – – – – – – – – – – – – –
The regression equation is assets = -17.1 + 0.0832 accts

Predictor      Coef      Stdev     t-ratio        p
Constant     -17.121     8.778      -1.95      0.087
accts       0.083205   0.007592     10.96      0.000

s = 20.19      R-sq = 93.8%     R-sq(adj) = 93.0%
– – – – – – – – – – – – – – –  Quadratic model  – – – – – – – – – – – – – – –
The regression equation is assets = 7.61 - 0.0046 accts + 0.000034 acctsqd

Predictor       Coef        Stdev     t-ratio       p
Constant       7.608        8.503       0.89      0.401
accts        -0.00457      0.02378     -0.19      0.853
acctsqd     0.00003361   0.00000893    3.76      0.007

s = 12.41      R-sq = 97.9%     R-sq(adj) = 97.3%
```

11.17. With the altered quadratic term, the regression equation is $\widehat{\text{ASSETS}} =$
$-13.558 - 0.04877\,\text{ACCTS} + 0.00003361(\text{ACCTS} - 793.6)^2$, with $s = 12.41$ and $R^2 = 0.979$.
The coefficient of the new quadratic term and its standard error (and therefore its t statistics
and P-value) are the same as for the old quadratic term. Also, the values of s and R^2 are
unchanged. The constant term and the coefficient of ACCTS are now both significantly
different from 0.

   Note: *The estimates b_0 and b_1 for the new model can be obtained from those in the old
model in a fairly simple way. Note that $(\text{ACCTS} - 793.6)^2 = \text{ACCTS}^2 - 1587.2\,\text{ACCTS} + 793.6^2$.
Therefore, new $b_0 = $ old $b_0 - 793.6^2 b_2$ and new $b_1 = $ old $b_1 + 1587.2 b_2$.*

Minitab output

```
– – – – – – – – – – – – –  Modified quadratic model   – – – – – – – – – – – –
The regression equation is assets = -13.6 + 0.0488 accts + 0.000034 accts2

Predictor       Coef        Stdev     t-ratio       p
Constant      -13.558       5.479      -2.47      0.043
accts        0.04877       0.01027      4.75      0.000
accts2     0.00003361   0.00000893     3.76      0.007

s = 12.41        R-sq = 97.9%     R-sq(adj) = 97.3%
```

11.18. Students might identify the two outliers differently. Some might choose the two points with 2300 and 2500 thousand accounts (Charles Schwab and Fidelity). If they do so, the regression results are shown below. (The quadratic regression was done using both of the models from the previous two exercises.) Without these points, the regression is less useful for prediction; the coefficients are, at best, on the borderline of significance, and R^2 is much smaller than before.

Minitab output

```
– – – – – – – – –   Linear model without Schwab and Fidelity   – – – – – – – – –
The regression equation is assets = 2.13 + 0.0297 accts

Predictor        Coef       Stdev      t-ratio        p
Constant        2.131       5.787        0.37      0.725
accts         0.02967     0.01211        2.45      0.050

s = 9.369        R-sq = 50.0%      R-sq(adj) = 41.7%
– – – – – – – –   Quadratic model without Schwab and Fidelity   – – – – – – – –
The regression equation is assets = -6.74 + 0.0887 accts - 0.000063 acctsqd

Predictor        Coef       Stdev      t-ratio        p
Constant       -6.737       9.204       -0.73      0.497
accts         0.08874     0.05016        1.77      0.137
acctsqd   -0.00006251  0.00005163       -1.21      0.280

s = 9.025        R-sq = 61.4%      R-sq(adj) = 45.9%
– – – – – –   Modified quadratic model without Schwab and Fidelity   – – – – – –
The regression equation is assets = 32.6 - 0.0105 accts - 0.000063 accts2

Predictor        Coef       Stdev      t-ratio        p
Constant        32.63      25.80         1.26      0.262
accts         -0.01048    0.03516       -0.30      0.778
accts2    -0.00006251  0.00005163       -1.21      0.280

s = 9.025        R-sq = 61.4%      R-sq(adj) = 45.9%
```

Other students might identify as outliers the two points that had the largest residuals in the original linear fit (Charles Schwab and E*Trade). Note, though, that these two points did *not* have the largest residuals for the quadratic fit, so this choice of outliers is perhaps not as good as the first. Without these two points, R^2 rises slightly for all models, but we see that the coefficients for the quadratic terms are not significantly different from 0—the linear model appears to be the best in this case.

Minitab output

```
– – – – – – – –   Linear model without Schwab and E*Trade   – – – – – – – –
The regression equation is assets = -9.66 + 0.0721 accts

Predictor        Coef       Stdev      t-ratio        p
Constant       -9.659       4.582       -2.11      0.080
accts         0.072072    0.005166      13.95      0.000

s = 9.978        R-sq = 97.0%      R-sq(adj) = 96.5%
```

```
------- Quadratic model without Schwab and E*Trade  --------
The regression equation is assets = -0.46 + 0.0345 accts + 0.000015 acctsqd

Predictor      Coef       Stdev     t-ratio        p
Constant      -0.463      6.639      -0.07       0.947
accts         0.03451     0.02219     1.56       0.181
acctsqd       0.00001533  0.00000887  1.73       0.144

s = 8.648      R-sq = 98.1%     R-sq(adj) = 97.4%
------- Modified quadratic model without Schwab and E*Trade  -------
The regression equation is assets = -10.1 + 0.0588 accts + 0.000015 accts2

Predictor      Coef       Stdev     t-ratio        p
Constant     -10.120      3.980      -2.54       0.052
accts         0.058847    0.008865    6.64       0.001
accts2        0.00001533  0.00000887  1.73       0.144

s = 8.648      R-sq = 98.1%     R-sq(adj) = 97.4%
```

11.19. The plot of log-assets against log-accounts (below, left) appears to be reasonably linear. The regression equation is $\hat{y} = -5.058 + 1.2885x$ with $s = 0.6291$, $R^2 = 0.858$, $t = 6.96$, and $P < 0.0005$. A plot of residuals against log-accounts (below, right) suggests no particular pattern.

Minitab output

```
The regression equation is logasset = -5.06 + 1.29 logaccts

Predictor      Coef       Stdev     t-ratio        p
Constant      -5.058      1.150      -4.40       0.002
logaccts       1.2885     0.1852      6.96       0.000

s = 0.6291     R-sq = 85.8%     R-sq(adj) = 84.0%
```

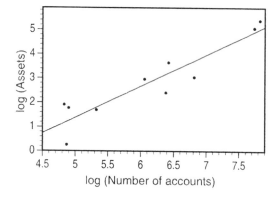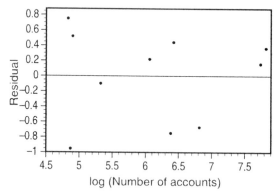

11.20. The three regression equations and associated results are:

	$\widehat{ASSETS} =$		s	R^2	t	P
(a)	$-17.12 + 0.0832$ ACCTS		20.19	0.938	10.96	$P < 0.0005$
(b)	-19.90	$+ 7.680$ MSHARE	50.54	0.609	3.53	$P = 0.008$
(c)	$-21.45 + 0.0756$ ACCTS $+ 1.158$ MSHARE		20.52	0.944	6.44	$P < 0.0005$
					0.86	$P = 0.418$

(d) Between the three models, (a) seems to be the best. Based on R^2, it is clearly better than (b), and only slightly worse than (c). The model in (c) is more complicated, and the market-share component does not make a significant contribution when the number of accounts is included in the model.

Minitab output

```
– – – – – – – – – – – – –   Number of accounts   – – – – – – – – – – – – – – –
The regression equation is assets = -17.1 + 0.0832 accts

Predictor       Coef        Stdev     t-ratio        p
Constant     -17.121        8.778       -1.95    0.087
accts       0.083205     0.007592       10.96    0.000

s = 20.19       R-sq = 93.8%      R-sq(adj) = 93.0%
– – – – – – – – – – – – – – –   Market share   – – – – – – – – – – – – – – –
The regression equation is assets = -19.9 + 7.68 mshare

Predictor       Coef        Stdev     t-ratio        p
Constant      -19.90        25.22       -0.79    0.453
mshare         7.680        2.177        3.53    0.008

s = 50.54       R-sq = 60.9%      R-sq(adj) = 56.0%
– – – – – – – – – – – – – – – – –   Both   – – – – – – – – – – – – – – – – –
The regression equation is assets = -21.5 + 0.0756 accts + 1.16 mshare

Predictor       Coef        Stdev     t-ratio        p
Constant      -21.45        10.24       -2.09    0.074
accts        0.07559      0.01173        6.44    0.000
mshare         1.158        1.344        0.86    0.418

s = 20.52       R-sq = 94.4%      R-sq(adj) = 92.7%
```

11.21. (a) H_0: $\beta_1 = \beta_2 = \cdots = \beta_{13} = 0$ vs. H_a: at least one $\beta_j \neq 0$. The degrees of freedom are 13 and 2215, and $P < 0.001$ (referring to an $F(12, 1000)$ distribution). We have strong evidence that at least one coefficient is not 0. (b) The regression explains 29.7% of the variation. (c) Each t statistic tests H_0: $\beta_j = 0$ vs. H_a: $\beta_j \neq 0$, and has df = 2215. The critical value is $t^* = 1.961$, so we reject H_0 if $|t| > 1.961$. (d) The only three coefficients that are *not* significantly different from 0 are those for "total payments," "male borrower," and "married." (e) Interest rates are lower for larger loans, for longer terms, with larger down payments, when there is a cosigner, when the loan is secured, when the borrower has a higher income, when the credit report is not considered "bad," for older borrowers, when the borrower owns a home, and for borrowers who have lived for a long time at their present address.

11.22. (a) H_0: $\beta_1 = \beta_2 = \cdots = \beta_{13} = 0$ vs. H_a: at least one $\beta_j \neq 0$. The degrees of freedom are 13 and 5650, and $P < 0.001$ (referring to an $F(12, 1000)$ distribution). We have strong evidence that at least one of the β_j is not 0. (b) The regression explains 14.1% of the variation—much less than for the direct loans. (c) Each t statistic tests H_0: $\beta_j = 0$ vs. H_a: $\beta_j \neq 0$, and has df = 5650. The critical value is $t^* = 1.9604$. (d) Only the coefficients of "loan size," "length of loan," "percent down payment," and "unsecured loan" are significantly different from 0. (e) Interest rates are lower for larger loans, for longer terms, with larger down payments, and when the loan is secured.

11.23. In 11.21, we found that ten factors have a significant effect on the interest rate for direct loans, while based on 11.22, only four of the factors examined have a significant impact on the interest rate for indirect loans. Furthermore, the proportion of variation in interest rates explained by the regression is greater for direct loans than for indirect loans.

11.24. (a) Between GPA and IQ, $r = 0.634$ (straight-line regression explains $r^2 = 40.2\%$ of the variation in GPA). Between GPA and self-concept, $r = 0.542$ (straight-line regression explains $r^2 = 29.4\%$ of the variation in GPA). Since gender is categorical, the correlation between GPA and gender is not meaningful. **(b)** The model is $\text{GPA} = \beta_0 + \beta_1 \text{IQ} + \beta_2 \text{SC} + \epsilon_i$, where ϵ_i are independent $N(0, \sigma)$ random variables. **(c)** Regression gives the equation $\widehat{\text{GPA}} = -3.88 + 0.0772 \, \text{IQ} + 0.0513 \, \text{SC}$. Based on the reported value of R^2, the regression explains 47.1% of the variation in GPA. (So the inclusion of self-concept only adds about 6.9% to the variation explained by the regression.) **(d)** We test $H_0: \beta_2 = 0$ vs. $H_a: \beta_2 \neq 0$. The test statistic $t = 3.14$ (df $= 75$) has $P = 0.002$; we conclude that the coefficient of self-concept is not 0.

Minitab output

```
The regression equation is GPA = -3.88 + 0.0772 IQ + 0.0513 SelfCcpt

Predictor      Coef       Stdev    t-ratio        p
Constant     -3.882       1.472      -2.64    0.010
IQ           0.07720     0.01539      5.02    0.000
SelfCcpt     0.05125     0.01633      3.14    0.002

s = 1.547      R-sq = 47.1%     R-sq(adj) = 45.7%
```

11.25. A 95% prediction interval is $\$2.136 \pm (1.984)(\$0.013)$, or $\$2.1102$ to $\$2.1618$. The actual price falls in this interval (in fact, it is less than one standard error below the predicted value), so there is not enough evidence to reject H_0, which in this situation would be "there was no manipulation."

11.26. (a) Stemplots (below) show that all four variables are right-skewed to some degree. The means and standard deviations are given in the table on the right. **(b)** Correlations and scatterplots (below) show that all six pairs of variables are positively associated. The strongest association is between VO+ and VO−, and the weakest is between OC and VO−.

	Mean	SD
VO+	985.806	579.858
VO−	889.194	427.616
OC	33.416	19.610
TRAP	13.248	6.528

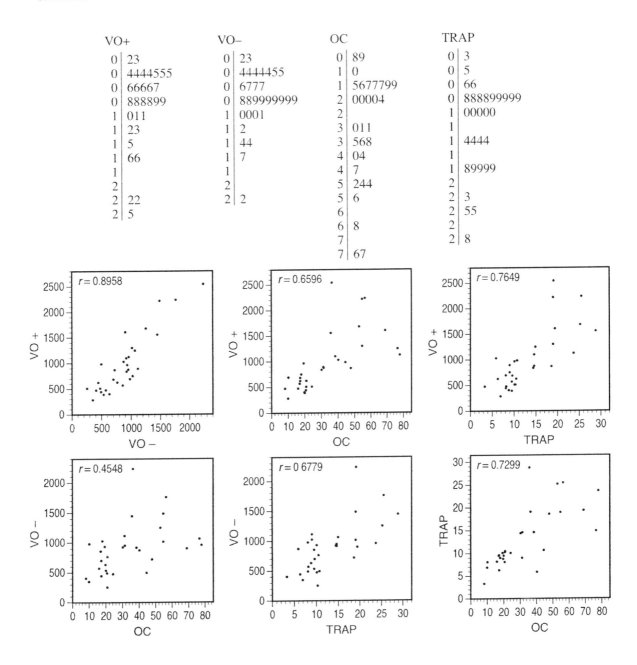

```
VO+              VO–              OC               TRAP
0 | 23           0 | 23           0 | 89           0 | 3
0 | 4444555      0 | 4444455      1 | 0            0 | 5
0 | 66667        0 | 6777         1 | 5677799      0 | 66
0 | 888899       0 | 889999999    2 | 00004        0 | 888899999
1 | 011          1 | 0001         2 |              1 | 00000
1 | 23           1 | 2            3 | 011          1 |
1 | 5            1 | 44           3 | 568          1 | 4444
1 | 66           1 | 7            4 | 04           1 |
1 |              1 |              4 | 7            1 | 89999
2 |              2 |              5 | 244          2 |
2 | 22           2 | 2            5 | 6            2 | 3
2 | 5                             6 |             2 | 55
                                  6 | 8            2 |
                                  7 |              2 | 8
                                  7 | 67
```

11.27. (a) See the previous solution for the scatterplot, which suggests greater variation in VO+ for large OC. The regression equation is $\widehat{\text{VOplus}} = 334.0 + 19.505\text{ OC}$ with $s \doteq 443.3$ and $R^2 \doteq 0.435$; the test statistic for the slope is $t = 4.73$ ($P < 0.0005$), so we conclude the slope is not zero. The plot of residuals against OC suggests a slight downward curve on the right end, as well as the increasing scatter as OC increases. The residuals are

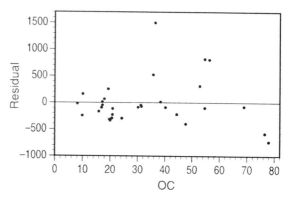

also somewhat right-skewed. A stemplot and normal quantile plot of the residuals are not shown here, but could be included as part of the analysis. **(b)** The regression equation is $\widehat{\text{VOplus}} = 57.7 + 6.415\text{ OC} + 53.87\text{ TRAP}$ with $s \doteq 376.3$ and $R^2 \doteq 0.607$. The coefficient of OC is not significantly different from 0 ($t = 1.25$, $P = 0.221$), but the coefficient of TRAP is ($t = 3.50$, $P = 0.002$). This is consistent with the correlations found in the solution to Exercise 11.26: TRAP is more highly correlated with VO+, and is also highly correlated with OC, so it is reasonable that if TRAP is present in the model, little additional information is gained from OC.

Minitab output

```
– – – – – – – – – – – – – –  Model 1: OC only  – – – – – – – – – – – – – –
The regression equation is VOplus = 334 + 19.5 OC

Predictor      Coef       Stdev     t-ratio        p
Constant       334.0      159.2        2.10     0.045
OC             19.505     4.127        4.73     0.000

s = 443.3       R-sq = 43.5%     R-sq(adj) = 41.6%
– – – – – – – – – – – – – –  Model 2: OC and TRAP  – – – – – – – – – – – – – –
The regression equation is VOplus = 58 + 6.41 OC + 53.9 TRAP

Predictor      Coef       Stdev     t-ratio        p
Constant       57.7       156.5        0.37     0.715
OC             6.415      5.125        1.25     0.221
TRAP           53.87      15.39        3.50     0.002

s = 376.3       R-sq = 60.7%     R-sq(adj) = 57.9%
```

11.28. (a) The model is $\text{VOplus} = \beta_0 + \beta_1\text{ OC} + \beta_2\text{ TRAP} + \beta_2\text{ VOminus} + \epsilon_i$, where ϵ_i are independent $N(0, \sigma)$ random variables. **(b)** See the table below for this regression equation and the significance test results. **(c) & (d)** The table below summarizes the results for the three regressions. The estimated coefficients and P-values can change rather drastically from one model to the next. Generally, R^2 increases (sometimes only slightly) as we add more explanatory variables to the model. **(e)** The results of the regression in (b) suggest that we remove TRAP from the model. This regression equation and associated results are also in the table below. Because R^2 drops only slightly for this simpler model, this is probably the best of all models we have considered to this point.

Equation: $\widehat{VOplus} =$				R^2	s
334.0	+ 19.505 OC			0.435	443.3
	SE = 4.127				
	$t = 4.73$				
	$P < 0.0005$				
57.7	+ 6.415 OC	+ 53.87 TRAP		0.607	376.3
	SE = 5.125	SE = 15.39			
	$t = 1.25$	$t = 3.50$			
	$P = 0.221$	$P = 0.002$			
−243.5	+ 8.235 OC	+ 6.61 TRAP	+ 0.975 VOminus	0.884	207.8
	SE = 2.840	SE = 10.33	SE = 0.1211		
	$t = 2.90$	$t = 0.64$	$t = 8.05$		
	$P = 0.007$	$P = 0.528$	$P < 0.0005$		
−234.1	+ 9.404 OC		+ 1.019 VOminus	0.883	205.6
	SE = 2.150		SE = 0.0986		
	$t = 4.37$		$t = 10.33$		
	$P < 0.0005$		$P < 0.0005$		

Minitab output

```
– – – – – – – – – –     Model 3: OC, TRAP and VOminus   – – – – – – – – – –
The regression equation is VOplus = -243 + 8.23 OC + 6.6 TRAP + 0.975 VOminus

Predictor      Coef      Stdev     t-ratio       p
Constant    -243.49      94.22      -2.58      0.015
OC            8.235      2.840       2.90      0.007
TRAP          6.61      10.33        0.64      0.528
VOminus      0.9746     0.1211       8.05      0.000

s = 207.8      R-sq = 88.4%     R-sq(adj) = 87.2%
– – – – – – – – – – – –     Model 4: OC and VOminus   – – – – – – – – – – – –
The regression equation is VOplus = -234 + 9.40 OC + 1.02 VOminus

Predictor      Coef      Stdev     t-ratio       p
Constant    -234.14      92.09      -2.54      0.017
OC            9.404      2.150       4.37      0.000
VOminus     1.01857    0.09858      10.33      0.000

s = 205.6      R-sq = 88.3%      R-sq(adj) = 87.4%
```

11.29. Stemplots (below) show that all four variables are noticeably less skewed. The means and standard deviations are
given in the table on the right. Correlations and scatterplots
(below) show that all six pairs of variables are positively
associated. The strongest association is between LVO+ and

	Mean	SD
logVO+	6.7418	0.5555
logVO–	6.6816	0.4832
logOC	3.3380	0.6085
logTRAP	2.4674	0.4978

LVO–, and the weakest is between LOC and LVO–. The regression equations for these transformed variables are given in the table below, along with significance test results. Residual
analysis for these regressions is not shown here.

The final conclusion is the same as for the untransformed data: When we use all three
explanatory variables to predict LVO+, the coefficient of LTRAP is not significantly different from 0, and we then find that the model which uses LOC and LVO– to predict LVO+ is
nearly as good (in terms of R^2), making it the best of the bunch.

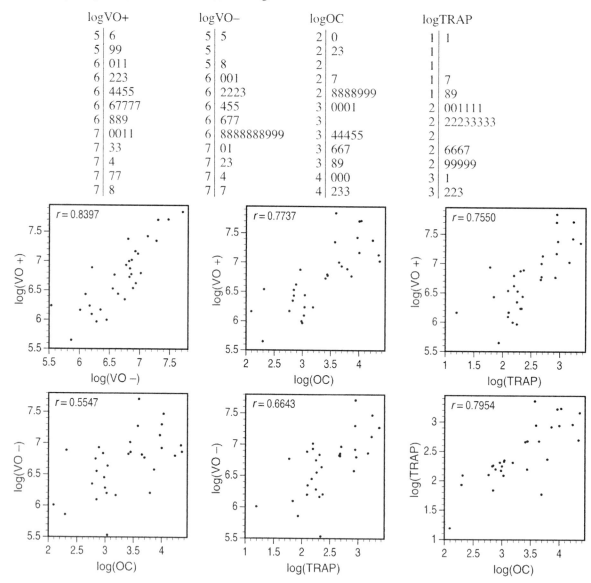

Equation: LVOplus =				R^2	s
4.3841	+ 0.7063 LOC			0.599	0.3580
	SE = 0.1074				
	$t = 6.58$				
	$P < 0.0005$				
4.2590	+ 0.4304 LOC	+ 0.4240 LTRAP		0.652	0.3394
	SE = 0.1680	SE = 0.2054			
	$t = 2.56$	$t = 2.06$			
	$P = 0.016$	$P = 0.048$			
0.8716	+ 0.3922 LOC	+ 0.0275 LTRAP	+ 0.6725 LVOminus	0.842	0.2326
	SE = 0.1154	SE = 0.1570	SE = 0.1178		
	$t = 3.40$	$t = 0.18$	$t = 5.71$		
	$P = 0.002$	$P = 0.862$	$P < 0.0005$		
0.8321	+ 0.4061 LOC		+ 0.6816 LVOminus	0.842	0.2286
	SE = 0.0824		SE = 0.1038		
	$t = 4.93$		$t = 6.57$		
	$P < 0.0005$		$P < 0.0005$		

11.30. Refer to the solution to Exercise 11.26 for the scatterplots. Note that, in this case, it really makes the most sense to use TRAP to predict VO– (because it is the appropriate biomarker), but many students might miss that detail. Both single-explanatory variable models are given in the table below. Residual analysis plots are not included. As before, we find the best model is to use OC and VO+ to predict VO–.

Equation: $\widehat{\text{VOminus}} =$				R^2	s
557.8	+ 9.917 OC			0.207	387.4
	SE = 3.606				
	t = 2.75				
	P = 0.010				
300.9		+ 44.41 TRAP		0.460	319.7
		SE = 8.942			
		t = 4.97			
		$P < 0.0005$			
309.1	− 1.868 OC	+ 48.50 TRAP		0.463	324.4
	SE = 4.418	SE = 13.27			
	t = −0.42	t = 3.66			
	P = 0.676	P = 0.001			
267.3	− 6.513 OC	+ 9.485 TRAP	+ 0.724 VOplus	0.842	179.2
	SE = 2.507	SE = 10.33	SE = 0.0900		
	t = −2.60	t = 1.08	t = 8.05		
	P = 0.015	P = 0.290	$P < 0.0005$		
298.0	− 5.254 OC		+ 0.778 VOplus	0.835	179.7
	SE = 2.226		SE = 0.0753		
	t = −2.36		t = 10.33		
	P = 0.025		$P < 0.0005$		

11.31. Refer to the solution to Exercise 11.28 for the scatterplots. Note that, in this case, it really makes the most sense to use LTRAP to predict LVO– (because it is the appropriate biomarker), but many students might miss that detail. Both single-explanatory variable models are given in the table below. Residual analysis plots are not included. This time, we might conclude that the best model is to predict LVO– from LVO+ alone; neither biomarker variable makes an indispensable contribution to the prediction.

Equation: $\widehat{\text{LVOminus}}$ =			R^2	s
5.2110 $\quad$ + 0.4406 LOC			0.308	0.4089
$\quad\quad\quad$ SE = 0.1227				
$\quad\quad\quad$ t = 3.59				
$\quad\quad\quad$ P = 0.001				
5.0905 $\quad\quad\quad\quad\quad\quad\quad$ + 0.6449 LTRAP			0.441	0.3674
$\quad\quad\quad\quad\quad\quad\quad\quad$ SE = 0.1347				
$\quad\quad\quad\quad\quad\quad\quad\quad$ t = 4.79				
$\quad\quad\quad\quad\quad\quad\quad\quad$ P < 0.0005				
5.0370 $\quad$ + 0.0569 LOC $\quad$ + 0.5896 LTRAP			0.443	0.3732
$\quad\quad\quad$ SE = 0.1848 $\quad\quad$ SE = 0.2259				
$\quad\quad\quad$ t = 0.31 $\quad\quad\quad\quad$ t = 2.61				
$\quad\quad\quad$ P = 0.761 $\quad\quad\quad$ P = 0.014				
1.5729 $\quad$ − 0.2932 LOC $\quad$ + 0.2447 LTRAP $\quad$ + 0.8134 LVOplus			0.748	0.2558
$\quad\quad\quad$ SE = 0.1407 $\quad\quad$ SE = 0.1662 $\quad\quad$ SE = 0.1425				
$\quad\quad\quad$ t = −2.08 $\quad\quad\quad$ t = 1.47 $\quad\quad\quad$ t = 5.71				
$\quad\quad\quad$ P = 0.047 $\quad\quad\quad$ P = 0.152 $\quad\quad$ P < 0.0005				
1.3109 $\quad$ − 0.1878 LOC $\quad\quad\quad\quad\quad\quad\quad$ + 0.8896 LVOplus			0.728	0.2611
$\quad\quad\quad$ SE = 0.1237 $\quad\quad\quad\quad\quad\quad\quad\quad$ SE = 0.1355				
$\quad\quad\quad$ t = −1.52 $\quad\quad\quad\quad\quad\quad\quad\quad$ t = 6.57				
$\quad\quad\quad$ P = 0.140 $\quad\quad\quad\quad\quad\quad\quad$ P < 0.0005				
1.7570 $\quad\quad\quad\quad\quad\quad\quad\quad\quad\quad\quad\quad$ + 0.7304 LVOplus			0.705	0.2669
$\quad\quad\quad\quad\quad\quad\quad\quad\quad\quad\quad\quad$ SE = 0.0877				
$\quad\quad\quad\quad\quad\quad\quad\quad\quad\quad\quad\quad$ t = 8.33				
$\quad\quad\quad\quad\quad\quad\quad\quad\quad\quad\quad$ P < 0.0005				

11.32. (a) Means and standard deviations are given in the table on the right; histograms are below. All distributions are sharply right-skewed. **(b)** Scatterplots and correlations below. All pairs of variables are positively associated, although some only weakly. In general, even when the association is strong, the plots show more variation for large values of the two variables. One correlation (PCB52/PCB180) is not significantly different from 0 (r = 0.0869, t = 0.71, P = 0.4775). The correlation between PCB52/PCB138 is significantly different from 0 at α = 0.05 but not 0.01 (r = 0.3009, t = 2.58, P = 0.0120). All others have P < 0.0005.

	Mean	SD
PCB	68.4674	59.3906
PCB52	0.9580	1.5983
PCB118	3.2563	3.0191
PCB138	6.8268	5.8627
PCB180	4.1584	4.9864

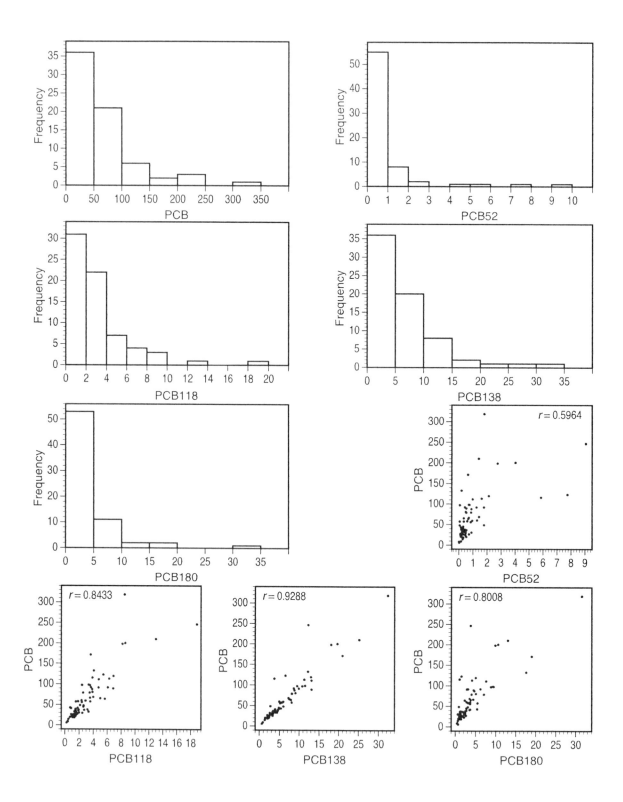

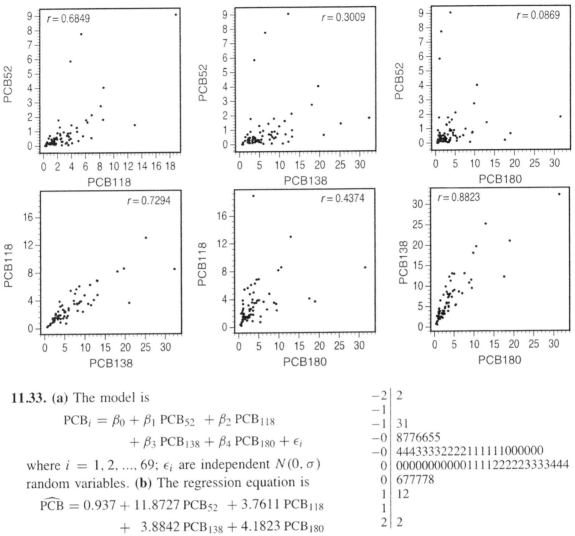

11.33. (a) The model is

$$PCB_i = \beta_0 + \beta_1\,PCB_{52} + \beta_2\,PCB_{118}$$
$$+ \beta_3\,PCB_{138} + \beta_4\,PCB_{180} + \epsilon_i$$

where $i = 1, 2, ..., 69$; ϵ_i are independent $N(0, \sigma)$ random variables. (b) The regression equation is

$$\widehat{PCB} = 0.937 + 11.8727\,PCB_{52} + 3.7611\,PCB_{118}$$
$$+ 3.8842\,PCB_{138} + 4.1823\,PCB_{180}$$

```
-2 | 2
-1 |
-1 | 31
-0 | 8776655
-0 | 4443333322221111111000000
 0 | 00000000000011112222223333444
 0 | 677778
 1 | 12
 1 |
 2 | 2
```

with $s = 6.382$ and $R^2 = 0.989$. All coefficients are significantly different from 0, although the constant 0.937 is not ($t = 0.76$, $P = 0.449$). That makes some sense—if none of these four congeners are present, it might be somewhat reasonable to predict that the total amount of PCB is 0. (c) The residuals appear to be roughly normal, but with two outliers. There are no clear patterns when plotted against the explanatory variables (these plots are not shown).

Minitab output

```
The regression equation is
PCB = 0.94 + 11.9 PCB52 + 3.76 PCB118 + 3.88 PCB138 + 4.18 PCB180

Predictor      Coef      Stdev     t-ratio        p
Constant      0.937      1.229        0.76    0.449
PCB52       11.8727     0.7290       16.29    0.000
PCB118       3.7611     0.6424        5.85    0.000
PCB138       3.8842     0.4978        7.80    0.000
PCB180       4.1823     0.4318        9.69    0.000

s = 6.382      R-sq = 98.9%      R-sq(adj) = 98.8%
```

11.34. (a) The outliers are specimen #50 (residual -22.0864) and #65 (22.5487). Because residuals are observed values minus predicted values, the negative residual (#50) is an overestimate. (The estimated PCB for this specimen is $\widehat{PCB} \doteq 144.882$, and the actual level was 122.796.) **(b)** The regression equation is

$$\widehat{PCB} = 1.6277 + 14.4420\,PCB_{52} + 2.5996\,PCB_{118}$$
$$+ 4.0541\,PCB_{138} + 4.1086\,PCB_{180}$$

with $s = 4.555$ and $R^2 = 0.994$. As before, all coefficients are significantly different from 0, although the constant is barely not different ($t = 1.84$, $P = 0.071$). The residuals again appear to be roughly normal, but two new specimens (#44 and #58) show up as outliers to replace the two we removed. There are no clear patterns when plotted against the explanatory variables (these plots are not shown).

```
-1 | 2
-1 |
-0 | 98
-0 | 76
-0 | 5544
-0 | 33332222
-0 | 111111111100000000000
 0 | 0000000000111111
 0 | 22233
 0 | 445
 0 | 677
 0 | 889
 1 |
 1 |
 1 | 4
```

Minitab output

```
The regression equation is
PCB = 1.63 + 14.4 PCB52 + 2.60 PCB118 + 4.05 PCB138 + 4.11 PCB180

Predictor       Coef        Stdev      t-ratio         p
Constant      1.6277       0.8858         1.84     0.071
PCB52        14.4420       0.6960        20.75     0.000
PCB118        2.5996       0.5164         5.03     0.000
PCB138        4.0541       0.3752        10.80     0.000
PCB180        4.1086       0.3175        12.94     0.000

s = 4.555       R-sq = 99.4%      R-sq(adj) = 99.4%
```

11.35. (a) The regression equation is

$$\widehat{PCB} = -1.018 + 12.644\,PCB_{52} + 0.3131\,PCB_{118} + 8.2546\,PCB_{138}$$

with $s = 9.945$ and $R^2 = 0.973$. Residual analysis (not shown) suggests a few areas of concern: The distribution of residuals has heavier tails than a normal distribution, and the scatter (that is, prediction error) is greater for larger values of the predicted PCB. **(b)** The estimated coefficient of PCB118 is $b_2 \doteq 0.3131$; its P-value is 0.708. (Details in Minitab output below.) **(c)** In Exercise 11.33, $b_2 \doteq 3.7611$ and $P < 0.0005$. **(d)** This illustrates how complicated multiple regression can be: When we add PCB180 to the model, it complements PCB118, making it useful for prediction.

Minitab output

```
The regression equation is
PCB = -1.02 + 12.6 PCB52 + 0.313 PCB118 + 8.25 PCB138

Predictor       Coef        Stdev      t-ratio         p
Constant     -1.018        1.890        -0.54     0.592
PCB52        12.644        1.129        11.20     0.000
PCB118        0.3131       0.8333        0.38     0.708
PCB138        8.2546       0.3279       25.18     0.000

s = 9.945       R-sq = 97.3%      R-sq(adj) = 97.2%
```

11.36. (a) Because TEQ is defined as the sum TEQPCB + TEQDIOXIN + TEQFURAN, we have $\beta_0 = 0$ and $\beta_1 = \beta_2 = \beta_3 = 1$. **(b)** The error terms are all zero, so they have no scatter; therefore, $\sigma = 0$. **(c)** Except for rounding error, the regression confirms the values in (a) and (b).

Minitab output

```
The regression equation is
TEQ =0.000000 + 1.00 TEQPCB + 1.00 TEQDIOXIN + 1.00 TEQFURAN

Predictor       Coef       Stdev    t-ratio        p
Constant  0.00000032  0.00000192       0.16    0.870
TEQPCB       1.00000     0.00000 1211707.25    0.000
TEQDIOXIN    1.00000     0.00000  566800.75    0.000
TEQFURAN     1.00000     0.00001  176270.48    0.000

s = 0.000007964   R-sq = 100.0%   R-sq(adj) = 100.0%
```

11.37. The model is

$$\text{TEQ}_i = \beta_0 + \beta_1\,\text{PCB}_{52} + \beta_2\,\text{PCB}_{118}$$
$$+ \beta_3\,\text{PCB}_{138} + \beta_4\,\text{PCB}_{180} + \epsilon_i$$

where $i = 1, 2, ..., 69$; ϵ_i are independent $N(0, \sigma)$ random variables. The regression equation is

$$\widehat{\text{TEQ}} = 1.0600 - 0.0973\,\text{PCB}_{52} + 0.3062\,\text{PCB}_{118}$$
$$+ 0.1058\,\text{PCB}_{138} - 0.0039\,\text{PCB}_{180}$$

```
-1 | 66
-1 | 4200
-0 | 987666666666555555
-0 | 44444333221111100
 0 | 0000222224
 0 | 566667788
 1 | 23334
 1 | 9
 2 | 3
 2 | 57
```

with $s = 0.9576$ and $R^2 = 0.677$. Only the constant and the PCB118 coefficient are significantly different from 0; see Minitab output below. Residuals (stemplot on the left) are slightly right-skewed and show no clear patterns when plotted with the explanatory variables (not shown).

Minitab output

```
The regression equation is
TEQ = 1.06 - 0.097 PCB52 + 0.306 PCB118 + 0.106 PCB138 - 0.0039 PCB180

Predictor      Coef      Stdev   t-ratio       p
Constant     1.0600     0.1845      5.75   0.000
PCB52       -0.0973     0.1094     -0.89   0.377
PCB118       0.30618    0.09639     3.18   0.002
PCB138       0.10579    0.07470     1.42   0.162
PCB180      -0.00391    0.06478    -0.06   0.952

s = 0.9576      R-sq = 67.7%    R-sq(adj) = 65.7%
```

11.38. (a) Results will vary with software. **(b)** Different software may produce different results, but (presumably) all software will ignore those 16 specimens, which is probably not a good approach. **(c)** The summary statistics (right) and stemplots (below) are based on natural logarithms; for common logarithms, multiply mean and standard deviation by 2.3026. For LPCB126, the zero terms were replaced $\ln 0.0026 \doteq -5.9522$, which accounts for the odd appearance of its stemplot.

	Mean	SD
LPCB28	−1.3345	1.1338
LPCB52	−0.7719	1.1891
LPCB118	0.8559	0.8272
LPCB126	−4.8457	0.7656
LPCB138	1.6139	0.8046
LPCB153	1.7034	0.9012
LPCB180	0.9752	0.9276
LPCB	3.9170	0.8020
LTEQ	0.8048	0.5966

```
LPCB28                          LPCB52                          LPCB118
-5 | 1                          -3 | 85                         -1 | 4
-4 |                            -3 |                            -0 | 996
-4 |                            -2 | 776                        -0 | 33110
-3 | 6                          -2 | 1100                        0 | 0112233334444444
-3 |                            -1 | 98877765                    0 | 556666788899999
-2 | 88765                      -1 | 4443211111000              1 | 012222222333334
-2 | 433331111100              -0 | 8777776666665              1 | 556678899
-1 | 8888776665555             -0 | 443332111100              2 | 111
-1 | 443222211111               0 | 22334                     2 | 59
-0 | 99998888766555             0 | 5557
-0 | 3100                       1 | 03
 0 | 4                          1 | 7
 0 | 56789                      2 | 02
 1 |
 1 | 9


LPCB126                         LPCB138                         LPCB153
-5 | 9999999999999999           -0 | 411                        -0 | 110
-5 |                             0 | 33                          0 | 134
-5 |                             0 | 6677788999                  0 | 5578899
-5 | 222                         1 | 0011112222333334            1 | 000112222222222333444
-5 | 111000                      1 | 5555566777789               1 | 5677888899999
-4 | 99999999998888              2 | 000001111222344             2 | 01222233444
-4 | 7776                        2 | 5555589                     2 | 55569
-4 | 54444                       3 | 024                         3 | 01244
-4 | 3322                                                        3 | 57
-4 | 11100
-3 | 999888
-3 | 666
-3 | 554


LPCB180                         LPCB                            LTEQ
-0 | 975                         1 | 8                           0 | 00000000111111
-0 | 443110                      2 | 12                          0 | 2223333333
 0 | 00001111222334              2 | 6999                        0 | 4455555
 0 | 567778889999                3 | 0011222233444444           0 | 66677
 1 | 0011122222233344            3 | 5556666777888              0 | 888899
 1 | 55666689                    4 | 000000111233344             1 | 0111111
 2 | 012223                      4 | 555555777788                1 | 22333
 2 | 589                         5 | 1233                        1 | 44455
 3 | 4                           5 | 57                          1 | 6667777
                                                                 1 | 888
```

11.39. (a) The correlations (all positive) are listed in the table below. The largest correlation is 0.956 (LPCB and LPCB138); the smallest (0.227, for LPCB28 and LPCB180) is not quite significantly different from 0 ($t = 1.91$, $P = 0.0607$), but with 28 correlations such a P-value could easily arise by chance, so we would not necessarily conclude that $\rho = 0$. Rather than showing all 28 scatterplots—which are all fairly linear, and confirm the positive associations suggested by the correlations—we have included only two of the interesting ones: LPCB against LPCB28, and LPCB against LPCB126. The former is notable because of one outlier (specimen 39) in LPCB28; the latter stands out because of the "stack" of values in the LPCB126 data set that arose from the adjustment of the zero terms. (The outlier in LPCB28 and the stack in LPCB126 can be seen in other plots involving those variables; the two plots shown are the most appropriate for using the PCB congeners to predict LPCB, as the next exercise asks.) **(b)** All correlations are higher with the transformed data. In part, this is because these scatterplots do not exhibit the "greater scatter in the upper right" that was seen in many of the scatterplots of the original data.

	LPCB28	LPCB52	LPCB118	LPCB126	LPCB138	LPCB153	LPCB180
LPCB52	0.795						
LPCB118	0.533	0.671					
LPCB126	0.272	0.331	0.739				
LPCB138	0.387	0.540	0.890	0.792			
LPCB153	0.326	0.519	0.780	0.647	0.922		
LPCB180	0.227	0.301	0.654	0.695	0.896	0.867	
LPCB	0.570	0.701	0.906	0.729	0.956	0.905	0.829

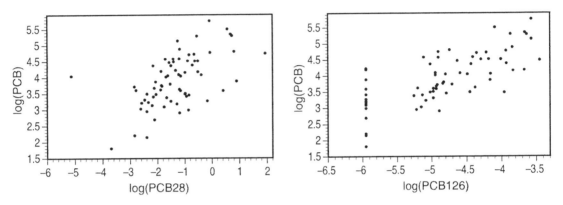

11.40. Student results will vary with how many different models they try, and what tradeoff they consider between "good" (in terms of large R^2) and "simple" (in terms of the number of variables included in the model). The first Minitab output below, produced with the BREG (best regression) command, gives some guidance as to likely answers; it shows the best models with 1, 2, 3, 4, 5, 6, and 7 explanatory variables. We can see, for example, that if all variables are used, $R^2 = 0.975$, but we can achieve similar values of R^2 with fewer variables. The best regressions with 2, 3, and 4 explanatory variables are shown in the Minitab output below.

Minitab output

```
– – – – – – – – – –      Best subsets regression    – – – – – – – – – – – – –
                                               L L L L L
                                           L L P P P P P
                                           P P C C C C C
                                           C C B B B B B
                                           B B 1 1 1 1 1
                          Adj.             2 5 1 2 3 5 8
     Vars  R-sq  R-sq  C-p        s        8 2 8 6 8 3 0

        1  91.4  91.3  141.4  0.23689              X
        2  96.2  96.1   28.5  0.15892          X   X
        3  96.8  96.6   16.1  0.14696      X X     X
        4  97.2  97.0    8.2  0.13826      X X       X X
        5  97.3  97.0    8.6  0.13776      X X X     X X
        6  97.5  97.2    6.0  0.13389      X X X     X X X
        7  97.5  97.2    8.0  0.13497      X X X X X X X
```

```
— — — — — — — — — — — — Two explanatory variables   — — — — — — — — — —
The regression equation is
LPCB = 2.74 + 0.175 LPCB52 + 0.813 LPCB138


Predictor       Coef      Stdev      t-ratio         p
Constant      2.74038    0.05860      46.76       0.000
LPCB52        0.17533    0.01926       9.10       0.000
LPCB138       0.81294    0.02846      28.56       0.000


s = 0.1589      R-sq = 96.2%     R-sq(adj) = 96.1%
— — — — — — — — — — — Three explanatory variables   — — — — — — — — — —
The regression equation is
LPCB = 2.79 + 0.0908 LPCB28 + 0.104 LPCB52 + 0.821 LPCB138


Predictor       Coef      Stdev      t-ratio         p
Constant      2.79394    0.05633      49.60       0.000
LPCB28        0.09078    0.02601       3.49       0.001
LPCB52        0.10371    0.02717       3.82       0.000
LPCB138       0.82056    0.02641      31.07       0.000


s = 0.1470      R-sq = 96.8%     R-sq(adj) = 96.6%
— — — — — — — — — — — Four explanatory variables   — — — — — — — — — — —
The regression equation is
LPCB = 2.79 + 0.107 LPCB28 + 0.0876 LPCB52 + 0.669 LPCB138 + 0.151 LPCB153


Predictor       Coef      Stdev      t-ratio         p
Constant      2.79081    0.05300      52.65       0.000
LPCB28        0.10684    0.02503       4.27       0.000
LPCB52        0.08763    0.02610       3.36       0.001
LPCB138       0.66854    0.05538      12.07       0.000
LPCB153       0.15118    0.04921       3.07       0.003


s = 0.1383      R-sq = 97.2%     R-sq(adj) = 97.0%
```

11.41. Using Minitab's BREG (best regression) command for guidance, we see that there is little improvement in R^2 beyond models with four explanatory variables. The best models with 2, 3, and 4 variables are given in the Minitab output below.

Minitab output

```
— — — — — — — — — — — — Best subsets regression   — — — — — — — — — — — —
                                              L L L L L
                                            L L P P P P P
                                            P P C C C C C
                                            C C B B B B B
                                            B B 1 1 1 1 1
                         Adj.                2 5 1 2 3 5 8
Vars    R-sq   R-sq   C-p        s           8 2 8 6 8 3 0

   1    72.9   72.5  10.8    0.31266               X
   2    76.8   76.1   2.0    0.29166         X     X
   3    77.6   76.6   1.6    0.28859         X   X X
   4    78.0   76.7   2.5    0.28816         X   X X     X
   5    78.1   76.4   4.2    0.28981         X X X X     X
   6    78.2   76.1   6.1    0.29188         X X X X     X X
   7    78.2   75.7   8.0    0.29400         X X X X X X X
```

```
– – – – – – – – – – – – – –        Two explanatory variables        – – – – – – – – – – – –
The regression equation is
LTEQ = 3.96 + 0.107 LPCB28 + 0.622 LPCB126

Predictor      Coef        Stdev      t-ratio        p
Constant       3.9637      0.2275       17.42      0.000
LPCB28         0.10749     0.03242       3.32      0.001
LPCB126        0.62231     0.04801      12.96      0.000

s = 0.2917      R-sq = 76.8%      R-sq(adj) = 76.1%
– – – – – – – – – – –        Three explanatory variables        – – – – – – – – – – – – –
The regression equation is
LTEQ = 3.44 + 0.0777 LPCB28 + 0.114 LPCB118 + 0.543 LPCB126

Predictor      Coef        Stdev      t-ratio        p
Constant       3.4445      0.4029        8.55      0.000
LPCB28         0.07773     0.03736       2.08      0.041
LPCB118        0.11371     0.07319       1.55      0.125
LPCB126        0.54345     0.06952       7.82      0.000

s = 0.2886      R-sq = 77.6%      R-sq(adj) = 76.6%
– – – – – – – – – – – –        Four explanatory variables        – – – – – – – – – – – – –
The regression equation is
LTEQ = 3.56 + 0.0720 LPCB28 + 0.170 LPCB118 + 0.554 LPCB126 - 0.0693 LPCB153

Predictor      Coef        Stdev      t-ratio        p
Constant       3.5568      0.4152        8.57      0.000
LPCB28         0.07199     0.03767       1.91      0.060
LPCB118        0.16973     0.08928       1.90      0.062
LPCB126        0.55374     0.07005       7.90      0.000
LPCB153       -0.06929     0.06344      -1.09      0.279

s = 0.2882      R-sq = 78.0%      R-sq(adj) = 76.7%
```

11.42. The degree of change in these elements of a regression can be readily seen by comparing the three regression results shown in the solution to Exercise 11.40; they will be even more visible if students have explored more models in their search for the best model. Student explanations might include observations of changes in particular coefficients from one model to another, and perhaps might attempt to paraphrase the text's comments about *why* this happens.

11.43. In the table, two *IQR*s are given; those in parentheses are based on quartiles reported by Minitab, which computes quartiles in a slightly different way from this text's method.

	$\bar{x}$	M	s	IQR
Taste	24.53	20.95	16.26	23.9 (or 24.58)
Acetic	5.498	5.425	0.571	0.656 (or 0.713)
H2S	5.942	5.329	2.127	3.689 (or 3.766)
Lactic	1.442	1.450	0.3035	0.430 (or 0.4625)

None of the variables show striking deviations from normality in the quantile plots (not shown). Taste and H2S are slightly right-skewed, and Acetic has two peaks. There are no outliers.

Taste	Acetic	H2S	Lactic
0 | 00	4 | 455	2 | 9	8 | 6
0 | 556	4 | 67	3 | 1268899	9 | 9
1 | 1234	4 | 8	4 | 17799	10 | 689
1 | 55688	5 | 1	5 | 024	11 | 56
2 | 011	5 | 2222333	6 | 11679	12 | 5599
2 | 556	5 | 444	7 | 4699	13 | 013
3 | 24	5 | 677	8 | 7	14 | 469
3 | 789	5 | 888	9 | 025	15 | 2378
4 | 0	6 | 0011	10 | 1	16 | 38
4 | 7	6 | 3		17 | 248
5 | 4	6 | 44		18 | 1
5 | 67			19 | 09
			20 | 1

11.44. The plots show positive associations between the variables. The correlations and P-values are in the plots; all correlations are positive (as expected) and significantly different from 0. (Recall that the P-values are correct if the two variables are normally distributed, in which case $t = r\sqrt{n-2}/\sqrt{1-r^2}$ has a $t(n-2)$ distribution if $\rho = 0$.)

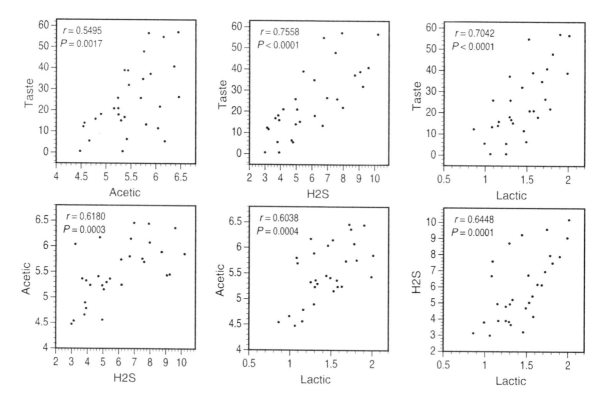

11.45. The regression equation is $\widehat{\text{Taste}} = -61.50 + 15.648$ Acetic with $s = 13.82$ and $R^2 = 0.302$. The slope is significantly different from 0 ($t = 3.48$, $P = 0.002$).

Based on a stemplot (right) and quantile plot (not shown), the residuals seem to have a normal distribution. Scatterplots (below) reveal positive associations between residuals and both H2S and Lactic. The plot of residuals against Acetic suggests greater scatter in the residuals for large Acetic values.

```
-2 | 9
-2 | 11
-1 | 65
-1 | 31
-0 | 7655
-0 | 21
 0 | 0122224
 0 | 5668
 1 |
 1 | 5679
 2 | 0
 2 | 6
```

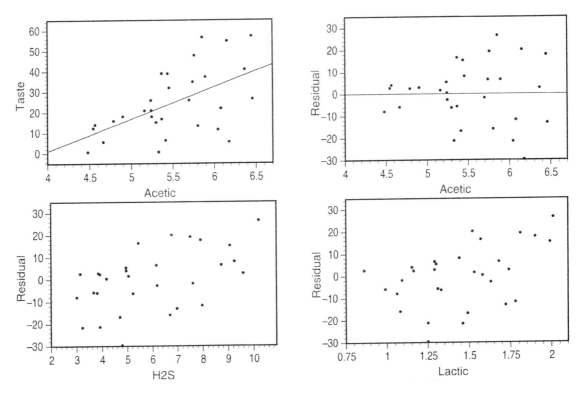

11.46. The regression equation is $\widehat{\text{Taste}} = -9.787 + 5.7761$ H2S with $s = 10.83$ and $R^2 = 0.571$. The slope is significantly different from 0 ($t = 6.11$, $P < 0.0005$).

Based on a stemplot (right) and quantile plot (not shown), the residuals may be slightly skewed, but do not differ greatly from a normal distribution. Scatterplots (below) reveal weak positive associations between residuals and both Acetic and Lactic. The plot of residuals against H2S suggests greater scatter in the residuals for large H2S values.

```
-1 | 5
-1 | 42210
-0 | 87665
-0 | 44333
 0 | 1233
 0 | 556779
 1 | 4
 1 | 7
 2 | 1
 2 | 5
```

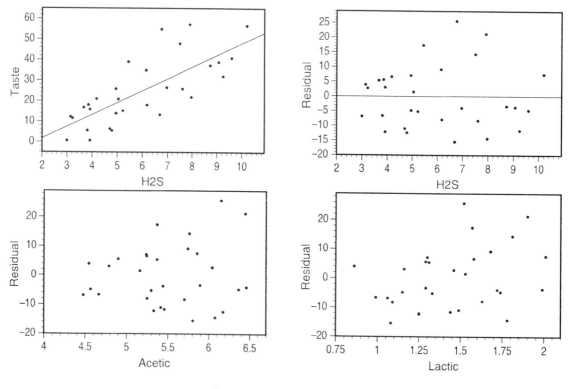

11.47. The regression equation is $\widehat{Taste} = -29.86 + 37.720$ Lactic with $s = 11.75$ and $R^2 = 0.496$. The slope is significantly different from 0 ($t = 5.25$, $P < 0.0005$).

Based on a stemplot (right) and quantile plot (not shown), the residuals appear to be roughly normal. Scatterplots (below) reveal no striking patterns for residuals vs. Acetic and H2S.

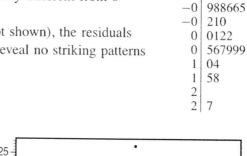

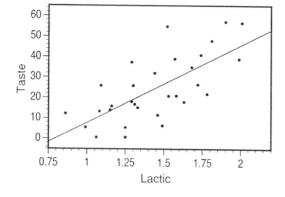

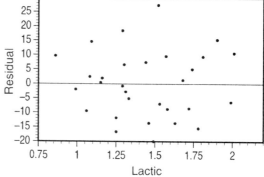

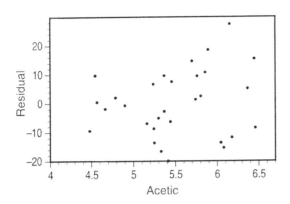 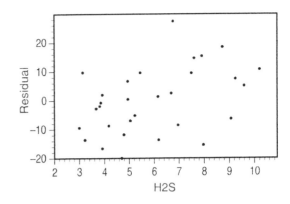

11.48. All information is in the table at the right. The intercepts differ from one model to the next because

x	$\widehat{\text{Taste}} =$	F	P	r^2	s
Acetic	$-61.50 + 15.648x$	12.11	0.002	30.2%	13.82
H2S	$-9.787 + 5.7761x$	37.29	<0.0005	57.1%	10.83
Lactic	$-29.86 + 37.720x$	27.55	<0.0005	49.6%	11.75

they represent different things—e.g., in the first model, the intercept is the predicted value of Taste with Acetic $= 0$, etc.

11.49. The regression equation is $\widehat{\text{Taste}} = -26.94 + 3.801$ Acetic $+ 5.146$ H2S with $s = 10.89$ and $R^2 = 0.582$. The t-value for the coefficient of Acetic is 0.84 ($P = 0.406$), indicating that it does not add significantly to the model when H2S is used, because Acetic and H2S are correlated (in fact, $r = 0.618$ for these two variables). This model does a better job than any of the three simple linear regression models, but it is not much better than the model with H2S alone (which explained 57.1% of the variation in Taste)—as we might expect from the t-test result.

Minitab output

```
The regression equation is taste = -26.9 + 3.80 acetic + 5.15 h2s

Predictor      Coef       Stdev     t-ratio        p
Constant     -26.94       21.19       -1.27    0.215
acetic         3.801       4.505        0.84    0.406
h2s            5.146       1.209        4.26    0.000

s = 10.89      R-sq = 58.2%     R-sq(adj) = 55.1%
```

11.50. The regression equation is $\widehat{\text{Taste}} = -27.592 + 3.946$ H2S $+ 19.887$ Lactic with $s = 9.942$. The model explains 65.2% of the variation in Taste, which is higher than for the two simple linear regressions. Both coefficients are significantly different from 0 ($P = 0.002$ for H2S, and $P = 0.019$ for Lactic).

Minitab output

```
The regression equation is taste = -27.6 + 3.95 h2s + 19.9 lactic

Predictor      Coef       Stdev     t-ratio        p
Constant     -27.592      8.982       -3.07    0.005
h2s            3.946       1.136        3.47    0.002
lactic        19.887       7.959        2.50    0.019

s = 9.942      R-sq = 65.2%     R-sq(adj) = 62.6%
```

11.51. The regression equation is $\widehat{\text{Taste}} = -28.88 + 0.328$ Acetic $+ 3.912$ H2S $+ 19.671$ Lactic with $s = 10.13$. The model explains 65.2% of the variation in Taste (the same as for the model with only H2S and Lactic). Residuals of this regression appear to be normally distributed and show no patterns in scatterplots with the explanatory variables. (These plots are not shown.)

The coefficient of Acetic is not significantly different from 0 ($P = 0.942$); there is no gain in adding Acetic to the model with H2S and Lactic. It appears that the best model is the H2S/Lactic model of Exercise 11.50.

Minitab output

```
The regression equation is
taste = -28.9 + 0.33 acetic + 3.91 h2s + 19.7 lactic

Predictor        Coef        Stdev      t-ratio          p
Constant       -28.88        19.74        -1.46      0.155
acetic          0.328        4.460         0.07      0.942
h2s             3.912        1.248         3.13      0.004
lactic         19.671        8.629         2.28      0.031

s = 10.13        R-sq = 65.2%      R-sq(adj) = 61.2%
```

Chapter 12 Solutions

12.1. (a) ANOVA is used when the explanatory variable has two *or more* values. **(b)** There is no theoretical limit to the number of means that can be compared. **(c)** The common population standard deviation σ (not its estimate s_p) is a parameter.

12.2. (a) The ANOVA F statistic tests the null hypothesis that *population* means are equal (and there can be two or more—not necessarily three). **(b)** The *sum of* squares (not the mean squares) in an ANOVA table will add. **(c)** This sentence describes *between*-group variation. Within-group variation is the variation that occurs by chance among members of the same group.

12.3. (a) With $I = 4$ groups and $N = 44$, we have df $I - 1 = 3$ and $N - I = 40$. In Table E, we see that $3.46 < F < 4.31$. **(b)** The sketch on the right shows the observed F value and the critical values from Table E. Shown is an actual $F(3, 40)$ density; student sketches will vary. **(c)** $0.010 < P < 0.025$ (software gives 0.0235). **(d)** The alternative hypothesis states that at least one mean is different, not that all means are different.

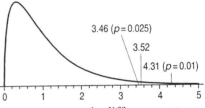

12.4. The answers are found in Table E (or using software) with $p = 0.05$ and degrees of freedom $I - 1$ and $N - I$. **(a)** $I = 6$, $N = 12$, df 5 and 6: $F > 4.39$ (software: 4.3874). **(b)** $I = 6$, $N = 24$, df 5 and 18: $F > 2.77$ (software: 2.7729). **(c)** $I = 6$, $N = 66$, df 5 and 60: $F > 2.37$ (software: 2.3683). **(d)** As the degrees of freedom increase, values from an F distribution tend to be smaller (closer to 1), so smaller values of F are statistically significant. In terms of ANOVA conclusions, we have learned that with smaller samples (fewer observations per group), the F statistic needs to be fairly large in order to reject H_0.

12.5. (a) $I = 5$ and $N = 40$, so the degrees of freedom are 4 and 35. $F = \frac{57}{50} = 1.14$. Comparing to the $F(4, 30)$ distribution in Table E, we find $F < 2.14$, so $P > 0.100$. (Software gives $P = 0.3538$.) **(b)** $I = 3$ and $N = 21$, so the degrees of freedom are 2 and 18. $F = \frac{40/2}{90/18} = 4$. Comparing to the $F(2, 18)$ distribution in Table E, we find $3.55 < F < 4.56$, so $0.025 < P < 0.050$. (Software gives $P = 0.0365$.)

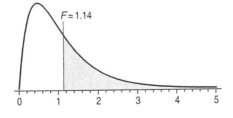

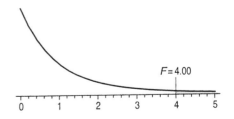

12.6. These pictures are shown below. Note that for (b), there are four curves, but two coincide almost exactly (one centered at 30, the other at 30.1).

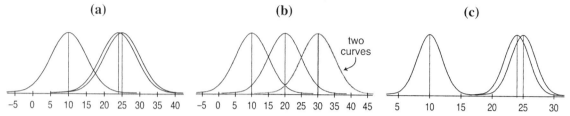

(a)   **(b)**   **(c)**

12.7. **(a)** Response: rating on five-point scale. Populations: The three groups of students. $I = 3, n_1 = 220, n_2 = 145, n_3 = 76, N = 441$. **(b)** Response: Change in cholesterol level. Populations: Pigs eating different varieties of onions. $I = 3, n_i = 5 \ (i = 1, 2, 3), N = 15$. **(c)** Response: Video game rating. Populations: Eighth graders, third-year high school students, second-year college students. $I = 3, n_i = 25 \ (i = 1, 2, 3), N = 75$.

12.8. **(a)** Response: Breaking strength. Populations: Cloth treated with one of the six treatments. $I = 6, n_i = 20 \ (i = 1, 2, 3, 4, 5, 6), N = 120$. **(b)** Response: Size of tip. Populations: Customers responding to one of three waiter behaviors. $I = 3, n_i = 10 \ (i = 1, 2, 3), N = 30$. **(c)** Response: Total sales between 5:00 and 6:00 p.m. (Presumably this is sales of cheddar cheese, or perhaps all cheese sales, but the problem does not make this clear.) Populations: Customers responding to one of four sample offers. $I = 4$, and if we assume that we make each offer five times, $n_i = 5 \ (i = 1, 2, 3, 4)$ and $N = 20$.

12.9. For all three situations, the hypotheses are H_0: $\mu_1 = \mu_2 = \mu_3$ vs. H_a: at least one mean is different. The other information is in the table below.

Situation	df	df for F statistic
(a) Alcohol awareness program	DFM 2, DFE 438, DFT 440	$F(2, 438)$
(b) Onions and cholesterol	DFM 2, DFE 12, DFT 14	$F(2, 12)$
(c) Video game ratings	DFM 2, DFE 72, DFT 74	$F(2, 72)$

12.10. For all three situations, the hypotheses are H_0: $\mu_1 = \cdots = \mu_I$ vs. H_a: at least one mean is different, where I is 6, 3, or 4, respectively. The other information is in the table below.

Situation	df	df for F statistic
(a) Fabric treatments	DFM 5, DFE 114, DFT 119	$F(5, 114)$
(b) Waiter behavior and tip	DFM 2, DFE 27, DFT 29	$F(2, 27)$
(c) Cheese samples	DFM 3, DFE 16, DFT 19	$F(3, 16)$

12.11. **(a)** Conclusions might not extend to students from schools that are geographically or demographically different from this one, or to students who are not in similar groups (statistics class, health class, coop housing). **(b)** The effects on humans might be different from the effects on pigs. **(c)** The key question is, how well do these groups represent other video game players?

12.12. (a) The results should apply to the type of fabric use in the sample (if it is consistently manufactured). It would not be safe to assume that we could apply the results to other types of fabric. (b) The waiter could probably assume that his conclusions would apply to his future customers at this restaurant, but they would not necessarily extend to other waiters or other restaurants. (c) The results *might* extend to similar supermarkets, and perhaps to other times of day, or to weekend sales.

12.13. (a) Yes: The guidelines for pooling standard deviations say that the ratio of largest to smallest should be less than 2; we have $\frac{220}{190} \doteq 1.16 < 2$. (b) Squaring the three standard deviations gives $s_1^2 = 48,400$, $s_2^2 = 36,100$, and $s_3^2 = 40,000$.
(c) $s_p^2 = \dfrac{19s_1^2 + 17s_2^2 + 14s_3^2}{19 + 17 + 14} = 41,866$. (d) $s_p = \sqrt{s_p^2} \doteq 204.6$.

12.14. (a) No: The guidelines for pooling standard deviations say that the ratio of largest to smallest should be less than 2; we have $\frac{21}{10} = 2.1$. (b) Squaring the four standard deviations gives $s_1^2 = 400$, $s_2^2 = 441$, $s_3^2 = 100$, and $s_4^2 = 361$.
(c) $s_p^2 = \dfrac{29s_1^2 + 21s_2^2 + 179s_3^2 + 24s_4^2}{29 + 21 + 179 + 24} \doteq 187.45$. (d) $s_p = \sqrt{s_p^2} \doteq 13.69$. (e) Because the third sample was over twice as large as the other three put together, the pooled standard deviation is closest to s_3.

12.15. (a) Use matched-pairs t methods; we examine the change in reaction time for each subject. (b) No: We cannot use ANOVA methods, because we do not have four independent samples. (The same group of subjects performed each of the four tasks.)

12.16. (a) It is useful to connect the points on the plot, to make the pattern (or lack thereof) more evident. There is some suggestion that average grade decreases as the number of accommodations increases. (b) Having too many decimal points is distracting; in this situation, no useful information is gained by having more than one or two digits after the decimal point. For example, the first mean and standard deviation would be more effectively presented as 2.79 and

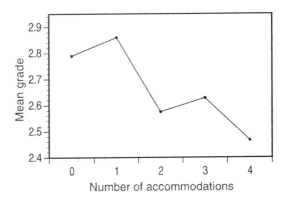

0.85. (c) The largest-to-smallest SD ratio is slightly over 2 (about 2.009), so pooling is not advisable. (If we pool in spite of this, we find $s_p \doteq 0.8589$.) (d) Eliminating data points (without a legitimate reason) is always risky, although we could run the analysis with and without them. Combining the last three groups would be a bad idea if the data suggested that grades rebounded after 2 accommodations (that is, if the average grades were higher for 3 and 4 accommodations), but as that is not the case, lumping 2, 3, and 4 accommodations seems reasonable. (e) ANOVA is not appropriate for these data, chiefly because we do not have 245 independent observations. (f) There may be a number of local factors (e.g., student demographics, or teachers' attitudes toward accommodations) which affected grades; these effects might not be the same elsewhere. (g) One weakness is that we do not have a control group for comparison; that is, we cannot tell what grades these students (or a similar group) would have had without accommodations.

12.17. **(a)** The variation in sample size is some cause for concern, but there can be no extreme outliers in a 1-to-7 scale, so ANOVA is probably reliable. **(b)** Pooling is reasonable: $\frac{1.26}{1.03} \doteq 1.22 < 2$. **(c)** With $I = 5$ groups and total sample size $N = 410$, we use an $F(4, 405)$ distribution. We can compare 5.69 to an

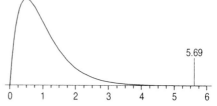

5.69

$F(4, 200)$ distribution in Table E and conclude that $P < 0.001$, or with software determine that $P \doteq 0.0002$. **(d)** Hispanic Americans have the highest emotion scores, Japanese are in the middle, and the other three cultures are the lowest (and very similar).

12.18. **(a)** The largest-to-smallest SD ratios are 2.84, 1.23, and 1.14, so the text's guidelines are satisfied for intensity and recall, but not for frequency. **(b)** As in the previous exercise, $I = 5$ and $N = 410$, so we use an $F(4, 405)$ distribution. From the $F(4, 200)$ distribution in Table E, we can conclude that $P < 0.001$ for all three response variables. With software, we find that the P-values are much smaller; all are less than 0.00002. We conclude that, for each variable, we have strong evidence that some group mean is different. (This conclusion is cautious in the case of frequency, because of our concern about the standard deviations.) **(c)** The table below shows one way of summarizing the means. For each variable, it attempts to identify low (underlined), medium, and high (boldface) values of that variable. Hispanic Americans were higher than other groups for all four variables. Asian Americans were low for all variables (the lowest in all but global score). Japanese were low on all but global score, while European Americans and Indians were in the middle for all but global score. **(d)** The results might not generalize to (e.g.) subjects who are not in a college or university community, or to subjects in different parts of their countries. **(e)** Create a two-way table with counts of men and women in each cultural group. The Minitab output on the right gives $X^2 = 11.353$, df = 4, $P = 0.023$, so we have evidence (significant at $\alpha = 0.05$) that the gender mix was not the same for all cultures. Specifically, Hispanic Americans and European Americans had higher percentages of women, which might further affect how much we can generalize the results.

Minitab output

	Women	Men	Total
1	38	8	46
	31.64	14.36	
2	22	11	33
	22.70	10.30	
3	57	34	91
	62.59	28.41	
4	102	58	160
	110.05	49.95	
5	63	17	80
	55.02	24.98	
Total	282	128	410

ChiSq = 1.279 + 2.817 +
         0.021 + 0.047 +
         0.499 + 1.100 +
         0.589 + 1.297 +
         1.156 + 2.547 = 11.353
df = 4, p = 0.023

	Score	Frequency	Intensity	Recall
European Amer.	<u>4.39</u>	82.87	2.79	49.12
Asian Amer.	<u>4.35</u>	<u>72.68</u>	<u>2.37</u>	<u>39.77</u>
Japanese	4.72	<u>73.36</u>	2.53	43.98
Indian	<u>4.34</u>	82.71	2.87	49.86
Hispanic Amer.	**5.04**	**92.25**	**3.21**	**59.99**

12.19. (a) Table below ($\bar{x}$, s, $s_{\bar{x}}$ in mg/100g). (b) To test H_0: $\mu_1 = \mu_2 = \mu_3 = \mu_4 = \mu_5$ vs. H_a: not all μ_i are equal, we have $F = 367.74$ with df 4 and 5, and $P < 0.0005$, so we reject the null hypothesis. Minitab output below. (c) Plot below. We conclude that vitamin C content decreases over time.

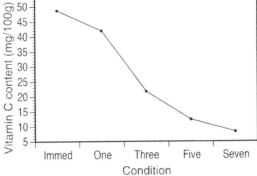

Condition	n	$\bar{x}$	s	$s_{\bar{x}}$
Immediate	2	48.705	1.534	1.085
One day	2	41.955	2.128	1.505
Three days	2	21.795	0.771	0.545
Five days	2	12.415	1.082	0.765
Seven days	2	8.320	0.269	0.190

Minitab output

```
Analysis of Variance on VitC
Source    DF       SS       MS       F       p
Days       4   2565.72   641.43   367.74   0.000
Error      5      8.72     1.74
Total      9   2574.44
```

12.20. We have 10 comparisons to make, and df $= 5$, so the Bonferroni critical value with $\alpha = 0.05$ is $t^{**} = 4.7733$. The pooled standard deviation is $s_p \doteq 1.3207$, and the standard error of each difference is $s_p\sqrt{1/2 + 1/2} = s_p$, so two means are significantly different if they differ by $t^{**}s_p \doteq 6.3041$. All differences are significant *except* the five-day/seven-day difference.

12.21. Means, etc. ($\bar{x}$, s, $s_{\bar{x}}$ in mg/100g) below, along with plots of means. The hypotheses are H_0: $\mu_1 = \cdots = \mu_5$ vs. H_a: not all μ_i are equal. For vitamin A, $F = 12.09$ (df 4 and 5), so $P = 0.009$—we reject H_0 and conclude that vitamin A content changes over time (it appears to decrease, except for the rise at "Five days"). For vitamin E, $F = 0.69$ (df 4 and 5), so $P = 0.630$—we cannot reject the null hypothesis.

Vitamin A	n	$\bar{x}$	s	$s_{\bar{x}}$
Immediate	2	3.350	0.01414	0.010
One day	2	3.240	0.05657	0.040
Three days	2	3.210	0.07071	0.050
Five days	2	3.305	0.07778	0.055
Seven days	2	2.965	0.06364	0.045

Vitamin E	n	$\bar{x}$	s	$s_{\bar{x}}$
Immediate	2	95.30	0.9900	0.700
One day	2	94.45	1.7678	1.250
Three days	2	95.85	2.1920	1.550
Five days	2	96.35	1.9092	1.350
Seven days	2	93.70	1.9799	1.400

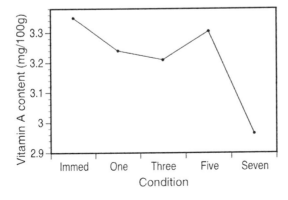

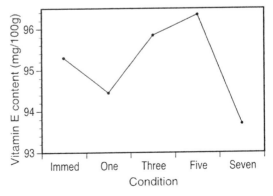

Minitab output
```
Analysis of Variance on VitA
Source    DF        SS        MS        F         p
Days       4   0.17894   0.04473    12.09     0.009
Error      5   0.01850   0.00370
Total      9   0.19744
-----------------------------------------------------
Analysis of Variance on VitE
Source    DF        SS        MS        F         p
Days       4      9.09      2.27     0.69     0.630
Error      5     16.47      3.29
Total      9     25.56
```

12.22. (a) We did not reject H_0 for vitamin E, so we have no reason to believe that any means are different. **(b)** As in Exercise 12.20, $t^{**} = 4.7733$. The pooled standard deviation is $s_p \doteq 0.06083$, and the standard error of each difference is $s_p\sqrt{1/2 + 1/2} = s_p$, so two means are significantly different if they differ by $t^{**}s_p \doteq 0.2903$. By this standard, only the immediate/seven-day and five-day/seven-day differences are significant.

12.23. There is no significant evidence of change in vitamin E content. Vitamin C content decreases over time, with significant change occurring over the first five days. For vitamin A, the fluctuations over the first five days are not significant, but the drop from day 5 to day 7 is.

12.24. We have $\bar{x}_1 = 4.77$, $s_1 = 1.5$, $n_1 = 66$, $\bar{x}_2 = 2.43$, $s_2 = 1.64$, and $n_2 = 61$. For the pooled t procedure, we find $s_p \doteq 1.5688$ and $t = 8.398$ (df $= 125$, $P < 0.0001$). The Minitab output below shows that $F = 70.53$ (t^2, up to rounding error).

Minitab output
```
Analysis of Variance
Source    DF        SS        MS        F         p
Factor     1    173.58    173.58    70.53     0.000
Error    125    307.63      2.46
Total    126    481.21
```

12.25. Assuming the t (ANOVA) test establishes that the means are different, contrasts and multiple comparison provide no further useful information. (With two means, there is only one comparison to make, and it has already been made by the t test.)

12.26. (a) Means, standard deviations, and standard errors of the mean are below, along with a plot of the means. Note that the standard deviations grossly violate our guideline for pooling: $\frac{1066.97}{89.94} \doteq 11.86$. As we might expect, spores are highest in the summer, and lowest in the winter. **(b)** ANOVA gives $F = 4.83$ (df 3 and 8) and $P = 0.033$—the differences are significant at the 5% level. (The small samples and large variation make the seemingly large differences not as significant as we might expect.)

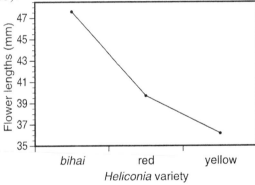

	n	$\bar{x}$	s	$s_{\bar{x}}$
Fall	3	1191	89.94	51.926
Winter	3	195	163.72	94.522
Spring	3	1216	773.12	446.360
Summer	3	2263.$\overline{6}$	1066.97	616.014

Minitab output

```
Analysis of Variance
Source   DF      SS        MS       F      p
Factor    3   6422013   2140671   4.83   0.033
Error     8   3542047    442756
Total    11   9964060
```

12.27. See also the solution to Exercise 1.59. The means, standard deviations, and standard errors (all in millimeters) are given below. We reject H_0 and conclude that at least one mean is different ($F = 259.12$, df 2 and 51, $P < 0.0005$).

Variety	n	$\bar{x}$	s	$s_{\bar{x}}$
bihai	16	47.5975	1.2129	0.3032
red	23	39.7113	1.7988	0.3751
yellow	15	36.1800	0.9753	0.2518

Minitab output

```
Analysis of Variance on length
Source   DF      SS       MS       F       p
Factor    2   1082.87   541.44   259.12   0.000
Error    51    106.57     2.09
Total    53   1189.44
```

12.28. Means, standard deviations, and standard errors of the mean are below, along with a plot of the means. ANOVA gives $F = 11.93$ (df 3 and 8) and $P = 0.003$—the differences are significant at the 1% level. Taking logarithms made the evidence against H_0 stronger, in part because the standard deviations were greatly reduced. (They are now in line with the text's guidelines for pooling.)

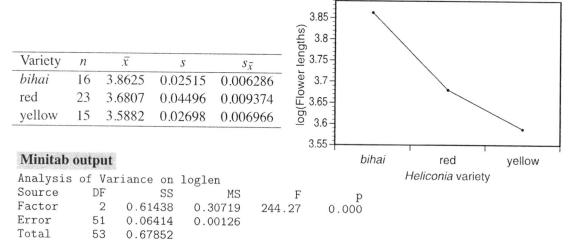

	n	$\bar{x}$	s	$s_{\bar{x}}$
Fall	3	7.0806	0.0772	0.0446
Winter	3	5.0566	0.7751	0.4475
Spring	3	6.9801	0.5891	0.3401
Summer	3	7.6305	0.5630	0.3250

Minitab output
```
Analysis of Variance
Source   DF      SS       MS       F       p
Factor    3   11.368    3.789   11.93   0.003
Error     8    2.541    0.318
Total    11   13.909
```

12.29. The means, standard deviations, and standard errors are given below. We reject H_0 and conclude that at least one mean is different ($F = 244.27$, df 2 and 51, $P < 0.0005$). These results are essentially the same as in Exercise 12.27.

Variety	n	$\bar{x}$	s	$s_{\bar{x}}$
bihai	16	3.8625	0.02515	0.006286
red	23	3.6807	0.04496	0.009374
yellow	15	3.5882	0.02698	0.006966

Minitab output
```
Analysis of Variance on loglen
Source   DF      SS       MS        F       p
Factor    2   0.61438  0.30719   244.27   0.000
Error    51   0.06414  0.00126
Total    53   0.67852
```

12.30. (a) Statistics and plots are below. (b) The standard deviations satisfy the text's guidelines for pooling. One concern is that all three distributions are slightly left-skewed, and the youngest nonfiction death is an outlier. (c) ANOVA gives $F = 6.56$ (df 2 and 120) and $P = 0.002$, so we conclude that at least one mean is different. (d) The appropriate contrast is $\psi_1 = \frac{1}{2}(\mu_{\text{nov}} + \mu_{\text{nf}}) - \mu_{\text{p}}$. (This is defined so that the $\psi_1 > 0$ if poets die younger. This is not absolutely necessary, but is in keeping with the text's advice.) The null hypothesis is $H_0: \psi_1 = 0$; the Yeats quote hardly seems like an adequate reason to choose a one-sided alternative, but students may have other opinions. For the test, we compute $c \doteq 10.9739$, $\text{SE}_c \doteq 3.0808$, and $t \doteq 3.56$ with df $= 120$. The P-value is very small regardless of whether H_a is one- or two-sided, so we conclude that the contrast is positive (and poets die young). (e) For this comparison, the contrast is $\psi_2 = \mu_{\text{nov}} - \mu_{\text{nf}}$, and the hypotheses are H_0: $\psi_2 = 0$ vs. H_a: $\psi_2 \neq 0$. (Because the alternative is two-sided, the subtraction in this contrast can go either way.) For the test, we compute $c \doteq -5.4272$, $SE_c \doteq 3.4397$, and $t \doteq -1.58$ with df = 120. This gives $P = 0.1172$; the difference between novelists and nonfiction writers is not significant. **(f)** With three comparisons and df = 120, the Bonferroni critical value is $t^{**} = 2.4280$. The pooled standard deviation is $s_p \doteq 14.4592$, so the differences, standard errors, and t values are

$$\bar{x}_{\text{nov}} - \bar{x}_{\text{p}} \doteq 8.2603, \quad SE_{\text{nov}-\text{p}} = s_p\sqrt{\tfrac{1}{67} + \tfrac{1}{32}} \doteq 3.1071, \quad t \doteq 2.66$$

$$\bar{x}_{\text{nov}} - \bar{x}_{\text{nf}} \doteq -5.4272, \quad SE_{\text{nov}-\text{nf}} = s_p\sqrt{\tfrac{1}{67} + \tfrac{1}{24}} \doteq 3.4397, \quad t \doteq -1.58$$

$$\bar{x}_{\text{p}} - \bar{x}_{\text{nf}} \doteq -13.6875, \quad SE_{\text{p}-\text{nf}} = s_p\sqrt{\tfrac{1}{32} + \tfrac{1}{24}} \doteq 3.9044, \quad t \doteq -3.51$$

The first and last differences are greater (in absolute value) than t^{**}, so those differences are significant. The second difference is the same one tested in the contrast of part (e); the standard error and the conclusion are the same.

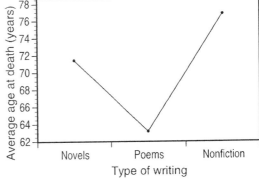

	n	$\bar{x}$	s	$s_{\bar{x}}$
Novels	67	71.4478	13.0515	1.5945
Poems	32	63.1875	17.2971	3.0577
Nonfiction	24	76.8750	14.0969	2.8775

Minitab output

```
Analysis of Variance on AgeDeath
Source    DF      SS      MS       F       p
Writer     2    2744    1372    6.56   0.002
Error    120   25088     209
Total    122   27832
```

12.31. (a) The means, standard deviations, and standard errors are given below (all in grams per cm^2). **(b)** All three distributions appear to reasonably close to normal, and the standard deviations are suitable for pooling. **(c)** ANOVA gives $F = 7.72$ (df 2 and 42) and $P = 0.001$, so we conclude that the means are not all the same. **(d)** With df = 42, 3 comparisons, and $\alpha = 0.05$, the Bonferroni critical value is $t^{**} = 2.4937$. The pooled standard deviation is $s_p \doteq 0.01437$, and the standard error of each difference is $SE_D = s_p\sqrt{1/15 + 1/15} \doteq 0.005246$, so two means are significantly different if they differ by $t^{**}SE_D \doteq 0.01308$. The high-dose mean is significantly different from the other two. **(e)** Briefly: High doses of kudzu isoflavones increase BMD.

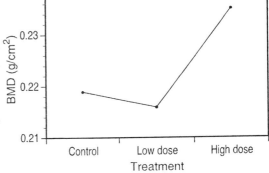

	n	$\bar{x}$	s	$s_{\bar{x}}$
Control	15	0.2189	0.01159	0.002992
Low dose	15	0.2159	0.01151	0.002972
High dose	15	0.2351	0.01877	0.004847

Minitab output

```
Analysis of Variance on BMD
Source    DF      SS        MS       F       p
Factor     2   0.003186  0.001593  7.72   0.001
Error     42   0.008668  0.000206
Total     44   0.011853
```

12.32. **(a)** All four data sets appear to be reasonably close to normal, although "3 promotions" seems to have a low outlier. Plots below. **(b)** At right ($\bar{x}$, s, $s_{\bar{x}}$ in dollars).
(c) The ratio of largest to smallest stan-

Promotions	n	$\bar{x}$	s	$s_{\bar{x}}$
One	40	4.2240	0.2734	0.0432
Three	40	4.0627	0.1742	0.0275
Five	40	3.7590	0.2526	0.0399
Seven	40	3.5487	0.2750	0.0435

dard deviations is about 1.58, so the assumption of equal standard deviations is reasonable.
(d) We test H_0: $\mu_1 = \cdots = \mu_4$ vs. H_a: not all μ_i are equal. Minitab output gives $F = 59.90$ with df 3 and 156, and $P < 0.0005$, so we reject the null hypothesis. With more promotions, expected price decreases.

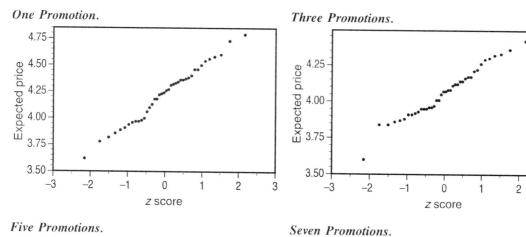

One Promotion.

Three Promotions.

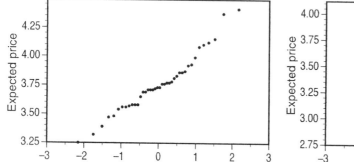

Five Promotions.

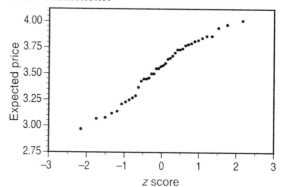

Seven Promotions.

Minitab output

```
Analysis of Variance on ExpPrice
Source    DF      SS        MS       F       p
NumPromo   3   10.9885   3.6628   59.90   0.000
Error    156    9.5388   0.0611
Total    159   20.5273
```

12.33. We have six comparisons to make, and df $= 156$, so the Bonferroni critical value with $\alpha = 0.05$ is $t^{**} = 2.6723$. The pooled standard deviation is $s_p \doteq 0.2473$, so the standard error of each difference is $SE_D = s_p \sqrt{1/40 + 1/40} \doteq 0.05529$. Two means must differ by $t^{**}SE_D \doteq 0.1477$ in order to be significantly different; all six differences are significant. (Note that because the means decrease, we could consider only the differences in consecutive means, i.e., $\bar{x}_1 - \bar{x}_3$, $\bar{x}_3 - \bar{x}_5$, and $\bar{x}_5 - \bar{x}_7$. Since these three differences are significant, it follows that the others must be, too.)

$\bar{x}_1 - \bar{x}_3 = 0.16125$	$t_{13} = 2.916$
$\bar{x}_1 - \bar{x}_5 = 0.46500$	$t_{15} = 8.410$
$\bar{x}_1 - \bar{x}_7 = 0.67525$	$t_{17} = 12.212$
$\bar{x}_3 - \bar{x}_5 = 0.30375$	$t_{35} = 5.493$
$\bar{x}_3 - \bar{x}_7 = 0.51400$	$t_{37} = 9.296$
$\bar{x}_5 - \bar{x}_7 = 0.21025$	$t_{57} = 3.802$

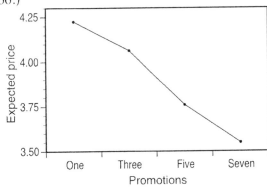

12.34. **(a)** At right. **(b)** We test H_0: $\mu_1 = \cdots = \mu_4$ vs. H_a: not all μ_i are equal. ANOVA gives $F = 9.24$ with df 3 and 74, for which $P < 0.0005$, so we reject the null hypothesis. The type of lesson does affect the mean score change; in particular, it appears that students who take piano lessons had significantly higher scores than the other students.

Lesson	n	$\bar{x}$	s	$s_{\bar{x}}$
Piano	34	3.6176	3.0552	0.5240
Singing	10	-0.3000	1.4944	0.4726
Computer	20	0.4500	2.2118	0.4946
None	14	0.7857	3.1908	0.8528

Minitab output

```
Analysis of Variance on Scores
Source    DF       SS       MS       F       p
Lesson     3    207.28    69.09    9.24    0.000
Error     74    553.44     7.48
Total     77    760.72
```

12.35. We have six comparisons to make, and df $= 74$, so the Bonferroni critical value with $\alpha = 0.05$ is $t^{**} = 2.7111$. The pooled standard deviation is $s_p \doteq 2.7348$. The table below shows the differences, their standard errors, and the t statistics.

The Piano mean is significantly higher than the other three, but the other three means are not significantly different.

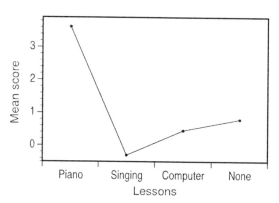

$D_{PS} =$	3.91765	$D_{PC} =$	3.16765	$D_{PN} =$	2.83193
$SE_{PS} =$	0.98380	$SE_{PC} =$	0.77066	$SE_{PN} =$	0.86843
$t_{PS} =$	3.982	$t_{PC} =$	4.110	$t_{PN} =$	3.261
		$D_{SC} =$	−0.75000	$D_{SN} =$	−1.08571
		$SE_{SC} =$	1.05917	$SE_{SN} =$	1.13230
		$t_{SC} =$	−0.708	$t_{SN} =$	−0.959
				$D_{CN} =$	−0.33571
				$SE_{CN} =$	0.95297
				$t_{CN} =$	−0.352

12.36. We test the hypothesis H_0: $\psi = \mu_P - \frac{1}{3}(\mu_S + \mu_C + \mu_N) = 0$; the sample contrast is $c \doteq 3.618 - \frac{1}{3}(-0.300 + 0.450 + 0.786) = 3.306$. The pooled standard deviation estimate is $s_p = 2.735$, so $SE_c = 2.735\sqrt{1/34 + \frac{1}{9}/10 + \frac{1}{9}/20 + \frac{1}{9}/14} \doteq 0.6356$. Then $t = 3.306/0.6356 \doteq 5.20$, with df $= 74$. This is enough evidence ($P < 0.001$) to reject H_0 in favor of H_a: $\psi > 0$, so we conclude that mean score changes for piano students are greater than the average of the means for the other three groups.

12.37. (a) Pooling is reasonable, as the largest-to-smallest ratio is about 1.31. **(b)** ANOVA gives $F = 2.72$ (df 2 and 42) for which $P = 0.078$. We cannot reject H_0.

	n	$\bar{x}$	s
4 months	19	570.00	122.96
5 months	18	483.00	112.95
6 months	8	541.88	93.96

Minitab output

```
Analysis of Variance on energy
Source      DF        SS       MS       F       p
Treatment    2     71288    35644    2.72   0.078
Error       42    550811    13115
Total       44    622099
```

12.38. (a) Aside from two low outliers, the residuals are reasonably normal. **(b)** We did not reject H_0, so we do not need comparisons to determine which means are different.

```
-3 | 6
-3 | 0
-2 |
-2 |
-1 | 6
-1 | 110
-0 | 9888776555
-0 | 2110
 0 | 0123333444
 0 | 555789
 1 | 000333
 1 | 566
```

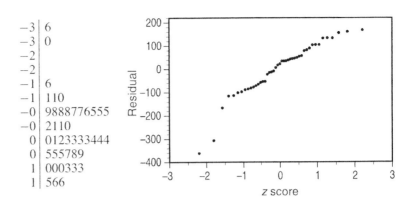

12.39. (a) Pooling is reasonable, as the largest-to-smallest ratio is about 1.65. **(b)** ANOVA gives $F = 7.98$ (df 2 and 27) for which $P = 0.002$. We reject H_0 and conclude that not all means are equal.

	n	$\bar{x}$	s
Control	10	601.1	27.364
Low jump	10	612.5	19.329
High jump	10	638.7	16.594

Minitab output

```
Analysis of Variance on density
Source      DF      SS       MS       F        p
Treatment    2     7434     3717     7.98    0.002
Error       27    12580      466
Total       29    20013
```

12.40. (a) The residuals appear to be reasonably normal. **(b)** With df $= 27$, 3 comparisons, and $\alpha = 0.05$, the Bonferroni critical value is $t^{**} = 2.5525$. The pooled standard deviation is $s_p \doteq 21.5849$, and the standard error of each difference is $\text{SE}_D = s_p\sqrt{1/10 + 1/10} \doteq 9.6531$, so two means are significantly different if they differ by $t^{**}\text{SE}_D \doteq 24.6390$. The high-jump mean is significantly different from the other two.

```
-4 | 7
-3 | 2
-2 | 4
-1 | 8666322
-0 | 887751
 0 | 1449
 1 | 112899
 2 | 25
 3 | 5
 4 |
 5 | 1
```

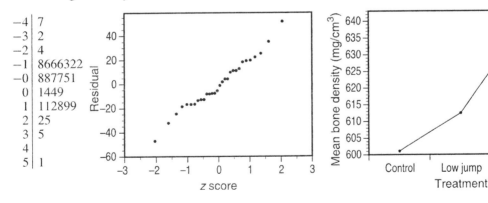

12.41. (a) Pooling is risky because $0.6283/0.2520 = 2.49 > 2$. **(b)** ANOVA gives $F = 31.16$ (df 2 and 9) for which $P < 0.0005$. We reject H_0 and conclude that not all means are equal.

	n	$\bar{x}$	s
Aluminum	4	2.0575	0.2520
Clay	4	2.1775	0.6213
Iron	4	4.6800	0.6283

Minitab output

```
Analysis of Variance on iron
Source      DF      SS       MS       F        p
Pot          2    17.539    8.770    31.16   0.000
Error        9     2.533    0.281
Total       11    20.072
```

12.42. (a) There are no clear violations of normality, but the number of residuals is so small that is difficult to draw any conclusions. **(b)** With df $= 9$, 3 comparisons, and $\alpha = 0.05$, the Bonferroni critical value is $t^{**} = 2.9333$. The pooled standard deviation is $s_p \doteq 0.5305$, and the standard error of each difference is $\text{SE}_D = s_p\sqrt{1/4 + 1/4} \doteq 0.3751$, so two means are significantly different if they differ by $t^{**}\text{SE}_D \doteq 1.1003$. The iron mean is significantly higher than the other two.

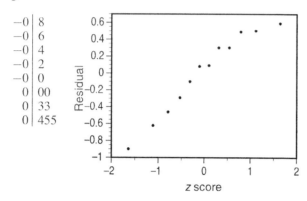
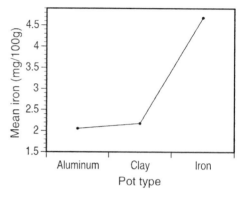

12.43. (a) Pooling is risky because $8.66/2.89 = 3 > 2$. **(b)** ANOVA gives $F = 137.94$ (df 5 and 12) for which $P < 0.0005$. We reject H_0 and conclude that not all means are equal.

	n	$\bar{x}$	s
ECM1	3	65.0%	8.6603%
ECM2	3	63.$\bar{3}$%	2.8868%
ECM3	3	73.$\bar{3}$%	2.8868%
MAT1	3	23.$\bar{3}$%	2.8868%
MAT2	3	6.$\bar{6}$%	2.8868%
MAT3	3	11.$\bar{6}$%	2.8868%

Minitab output

```
Analysis of Variance on gpi
Source      DF        SS        MS        F        p
Treatment    5    13411.1    2682.2    137.94    0.000
Error       12      233.3      19.4
Total       17    13644.4
```

12.44. (a) The residuals have one low outlier, and a lot of granularity, so normality is difficult to assess. **(b)** With df $= 12$, 15 comparisons, and $\alpha = 0.05$, the Bonferroni critical value is $t^{**} = 3.6489$. The pooled standard deviation is $s_p \doteq 4.4096\%$, and the standard error of each difference is $\text{SE}_D = s_p\sqrt{1/3 + 1/3} \doteq 3.6004\%$, so two means are significantly different if they differ by $t^{**}\text{SE}_D \doteq 13.1375\%$. The three ECM means are significantly higher than the three MAT means.

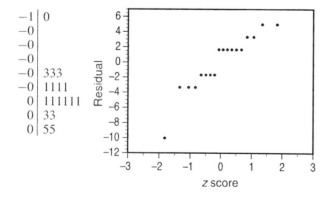
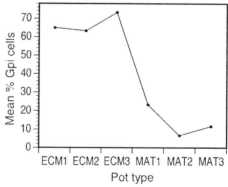

12.45. The contrast is $\psi = \frac{1}{3}(\mu_{ECM1} + \mu_{ECM2} + \mu_{ECM3}) - \frac{1}{3}(\mu_{MAT1} + \mu_{MAT2} + \mu_{MAT3})$, and the hypotheses are H_0: $\psi = 0$ vs. H_a: $\psi \neq 0$. For the test, we compute $c \doteq 53.33\%$, $SE_c \doteq 2.0787\%$, and $t \doteq 25.66$ with df = 12. This has a tiny P-value; the difference between ECM and MAT is highly significant. This is consistent with the Bonferroni results from the previous exercise.

12.46. (a) Below. **(b)** To test H_0: $\mu_1 = \cdots = \mu_4$ vs. H_a: not all μ_i are equal, ANOVA (Minitab output below) gives $F = 967.82$ (df 3 and 351), which has $P < 0.0005$. We conclude that not all means are equal; specifically, the 'Placebo' mean is much higher than the other three means.

Shampoo	n	$\bar{x}$	s	$s_{\bar{x}}$
PyrI	112	17.393	1.142	0.108
PyrII	109	17.202	1.352	0.130
Keto	106	16.028	0.931	0.090
Placebo	28	29.393	1.595	0.301

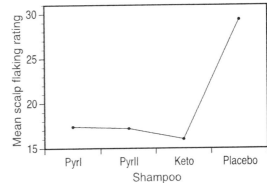

Minitab output

```
Analysis of Variance on Flaking
Source    DF        SS        MS        F        P
Code       3   4151.43   1383.81   967.82    0.000
Error    351    501.87      1.43
Total    354   4653.30
```

12.47. (a) The plot (below) shows granularity (which varies between groups), but that should not make us question independence; it is due to the fact that the scores are all integers. **(b)** The ratio of the largest to the smallest standard deviations is $1.595/0.931 \doteq 1.714$—less than 2. **(c)** Apart from the granularity, the quantile plots (below) are reasonably straight. **(d)** Again, apart from the granularity, the quantile plot looks pretty good.

For 12.47(a).

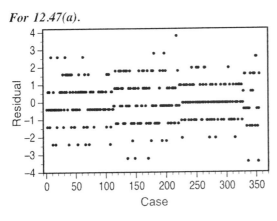

For 12.47(d).

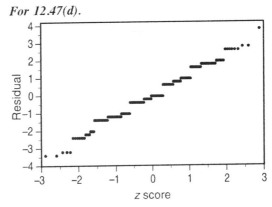

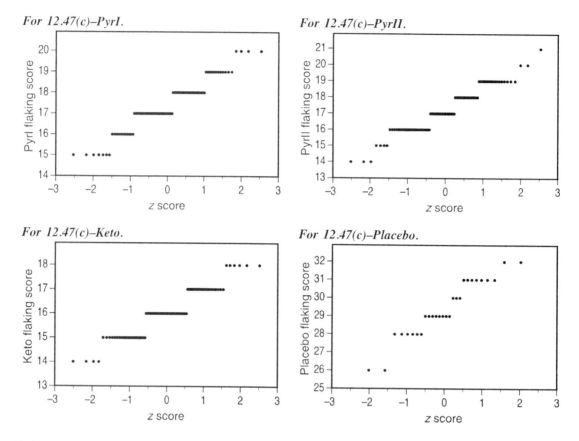

For 12.47(c)–PyrI.

For 12.47(c)–PyrII.

For 12.47(c)–Keto.

For 12.47(c)–Placebo.

12.48. We have six comparisons to make, and df $= 351$, so the Bonferroni critical value with $\alpha = 0.05$ is $t^{**} = 2.6533$. The pooled standard deviation is $s_p = \sqrt{\text{MSE}} \doteq 1.1958$; the differences, standard errors, and t statistics are below. The only *non*significant difference is between the two Pyr treatments (meaning the second application of the shampoo is of little benefit). The Keto shampoo mean is the lowest; the placebo mean is by far the highest.

$D_{\text{Py1–Py2}} = 0.19102$	$D_{\text{Py1–K}} = 1.36456$	$D_{\text{Py1–P}} = -12.0000$
$\text{SE}_{\text{Py1–Py2}} = 0.16088$	$\text{SE}_{\text{Py1–K}} = 0.16203$	$\text{SE}_{\text{Py1–P}} = 0.25265$
$t_{\text{Py1–Py2}} = 1.187$	$t_{\text{Py1–K}} = 8.421$	$t_{\text{Py1–P}} = -47.497$
	$D_{\text{Py2–K}} = 1.17353$	$D_{\text{Py2–P}} = -12.1910$
	$\text{SE}_{\text{Py2–K}} = 0.16312$	$\text{SE}_{\text{Py2–P}} = 0.25334$
	$t_{\text{Py2–K}} = 7.195$	$t_{\text{Py2–P}} = -48.121$
		$D_{\text{K–P}} = -13.3646$
		$\text{SE}_{\text{K–P}} = 0.25407$
		$t_{\text{K–P}} = -52.601$

12.49. (a) The three contrasts are

$\psi_1 = \frac{1}{3}\mu_{Py1} + \frac{1}{3}\mu_{Py2} + \frac{1}{3}\mu_K - \mu_P,$

$\psi_2 = \frac{1}{2}\mu_{Py1} + \frac{1}{2}\mu_{Py2} - \mu_K,$

$\psi_3 = \mu_{Py1} - \mu_{Py2}.$

$c_1 = -12.51$	$c_2 = 1.269$	$c_3 = 0.191$
$SE_{c_1} \doteq 0.2355$	$SE_{c_2} \doteq 0.1413$	$SE_{c_3} \doteq 0.1609$
$t_1 = -53.17$	$t_2 = 8.98$	$t_3 = 1.19$
$P_1 < 0.0005$	$P_2 < 0.0005$	$P_3 \doteq 0.2359$

(b) The pooled standard deviation is $s_p = \sqrt{MSE} \doteq 1.1958$. The estimated contrasts and their standard errors are in the table. For example,

$$SE_{c_1} = s_p\sqrt{\tfrac{1}{9}/112 + \tfrac{1}{9}/109 + \tfrac{1}{9}/106 + 1/28} \doteq 0.2355.$$

(c) We test H_0: $\psi_i = 0$ vs. H_a: $\psi_i \neq 0$ for each contrast. The t and P values are given in the table.

The Placebo mean is significantly higher than the average of the other three, while the Keto mean is significantly lower than the average of the two Pyr means. The difference between the Pyr means is not significant (meaning the second application of the shampoo is of little benefit)—this agrees with our conclusion from Exercise 12.48.

12.50. (a) At right. **(b)** Each new value (except for n) is simply

(old value)/64 × 100%

(c) The SS and MS entries differ from those of Exercise 12.19—by a factor of $(100/64)^2$. However, everything else is the same: $F = 367.74$ with df 4 and 5; $P < 0.0005$, so we (again) reject H_0 and conclude that vitamin C content decreases over time.

Condition	n	$\bar{x}$	s	$s_{\bar{x}}$
Immediate	2	76.102%	2.3975%	1.6953%
One day	2	65.555%	3.3256%	2.3516%
Three days	2	34.055%	1.2043%	0.8516%
Five days	2	19.398%	1.6904%	1.1953%
Seven days	2	13.000%	0.4198%	0.2969%

Minitab output

```
Analysis of Variance on VitCPct
Source    DF      SS       MS       F        p
Days       4   6263.97  1565.99  367.74   0.000
Error      5     21.29     4.26
Total      9   6285.26
```

12.51. Transformed values for vitamin A are at right; each value is

(old value)/5 × 100%

(or equivalently, multiply by 20%). The transformation has no effect on vitamin E, since the

Condition	n	$\bar{x}$	s	$s_{\bar{x}}$
Immediate	2	67.0%	0.2828%	0.2%
One day	2	64.8%	1.1314%	0.8%
Three days	2	64.2%	1.4142%	1.0%
Five days	2	66.1%	1.5556%	1.1%
Seven days	2	59.3%	1.2728%	0.9%

number of milligrams remaining is also the percentage of the original 100 mg.

For vitamin A, the SS and MS entries differ from those of Exercise 12.21—by a factor of $(100/5)^2 = 400$. Everything else is the same: $F = 12.09$ with df 4 and 5; $P = 0.009$, so we (again) reject H_0 and conclude that vitamin A content decreases over time.

Since the vitamin E numbers are unchanged, the ANOVA table is unchanged, and we again fail to reject H_0 ($F = 0.69$ with df 4 and 5; $P = 0.630$).

In summary, transforming to percents (or doing any linear transformation) has no effect on the results of the ANOVA.

Minitab output

```
Analysis of Variance on VitAPct
Source      DF        SS        MS        F        p
Days         4     71.58     17.89     12.09    0.009
Error        5      7.40      1.48
Total        9     78.98
```

12.52. There is no effect on the test statistic, df, P-value, and conclusion. The degrees of freedom are not affected, since the number of groups and sample sizes are unchanged; meanwhile, the SS and MS values change (by a factor of b^2), but this change does not affect F, since the factors of b^2 cancel out in the ratio $F = \text{MSG}/\text{MSE}$. With the same F and df values, the P-value and conclusion are necessarily unchanged.

Proof of these statements is not too difficult, but it requires careful use of the SS formulas. For most students, a demonstration with several choices of a and b would probably be more convincing than a proof. However, here is the basic idea: Using results of Chapter 1, we know that the means undergo the same transformation as the data $(\bar{x}_i^* = a + b\bar{x}_i)$, while the standard deviations are changed by a factor of $|b|$. Let $\bar{x}$ be the average of *all* the data; note that $\bar{x}^* = a + b\bar{x}$. Now $\text{SSG} = \sum_{i=1}^{I} n_i(\bar{x}_i - \bar{x})^2$, so

$$\text{SSG}^* = \sum_i n_i(\bar{x}_i^* - \bar{x}^*)^2 = \sum_i n_i(b\bar{x}_i - b\bar{x})^2 = \sum_i n_i b^2(\bar{x}_i - \bar{x})^2 = b^2\text{SSG}.$$

Similarly, we can establish that $\text{SSE}^* = b^2\text{SSE}$ and $\text{SST}^* = b^2\text{SST}$. Since the MS values are merely SS values divided by the (unchanged) degrees of freedom, these also change by a factor of b^2.

12.53. A table of means and standard deviations is given below. Quantile plots are not shown, but apart from the granularity of the scores, and a few possible outliers, there are no marked deviations from normality. Pooling is reasonable for both PRE1 and PRE2; the ratios are 1.24 and 1.48.

For both PRE1 and PRE2, we test H_0: $\mu_B = \mu_D = \mu_S$ vs. H_a: at least one mean is different. Both tests have df 2 and 63. For PRE1, $F = 1.13$ and $P = 0.329$; for PRE2, $F = 0.11$ and $P = 0.895$. There is no reason to believe that the mean pretest scores differ between methods.

Method	n	PRE1 $\bar{x}$	PRE1 s	PRE2 $\bar{x}$	PRE2 s
Basal	22	10.5	2.9721	5.$\overline{27}$	2.7634
DRTA	22	9.$\overline{72}$	2.6936	5.$\overline{09}$	1.9978
Strat	22	9.1$\overline{36}$	3.3423	4.9$\overline{54}$	1.8639

Minitab output

```
Analysis of Variance on pre1
Source      DF        SS        MS        F        p
Group        2     20.58     10.29      1.13    0.329
Error       63    572.45      9.09
Total       65    593.03

Analysis of Variance on pre2
Source      DF        SS        MS        F        p
Group        2      1.12      0.56      0.11    0.895
Error       63    317.14      5.03
Total       65    318.26
```

12.54. Some of the distributions have mild outliers or skewness, but there are no serious violations of normality evident. Pooling is appropriate for all three response variables.

Variable	s_p	SE_D	$t^{**}SE_D$
POST1	3.1885	0.9614	2.3646
POST2	2.3785	0.7171	1.7639
POST3	6.3141	1.9038	4.6825

The three F statistics, all with df 2 and 63, are 5.32 ($P = 0.007$), 8.41 ($P = 0.001$), and 4.48 ($P = 0.015$). We conclude that at least one mean is different for each posttest.

For multiple comparisons, we have 3 comparisons, df 63, and $\alpha = 0.05$, so the Bonferroni critical value is $t^{**} = 2.4596$. In the table on the right are the pooled standard deviations, standard error of each difference, and values of $t^{**}SE_D$ (the "minimum significant difference," or MSD) for each response variable. For both POST1 and POST3, DRTA is significantly greater than Basal, but no other comparisons are significant. For POST2, Strat is significantly greater than both Basal and DRTA.

We also may examine the contrasts $\psi_1 = -\mu_B + \frac{1}{2}(\mu_D + \mu_S)$, which is positive if the average of the new methods is greater than the basal mean, and $\psi_2 = \mu_D - \mu_S$, which compares the two new methods. Estimated contrasts, standard errors, t, and P are given in the table below. (The P-values are one-sided for ψ_1 and two-sided for ψ_2.) We see that c_1 is significantly positive for all three variables. The second contrast was included in our multiple comparisons, where we found the difference significant only for POST2, but this time, when we are testing *only* this difference, rather than all three possible differences, we conclude that $\mu_D > \mu_S$ for POST1, in addition to the difference for POST2.

Variable	c_1	SE_{c_1}	t_1	P_1	c_2	SE_{c_2}	t_2	P_2
POST1	2.0909	0.8326	2.51	0.0073	2.0000	0.9614	2.08	0.0415
POST2	1.7500	0.6211	2.82	0.0032	−2.1364	0.7171	−2.98	0.0041
POST3	4.4545	1.6487	2.70	0.0044	2.4545	1.9038	1.29	0.2019

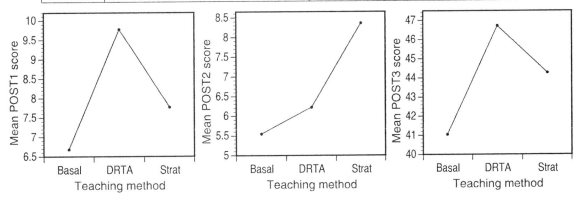

Test	Method	$\bar{x}$	s
POST1	Basal	6.6818	2.7669
	DRTA	9.7727	2.7243
	Strat	7.7727	3.9271
POST2	Basal	5.5455	2.0407
	DRTA	6.2273	2.0915
	Strat	8.3636	2.9040
POST3	Basal	41.0455	5.6356
	DRTA	46.7273	7.3884
	Strat	44.2727	5.7668

```
Basal/POST1      DRTA/POST1      Strat/POST1
 1|               1|              1|0
 2|0              2|              2|
 3|0              3|              3|0
 4|000            4|              4|0000
 5|00000          5|00            5|00
 6|0              6|              6|0
 7|00             7|000           7|000
 8|000            8|0000          8|0
 9|000            9|              9|00
10|0             10|0000         10|
11|              11|00           11|00
12|00            12|000          12|00
                 13|00           13|0
                 14|00           14|0
                                 15|0
```

```
Basal/POST2      DRTA/POST2        Strat/POST2
 0|               0|0               0|
 1|               1|                1|0
 2|               2|                2|
 3|000            3|0               3|
 4|00000          4|                4|0
 5|000000         5|00              5|00
 6|0              6|0000000000      6|0
 7|00             7|0000            7|00
 8|000            8|00              8|000
 9|0              9|0               9|0000
10|0             10|               10|000
                 11|0              11|00
                                   12|00
                                   13|0
```

```
Basal/POST3      DRTA/POST3       Strat/POST3
 3|               3|01             3|
 3|223            3|               3|33
 3|5              3|               3|4
 3|66             3|7              3|
 3|99             3|               3|8
 4|0011           4|01             4|1
 4|23             4|23             4|2223
 4|4555           4|               4|455
 4|66             4|7              4|7
 4|9              4|8889999        4|888999
 5|               5|0              5|01
 5|               5|33             5|3
 5|4              5|455
                  5|7
```

Minitab output

```
Analysis of Variance on POST1
Source    DF        SS        MS        F        p
Method     2     108.1      54.1     5.32    0.007
Error     63     640.5      10.2
Total     65     748.6


Analysis of Variance on POST2
Source    DF        SS        MS        F        p
Method     2     95.12     47.56     8.41    0.001
Error     63    356.41      5.66
Total     65    451.53


Analysis of Variance on POST3
Source    DF        SS        MS        F        p
Method     2     357.3     178.7     4.48    0.015
Error     63    2511.7      39.9
Total     65    2869.0
```

12.55. The regression equation is

$$\hat{y} = 4.3645 - 0.1165x$$

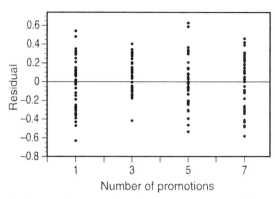

($\hat{y}$ is the expected price, and x is the number of promotions). The regression is significant (i.e., the slope is significantly different from 0): $t = -13.31$ with df $= 158$, giving $P < 0.0005$. The regression on number of promotions explains $r^2 = 52.9\%$ of the variation in expected price. (This is similar to the ANOVA value: $R^2 = 53.5\%$.)

The granularity of the "Number of promotions" observations makes interpreting the residual plot a bit tricky. For five promotions, the residuals seem to be more likely to be negative (in fact, 26 of the 40 residuals are negative), while for 3 promotions, the residuals are weighted toward the positive side. (We also observe that in the plot of mean expected price vs. number of promotions—see the solution to Exercise 12.32—the mean for three promotions is not as small as one would predict from a line near the other three points.) This suggests that a linear model may not be appropriate.

Minitab output

The regression equation is ExpPrice = 4.36 - 0.116 NumPromo

Predictor	Coef	Stdev	t-ratio	p
Constant	4.36452	0.04009	108.87	0.000
NumPromo	-0.116475	0.008748	-13.31	0.000

s = 0.2474   R-sq = 52.9%   R-sq(adj) = 52.6%

Analysis of Variance

SOURCE	DF	SS	MS	F	p
Regression	1	10.853	10.853	177.26	0.000
Error	158	9.674	0.061		
Total	159	20.527			

12.56. (a) *P*-values close to 0.01 occur when F is close to 5.483. (This is the value for df 2 and 27; this applet seems to have three samples with 10 observations each.) How close students can get to this depends on how much they play around with the applet, and the pooled standard error setting. **(b)** As variation increases, F decreases and P increases.

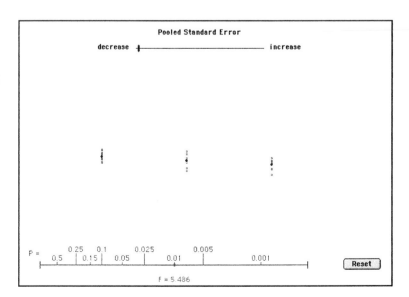

12.57. (a) *F* can be made
very small (close to
0), and *P* close to 1.
(b) *F* increases, and
P decreases. Moving
the means farther apart
means that (even with
moderate spread) it is
easier to see that the
three groups represent
three different popula-
tions (that is, populations
having different means).
Therefore, the evidence
against H_0 becomes
stronger.

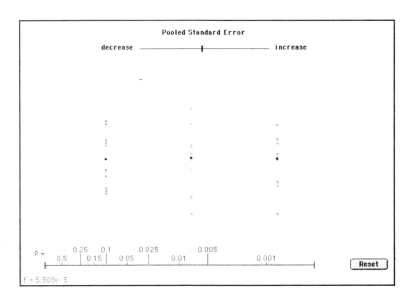

12.58. The pooled standard deviation s_p is found by looking at the spread of each observation about its *group* mean $\bar{x}_i$. The "total" standard deviation s given in Exercise 12.16 is the spread about the grand mean (the mean of all the data values, ignoring distinctions between groups). When we ignore group differences, we have more variation (uncertainty) in our data, so s is *almost always* larger than s_p.

This can be made clearer (to sufficiently mathematical students) by noting that the total variance s^2 can be found in the ANOVA table: Just as $s_p^2 = \dfrac{\text{SSE}}{\text{DFE}} = \text{MSE}$, $s^2 = \dfrac{\text{SST}}{\text{DFT}} = \text{MST}$. (The total mean square is not included in the ANOVA table but is easily computed from the values on the bottom line.) Because SSM + SSE = SST, we always have SSE ≤ SST, with equality only when the model is completely worthless (that is, when all group means equal the grand mean). Because DFE < DFT, it might be that MSE ≥ MST but that does not happen very often.

12.60. With $\sigma = 7$ and means $\mu_1 = 40$, $\mu_2 = 48$, and $\mu_3 = 44$, we have $\bar{\mu} = \dfrac{40 + 48 + 44}{3} = 44$ and noncentrality parameter

$$\lambda = \frac{n \sum (\mu_i - \bar{\mu})^2}{\sigma^2} = \frac{(10)[(40 - 44)^2 + (48 - 44)^2 + (44 - 44)^2]}{49} = \frac{(10)(32)}{49} \doteq 6.5306$$

(The value of λ in the G•Power output below is slightly different due to rounding.) The degrees of freedom and critical value are the same as in Example 12.27: df 2 and 27, $F^* = 3.35$. Software reports the power as about 57%. Samples of size 10 are not adequate for this alternative; we should increase the sample size so that we have a better chance of detecting it. (For example, samples of size 20 give power 89% for this alternative.)

G•Power output

```
Post-hoc analysis for "F-Test (ANOVA)", Global, Groups: 3:
Alpha: 0.0500
Power (1-beta): 0.5717
Effect size "f": 0.4666
Total sample size: 30
Critical value: F(2,27) = 3.3541
Lambda: 6.5315
```

12.61. (a) Sampling plans will vary but should attempt to address how cultural groups will be determined: Can we obtain such demographic information from the school administration? Do we simply select a large sample, then poll each student to determine if he or she belongs to one of these groups? (b) Answers will vary with choice of H_a and desired power. For example, with the alternative $\mu_1 = \mu_2 = 4.4$, $\mu_3 = 5$, and standard deviation $\sigma = 1.2$, three samples of size 75 will produce power 0.89. (See G•Power output below.) (c) The report should make an attempt to explain the statistical issues involved; specifically, it should convey that sample sizes are sufficient to detect anticipated differences among the groups.

G•Power output

```
Post-hoc analysis for "F-Test (ANOVA)", Global, Groups: 3:
Alpha: 0.0500
Power (1-beta): 0.8920
Effect size "f": 0.2357
Total sample size: 225
Critical value: F(2,222) = 3.0365
Lambda: 12.4998
```

12.62. Recommended sample sizes will vary with choice of H_a and desired power. For example, with the alternative $\mu_1 = \mu_2 = 0.22$, $\mu_3 = 0.24$, and standard deviation $\sigma = 0.015$, three samples of size 10 will produce power 0.84, and samples of size 15 increase the power to 0.96. (See G•Power output below.) The report should make an attempt to explain the statistical issues involved; specifically, it should convey that sample sizes are sufficient to detect anticipated differences among the groups.

G•Power output

```
Post-hoc analysis for F-Test (ANOVA), Global, Groups: 3:
Alpha: 0.0500
Power (1-beta): 0.8379
Effect size f: 0.6285
Total sample size: 30
Critical value: F(2,27) = 3.3541
Lambda: 11.8504
Note: Accuracy mode calculation.

Post-hoc analysis for F-Test (ANOVA), Global, Groups: 3:
Alpha: 0.0500
Power (1-beta): 0.9622
Effect size f: 0.6285
Total sample size: 45
Critical value: F(2,42) = 3.2199
Lambda: 17.7756
```

Chapter 13 Solutions

13.1. (a) The RESIDUAL part of the model represents the error. **(b)** Large F (not small) is needed to reject H_0. **(c)** The given statement is backwards; it should be: Mean squares are equal to sum of squares divided by degrees of freedom.

13.2. (a) The tests for the main effects (and the test for interactions) involve an F distribution if H_0 is true. **(b)** It is not necessary that all sample sizes be the same. **(c)** The means $\bar{x}_{ij}$ are *estimates of* the parameters μ_{ij}.

13.3. A 2×4 ANOVA with five observations per cell has $I = 2$, $J = 4$, and $N = 40$. **(a)** The degrees of freedom for interaction are DFAB $= (I-1)(J-1) = 3$ and DFE $= N - IJ = 32$. In Table E, use df 3 and 30. **(b)** The sketch on the right shows the observed F value given in part (c) and the bounding critical 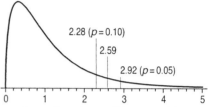 values from Table E. Shown is an actual $F(3, 32)$ density; student sketches will vary. **(c)** In Table E, we see that $2.28 < F < 2.92$, so $0.05 < P < 0.10$. (Software gives 0.0700.) **(d)** The plot of means would look somewhat parallel, because the interaction term is not significantly different from 0. (Because the P-value is pretty small, the means will not be perfectly parallel.)

13.4. The answers are found in Table E (or using software) with $p = 0.05$. **(a)** We have $I = J = 3$ and $N = 36$, so DFA $= 2$ and DFE $= 27$. We would reject H_0 if $F > 3.35$ (software: 3.3541). **(b)** We have $I = J = 3$ and $N = 36$, so DFAB $= 4$ and DFE $= 27$. We would reject H_0 if $F > 2.73$ (software: 2.7278). **(c)** We have $I = J = 2$ and $N = 1004$, so DFAB $= 1$ and DFE $= 1000$. We would reject H_0 if $F > 3.85$ (software: 3.8508).

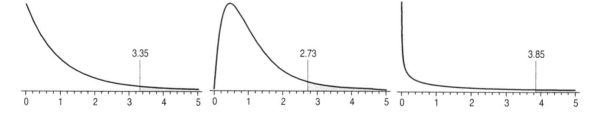

13.5. **(a)** The marginal means (as well as the individual cell means) are in the table below. The first two means suggest that the intervention group showed improvement over the control group. **(b)** Interaction means that the mean number of actions changes differently over time for the two groups. We see this in the plot below because the lines connecting the means are not parallel.

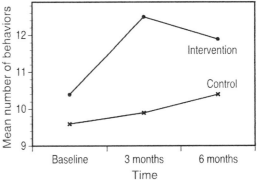

Group	Time Baseline	3 mo.	6 mo.	Mean
Intervention	10.4	12.5	11.9	11.6
Control	9.6	9.9	10.4	9.967
Mean	10.0	11.2	11.15	10.783

13.6. **(a)** The data might be displayed in a variety of ways. Because there are so many numbers (intervention and control groups, at baseline, 3 months, and 6 months), the graph can very easily become overwhelmingly crowded; in order to avoid this, the graph on the right shows the percentage for each group averaged over the three times. Any reasonable graphical display will likely be judged more effective than Table 13.1; for the most part, it is easier to interpret pictures than lists of numbers.

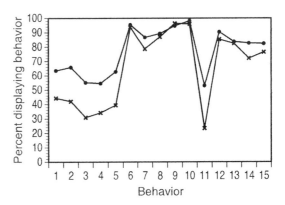

(b) The behaviors seemed to fall into two categories: Those which both groups did most of the time, and those which were less common. The biggest differences between the control and intervention groups are in the latter group, which includes the first five and the 11th behaviors: hide money, hide extra keys, abuse code to alert family, hide extra clothing, asked neighbors to call police, removed weapons. These behaviors should receive special attention in future programs. **(c)** Perhaps the results of this study may be less applicable to smaller communities, or to those which are less diverse.

13.7. We have $I = 3$, $J = 2$ and $N = 30$, so the degrees of freedom are DFA $= 2$, DFB $= 1$, DFAB $= 2$, and DFE $= 24$. This allows us to determine P-values (or to compare to Table E), and we find that there are no significant effects:

$$F_A = 1.21 \text{ has df 2 and 24, so } P = 0.3157.$$

$$F_B = 3.63 \text{ has df 1 and 24, so } P = 0.0688.$$

$$F_{AB} = 2.04 \text{ has df 2 and 24, so } P = 0.1520.$$

13.8. **(a)** Based on the given P-values, all three effects are significant at $\alpha = 0.05$. (The interaction effect would not be significant at $\alpha = 0.01$.) **(b)** In order to summarize the results, we would need to know the number of levels for each factor (I and J) and the sample sizes in each cell (n_{ij}). We also would want to know the sample cell means $\bar{x}_{ij}$, so that we could interpret the significant main effects and the nature of the interaction.

13.9. **(a)** For familiar ads, mean attitude increases with repetition. Familiar ads had the higher mean rating for 1 and 3 repetitions, while unfamiliar ads were rated higher for 2 repetitions. **(b)** The interaction is that unfamiliar does better with 2 repetitions, and worse for 1 and 3. (If there were no interaction, the lines connecting the means would be close to parallel.)

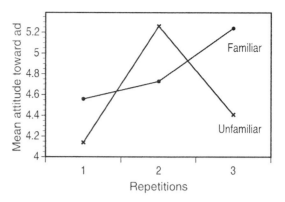

13.10. All four mean plots show evidence of interaction (the lines connecting the means are not parallel). The first and third exhibit a pattern similar to the plot in the previous exercise: For familiar ads, the response variable increases (or decreases only slightly) with increasing repetition, while for unfamiliar ads, the response variable is sharply higher for 2 repetitions. Mean counter arguments displays nearly the opposite pattern: increasing for unfamiliar ads, and higher at 2 repetitions for familiar ads. Mean total thoughts increases with repetitions for both familiar and unfamiliar ads.

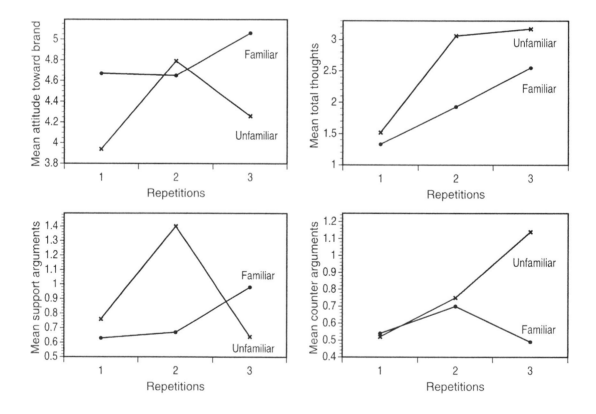

13.11. Pooling is reasonable, as $1.46/1.16 \doteq 1.26 < 2$. If we assume that all sample sizes were equal, the pooled standard deviation is $s_p \doteq 1.3077$. As long as the sample sizes were approximately equal, we get a similar answer.

Note: *The published paper from which these numbers were taken only mentions that there were 94 subjects, randomly assigned into groups. Also, the value of s_p is the same regardless of the sample size; that is, we do not need to know the sample sizes in order to compute this. It is simplest to do the computation assuming that all sample sizes were 2; in that case, we simply square the six given standard deviations, find the average, and then take the square root.*

13.12. Pooling is reasonable, as $2.16/1.42 \doteq 1.52 < 2$. If we assume that all sample sizes were equal (see the comment in the previous solution), the pooled standard deviation is $s_p \doteq 1.6767$.

13.13. Questions raised by this background information might include: Are opinions of university employees (and/or west coast residents) similar to other groups? What do experts consider to be "good" ads? Did the content of the news show affect responses to the ads?

13.14. The data cannot be normally distributed, as we have whole numbers from 1 to 7. However, there can be no extreme outliers on such a scale, and we have averaged the ratings of three ads, so ANOVA would be fairly safe.

13.15. (a) Plot on the right. (b) There seems to be a fairly large difference between the means based on how much the rats were allowed to eat, but not very much difference based on the chromium level. There may be an interaction: the NM mean is lower than the LM mean, while the NR mean is higher than the LR mean. (c) The marginal means are L: 4.86, N: 4.871, M: 4.485, R: 5.246. For low chromium level (L), R minus M is 0.63; for normal chromium (N), R minus M is 0.892. Mean GITH levels are lower for M than for R; there is not much difference for L *versus* N. The difference between M and R is greater among rats who had normal chromium levels in their diets (N).

13.16. The "Other" category had the lowest mean HS math grades for both genders; this is apparent from the graph (right) as well as from the marginal means (CS: 8.895, EO: 8.855, O: 7.845). Females had higher mean grades; the female marginal mean is $8.83\overline{6}$ compared to $8.22\overline{6}$ for males. The female − male difference is similar for CS and O (about 0.5) but is about twice as big for EO (an interaction).

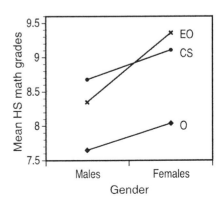

13.17. The "Other" category had the lowest mean SATM score for both genders; this is apparent from the graph (right) as well as from the marginal means (CS: 605, EO: 624.5, O: 566.) Males had higher mean scores in CS and O, while females are slightly higher in EO; this indicates an interaction. Overall, the marginal means by gender are 611.7 (males) and 585.3 (females).

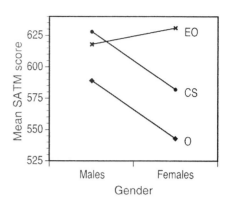

13.18. A study today might include a category for those who declared a major such as Information Technology (which probably did not exist at the time of the initial study). Some variables that might be useful to consider: grade in first programming course, high school physics grades, etc.

13.19. **(a)** For all cells, $n = 3$; the means, standard deviations, and standard errors are in the table below. The ratio of the largest to smallest standard deviations is $8.66/2.88 = 3$, but apart from the first standard deviation, the ratio is 2. **(b)** ECM means are all higher than MAT means. Time and interaction effects are not clearly suggested in the plot (the means are pretty close to parallel, and for a given material, there is little difference between four and eight weeks). **(c)** As the plot suggests, only Material ($F = 251.26$, df 5 and 24, $P < 0.0005$) is significant. For Time, $F = 0.29$, df 1 and 24, $P = 0.595$. For interaction, $F = 0.06$, df 5 and 24, $P = 0.998$. Based on this, we see clearly that the best results come from ECM scaffolds; no additional benefit is obtained from leaving the scaffold in place for eight weeks.

| Gpi (%) | | | | | | |
| Material | | 4 weeks | | | 8 weeks | |
	$\bar{x}$	s	$s_{\bar{x}}$	$\bar{x}$	s	$s_{\bar{x}}$
ECM1	65	8.6603	5	$63.\overline{3}$	2.8868	$1.\overline{6}$
ECM2	$63.\overline{3}$	2.8868	$1.\overline{6}$	$63.\overline{3}$	5.7735	$3.\overline{3}$
ECM3	$73.\overline{3}$	2.8868	$1.\overline{6}$	$73.\overline{3}$	5.7735	$3.\overline{3}$
MAT1	$23.\overline{3}$	2.8868	$1.\overline{6}$	$21.\overline{6}$	5.7735	$3.\overline{3}$
MAT2	$6.\overline{6}$	2.8868	$1.\overline{6}$	$6.\overline{6}$	2.8868	$1.\overline{6}$
MAT3	$11.\overline{6}$	2.8868	$1.\overline{6}$	10	5	2.8868

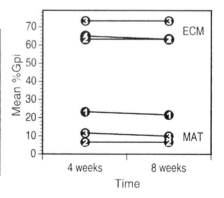

Minitab output

```
Analysis of Variance for Gpi

Source          DF       SS       MS       F       P
Material         5   27045.1   5409.0  251.26   0.000
Weeks            1       6.2      6.2    0.29   0.595
Weeks*Material   5       6.2      1.3    0.06   0.998
Error           24     516.7     21.5
Total           35   27574.3
```

13.20. The means, standard deviations, and standard errors for two weeks are in the table below; as in the previous exercise, $n = 3$ for all cells. Because of the large standard deviation for ECM3 at 2 weeks, the ratio of the largest to smallest standard deviations is now 3.6. The means plot again shows that ECM means are all higher than MAT means. In this plot, there appears to be a time effect (%Gpi decreases over time, at least for MAT1 and MAT3) and an interaction (the amount of decrease varies). ANOVA reveals that all three effects are significant: material ($F = 262.65$, df 5 and 36, $P < 0.0005$), time ($F = 16.93$, df 2 and 36, $P < 0.0005$), and interaction ($F = 3.81$, df 10 and 36, $P = 0.001$). Our conclusions are still the same (ECM scaffolds are better, and for ECM, time does not matter), but the addition of the two-week data adds a cautionary note: Not only are the inert-material scaffolds MAT1, MAT2, and MAT3 less effective than the ECM scaffolds, but they seem to do worse over time.

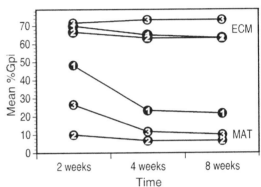

Gpi (%) at 2 weeks

Material	$\bar{x}$	s	$s_{\bar{x}}$
ECM1	70	5	2.8868
ECM2	$66.\overline{6}$	7.6376	4.4096
ECM3	$71.\overline{6}$	10.4083	6.0093
MAT1	$48.\overline{3}$	2.8868	$1.\overline{6}$
MAT2	10	5	2.8868
MAT3	$26.\overline{6}$	2.8868	$1.\overline{6}$

Minitab output

```
Analysis of Variance for Gpi

Source           DF        SS        MS       F       P
Material          5   35870.8    7174.2  262.65   0.000
Weeks             2     925.0     462.5   16.93   0.000
Material*Weeks   10    1041.7     104.2    3.81   0.001
Error            36     983.3      27.3
Total            53   38820.8
```

13.21. For each time period, there is a significant difference among materials (Minitab output below). The one-way ANOVA for the four-week time period also appears in the solution to Exercise 12.43.

Time period	s_p	SE_D	MSD
2 weeks	6.2361	5.0918	18.5793
4 weeks	4.4096	3.6004	13.1375
8 weeks	4.8591	3.9675	14.4768

With df $= 12$, 15 comparisons, and $\alpha = 0.05$, the Bonferroni critical value is $t^{**} = 3.6489$. The table on the right gives the pooled standard deviations s_p, the standard errors of each difference $SE_D = s_p\sqrt{1/3 + 1/3}$, and the "minimum significant difference" $MSD = t^{**}SE_D$ (two means are significantly different if they differ by at least this amount). For a given time period, the ECM means are not significantly different from one another. MAT1 is significantly larger than MAT2 for all time periods, and is also greater than MAT3 at 2 weeks. The only ECM/MAT difference that is *not* significant is ECM2 and MAT1 at 2 weeks.

Minitab output

```
– – – – – – – – – – – – –          Two weeks          – – – – – – – – – – – – – – –
Analysis of Variance on Gpi2
Source      DF        SS         MS         F          p
Material     5      9861.1     1972.2     50.71     0.000
Error       12       466.7       38.9
Total       17     10327.8
– – – – – – – – – – – – – –          Four weeks          – – – – – – – – – – – – – –
Analysis of Variance on Gpi4
Source      DF        SS         MS         F          p
Material     5     13411.1     2682.2    137.94     0.000
Error       12       233.3       19.4
Total       17     13644.4
– – – – – – – – – – – – – –          Eight weeks          – – – – – – – – – – – – – –
Analysis of Variance on Gpi8
Source      DF        SS         MS         F          p
Material     5     13640.3     2728.1    115.54     0.000
Error       12       283.3       23.6
Total       17     13923.6
```

13.22. (a) The sample size is $n = 4$ for all pot/food combinations; means and standard deviations are given in the table below. The largest-to-smallest ratio is $0.63/0.07 \doteq 8.8$, which is well above our guideline for pooling. **(b)** The iron levels differed among the three food types, and for all food types, aluminum and clay pots produced similar iron levels, while iron pots resulted in much higher iron levels. There is also evidence of an interaction: Iron levels in iron pots rose much more for meat than for legumes or vegetables. **(c)** The ANOVA table (below) shows that all three effects are quite significant.

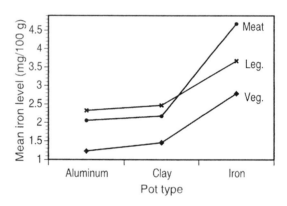

Iron (mg per 100 g)						
	Meat		Legumes		Vegetables	
Pot type	$\bar{x}$	s	$\bar{x}$	s	$\bar{x}$	s
Aluminum	2.0575	0.2520	2.3300	0.1111	1.2325	0.2313
Clay	2.1775	0.6213	2.4725	0.0714	1.4600	0.4601
Iron	4.6800	0.6283	3.6700	0.1726	2.7900	0.2399

Minitab output

```
Analysis of Variance for Iron

Source      DF        SS         MS         F         P
Pot          2     24.8940    12.4470    92.26     0.000
Food         2      9.2969     4.6484    34.46     0.000
Pot*Food     4      2.6404     0.6601     4.89     0.004
Error       27      3.6425     0.1349
Total       35     40.4738
```

13.23. Yes: The iron-pot means are the highest, and the F statistic for testing the effect of the pot type is very large. (In this case, the interaction does not weaken any evidence that iron-pot foods contain more iron; it only suggests that while iron pots increase iron levels in all foods, the effect is strongest for meats.)

13.24. The ANOVA table (below) shows significant evidence that at least one group mean is different. With df $= 27$, 36 comparisons, and $\alpha = 0.05$, the Bonferroni critical value is $t^{**} = 3.5629$. The pooled standard deviation is $s_p \doteq 0.3673$, the standard error of each difference $SE_D = s_p\sqrt{1/4 + 1/4} \doteq 0.2597$, so two means are significantly different if they differ by $t^{**}SE_D \doteq 0.9253$. The "error bars" in the plot on the right are drawn with this length (above and below each mean), so two means are significantly different if the "dot" for one mean does not fall within the other mean's error bars. For example, we find that iron/meat is significantly larger than everything else, and iron/legumes is significantly different from everything except iron/vegetable. These conclusions are consistent with the results of the two-way ANOVA.

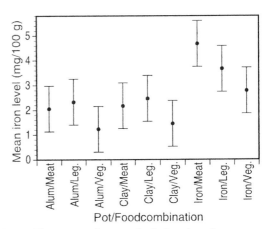

Minitab output

```
Analysis of Variance on Iron
Source    DF       SS        MS       F       p
Potfood    8    36.831     4.604   34.13   0.000
Error     27     3.643     0.135
Total     35    40.474
```

13.25. **(a)** For all tool/time combinations, $n = 3$. Means and standard deviations are in the table below. Note that five cells had no variability ($s = 0$). **(b)** Plot on the right. Except for tool 1, mean diameter is highest at time 2. Tool 1 had the highest mean diameters, followed by tool 2, tool 4, tool 3, and tool 5. **(c)** Minitab output below; all F statistics are highly significant. **(d)** There is strong evidence of a difference in mean diameter among the tools and among the times. There is also an interaction (specifically, tool 1's mean diameters changed differently over time compared to the other tools).

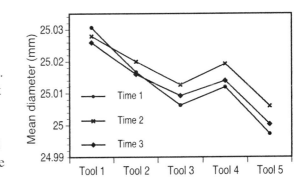

Minitab output

```
Analysis of Variance for Diameter

Source       DF        SS          MS        F       P
Tool          4  0.00359720  0.00089930  412.94   0.000
Time          2  0.00018991  0.00009496   43.60   0.000
Tool*Time     8  0.00013320  0.00001665    7.65   0.000
Error        30  0.00006533  0.00000218
Total        44  0.00398564
```

Diameter (mm)

Tool	Time 1 (8:00AM) $\bar{x}$	s	Time 2 (11:00AM) $\bar{x}$	s	Time 3 (3:00PM) $\bar{x}$	s
1	25.0307	0.001155	25.0280	0	25.0260	0
2	25.0167	0.001155	25.0200	0.002000	25.0160	0
3	25.0063	0.001528	25.0127	0.001155	25.0093	0.001155
4	25.0120	0	25.0193	0.001155	25.0140	0.004000
5	24.9973	0.001155	25.0060	0	25.0003	0.001528

13.26. All means and standard deviations will change by a factor of 0.04; the plot is identical to that in Exercise 13.25, except that the vertical scale is different. All SS and MS values change by a factor of $0.04^2 = 0.0016$, but the F (and P) values are the same.

Minitab output

```
Two-way ANOVA: diameter versus tool, time

Source        DF         SS          MS         F       P
tool           4  0.0000058   0.0000014    412.94   0.000
time           2  0.0000003   0.0000002     43.60   0.000
Interaction    8  0.0000002   0.0000000      7.65   0.000
Error         30  0.0000001   0.0000000
Total         44  0.0000064

S = 0.00005903    R-Sq = 98.36%    R-Sq(adj) = 97.60%
```

13.27. (a) Table below, plot on the right. The mean expected price decreases as the number of promotions increases, and also as the percent discount increases up to 30%. The expected price is higher for 40% than for 30%. **(b)** Minitab output below. Both main effects are significant, but there was no significant interaction. **(c)** There is strong evidence of a difference in mean expected price based on the number of promotions and the percent discount. Specifically, the two effects noted in (a) are significant: More promotions and higher discounts (up to a point) decrease the expected price. There is no evidence of an interaction.

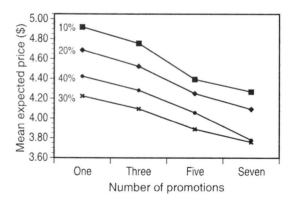

Expected price ($)

Promotions	40% discount $\bar{x}$	s	30% discount $\bar{x}$	s	20% discount $\bar{x}$	s	10% discount $\bar{x}$	s
1	4.423	0.1848	4.225	0.3856	4.689	0.2331	4.920	0.1520
3	4.284	0.2040	4.097	0.2346	4.524	0.2707	4.756	0.2429
5	4.058	0.1760	3.890	0.1629	4.251	0.2648	4.393	0.2685
7	3.780	0.2144	3.760	0.2618	4.094	0.2407	4.269	0.2699

Minitab output

Analysis of Variance for ExpPrice

Source	DF	SS	MS	F	P
Promos	3	8.3605	2.7868	47.73	0.000
Discount	3	8.3069	2.7690	47.42	0.000
Promos*Discount	9	0.2306	0.0256	0.44	0.912
Error	144	8.4087	0.0584		
Total	159	25.3067			

13.28. ANOVA gives $F = 19.29$ (df 15 and 144), which has $P < 0.0005$—there is significant evidence that some means are different. With df = 144, 120 comparisons, and $\alpha = 0.05$, the Bonferroni critical value is $t^{**} = 3.6135$. The pooled standard deviation is $s_p \doteq 0.2416$, and the standard error of each difference $SE_D = s_p\sqrt{1/10 + 1/10} \doteq 0.1081$, so two means are significantly different if they differ by $t^{**}SE_D \doteq 0.3905$. The "error bars" in the plot on the right are drawn with this length (above and below each mean), so two means are significantly different if the "dot" for one mean does not fall within the other mean's error bars. For example, we find that the 1 promotion/10% discount mean differs from all means except 1/20% and 3/10%.

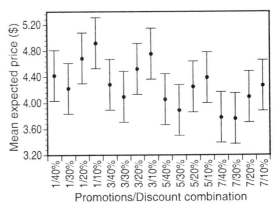

Minitab output

Analysis of Variance on ExpPrice

Source	DF	SS	MS	F	p
PromDisc	15	16.8980	1.1265	19.29	0.000
Error	144	8.4087	0.0584		
Total	159	25.3067			

13.29. (a) All three F values have df 1 and 945, and the P-values are < 0.001, < 0.001, and 0.1477. Gender and handedness both have significant effects on mean lifetime, but there is no significant interaction. **(b)** Women live about 6 years longer than men (on the average), while right-handed people average 9 more years of life than left-handed people. "There is no interaction" means that handedness affects both genders in the same way, and vice versa.

13.30. (a) $F_{\text{series}} = 7.02$ with df 3 and 61; this has $P = 0.0004$. $F_{\text{holder}} = 1.96$ with df 1 and 61; this has $P = 0.1665$. $F_{\text{interaction}} = 1.24$ with df 3 and 61; this has $P = 0.3026$. Only the series had a significant effect; the presence or absence of a holder and series/holder interaction did not significantly affect the mean radon reading. **(b)** Because the ANOVA indicates that these means are significantly different, we conclude that detectors produced in different production runs give different readings for the same radon level. This inconsistency may indicate poor quality control in production.

    Note: *In the initial printing of the text, the total sample size (N = 69) was not given, without which we cannot determine the denominator degrees of freedom for part (a).*

13.31. (a) & (b) The table below lists the means and standard deviations (the latter in parentheses). The two plots below suggest that plant 1 and plant 3 have the highest nitrogen content, plant 2 is in the middle, and plant 4 is the lowest. (In the second plot, the points are so crowded together that no attempt was made to differentiate among the different water levels.) There is no consistent effect of water level on nitrogen content. Standard deviations range from 0.0666 to 0.3437, for a ratio of 5.16—larger than we like. **(c)** Minitab output below. Both main effects and the interaction are highly significant.

Percent nitrogen

Species	50mm	150mm	250mm	350mm	450mm	550mm	650mm
1	3.2543	2.7636	2.8429	2.9362	3.0519	3.0963	3.3334
	(0.2287)	(0.0666)	(0.2333)	(0.0709)	(0.0909)	(0.0815)	(0.2482)
2	2.4216	2.0502	2.0524	1.9673	1.9560	1.9839	2.2184
	(0.1654)	(0.1454)	(0.1481)	(0.2203)	(0.1571)	(0.2895)	(0.1238)
3	3.0589	3.1541	3.2003	3.1419	3.3956	3.4961	3.5437
	(0.1525)	(0.3324)	(0.2341)	(0.2965)	(0.2533)	(0.3437)	(0.3116)
4	1.4230	1.3037	1.1253	1.0087	1.2584	1.2712	0.9788
	(0.1738)	(0.2661)	(0.1230)	(0.1310)	(0.2489)	(0.0795)	(0.2090)

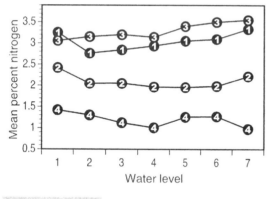
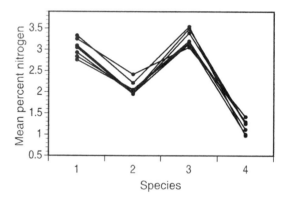

Minitab output

```
Analysis of Variance for Pctnit

Source          DF        SS        MS        F      P
Species          3  172.3916   57.4639  1301.32  0.000
Water            6    2.5866    0.4311     9.76  0.000
Species*Water   18    4.7446    0.2636     5.97  0.000
Error          224    9.8914    0.0442
Total          251  189.6143
```

13.32. The residuals appear to be reasonably normal, with no apparent outliers and no clear patterns.

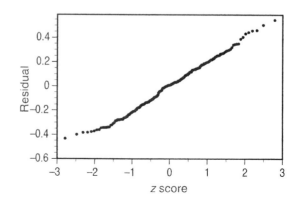

13.33. For each water level, there is highly significant evidence of variation in nitrogen level among plant species (Minitab output below). For each water level, we have df $= 32$, 6 comparisons, and $\alpha = 0.05$, so the Bonferroni critical value is $t^{**} = 2.8123$. (If we take into account that there are 7 water levels, so that overall we are performing $6 \times 7 = 42$ comparisons, we should take $t^{**} = 3.5579$.)

Water level	s_p	SE_D	MSD1	MSD2
1	0.1824	0.0860	0.2418	0.3059
2	0.2274	0.1072	0.3015	0.3814
3	0.1912	0.0902	0.2535	0.3208
4	0.1991	0.0939	0.2640	0.3340
5	0.1994	0.0940	0.2643	0.3344
6	0.2318	0.1093	0.3073	0.3887
7	0.2333	0.1100	0.3093	0.3913

The table on the right gives the pooled standard deviations s_p, the standard errors of each difference $SE_D = s_p\sqrt{1/9 + 1/9}$, and the "minimum significant difference" $MSD = t^{**}SE_D$ (two means are significantly different if they differ by at least this amount). MSD1 uses $t^{**} = 2.8123$, and MSD2 uses $t^{**} = 3.5579$. As it happens, for either choice of MSD, the only *non*significant differences are between species 1 and 3 for water levels 1, 4, and 7. (These are the three closest pairs of points in the plot from the solution to Exercise 13.31.) Therefore, for every water level, species 4 has the lowest nitrogen level, and species 2 is next. For water levels 1, 4, and 7, species 1 and 3 are statistically tied for the highest level; for the other levels, species 3 is the highest, with species 1 coming in second.

Minitab output

```
— — — — — — — — — — — — Water level 1  — — — — — — — — — — — — —
Source    DF      SS        MS        F        p
Species    3   18.3711    6.1237    184.05   0.000
Error     32    1.0647    0.0333
Total     35   19.4358
— — — — — — — — — — — — Water level 2  — — — — — — — — — — — — —
Source    DF      SS        MS        F        p
Species    3   17.9836    5.9945    115.93   0.000
Error     32    1.6546    0.0517
Total     35   19.6382
— — — — — — — — — — — — Water level 3  — — — — — — — — — — — — —
Source    DF      SS        MS        F        p
Species    3   22.9171    7.6390    208.87   0.000
Error     32    1.1704    0.0366
Total     35   24.0875
— — — — — — — — — — — — Water level 4  — — — — — — — — — — — — —
Source    DF      SS        MS        F        p
Species    3   25.9780    8.6593    218.37   0.000
Error     32    1.2689    0.0397
Total     35   27.2469
— — — — — — — — — — — — Water level 5  — — — — — — — — — — — — —
Source    DF      SS        MS        F        p
Species    3   26.2388    8.7463    220.01   0.000
Error     32    1.2721    0.0398
Total     35   27.5109
— — — — — — — — — — — — Water level 6  — — — — — — — — — — — — —
Source    DF      SS        MS        F        p
Species    3   28.0648    9.3549    174.14   0.000
Error     32    1.7191    0.0537
Total     35   29.7838
— — — — — — — — — — — — Water level 7  — — — — — — — — — — — — —
Source    DF      SS        MS        F        p
Species    3   37.5829   12.5276    230.17   0.000
Error     32    1.7417    0.0544
Total     35   39.3246
```

13.34. The F statistics for all four ANOVAs are significant, and all four regressions are significant, as well. However, the regressions all have low R^2 (varying from 6.4% to 27.3%), and plots indicate that a straight line is not really appropriate except perhaps for Plant 3 (which had the highest R^2 value).

Minitab output

```
— — — — — — — — — — — ANOVA: Plant species 1  — — — — — — — — — — — — — —
Source    DF       SS       MS        F        p
Water      6    2.3527    0.3921    14.25    0.000
Error     56    1.5413    0.0275
Total     62    3.8940
— — — — — — — — — — — — ANOVA: Plant species 2  — — — — — — — — — — — — —
Source    DF       SS       MS        F        p
Water      6    1.5626    0.2604     7.51    0.000
Error     56    1.9420    0.0347
Total     62    3.5046
— — — — — — — — — — — — ANOVA: Plant species 3  — — — — — — — — — — — — —
Source    DF       SS       MS        F        p
Water      6    1.9764    0.3294     4.15    0.002
Error     56    4.4464    0.0794
Total     62    6.4228
— — — — — — — — — — — ANOVA: Plant species 4  — — — — — — — — — — — — —
Source    DF       SS       MS        F        p
Water      6    1.4396    0.2399     6.85    0.000
Error     56    1.9618    0.0350
Total     62    3.4013
— — — — — — — — — — — — Regression: Plant species 1  — — — — — — — — — — — —
The regression equation is plant1 = 2.88 + 0.0397 Water

Predictor      Coef      Stdev    t-ratio       p
Constant    2.88097    0.06745     42.71    0.000
Water       0.03971    0.01508      2.63    0.011

s = 0.2394      R-sq = 10.2%    R-sq(adj) = 8.7%
— — — — — — — — — — — Regression: Plant species 2  — — — — — — — — — — — —
The regression equation is plant2 = 2.21 - 0.0299 Water

Predictor      Coef      Stdev    t-ratio       p
Constant    2.21262    0.06531     33.88    0.000
Water      -0.02994    0.01460     -2.05    0.045

s = 0.2318      R-sq = 6.4%     R-sq(adj) = 4.9%
— — — — — — — — — — — Regression: Plant species 3  — — — — — — — — — — — —
The regression equation is plant3 = 2.95 + 0.0833 Water

Predictor      Coef      Stdev    t-ratio       p
Constant    2.95100    0.07797     37.85    0.000
Water       0.08334    0.01743      4.78    0.000

s = 0.2768      R-sq = 27.3%    R-sq(adj) = 26.1%
— — — — — — — — — — — Regression: Plant species 4  — — — — — — — — — — — —
The regression equation is plant4 = 1.38 - 0.0452 Water

Predictor      Coef      Stdev    t-ratio       p
Constant    1.37622    0.06129     22.45    0.000
Water      -0.04516    0.01371     -3.29    0.002

s = 0.2176      R-sq = 15.1%    R-sq(adj) = 13.7%
```

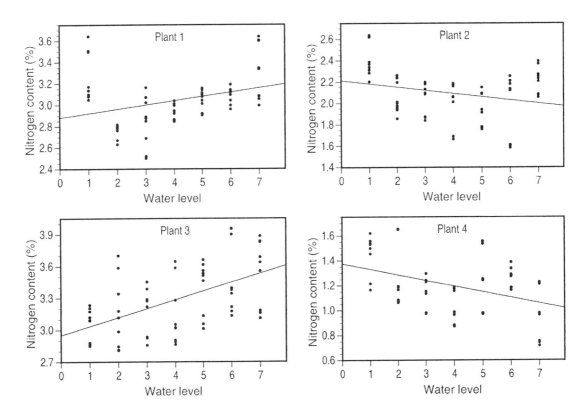

13.35. (a) & (b) The tables below list the means and standard deviations (the latter in parentheses). The means plots show that biomass (both fresh and dry) increases with water level for all plants. Generally, plants 1 and 2 have higher biomass for each water level, while plants 3 and 4 are lower. Standard deviation ratios are quite high for both fresh and dry biomass: $108.01/6.79 \doteq 15.9$ and $35.76/3.12 \doteq 11.5$. **(c)** Minitab output below. For both fresh and dry biomass, main effects and the interaction are significant. (The interaction for fresh biomass has $P = 0.04$; other P-values are smaller.)

Minitab output

```
– – – – – – – – – – – – – – – – Fresh biomass  – – – – – – – – – – – – – – – –
Source          DF        SS        MS      F      P
Species          3    458295    152765  81.45  0.000
Water            6    491948     81991  43.71  0.000
Species*Water   18     60334      3352   1.79  0.040
Error           84    157551      1876
Total          111   1168129
– – – – – – – – – – – – – – – Dry biomass  – – – – – – – – – – – – – – – – –
Source          DF        SS        MS      F      P
Species          3   50523.8   16841.3  79.93  0.000
Water            6   56623.6    9437.3  44.79  0.000
Species*Water   18    8418.8     467.7   2.22  0.008
Error           84   17698.4     210.7
Total          111  133264.6
```

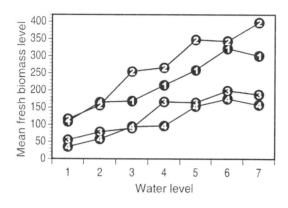
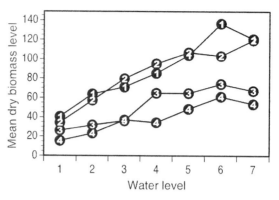

Fresh biomass

Species	50mm	150mm	250mm	350mm	450mm	550mm	650mm
1	109.095	165.138	168.825	215.133	258.900	321.875	300.880
	(20.949)	(29.084)	(18.866)	(42.687)	(45.292)	(46.727)	(29.896)
2	116.398	156.750	254.875	265.995	347.628	343.263	397.365
	(29.250)	(46.922)	(13.944)	(59.686)	(54.416)	(98.553)	(108.011)
3	55.600	78.858	90.300	166.785	164.425	198.910	188.138
	(13.197)	(29.458)	(28.280)	(41.079)	(18.646)	(33.358)	(18.070)
4	35.128	58.325	94.543	96.740	153.648	175.360	158.048
	(11.626)	(6.789)	(13.932)	(24.477)	(22.028)	(32.873)	(70.105)

Dry biomass

Species	50mm	150mm	250mm	350mm	450mm	550mm	650mm
1	40.565	63.863	71.003	85.280	103.850	136.615	120.860
	(5.581)	(7.508)	(6.032)	(10.868)	(15.715)	(16.203)	(17.137)
2	34.495	57.365	79.603	95.098	106.813	103.180	119.625
	(11.612)	(6.149)	(13.094)	(25.198)	(18.347)	(25.606)	(35.764)
3	26.245	31.865	36.238	64.800	64.740	74.285	67.258
	(6.430)	(11.322)	(11.268)	(9.010)	(3.122)	(12.277)	(7.076)
4	15.530	23.290	37.050	34.390	48.538	61.195	53.600
	(4.887)	(3.329)	(5.194)	(11.667)	(5.658)	(12.084)	(25.290)

13.36. Both sets of residuals have a high outlier (observation #53); observation #52 is a low outlier for fresh biomass. The other residuals look reasonably normal.

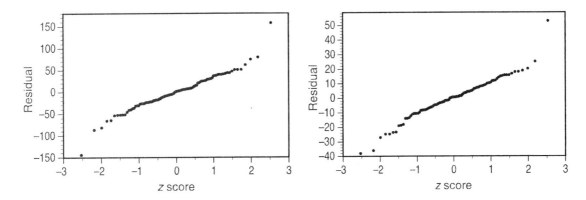

13.37. For each water level, there is highly significant evidence of variation in biomass level (both fresh and dry) among plant species (Minitab output below). For each water level, we have df = 12, 6 comparisons, and $\alpha = 0.05$, so the Bonferroni critical value is $t^{**} = 3.1527$. (If we take into account that there are 7 water levels, so that overall we are performing $6 \times 7 = 42$ comparisons, we should take $t^{**} = 4.2192$.) The table below gives the pooled standard deviations s_p, the standard errors of each difference $SE_D = s_p\sqrt{1/4 + 1/4}$, and the "minimum significant difference" $MSD = t^{**}SE_D$ (two means are significantly different if they differ by at least this amount). MSD1 uses $t^{**} = 3.1527$, and MSD2 uses $t^{**} = 4.2192$. Rather than give a full listing of which differences are significant, we note that plants 3 and 4 are *not* significantly different, nor are 1 and 3 (except for one or two water levels). All other plant combinations are significantly different for at least three water levels. For fresh biomass, plants 2 and 4 are different for *all* levels, and for dry biomass, 1 and 4 differ for all levels.

Water level	Fresh biomass				Dry biomass			
	s_p	SE_D	MSD1	MSD2	s_p	SE_D	MSD1	MSD2
1	20.0236	14.1588	44.6382	50.3764	7.6028	5.3760	16.9487	19.1274
2	31.4699	22.2526	70.1552	79.1735	7.6395	5.4019	17.0305	19.2197
3	19.6482	13.8934	43.8012	49.4318	9.5103	6.7248	21.2010	23.9263
4	43.7929	30.9663	97.6265	110.1762	15.5751	11.0133	34.7213	39.1846
5	38.2275	27.0310	85.2197	96.1746	12.5034	8.8412	27.8734	31.4565
6	59.3497	41.9666	132.3068	149.3147	17.4280	12.3235	38.8518	43.8462
7	66.7111	47.1719	148.7174	167.8348	23.7824	16.8167	53.0176	59.8329

Minitab output

```
— — — — — — — — — — — Fresh biomass — Water level 1  — — — — — — — — — —
Source     DF      SS       MS       F       p
Species     3    19107    6369    15.88   0.000
Error      12     4811     401
Total      15    23918
— — — — — — — — — — — Fresh biomass — Water level 2  — — — — — — — — — —
Source     DF      SS       MS       F       p
Species     3    35100   11700    11.81   0.001
Error      12    11884     990
Total      15    46984
```

— — — — — — — — Fresh biomass — Water level 3 — — — — — — — —

Source	DF	SS	MS	F	p
Species	3	71898	23966	62.08	0.000
Error	12	4633	386		
Total	15	76531			

— — — — — — — — Fresh biomass — Water level 4 — — — — — — — —

Source	DF	SS	MS	F	p
Species	3	62337	20779	10.83	0.001
Error	12	23014	1918		
Total	15	85351			

— — — — — — — — Fresh biomass — Water level 5 — — — — — — — —

Source	DF	SS	MS	F	p
Species	3	99184	33061	22.62	0.000
Error	12	17536	1461		
Total	15	116720			

— — — — — — — — Fresh biomass — Water level 6 — — — — — — — —

Source	DF	SS	MS	F	p
Species	3	86628	28876	8.20	0.003
Error	12	42269	3522		
Total	15	128897			

— — — — — — — — Fresh biomass — Water level 7 — — — — — — — —

Source	DF	SS	MS	F	p
Species	3	144376	48125	10.81	0.001
Error	12	53404	4450		
Total	15	197780			

— — — — — — — — Dry biomass — Water level 1 — — — — — — — —

Source	DF	SS	MS	F	p
Species	3	1411.2	470.4	8.14	0.003
Error	12	693.6	57.8		
Total	15	2104.8			

— — — — — — — — Dry biomass — Water level 2 — — — — — — — —

Source	DF	SS	MS	F	p
Species	3	4597.1	1532.4	26.26	0.000
Error	12	700.3	58.4		
Total	15	5297.4			

— — — — — — — — Dry biomass — Water level 3 — — — — — — — —

Source	DF	SS	MS	F	p
Species	3	6127.2	2042.4	22.58	0.000
Error	12	1085.3	90.4		
Total	15	7212.6			

— — — — — — — — Dry biomass — Water level 4 — — — — — — — —

Source	DF	SS	MS	F	p
Species	3	8634	2878	11.86	0.001
Error	12	2911	243		
Total	15	11545			

— — — — — — — — Dry biomass — Water level 5 — — — — — — — —

Source	DF	SS	MS	F	p
Species	3	10026	3342	21.38	0.000
Error	12	1876	156		
Total	15	11902			

— — — — — — — — Dry biomass — Water level 6 — — — — — — — —

Source	DF	SS	MS	F	p
Species	3	13460	4487	14.77	0.000
Error	12	3645	304		
Total	15	17105			

— — — — — — — — Dry biomass — Water level 7 — — — — — — — —

Source	DF	SS	MS	F	p
Species	3	14687	4896	8.66	0.002
Error	12	6787	566		
Total	15	21474			

13.38. The F statistics for all eight ANOVAs are significant, and all eight regressions are significant, as well. Unlike the nitrogen level (Exercises 13.31 through 13.34), all of these regressions have reasonably large values of R^2, and the scatterplots suggest that a straight line is an appropriate model for the relationship.

Minitab output

```
— — — — — — — — ANOVA: Fresh biomass, plant species 1  — — — — — — — — —
Source    DF      SS       MS       F       p
Water     6     145543    24257   19.76   0.000
Error    21      25774     1227
Total    27     171317
— — — — — — — — ANOVA: Fresh biomass, plant species 2  — — — — — — — — —
Source    DF      SS       MS       F       p
Water     6     257083    42847    9.63   0.000
Error    21      93463     4451
Total    27     350546
— — — — — — — — ANOVA: Fresh biomass, plant species 3  — — — — — — — — —
Source    DF      SS       MS       F       p
Water     6      80952    13492   17.77   0.000
Error    21      15948      759
Total    27      96901
— — — — — — — — ANOVA: Fresh biomass, plant species 4  — — — — — — — — —
Source    DF      SS       MS       F       p
Water     6      68704    11451   10.75   0.000
Error    21      22365     1065
Total    27      91070
— — — — — — — — ANOVA: Dry biomass, plant species 1  — — — — — — — — —
Source    DF      SS       MS       F       p
Water     6      27273     4545   30.44   0.000
Error    21       3136      149
Total    27      30408
— — — — — — — — ANOVA: Dry biomass, plant species 2  — — — — — — — — —
Source    DF      SS       MS       F       p
Water     6      21802     3634    7.83   0.000
Error    21       9751      464
Total    27      31553
— — — — — — — — ANOVA: Dry biomass, plant species 3  — — — — — — — — —
Source    DF      SS       MS       F       p
Water     6     9489.9    1581.6  18.82   0.000
Error    21     1764.6      84.0
Total    27    11254.5
— — — — — — — — ANOVA: Dry biomass, plant species 4  — — — — — — — — —
Source    DF      SS       MS       F       p
Water     6       6478     1080    7.44   0.000
Error    21       3047      145
Total    27       9525
— — — — — — — — Regression: Fresh biomass, plant species 1  — — — — — — — —
The regression equation is plant1 = 80.1 + 35.0 Water

Predictor      Coef      Stdev    t-ratio      p
Constant      80.13      15.38      5.21     0.000
Water        34.961      3.438     10.17     0.000

s = 36.39      R-sq = 79.9%     R-sq(adj) = 79.1%
```

— — — — — — — —   Regression: Fresh biomass, plant species 2   — — — — — — — —
The regression equation is plant2 = 81.9 + 46.7 Water

```
Predictor        Coef       Stdev      t-ratio        p
Constant         81.94      26.97         3.04     0.005
Water            46.739      6.030        7.75     0.000
```

s = 63.82   R-sq = 69.8%   R-sq(adj) = 68.6%
— — — — — — — —   Regression: Fresh biomass, plant species 3   — — — — — — — —
The regression equation is plant3 = 33.0 + 25.4 Water

```
Predictor        Coef       Stdev      t-ratio        p
Constant         33.02      12.98         2.55     0.017
Water            25.423      2.901        8.76     0.000
```

s = 30.70   R-sq = 74.7%   R-sq(adj) = 73.7%
— — — — — — — —   Regression: Fresh biomass, plant species 4   — — — — — — — —
The regression equation is plant4 = 15.7 + 23.6 Water

```
Predictor        Coef       Stdev      t-ratio        p
Constant         15.69      13.98         1.12     0.272
Water            23.641      3.127        7.56     0.000
```

s = 33.09   R-sq = 68.7%   R-sq(adj) = 67.5%
— — — — — — — —   Regression: Dry biomass, plant species 1   — — — — — — — —
The regression equation is plant1 = 29.0 + 15.0 Water

```
Predictor        Coef       Stdev      t-ratio        p
Constant         28.971      6.033        4.80     0.000
Water            14.973      1.349       11.10     0.000
```

s = 14.28   R-sq = 82.6%   R-sq(adj) = 81.9%
— — — — — — — —   Regression: Dry biomass, plant species 2   — — — — — — — —
The regression equation is plant2 = 31.7 + 13.4 Water

```
Predictor        Coef       Stdev      t-ratio        p
Constant         31.707      8.905        3.56     0.001
Water            13.365      1.991        6.71     0.000
```

s = 21.07   R-sq = 63.4%   R-sq(adj) = 62.0%
— — — — — — — —   Regression: Dry biomass, plant species 3   — — — — — — — —
The regression equation is plant3 = 18.4 + 8.44 Water

```
Predictor        Coef       Stdev      t-ratio        p
Constant         18.436      4.741        3.89     0.001
Water             8.442      1.060        7.96     0.000
```

s = 11.22   R-sq = 70.9%   R-sq(adj) = 69.8%
— — — — — — — —   Regression: Dry biomass, plant species 4   — — — — — — — —
The regression equation is plant4 = 10.3 + 7.20 Water

```
Predictor        Coef       Stdev      t-ratio        p
Constant         10.298      5.057        2.04     0.052
Water             7.197      1.131        6.36     0.000
```

s = 11.97   R-sq = 60.9%   R-sq(adj) = 59.4%

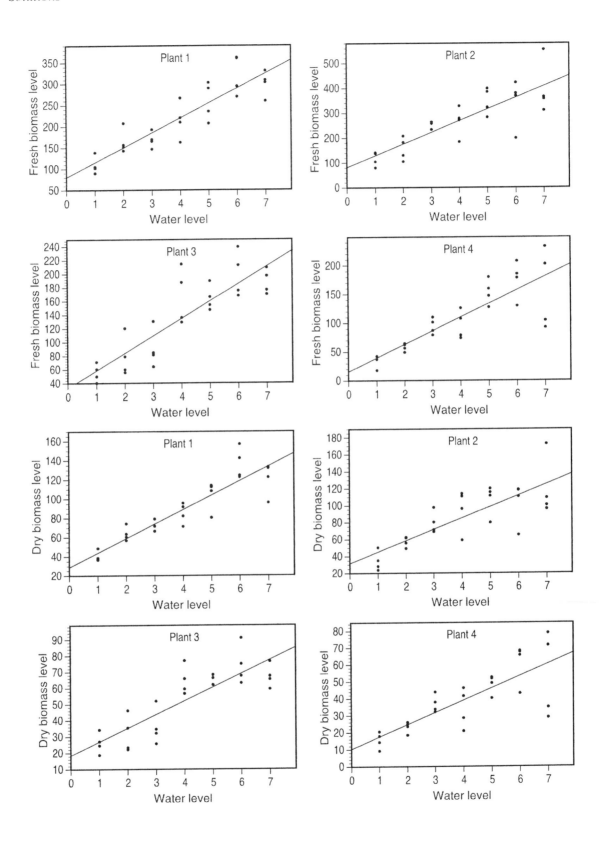

13.39. The table and plot of the means below suggest that students who stay in the sciences have higher mean SATV scores than those who end up in the "Other" group. Female CS and EO students have higher scores than males in those majors, but males have the higher mean in the Other group. Normal quantile plots suggest some right-skewness in the "Women in CS" group, and also some nonnormality in the tails of the "Women in EO" group. Other groups look reasonably normal. In the ANOVA table, only the effect of major is significant.

Minitab output

```
Analysis of Variance for SATV

Source      DF          SS         MS       F       P
Maj          2      150723      75362    9.32   0.000
Sex          1        3824       3824    0.47   0.492
Maj*Sex      2       29321      14661    1.81   0.166
Error      228     1843979       8088
Total      233     2027848
```

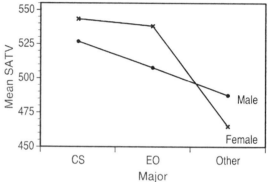

Gender	Major		
	CS	EO	Other
Male	$n =$ 39	39	39
	$\bar{x} =$ 526.949	507.846	487.564
	$s =$ 100.937	57.213	108.779
Female	$n =$ 39	39	39
	$\bar{x} =$ 543.385	538.205	465.026
	$s =$ 77.654	102.209	82.184

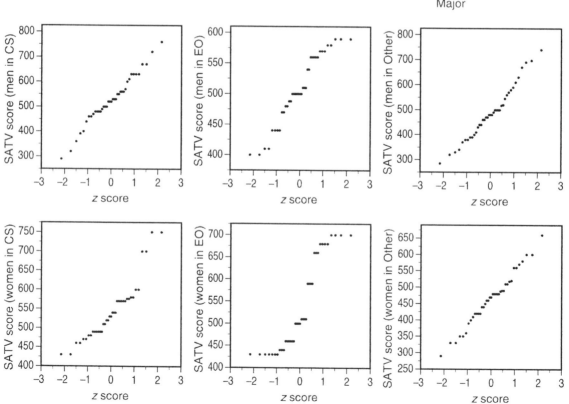

13.40. The table and plot of the means below suggest that, within a given gender, students who stay in the sciences have higher HSS grades than those who end up in the "Other" group. Males have a slightly higher mean in the CS group, but females have the edge in the other two. Normal quantile plots show no great deviations from normality, apart from the granularity of the grades (most evident among women in EO). In the ANOVA, both main effects and the interaction are all significant. Residual analysis (not shown) shows that they are left-skewed.

Minitab output

```
Analysis of Variance for HSS

Source      DF        SS        MS       F       P
Sex          1    12.927    12.927    5.06   0.025
Maj          2    44.410    22.205    8.69   0.000
Sex*Maj      2    24.855    12.427    4.86   0.009
Error      228   582.923     2.557
Total      233   665.115
```

Gender		Major	
	CS	EO	Other
Male	$n = 39$	39	39
	$\bar{x} = 8.6667$	7.9231	7.4359
	$s = 1.2842$	2.0569	1.7136
Female	$n = 39$	39	39
	$\bar{x} = 8.3846$	9.2308	7.8205
	$s = 1.6641$	0.7057	1.8046

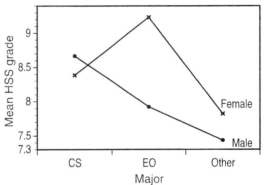

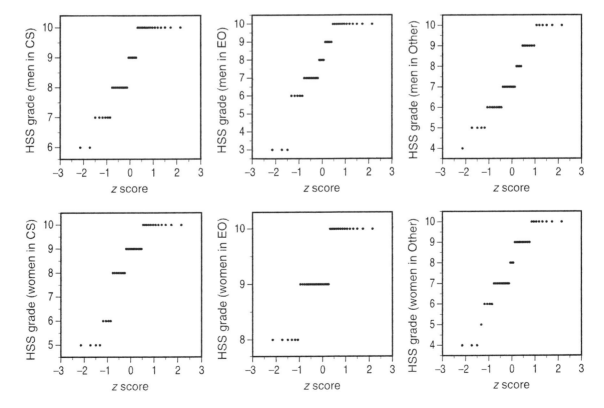

13.41. The table and plot of the means suggest that females have higher HSE grades than males. For a given gender, there is not too much difference among majors. Normal quantile plots show no great deviations from normality, apart from the granularity of the grades (most evident among women in EO). In the ANOVA, only the effect of gender is significant. Residual analysis (not shown) reveals some causes for concern; for example, the variance does not appear to be constant.

Minitab output
```
Analysis of Variance for HSE

Source    DF        SS        MS       F       P
Sex        1   105.338   105.338   50.32   0.000
Maj        2     5.880     2.940    1.40   0.248
Sex*Maj    2     5.573     2.786    1.33   0.266
Error    228   477.282     2.093
Total    233   594.073
```

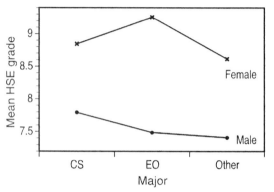

Gender	Major		
	CS	EO	Other
Male	$n = 39$	39	39
	$\bar{x} = 7.7949$	7.4872	7.4103
	$s = 1.5075$	2.1505	1.5681
Female	$n = 39$	39	39
	$\bar{x} = 8.8462$	9.2564	8.6154
	$s = 1.1364$	0.7511	1.1611

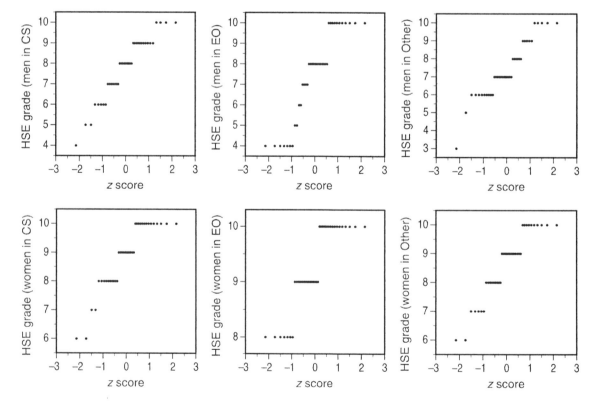

13.42. The table and plot of the means suggest that students who stay in the sciences have higher mean GPAs than those who end up in the "Other" group. Both genders have similar mean GPAs in the EO group, but in the other two groups, females perform better. Normal quantile plots show no great deviations from normality, apart from a few low outliers in the two EO groups. In the ANOVA, sex and major are significant, while there is some (not quite significant) evidence for the interaction.

Minitab output

Analysis of Variance for GPA

Source	DF	SS	MS	F	P
Sex	1	3.1131	3.1131	7.31	0.007
Maj	2	26.7591	13.3795	31.42	0.000
Sex*Maj	2	2.3557	1.1779	2.77	0.065
Error	228	97.0986	0.4259		
Total	233	129.3265			

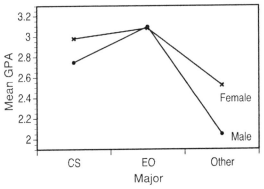

Gender		CS	EO	Other
Male	$n = 39$		39	39
	$\bar{x} = 2.7474$		3.0964	2.0477
	$s = 0.6840$		0.5130	0.7304
Female	$n = 39$		39	39
	$\bar{x} = 2.9792$		3.0808	2.5236
	$s = 0.5335$		0.6481	0.7656

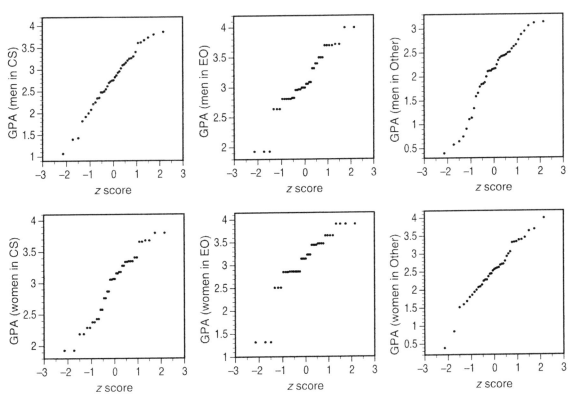

Chapter 14 Solutions

Editor's note: These solutions were prepared using Microsoft Word rather than T$_{E}$X, so formatting is slightly different throughout this chapter.

This chapter uses computationally demanding resampling procedures, for which the use of a computer is critical. We used S-PLUS while writing this chapter, and give commands below for performing the analyses in S-PLUS. Our goal is to make it as easy as possible for you, and students, to focus on the statistical aspects of this chapter. You may use S-PLUS for this chapter even if you use other software for other chapters.

To use S-PLUS you need:
- a copy of S-PLUS; there is a free version for students at
  `http://elms03.e-academy.com/splus`
- Instructors should see:
  `http://www.insightful.com/industry/academic`
- the new S+Resample library:
  `http://www.insightful.com/downloads/libraries`
- the data, as an S-PLUS library:
  `http://www.insightful.com/Hesterberg/bootstrap/IPSdata.zip`

The Web site for resampling within *Introduction to the Practice of Statistics*, 5th edition, is:
     `http://www.whfreeman.com/ips5e_resample`
You may check that page for updated information.

In these solutions, we provide answers, example figures, and S-PLUS code used to obtain the answers and figures. The S-PLUS code is largely identical to example code included in the S+IPSdata library in file
     `IPSdata/doc/exercises14.ssc`
That script file is intended for student use. There are two differences between examples below and those in `exercises14.ssc`:
- here we specify random number seeds to make results reproducible; in the examples shown to students we do not, because we want them to experience randomness
- the examples here include a few more details, or calculations that would give away the answers.

A few exercises here (3, 9, 11, 49) contain general comments that apply to many other exercises.

To use a script file such as `exercises14.ssc`, open it in S-PLUS (double-click it within Windows to open S-PLUS). To run code in a script window, select the lines you want to run, then hit F10 or click the triangle in the S-PLUS menu bar.

Here and in `exercises14.ssc` we use command-line code, but the menu-driven interface is easier to use. Documentation on using the menu interface is contained in *Student Guide to Use of Menus for Resampling*, stored as IPSdata.pdf in the S+IPSdata library, and in the *S-PLUS Manual for Moore and McCabe's Introduction to the Practice of Statistics*, available from W. H. Freeman and Company.

14.1. Student answers in this problem will vary substantially due to using different random numbers. **(c)** Here is a stemplot for 200 resamples (the students do 20):

```
 0 : 677889999
 1 : 0000111112222344444455555566678889999
 2 : 000001122236
 3 : 4678899
 4 : 0001111111122222223333344444455555555555555566667777788888888899
 5 : 001122455579
 6 : 899
 7 : 00112223334445566667777788899
 8 : 00001234
 9 :
10 : 122244467779
11 : 002
12 :
13 : 4
```

(d) The standard error (SE) for 1000 resamples is 2.8

This is normally done by hand, but the following commands would work:

```
Exercise14.1 = data.frame(Time = c(3.12, 0, 1.57, 19.67, 0.22, 2.20))
boot1 = bootstrap(Exercise14.1$Time, mean, B=20)
stem(boot1$replicates)
boot1  # The standard error is the printed "SE"
```

14.2. The bootstrap distribution is close to normal (except in the left tail), so we expect the sampling distribution to also be close to normal.

```
boot2 = bootstrap(Table1.3$iq, mean, seed=0)
plot(boot2)
qqnorm(boot2)
# Note - the book does not ask for this, but to view a histogram and
# Normal quantile plot of the original data, we do:
hist(Table1.3$iq)
qqnorm(Table1.3$iq)
```

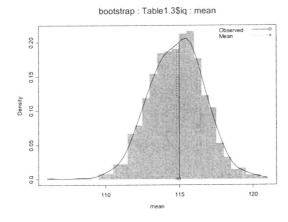

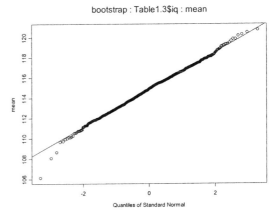

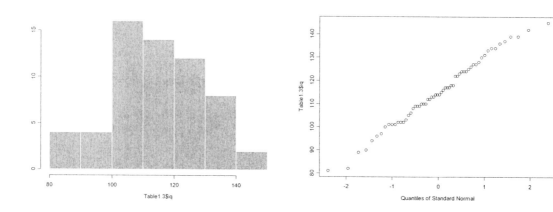

14.3. The bootstrap distribution shows some departures from normality, so we expect the sampling distribution to also be somewhat nonnormal. Normal approximations would suffice for quick-and-dirty work but not for high-accuracy applications.

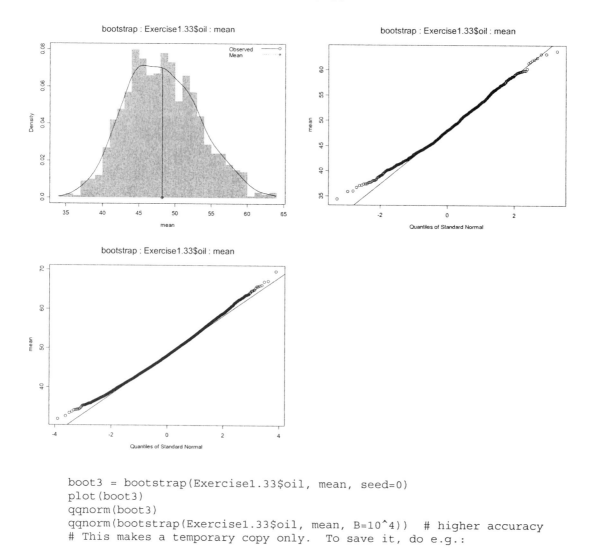

```
boot3 = bootstrap(Exercise1.33$oil, mean, seed=0)
plot(boot3)
qqnorm(boot3)
qqnorm(bootstrap(Exercise1.33$oil, mean, B=10^4))  # higher accuracy
# This makes a temporary copy only.  To save it, do e.g.:
```

```
# boot3b = bootstrap(Exercise1.33$oil, mean, B=10^4)
#
# You can use update() to rerun a command and change only
# some values.  E.g. we could do
# boot3b = update(boot3, B=10^4)
```

General Comment — Normal quantile plots for bootstrap distributions.
We are looking here at a bootstrap distribution, not a data distribution. This amount of
nonnormality in data would not be a concern. But what we are seeing here is after the central
limit theorem has already had its only chance to work. This applies throughout this chapter.

For a quick assessment of how far from normality this is, and what affect that might have on
confidence intervals, do:
```
cdf(boot3$replicates, limits.t(boot3, z=T))
# gives: 0.017 0.032 0.939 0.966
# for nominal .025, .05, .95, .975 values
```
Here we get (.017, .966). In rough terms, this means that a confidence interval that should miss
2.5% of the time on either side would miss 1.7% on one side and 3.4% of the time on the other,
for a sum of errors of 1.7%. (Actually this is an underestimate, based on the bootstrap percentile
interval; the more accurate BCa and tilting intervals are affected even more by skewness. These
intervals are discussed later in the chapter.)

The errors on the two sides combine to give a biased picture of where the parameter is likely to
be.

14.4. The bootstrap distribution shows some departures from normality on the right, so we expect
the sampling distribution to also be somewhat nonnormal. However some of the nonnormality
disappears with more bootstrap samples.

```
boot4 = bootstrap(Example7.1, mean, seed=0)
plot(boot4)
qqnorm(boot4)
cdf(boot4$replicates, limits.t(boot4, z=T))
# 0.029 0.063 0.957 0.988 -- 1.2% instead of 2.5% on the right
qqnorm(update(boot4, B=10^4))  # Optional, for higher accuracy
```

14.5. The bootstrap distribution is strongly nonnormal, so we expect the sampling distribution to
also be strongly nonnormal.

```
boot5 = bootstrap(Exercise7.2$CRP, mean, seed=0)
plot(boot5)
qqnorm(boot5)
cdf(boot5$replicates, limits.t(boot5, z=T))
# 0.012 0.029 0.944 0.957 -- 1.2% on the left, 4.3% on the right
```

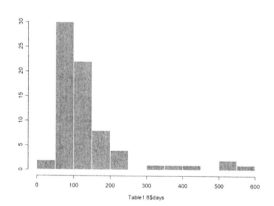

14.6. (a) The histogram is below; it does show strong skewness. **(b)** There is right skewness, but much less than for the data distribution. The right tail is longer and the left tail shorter than for a normal distribution.

```
hist(Table1.8$days)
boot6 = bootstrap(Table1.8$days, mean, seed=0)
plot(boot6)
qqnorm(boot6)
qqnorm(update(boot6, B=10^4))
```

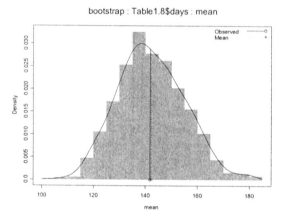

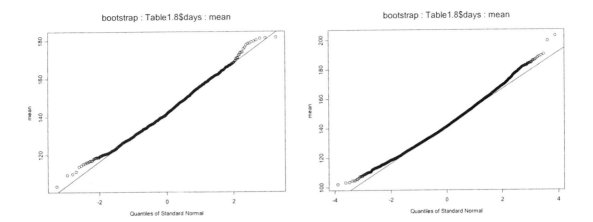

14.7. (a) It is roughly normal, but with right skewness. It is less normal, with greater skewness, than for Exercise 14.6. **(b)** The two SEs are 12.8 and 33. The second one is larger for two reasons: a smaller sample size, and a larger standard deviation in the data (153 vs. 109).

```
boot7 = bootstrap(Exercise14.7$days, mean, seed=0)
plot(boot7)
qqnorm(boot7)
boot6                     # SE is 12.82
boot7                     # SE is 33.14
stdev(Table1.8$days)      # 109.2
stdev(Exercise14.7$days)  # 153.4
```

14.8. $s = 153$, and the formula SE is 34.3, slightly larger than the bootstrap SE of 33.1.

```
stdev(Exercise14.7$days)             # 153.4
stdev(Exercise14.7$days) / sqrt(20)  # 34.29
boot7
```

14.9. (a) The estimated bias is 0.45 (this answer will vary randomly above or below zero, but should be close to zero). This is small compared to the SE of 12.8. This indicates that the bias is small; in this case only 3% of a standard error. **(b)** The bootstrap *t* interval is (116.3, 167.4). **(c)** The bootstrap SE is 12.82; the formula SE is 12.87. The formula *t* interval is (116.2, 167.5), just slightly wider than the bootstrap *t*.

```
boot6  # See Exercise14.6 above to create this
plot(boot6)
qqnorm(boot6)
qqnorm(update(boot6, B=10^4, trace=F))
limits.t(boot6)
boot6
stdev(Table1.8$days) / sqrt(nrow(Table1.8))
t.test(Table1.8$days)
```

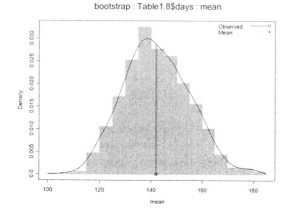

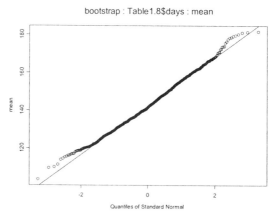

General Comment: Bootstrap Standard Errors Are Too Small

Aside from randomness, the bootstrap estimate of SE for a single mean is $\hat{\sigma}/\sqrt{n}$ rather than

$s/\sqrt{n}$, where $\hat{\sigma} = \sqrt{\frac{1}{n}\sum(x_i - \bar{x})^2}$. This is because the bootstrap plugs in the empirical

distribution as an estimate of the population, and the standard deviation of the empirical distribution is $\hat{\sigma}$. So bootstrap SEs are too small by a factor of about $(1-1/(2n))$. Throughout this document you'll find that bootstrap SEs are slightly smaller than formula SEs (or substantially smaller, for example when $n = 8$ in Exercise14.18). There are ways around this, but we don't tell students about them because we want to keep things simple.

One remedy is "bootknife sampling"—to draw a (bootknife) bootstrap sample, first omit one random observation, then draw a sample of size n with replacement from the remaining $n-1$ observations. In S+Resample you can select this option from the resampling menus, or use it from the command line by specifying `sampler=samp.bootknife` when calling `bootstrap`.

14.10. (a) The new bootstrap distribution should be similar to Figure 14.7. The histogram may have superficial differences — heights of individual bars, for example. The normal quantile plot appears a bit different, in part because the comparison line is different. But the general pattern — normal except for some right skewness — is the same. **(b)** The results now are:

```
              Observed  Mean   Bias     SE
TrimMean        244    244.9  0.8987  17.29
```

in contrast to before:

```
              Observed  Mean   Bias     SE
TrimMean        244    244.7  0.7171  16.83
```

The bias estimates are similar. The SEs differ by more than we like to see. For a few additional runs of 1000 bootstrap samples the SEs are 16.9, 18.7, 17.5, 18.1. **(c)** The bootstrap *t* interval is (209.2, 278.8). This is slightly wider, reflecting the larger SE.

```
boot10 = bootstrap(Table14.1, mean(Price02, trim=.25),
                   statisticName = "TrimMean", seed=0)
plot(boot10)
qqnorm(boot10)
boot10
limits.t(boot10)
```

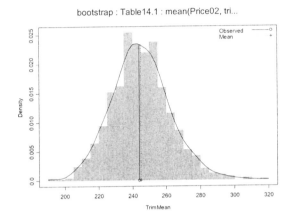

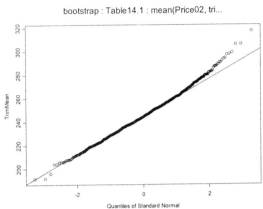

14.11. The shape is roughly normal, but with some odd departures at the lower end, and a shorter tail at the upper end. (These still occur for $B=10^4$, so are probably not random artifacts.) The estimated bias is -10.7, which is substantial, and a large fraction of the SE (83) and the observed s (317). That downward bias may be surprising; we expect that under simple random sampling that s^2 is an unbiased estimate of σ^2, and s is nearly unbiased for σ. We comment on this below; first we answer the rest of the question. There does appear to be moderate bias, so the bootstrap t interval should only be used in applications where high accuracy is not necessary. The bootstrap t interval is (149, 484). This is a large fraction above and below the estimated standard deviation of 316, indicating that the estimated standard deviation is imprecise.

```
boot11 = bootstrap(Table14.1$Price02, stdev, seed=0)
plot(boot11)
qqnorm(boot11)
boot11
limits.t(boot11)
```

Printouts from the last two commands are:

	Observed	Mean	Bias	SE
stdev	316.8	306.1	-10.72	83.2

	2.5%	5%	95%	97.5%
stdev	149.4278	177.2108	456.4493	484.2323

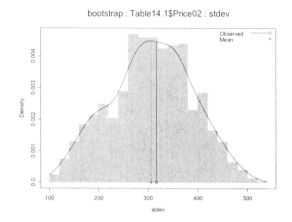
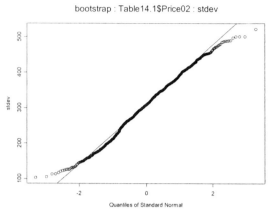

Comment About the Bias in the Bootstrap Distribution of s

The reason the bootstrap finds bias here is somewhat technical. The bootstrap assumes that the statistic being bootstrapped is a plug-in statistic that works in exactly the same way for the sample as for the population. This is true for the mean but not for s. The usual "unbiased" estimate of sample variance, with a divisor of $(n-1)$, is not a plug-in statistic. We calculate variance and standard deviation differently for a sample than for the equivalent discrete population, using a divisor of $(n-1)$ for one and n for the other.

More formally, the bootstrap is designed for functional statistics, whose value depends solely on the empirical distribution, not on other factors such as the sample size. If you get a different answer by repeating each observation twice before calculating the statistic, the statistic is not functional. $\hat{\sigma} = \sqrt{\frac{1}{n}\sum(x_i - \overline{x})^2}$ is a functional statistic — it is the standard deviation of a population where each value x_i has probability $1/n$. s is a multiple of the functional statistic, $s = \sqrt{n/(n-1)}\hat{\sigma}$. The bootstrap implicitly assumes that s is an estimate of $\sqrt{n/(n-1)}\sigma$, and indicates that s is negatively biased as an estimate of that parameter.

There is a second factor, that while s^2 is unbiased for σ^2, s is not unbiased for σ. The bias is approximately $-\sigma/(4n)$ if the underlying data are normally distributed, or larger (more negative) if the distribution has longer tails. In other words, using a divisor of $(n-1)$ in place of n still leaves about 1/3 or more of the bias for estimating σ.

14.12. The bootstrap distribution is quite nonnormal. It appears to have multiple modes. The normal quantile plot shows that it is also discrete.

```
boot12 = bootstrap(Table14.1$Price02, median, seed=0)
plot(boot12)
qqnorm(boot12)
boot12
```

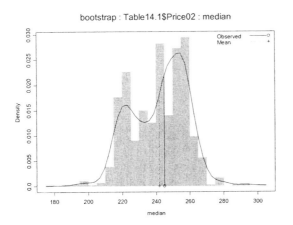

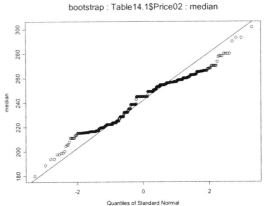

14.13. The formula SE is 4.08; the bootstrap SE is 3.89. The bootstrap SE is slightly smaller.

```
# First, split into two data sets
x1 = Example14.6$Time[ Example14.6$Group == "ILEC" ]
x2 = Example14.6$Time[ Example14.6$Group == "CLEC" ]
sqrt( var(x1) / length(x1) + var(x2) / length(x2) )
boot13 = bootstrap2(x1, data2=x2, mean, seed=0)
# another way, that doesn't require splitting the data:
# boot13 = bootstrap2(Example14.6$Time, mean,
#                 treatment = Example14.6Group, seed=0)
boot13
```

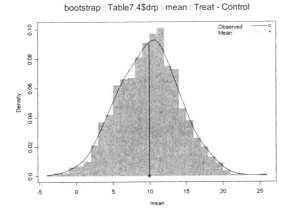

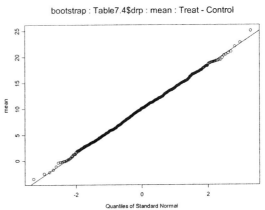

14.14. (a) The bootstrap SE is 4.2. **(b)** Yes — the bootstrap distribution is very normal, with no appreciable bias. The interval is (1.36, 18.55). **(c)** The *t* interval reported on page 492 is (1.2, 18.7). The bootstrap *t* interval is slightly shorter.

```
Table7.4   # has columns group, g, drp
boot14 = bootstrap2(Table7.4$drp, mean,
                treatment = Table7.4$group, seed=0)
boot14
plot(boot14)
qqnorm(boot14)
limits.t(boot14)
t.test(Table7.4$drp, treatment = Table7.4$group, var.equal=F)
```

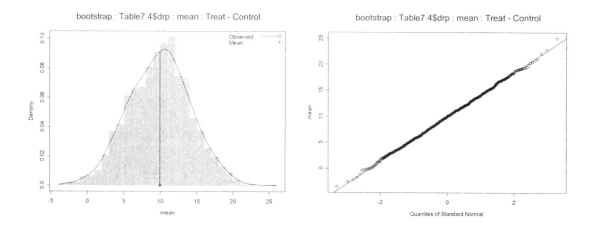

14.15. (a) Yes, the distribution appears to be quite close to normal (the normal quantile plot shows this better than the histogram does), with no appreciable bias. **(b)** The observed difference is 0.902 and the standard error is SE = 0.113. The bootstrap t confidence interval is (0.67, 1.13). **(c)** The bootstrap t interval is nearly identical to the formula t confidence interval, which also rounds to (0.67, 1.13).

```
Table7.6  # has columns status and ratio
boot15 = bootstrap2(Table7.6$ratio, mean,
                treatment = Table7.6$status, seed=0)
plot(boot15)
qqnorm(boot15)
boot15
limits.t(boot15)
t.test(Table7.6$ratio, treatment = Table7.6$status, var.equal=F)
```

14.16. The standard deviation of a sample measures the spread of that sample. The SE estimates how much a sample mean would vary, if you take the means of many samples from the same population. The SE is smaller by a factor of $\sqrt{n}$.

14.17. (a) The data appear roughly normal, though with the typical random gaps and bunches that usually occur with random data. This is more apparent from the normal quantile plot than from the histogram. It appears from both the histogram and normal quantile plot that the mean is slightly larger than zero, but the difference is not large enough to rule out an $N(0,1)$

distribution. **(b)** Yes; the bootstrap distribution is extremely close to normal with no appreciable bias. **(c)** The bootstrap *t* interval is (–0.13, 0.38); the formula *t* interval is (–0.14, 0.39).

```
hist(Exercise14.17$value)
qqnorm(Exercise14.17$value)
boot17 = bootstrap(Exercise14.17$value, mean, seed=0)
plot(boot17)
qqnorm(boot17)
boot17
stdev(Exercise14.17$value) / sqrt(length(Exercise14.17$value))
limits.t(boot17)
t.test(Exercise14.17$value)
```

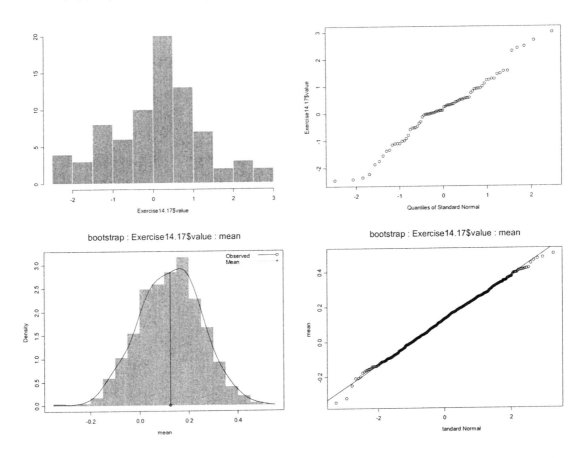

14.18. (a) The bootstrap distribution is approximately normal, with no bias. The distribution is slightly shorter than normal in the right tail; this would be a concern in high-accuracy applications. For other applications a *t* interval should be adequate. **(b)** The SE is 2.4, and bootstrap *t* interval is (16.9, 28.0). This is shorter than the usual *t* interval of (16.5, 28.5). (The sample size here is small so the bootstrap SE is much smaller; see the general comment after Exercise 14.9.)

```
#boot4 = bootstrap(Example7.1, mean, seed=0)
plot(boot4)
qqnorm(boot4)
boot4
limits.t(boot4)
```

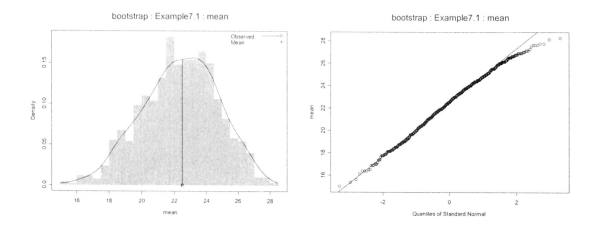

14.19. Yes, it is justified — the bootstrap distribution is very normal, with no bias. The bootstrap *t* interval is (5.00, 6.82); the usual *t* interval is (4.93, 6.87). The formula *t* interval is slightly longer.

```
Exercise7.5  # variable luck
boot19 = bootstrap(Exercise7.5$luck, mean, seed=0)
plot(boot19)
qqnorm(boot19)
limits.t(boot19)
t.test(Exercise7.5$luck)
```

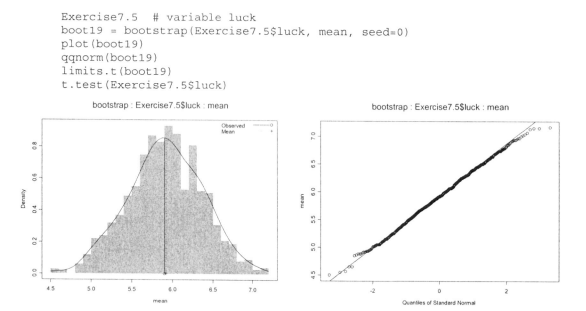

14.20. (a) *s* = 7.71. **(b)** The bootstrap SE for *s* is 2.23. **(c)** The bootstrap SE is almost one-third the value of the sample standard deviation. This suggests that the sample standard deviation is not accurate as an estimate of the population standard deviation. A 95% confidence interval would have endpoints that differ by a ratio of about 5 to 1. **(d)** It would not be appropriate to give a bootstrap *t* interval for the population standard deviation. The bootstrap distribution is not normal.

```
stdev(Exercise14.20$kg)
boot20 = bootstrap(Exercise14.20$kg, stdev, seed=0)
boot20
plot(boot20)
qqnorm(boot20)
qqnorm(Exercise14.20$kg)
```

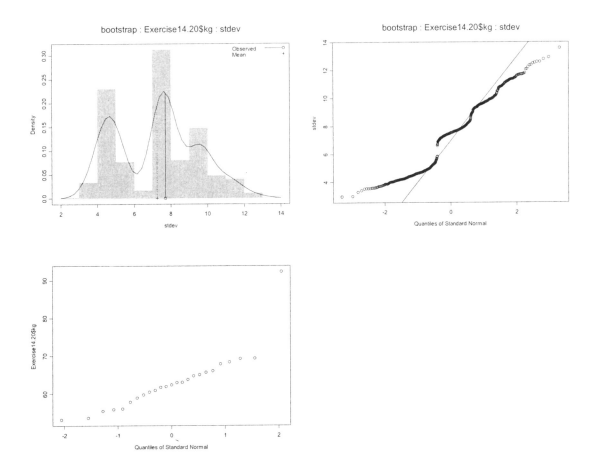

14.21. The distribution is right skewed, so we will use a trimmed mean rather than an ordinary mean. The trimmed mean is 1.95, SE is 0.37, and estimated bias is 0.08 — note that the bias is a substantial fraction of the SE. The bootstrap distribution is very skewed, so a bootstrap *t* interval would not be appropriate if accuracy is important. For now we calculate one anyway in order to get a rough idea; it gives a 95% confidence interval of (1.17, 2.72) for the average wealth of the middle 50% of billionaires. For comparison, the ordinary mean is 2.6 with a SE of 0.43. Curiously, this is an example where the bootstrap distribution for the trimmed mean is more skewed than for the ordinary mean. Here is why. Four of the 20 numbers are much larger than the rest; call these The Rich. The trimmed mean for the original data omits all four of The Rich, so is small. Similarly, most of the bootstrap samples (80%) include five or fewer copies of The Rich, so the trimmed mean for those bootstrap samples are also small. A minority of the bootstrap samples include enough copies of The Rich to affect the trimmed means, giving a long right tail.

```
hist(Exercise14.21$wealth)
qqnorm(Exercise14.21$wealth)
boot21a = bootstrap(Exercise14.21, mean(wealth), seed=0)
boot21b = bootstrap(Exercise14.21, mean(wealth, trim=.25), seed=0)
plot(boot21a)
qqnorm(boot21a)
boot21a
limits.t(boot21a)
plot(boot21b)
qqnorm(boot21b)
boot21b
limits.t(boot21b)
```

```
pbinom(5, 20, 4/20)  # 0.80 = P(X <= 5)
# where X=number of copies of the four largest fortunes
```

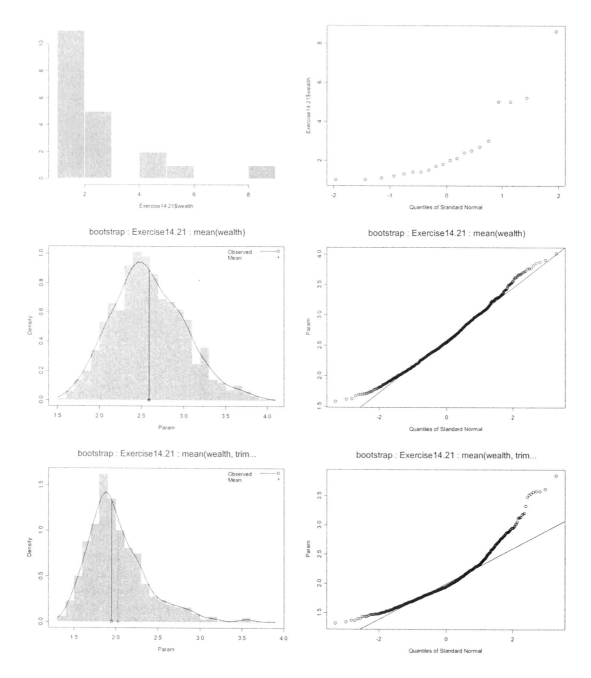

14.22. (a) The bootstrap distribution for CLEC mean is strongly right skewed, with a mean of 16.5 and SE of 4.1. For comparison, the bootstrap distribution for ILEC mean is barely skewed, with a mean of 8.4 and SE of 0.37. **(b)** Because the CLEC bootstrap means vary so little, what really matters when you take (ILEC mean) – (CLEC mean) is the CLEC mean. Because of the minus sign, the right skewness of the CLEC means makes the difference have left skewness.

```
boot22 = bootstrap(CLEC$Time, mean, seed=0)
plot(boot22)
```

```
qqnorm(boot22)
boot22
boot22b = bootstrap(ILEC$Time, mean, seed=0)
boot22b
plot(boot22b)
qqnorm(boot22b)
```

14.23. **(a)** Normal with mean 8.4 and standard deviation $14.7/\sqrt{n}$. **(b)** & **(c)** See figures.
(d) Student answers may vary a lot, depending on their samples. There may be some skewness (right or left) for smaller samples. There should be almost no bias, and SE should decrease by approximately a factor of 2 each time the sample size increases by a factor of 4, except that the SE for small samples may be higher or lower than the geometric progression would indicate.

```
set.seed(1)  # So can reproduce results (but do not use seed 0, use that
below)
x10 = rnorm(10, mean = 8.4, sd = 14.7)
boot23a = bootstrap(x10, mean, seed=0)
plot(boot23a)
qqnorm(boot23a)
boot23a
x40 = rnorm(40, mean = 8.4, sd = 14.7)
boot23b = bootstrap(x40, mean, seed=0)
plot(boot23b)
qqnorm(boot23b)
boot23b
x160 = rnorm(160, mean = 8.4, sd = 14.7)
boot23c = bootstrap(x160, mean, seed=0)
plot(boot23c)
```

```
qqnorm(boot23c)
boot23c
```

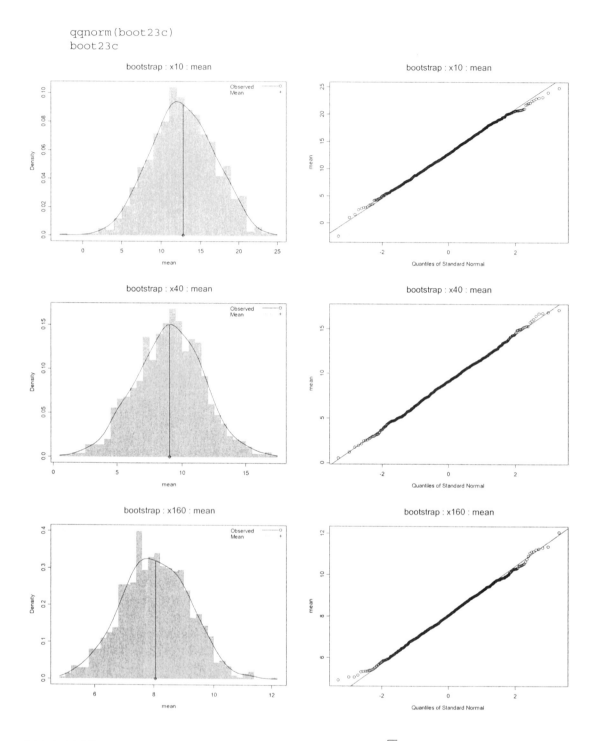

14.24. (a) The mean is 8.4, and the standard deviation is $14.7/\sqrt{n}$. **(b)** & **(c)** See figures.
(d) Student answers may vary, depending on their samples. There should be substantial right
skewness for smaller samples, closer to normal for large samples. There should be almost no
bias, and SE should decrease by approximately a factor of 2 each time the sample size increases
by a factor of 4, except that the SE for small samples may be higher or lower than indicated by
the geometric progression.

```
y10 = sample(ILEC$Time, size=10)
boot24a = bootstrap(y10, mean, seed=0)
```

```
plot(boot24a)
qqnorm(boot24a)
boot24a
y40 = sample(ILEC$Time, size=40)
boot24b = bootstrap(y40, mean, seed=0)
plot(boot24b)
qqnorm(boot24b)
boot24b
y160 = sample(ILEC$Time, size=160)
boot24c = bootstrap(y160, mean, seed=0)
plot(boot24c)
qqnorm(boot24c)
boot24c
```

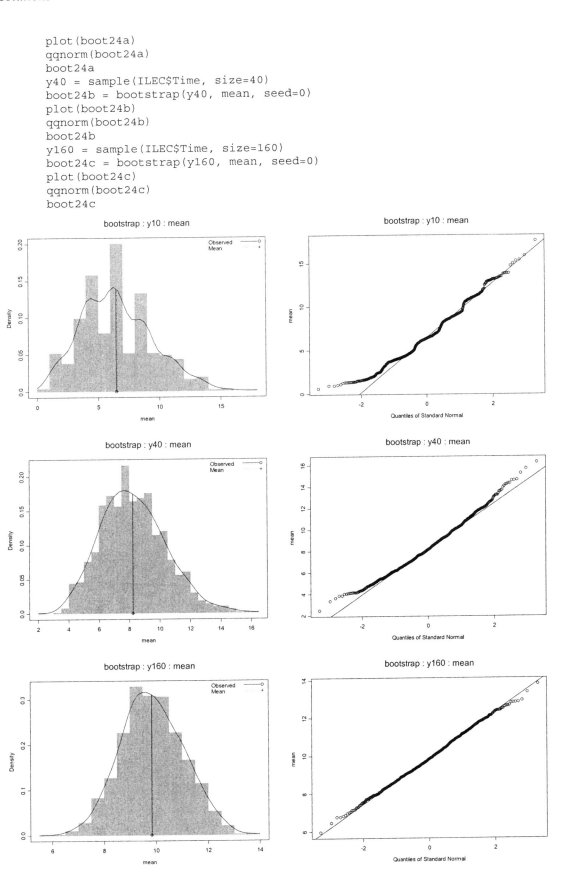

14.25. Student answers should vary depending on their samples. They should notice that the bootstrap distributions are approximately normal for larger sample sizes. For small samples, the sample could be skewed one way or the other in Exercise 14.23, and most should be right skewed for Exercise 14.24. Some of that skewness should come through into the bootstrap distribution.

14.26. 5% and 95%.

14.27. (a) The bootstrap percentile interval is (–0.13, 0.37). For comparison the bootstrap *t* interval is (–0.13, 0.38). These are very close, suggesting that the *t* intervals are acceptable. **(b)** Yes.

```
#boot17 = bootstrap(Exercise14.17$value, mean, seed=0)
limits.percentile(boot17)
```

14.28. (a) There is a small amount of right skewness, probably not enough to matter except for situations where high accuracy is needed. **(b)** The usual *t* interval is (116.3, 124.8). **(c)** The bootstrap distribution is approximately normal (with a slightly short left tail) with no appreciable bias; a *t* interval should be accurate. **(d)** The bootstrap percentile interval is (116.6, 124.5), and bootstrap *t* interval is (116.6, 124.5). These are similar to (and slightly narrower than) the usual *t* interval. We conclude that the usual *t* interval is accurate.

```
hist(Exercise14.28$value)
qqnorm(Exercise14.28$value)
t.test(Exercise14.28$value)
boot28 = bootstrap(Exercise14.28$value, mean, seed=0)
plot(boot28)
qqnorm(boot28)
limits.percentile(boot28)
limits.t(boot28)
```

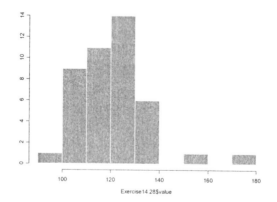
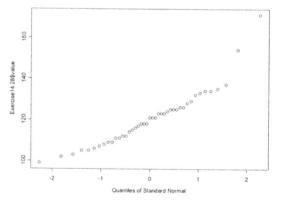

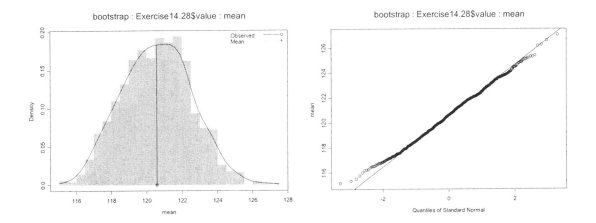

bootstrap : Exercise14.28$value : mean   bootstrap : Exercise14.28$value : mean

14.29. The bootstrap *t* interval is (–0.144, 0.358) and the percentile interval is (–0.128, 0.356). The differences are relatively small relative to the width of the intervals, so do not indicate appreciable skewness.

14.30. (a) The BCa interval is (117.0, 124.7) and the tilting interval is (116.8, 125.6). **(b)** The usual *t* interval is (116.3, 124.8). The tilting interval is slightly farther to the right on both ends than the *t* interval, suggesting that there is some skewness which should be taken into account in high-accuracy situations. **(c)** For a quick check we use the percentile interval. For a more accurate check we use one of the other intervals.

```
limits.bca(boot28)
limits.tilt(boot28)
```

14.31. The BCa interval is (–0.165, 0.356) and tilting interval is (–0.136, 0.362). For comparison, the bootstrap *t* interval is (–0.158, 0.371) and percentile interval is (–0.159, 0.360). The BCa and percentile are in close agreement, and *t* interval is not far off. This suggests that the simpler intervals are adequate. The tilting interval is substantially shorter on the left side. This is probably due to a weakness in the tilting intervals. There are different variations of tilting intervals. At the time these exercises are written the version implemented in S-PLUS gives intervals which are too short for small samples for some nonlinear statistics.

```
boot31 = bootstrap(Table14.2, cor(Salary,Average), seed=0)
plot(boot31)
qqnorm(boot31)
limits.t(boot31)
limits.percentile(boot31)
limits.bca(boot31)
limits.tilt(boot31)
```

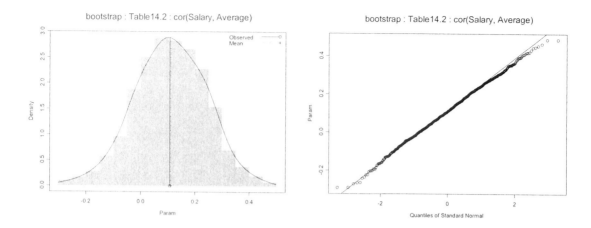

bootstrap : Table14.2 : cor(Salary, Average)   bootstrap : Table14.2 : cor(Salary, Average)

14.32. (a) The formula SE is 1.91, and formula *t* confidence interval is (111.2, 118.8). **(b)** The bootstrap distribution appears normal, except for a long tail on the far left. The bootstrap SE is 1.88, and bootstrap *t* confidence interval is (111.2, 118.7).   **(c)** The intervals agree fairly well, except that the percentile interval is shorter on the right side. Here the formula interval would be fine.

```
stdev(Exercise14.32$IQ) / sqrt(length(Exercise14.32$IQ))
t.test(Exercise14.32$IQ)
boot32 = bootstrap(Exercise14.32$IQ, mean, seed=0)
plot(boot32)
qqnorm(boot32)
boot32
limits.t(boot32)
limits.percentile(boot32)
limits.bca(boot32)
limits.tilt(boot32)
# Create a function to automate the process of showing intervals
graphically
plotWithIntervals = function(boot, usualT=NULL, ...){
  # Do bootstrap plot, and add all four bootstrap intervals,
  # and optionally the usual t interval.
  # ... may be used for the subset.statistic argument
  plot(boot, ...)
  ymax = par("usr")[4]
  f = function(x, y, label=""){
    # Draw a horizontal line for one interval
    lines(x=x, y=rep(y, length=length(x)))
    text(min(x), y, paste(label," "), adj=1)
  }
  f(limits.t(boot, ...), ymax*.9, "boot t")
  f(limits.percentile(boot, ...), ymax*.84, "percentile")
  f(limits.bca(boot, ...), ymax*.77, "BCa")
  f(limits.tilt(boot, ...), ymax*.70, "tilting")
  if(!is.null(usualT))
    f(usualT, ymax*.63, "usual t")
}
plotWithIntervals(boot32, t.test(Exercise14.32$IQ)$conf.int)
```

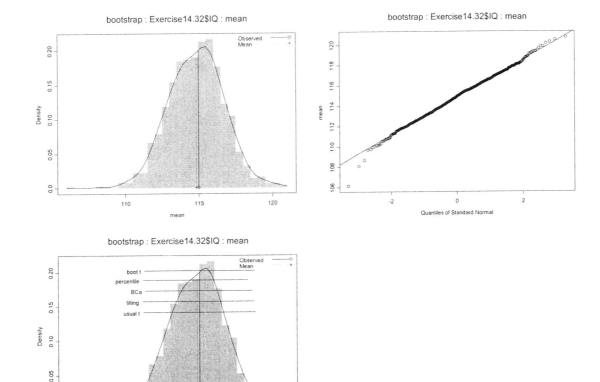

14.33. We previously found that the bootstrap *t* interval is (116.3, 167.4), and the formula *t* interval is (116.2, 167.5). The BCa interval is (120.7, 173.7) and the tilting interval is (121.4, 173.4). The bootstrap *t* and percentile intervals do not agree; the percentile interval is farther to the right, especially on the left side. The BCa and tilting intervals reach even farther to the right, on both sides. This is a case where the percentile interval makes part of the correction for skewness that the BCa and tilting intervals make. (This is what we expect from statistical theory.)

```
#boot6  # See Exercise14.6 above to create this
limits.t(boot6)
limits.percentile(boot6)
limits.bca(boot6)
limits.tilt(boot6)
plotWithIntervals(boot6, t.test(Table1.8$days)$conf.int)
```

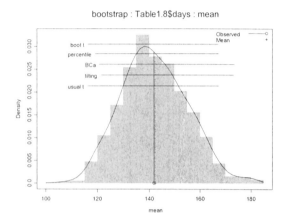

14.34. The percentile interval is shorter on the right side than is the bootstrap *t* interval. The BCa and tilting intervals are farther to the right than either of the simpler intervals. One issue is that the bootstrap is designed for a functional statistic; this is discussed in Exercise 14.11 above.

Hence the BCa interval is actually an interval for a different parameter, $\sqrt{n/(n-1)}\sigma$, rather than for σ. This would be true for tilting as well, except that the `limits.tilt` function in S-PLUS checks whether the statistic appears to be functional, and makes a correction when it is not. Students should notice the difference between intervals, and recommend using BCa or tilting. In practice we recommend being conservative, and using the left endpoint from the percentile interval and right endpoint from tilting (i.e., on each side use the most extreme of the three bootstrap endpoints).

```
# boot11 = bootstrap(Table14.1$Price02, stdev, seed=0)
plotWithIntervals(boot11)
# Now bootstrap the functional versions of standard deviation.
boot11b = bootstrap(Table14.1$Price02, stdev(data, unbiased=F), seed=0)
qqnorm(boot11b)
plotWithIntervals(boot11b)
# The tilting intervals are the same for boot11 and boot11b.
```

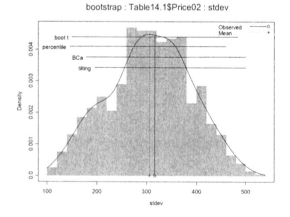

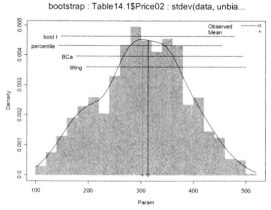

14.35. The bootstrap distribution is very skewed, indicating that the sampling distribution probably is too, so we should not use *t* intervals. The formula *t* interval is (97.5, 241.1); bootstrap *t* is (99.8, 238.8), percentile is (112.6, 239.9), BCa is (122.3, 268.3), and tilting is (121.2, 257.2). These intervals are much wider than for the full dataset. The BCa and tilting intervals are also more asymmetrical than for the full data set. For the full dataset the intervals are somewhat less dissimilar.

```
# boot7 = bootstrap(Exercise14.7$days, mean, seed=0)
plot(boot7)
qqnorm(boot7)
t.test(Exercise14.7$days)
limits.t(boot7)
limits.percentile(boot7)
limits.bca(boot7)
limits.tilt(boot7)
plotWithIntervals(boot7)
plotWithIntervals(boot6) # full dataset, for comparison
```

bootstrap : Exercise14.7$days : mean

bootstrap : Exercise14.7$days : mean

bootstrap : Exercise14.7$days : mean

bootstrap : Table1.8$days : mean

14.36. (a) The bootstrap distribution shows strong right skewness. The formula t, bootstrap t, and (to a lesser extent) the percentile intervals would not be accurate. The BCa and tilting intervals adjust for skewness so should be accurate. **(b)** The bootstrap t interval is (8.0, 25.0), percentile interval is (10.1, 26.2), BCa interval is (11.4, 31.7), and tilting interval is (10.7, 29.1). The BCa and tilting intervals are much more asymmetrical than the other intervals, because they take into account the skewness in the data; the bootstrap t ignores the skewness, and the percentile interval only catches part of the skewness. In practical terms a t interval would underestimate the true value. A t interval would not stretch far enough to the right, and would have a much higher than 2.5% probability of missing the population mean, because the interval is too low. This is true to a lesser extent for the percentile interval.

```
boot36 = bootstrap(Exercise14.22$Time, mean, seed=0)
plot(boot36)
```

```
qqnorm(boot36)
limits.t(boot36)
limits.percentile(boot36)
limits.bca(boot36)
limits.tilt(boot36)
plotWithIntervals(boot36)
```

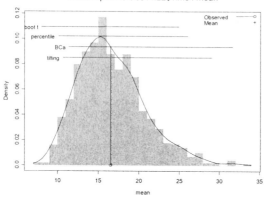 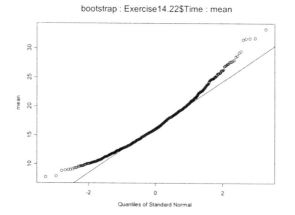

14.37. The observed difference is –8.1 (mean of ILEC – mean of CLEC). The BCa interval for the population difference is (–17.3, –2.1). A *t* interval does not reach far enough to the left and reaches too far to the right. In practical terms, the effect of using a *t* interval would be that the interval would be too high too often, effectively overestimating where the true difference lies.

```
boot37 = bootstrap2(Exercise14.37$Time, mean,
                    treatment = Exercise14.37$Group, seed=0)
limits.bca(boot37)
plotWithIntervals(boot37)
```

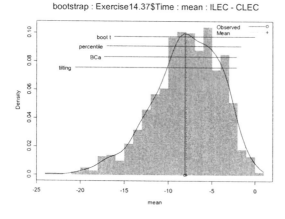

14.38. **(a)** The bootstrap distribution is approximately normal, with some left skewness, and no appreciable bias. The simpler intervals would be appropriate except in situations where high accuracy is needed. **(b)** The bootstrap *t* interval is (0.925, 0.964), percentile interval is (0.924, 0.962), BCa interval is (0.922, 0.960) and tilting interval is (0.921, 0.961). The BCa and tilting intervals reach farther to the left than the other intervals, rather more than expected from the amount of skewness in the bootstrap distribution. It appears that the simpler intervals are not particularly accurate; those intervals are biased, and they would be too high too often. A BCa or tilting interval should be used if accuracy is needed.

```
boot38 = bootstrap(Exercise14.38, cor(field, lab), seed=0)
plot(boot38)
qqnorm(boot38)
limits.t(boot38)
limits.percentile(boot38)
limits.bca(boot38)
limits.tilt(boot38)
plotWithIntervals(boot38) # defined in Exercise 14.32
```

bootstrap : Exercise14.38 : cor(field, lab)

ap distribution appears approximately normal (with a small amount of right skewness), with no appreciable bias. Hence the assumptions underlying the *t* interval are approximately met. **(b)** The BCa interval is (–0.37, 0.18) and the tilting interval is (–0.36, 0.17). These agree well, with the tilting interval slightly narrower. These intervals do not provide significant evidence that the population correlation is not zero; in fact they indicate that zero is well within the range of likely values of the population correlation.

```
boot39 = bootstrap(Exercise14.39, cor(tbill, stocks), seed=0)
plot(boot39)
qqnorm(boot39)
limits.t(boot39)
limits.percentile(boot39)
limits.bca(boot39)
limits.tilt(boot39)
plotWithIntervals(boot39)
```

bootstrap : Exercise14.39 : cor(tbill, stocks)

14.40. We should resample whole observations. If the data are stored in a spreadsheet with observations in rows and the *x* and *y* variables in two columns, then we should pick a random sample of rows with replacement. When a row is picked, we put the whole row into a bootstrap data set. By doing so we maintain the relationship between *x* and *y*.

```
# Regression problems follow.  Here is command-line code, but it would
# be more natural to do this using menus, under:
#        Statistics:Resample:Linear Regression
```

14.41. (a) The residuals appear quite normal. **(b)** The bootstrap distribution has no appreciable bias but does have somewhat longer tails than a normal distribution. But there is no skewness, and most of the long tails happen outside the range of ±2 standard deviations, so the *t* interval should be accurate. **(c)** The regression slope is –0.68, and SE is 0.83. The formula *t* interval is (–2.34, 0.98). The bootstrap *t* interval is (–2.46, 1.10), the percentile interval is (–2.53, 1.07), and the BCa interval is (–2.49, 1.08). The intervals are similar, except the formula *t* interval is shorter than the others. All of the intervals include 0, well within the interval. They do not provide evidence that the population slope is nonzero.

```
lm41 = lm(stocks ~ tbill, data=Exercise14.39)
plot(lm41) # This gives a variety of plots
plot(Exercise14.39$tbill, resid(lm41))
qqnorm(resid(lm41))
boot41 = bootstrap(lm41, coef, seed=0)
plot(boot41)
qqnorm(boot41)
qqnorm(boot41, subset.statistic = 2)
lm41
summary(lm41)   # This prints the std. error for slope
coef(lm41)[2] +
      qt(c(.025,.975), nrow(Exercise14.39)-2) * 0.8292
limits.t(boot41, subset.statistic = 2)
limits.percentile(boot41, subset.statistic = 2)
limits.bca(boot41, subset.statistic = 2)
plotWithIntervals(boot41, coef(lm41)[2] +
                qt(c(.025,.975), nrow(Exercise14.39)-2) * 0.8292,
                subset.statistic = 2)
```

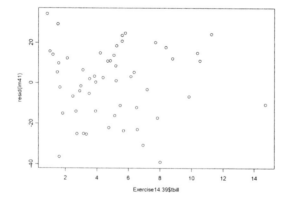

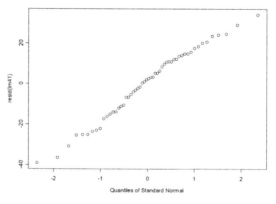

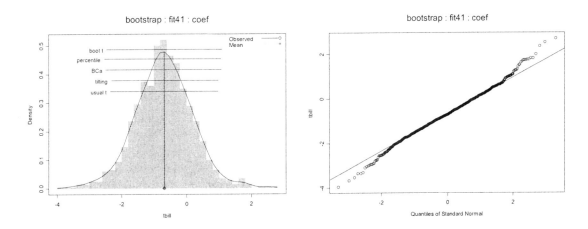

14.42. (a) There is heteroskedasticity — the residual variance is much larger when the predicted values are larger (or equivalently, when the explanatory variable is larger). There is one outlier in the residuals. **(b)** The bootstrap distribution looks quite normal. The bootstrap estimate of bias for b_1 is -0.0016, about 0.05 SEs. This amount of bias would cause a nominal 95% interval to have miss rates of 2.8% and 2.2%, not far from the desired 2.5%. Bootstrap t and percentile intervals do seem appropriate. **(c)** Short answer — the bootstrap t and percentile should be fine, while the formula t is too short. Details: the formula SE for b_1 is 0.0255; the bootstrap SE is 0.0323. This difference is probably due to the heteroskedasticity — the assumptions underlying the formula t interval are violated. The formula t interval for b_1 is (0.676, 0.777), the bootstrap t interval is (0.662, 0.791), the percentile interval is (0.664, 0.787), BCa interval is (0.669, 0.791), and tilting interval is (0.665, 0.795). The formula t is much shorter than the other intervals. The left endpoint of the BCa differs from the other bootstrap intervals; this may be due to Monte Carlo variability with only 1000 resamples (the BCa really needs more).

```
plot(Exercise14.38$lab, Exercise14.38$field)
lm42 = lm(field ~ lab, data=Exercise14.38)
abline(lm42)
plot(lm42) # This gives a variety of plots
plot(Exercise14.38$lab, resid(lm42))
qqnorm(resid(lm42))
boot42 = bootstrap(lm42, coef, seed=0)
plot(boot42)
qqnorm(boot42)
plot(boot42, subset.statistic = 2)
qqnorm(boot42, subset.statistic = 2)
boot42
pnorm(.05 + qnorm(c(.025,.975)))  # miss rates due to bias
lm42
summary(lm42)  # This prints the std. error for slope, 0.0255
coef(lm42)[2] +
     qt(c(.025,.975), nrow(Exercise14.38)-2) * 0.0255
limits.t(boot42, subset.statistic = 2)
limits.percentile(boot42, subset.statistic = 2)
limits.bca(boot42, subset.statistic = 2)
limits.tilt(boot42, subset.statistic = 2)
plotWithIntervals(boot42, coef(lm42)[2] +
               qt(c(.025,.975), nrow(Exercise14.32)-2) * 0.0255,
               subset.statistic = 2)
```

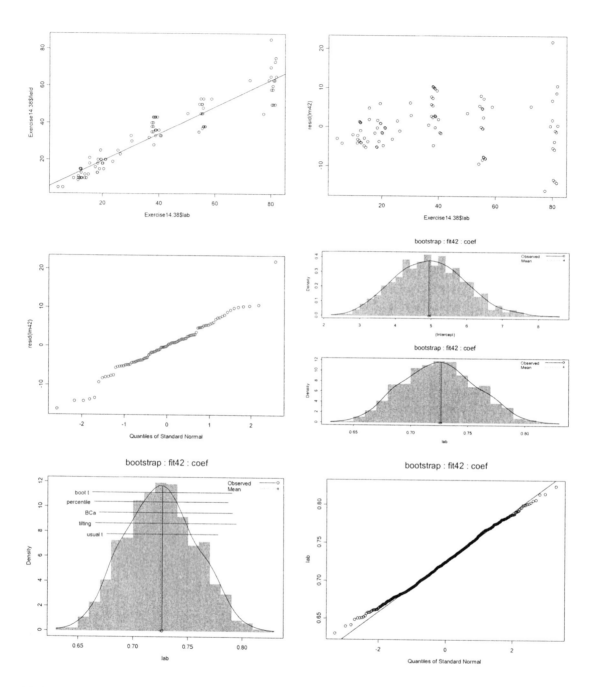

14.43. **(a)** The line is (predicted BA) = 0.253 + 0.00148(salary). Each $1 million in salary increases the predicted batting average by 0.00148. **(b)** The bootstrap distribution suggests that any of the intervals would be reasonably accurate. The 95% intervals are bootstrap t: (−0.0022, 0.0052), percentile (−0.0023, 0.0050), BCa (−0.0023, 0.0050), tilting (−0.0021, 0.0050). **(c)** This agrees; all intervals include zero, which corresponds to no (linear) relationship between batting average and salary.

As a side note (the exercise does not ask about this): the formula t interval is wider than the others. This is the opposite of the situation from Exercise 14.42. Here it appears that the residual variance is smaller for large values of the predictor variable, a violation of the usual regression assumptions, causing the formula SE to be an overestimate.

```
Table14.2 # variables Salary, Average
plot(Table14.2$Salary/10^6, Table14.2$Average)
lm43 = lm(Average ~ I(Salary/10^6), data=Table14.2)
lm43
abline(lm43)
bootstrap(lm43, abline, B=20, seed=0) # graphical bootstrap
abline(lm43, lwd=3, lty=3) # original line, darker, dashed
boot43 = bootstrap(lm43, coef, seed=0)
plot(boot43, subset.statistic = 2)
qqnorm(boot43, subset.statistic = 2)
limits.t(boot43)
limits.percentile(boot43)
limits.bca(boot43)
limits.tilt(boot43)
summary(lm43)  # This prints the std. error for slope, 0.0020
plotWithIntervals(boot43, coef(lm43)[2] +
             qt(c(.025,.975), nrow(Table14.2)-2) * 0.0020,
             subset.statistic = 2)
```

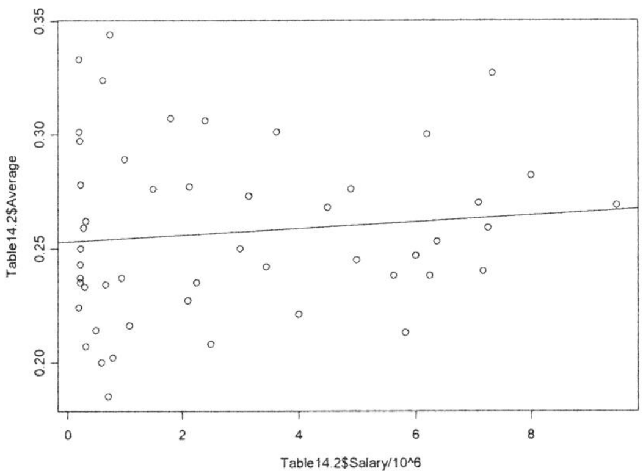

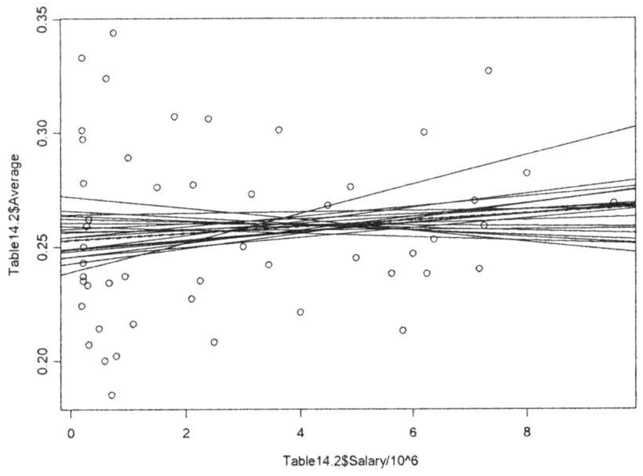

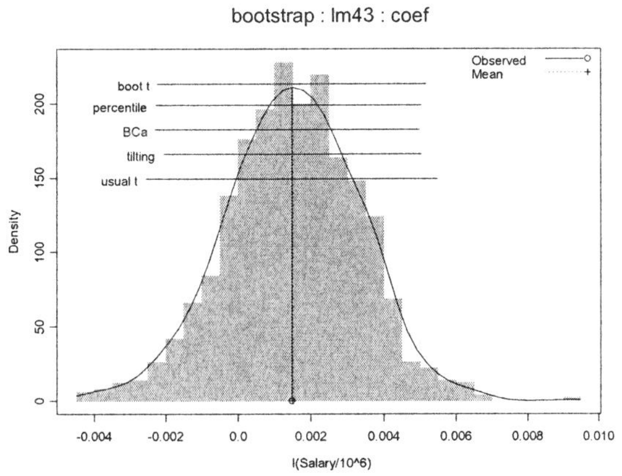

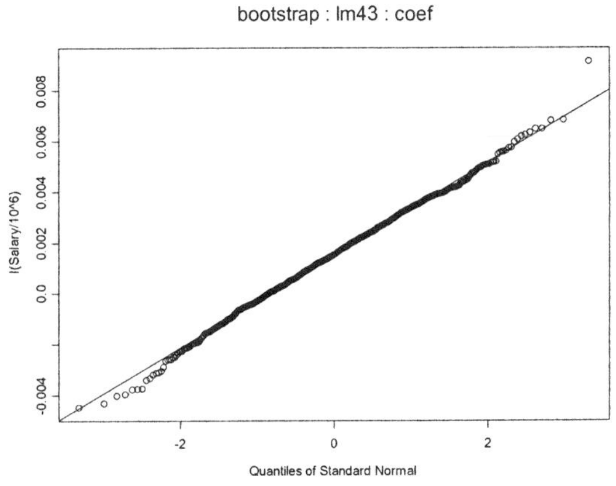

bootstrap : lm43 : coef

bootstrap : lm43 : coef

14.44. (a) The bootstrap distribution has slight left skewness for the full data set, and is close to normal with the outliers removed. The bias is close to zero in each case. The spread differs substantially — the two SEs are 0.37 and 0.24 with outliers included and excluded. **(b)** The BCa intervals are (1.58, 3.08) and (2.56, 3.50); the interval is higher and much narrower with low outliers excluded. The tilting intervals are (1.66, 3.11) and (2.55, 352); again, the intervals are higher and narrower with the lower outliers excluded.

```
boot44a = bootstrap(Table7.2$aggdiff, mean, seed=0)
boot44b = bootstrap(Table7.2$aggdiff[c(1:11,15)], mean, seed=0)
plot(boot44a)
qqnorm(boot44a)
plot(boot44b)
qqnorm(boot44b)
boot44a  # bias  0.0045, SE 0.366
boot44b  # bias -0.0020, SE 0.241
limits.bca(boot44a)
limits.bca(boot44b)
limits.tilt(boot44a)
limits.tilt(boot44b)
par(mfrow=c(2,1))  # plot both distributions with common axes
plot(boot44a, xlim=c(1.2, 3.8))
plot(boot44b, xlim=c(1.2, 3.8))
par(mfrow=c(1,1))
plotWithIntervals(boot44a)
plotWithIntervals(boot44b)
```

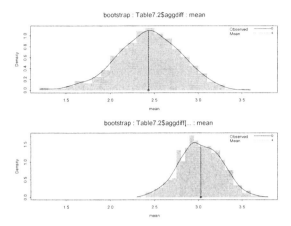

14.45. (a) 3. **(b), (c), & (d)** Answers will vary substantially. In this example there are only 15 possible combinations, which give differences in means equal to (–18.00, –15.00, –11.25, –8.25, –8.25, –4.50, –1.50, –1.50, 1.50, 3.00, 5.25, 9.75, 12.75, 16.50, 19.50), and the exact *P*-value is 0.4. This is normally done by hand, but the following commands would work:

```
mean( c(24, 61)) - mean( c(42, 33, 46, 37))
perm45 = permutationTestMeans(c(24,61), data2=c(42,33,46,37),
                              alternative="greater", seed=0)
perm45
sort(unique(perm45$replicates))
```

14.46. (a) Let μ_1 denote the mean selling price for all Seattle real estate transactions in 2001, and μ_2 the mean selling price for all Seattle real estate transactions in 2002. We test H_0: $\mu_1 = \mu_2$ vs. H_a: $\mu_1 \neq \mu_2$. **(b)** 0.423 (not pooling variances). **(c)** The *P*-value is 0.462. This is consistent with the *P*-value we computed in (b). We conclude that there is little evidence that the population means μ_1 and μ_2 differ. **(d)** A BCa 95% confidence interval for the change from 2001 to 2002 is (–40.1, 164.8). This interval includes 0 and suggests that the two means are not significantly different at the 0.05 level. This is consistent with the conclusions in (c).

```
t.test(Table14.1$Price02, Table14.5$Price01, var.equal = F)
perm46 = permutationTestMeans(Table14.1$Price02,
                              data2 = Table14.5$Price01, seed=0)
perm46
plot(perm46)
boot46 = bootstrap2(Table14.1$Price02,
                    data2=Table14.5$Price01, mean, seed=0)
plot(boot46)
qqnorm(boot46)
limits.bca(boot46)
limits.tilt(boot46)
```

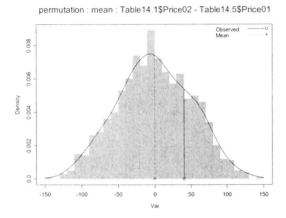

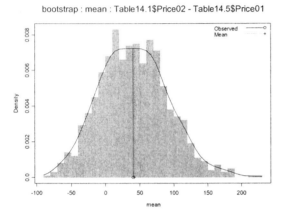

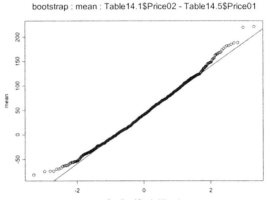

14.47. (a) The averages of the two groups appear about the same; the heights of the forwards are a bit more spread out.

```
        Forwards              Centers
             45  :  6  :
         666677  :  6  :  6
        8888999  :  6  :  888889
 000000011111    :  7  :  000111
         222223  :  7  :  222333
          44555  :  7  :  5
              6  :  7
```

(b) H_0: $\mu_1=\mu_2$, H_a: $\mu_1 < \mu_2$, where μ_1 is the mean height of forwards and μ_2 of centers. (We could also do a two-sided test, but we presume here that one would expect centers to be taller.) The P-value is 0.35. We conclude that there is not significant evidence that the mean height of forwards is less than that of centers.

```
Exercise14.47 # variables Height and Position
stem(Exercise14.47$Height[ Exercise14.47$Position == "Forward" ],
     scale = -1, nl=2)
stem(Exercise14.47$Height[ Exercise14.47$Position == "Center" ],
     scale = -1, nl=2)
# Put those together back-to-back by hand.
perm47 = permutationTestMeans(Exercise14.47, treatment = Position,
                    alternative="less", seed=0)
perm47
plot(perm47)
```

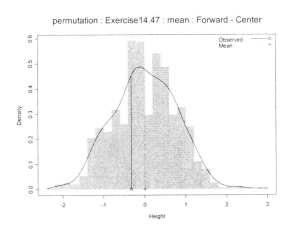

permutation : Exercise14.47 : mean : Forward - Center

14.48. (a) It appears that the weights are somewhat larger for the younger customers.

```
Age < 60          Age >= 60
        9 : 6 : 8
       34 : 7 : 1234
    55678 : 7 : 5778
       01 : 8 : 0
```

(b) Greater, because the goal of this significance test is to test the hypothesis that the weight of fries given to younger customers is greater than that for older customers. **(c)** The *P*-value is 0.223. This does not provide significant evidence against the null hypothesis. We would fail to reject the null hypothesis of equality. However, it is possible that there is an effect, just not large enough to be detected with a sample of this size.

```
Exercise14.48 # variables Weight and Age, either "<60" or ">=60"
stem(Exercise14.48$Weight[ Exercise14.48$Age == "<60" ])
stem(Exercise14.48$Weight[ Exercise14.48$Age == ">=60" ])
# do back-to-back by hand
perm48 = permutationTestMeans(Exercise14.48, treatment=Age,
            alternative="greater", seed=0)
plot(perm48)
perm48
```

permutation : Exercise14.48 : mean : <60 - >=60

14.49. (a) The ILEC distribution is clearly skewed to the right. The CLEC distribution is skewed slightly to the left. The means and spreads appear to be similar. **(b)** The *P*-value is 0.004 for a one-sided test against the alternative that the mean for the CLEC distribution is greater. **(c)** The *P*-value is 0.0073. The permutation test does not require normal distributions, and gives more accurate answers in the case of skewness. A plot of the permutation distributions shows there is substantial skewness. **(d)** The difference is significant at both the 5% and 1% levels.

```
Exercise14.49 # variables Time and Group (ILEC or CLEC)
histogram(~Time | Group, data=Exercise14.49)
qqmath(~Time | Group, data=Exercise14.49)
t.test(Exercise14.49$Time, treatment = Exercise14.49$Group,
        alternative="less", var.equal=F)
# It is easy to do perm test for difference in means:
perm49a = permutationTestMeans(Exercise14.49, treatment=Group,
        alternative="less", seed=0)
perm49a
permutationTestMeans(Exercise14.49, treatment=Group, B=99999,
        alternative="less", seed=0) # higher accuracy
perm49b = permutationTest(Exercise14.49, resampleColumns = "Time",
        alternative="less",
        t.test(Time[Group == "ILEC"],
            Time[Group == "CLEC"],
            alternative="less", var.equal=T)$statistic, seed=0)
perm49b
plot(perm49a)
plot(perm49b)
# permutation distributions are very skewed
```

permutation : Exercise14.49 : mean : ILEC - CLEC

permutation : Exercise14.49 : t.test(Time[Group...

General Comment—Permutation Tests Using Difference in Means or *t* statistic

For permutation testing comparing two groups, the test statistic can be the difference in means, or a *t* statistic. It is easier to do the former. And what is particularly interesting is that the *P*-value is exactly the same if you use the difference in means, or the *t* statistic with pooled variance, as long as you use the same random numbers. That is because in permutation tests, there is a 1-1 monotone relationship between the difference in means and the pooled-variance *t* statistic. For that matter, we could use just one of the means as the test statistic. As a check of this in S-PLUS, do:

```
perm49c = update(perm49b,
  statistic = mean(Time[Group == "ILEC"]) - mean(Time[Group == "CLEC"]))
perm49c  # Note the same p-value
plot(perm49b$replicates, perm49c$replicates)
points(perm49b$observed, perm49c$observed, pch=2)
```

That creates `perm49c` using the same inputs as `perm49b` except for a different statistic. We have to use `permutationTest` rather than the more convenient `permutationTest2` or `permutationTestMeans` in order to use the same random numbers.

14.50. The SEs are $\sqrt{p(1-p)/(B+1)}$, or approximately $\sqrt{p(1-p)/B}$. The SEs are 0.0038 and 0.00019 for DRP and Verizon respectively.

```
sqrt(.015*(1-.015)/1000)      # 0.003843826
sqrt(.0183*(1-.0183)/500000)  # 0.0001895527
```

14.51. (a) When the two populations are the same and skewed. **(b)** When the two populations are the same and normal. **(c)** When the two populations have the same mean but different standard deviations (assuming the *t* test is not pooling variances; if it is, then the standard deviations must be the same for the test to be valid, unless the sample sizes are the same).

```
x = seq(0, 4, length=100); plot(x, dexp(x), type="l") # exponential
x = seq(-3, 3, length=100); plot(x, dnorm(x), type="l") # normal
x = seq(-5, 5, length=100); plot(x, dnorm(x), type="l")
lines(x, dnorm(x, sd=2), lty=3)
```

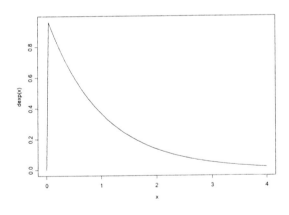
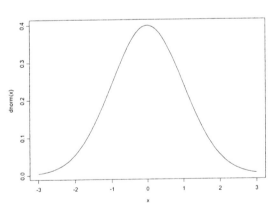

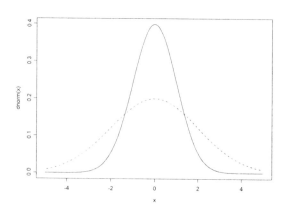

14.52. The *P*-value is 0.608 for a two-sided test. Pure random chance would produce a difference in medians as large as that in the actual data about 61% of the time; we conclude that the difference is easily explained by chance, and is therefore not statistically significant. The permutation distribution is bimodal; that does not matter.

```
perm52 = permutationTest2(Table14.1$Price02,
                       data2=Table14.5$Price01, median, seed=0)
perm52
plot(perm52)
```

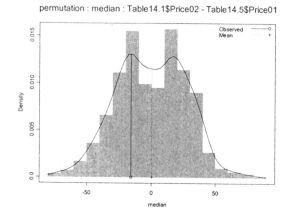

14.53. (a) H_0: $\mu = 0$, and H_a: $\mu > 0$, where μ is the population mean difference before and after the summer language institute. The matched-pairs *t*-value is 3.86 on 19 degrees of freedom, with a *P*-value of 0.0005. **(b)** See figure. **(c)** The odd appearance is because the mean difference can only be a multiple of 0.1, so the permutation distribution has many evenly spaced modes. The histogram bars include different numbers of these modes. The *P*-value is 0.001. Both tests lead to the same conclusion: that the difference is statistically significant. As a side note, the phenomenon of histogram bars including different numbers of modes is common. But this is a rare case where the mode counts differ by as much as 2, rather than 1. Here both the histogram bars and the modes have a spacing of 0.1. Algebraically the modes and bar edges are multiples of 0.1. But decimal numbers are rounded on a computer that uses binary arithmetic, and the rounding occurs differently for bar edges and modes, which are differences of two means. After floating-point arithmetic comparisons, some histogram bars end up including the modes at both edges, other bars include the mode at just one edge, and still others none.

```
t.test(Exercise7.41$gain, alternative = "greater")
qqnorm(Exercise7.41$gain)
perm53 = permutationTestMeans(Exercise7.41$post,
                data2 = Exercise7.41$pre, paired = T, B=9999,
                alternative = "greater", seed = 0)
plot(perm53)
qqnorm(perm53)
perm53
```

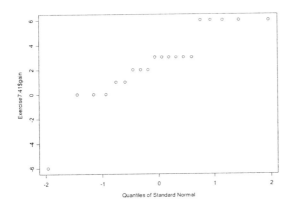

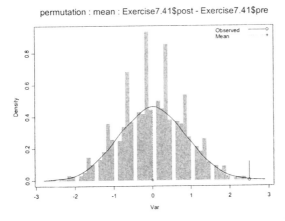

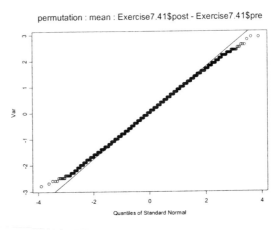

14.54. **(a)** H_0: $\rho = 0$, where ρ is the population correlation. H_a: $\rho > 0$. **(b)** The *P*-value is 0.226. This does not provide significant evidence against the null hypothesis.

```
Table14.2 # variables Salary and Average
# must permute only one of the variables
perm54 = permutationTest(Table14.2, resampleColumns = "Average",
                cor(Salary, Average), alternative="greater", seed=0)
plot(perm54)
perm54
```

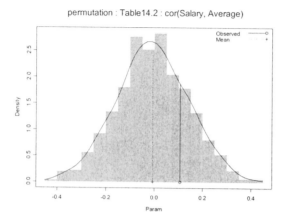

14.55. H_0: $\rho = 0$, H_a: $\rho \neq 0$. The two-sided P-value is 0.338. We conclude that there is not significant evidence against the null hypothesis; the true correlation could well be zero. This is consistent with the earlier conclusion.

```
perm55 = permutationTest(Exercise14.39, resampleColumns = "tbill",
                cor(tbill, stocks), seed=0)
plot(perm55)
perm55
```

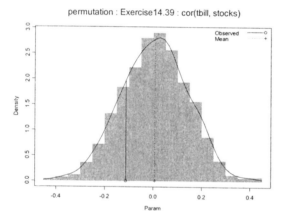

14.56. (a) The means for the two groups are 0.620 and 0.778. **(b)** H_0: $r = 1$, where r is the ratio of means between the two groups. H_a: $r > 1$. The one-sided P-value is 0.019. The permutation distribution is centered at about 1, standard deviation 0.11, and approximately normal with some right skewness. We expect the permutation distribution to be centered at about 1, because that is the null hypothesis value for the ratio. When we do permutation sampling, we sample in a way that is consistent with the null hypothesis.

```
Table14.6 # variables retinol and group
groupMeans(Table14.6$retinol, Table14.6$group)
perm56 = permutationTestMeans(Table14.6$retinol,
    treatment = Table14.6$group, ratio=T, alternative="greater", seed=0)
plot(perm56)
perm56
```

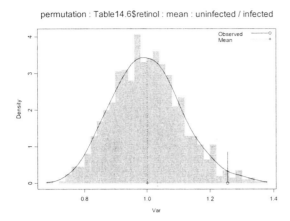

permutation : Table14.6$retinol : mean : uninfected / infected

14.57. For the permutation test, we must resample in a way that is consistent with the null hypothesis. Hence we pool the data (assuming that the two populations are the same), and draw data for each group from the pooled data. For the bootstrap we do not assume the null hypothesis is true, so we do not assume that the two populations are the same. We sample from each of the two datasets separately, rather than pooling the data first.

14.58. (a) The BCa interval is (1.018, 1.532), so we would finish the sentence: "is (1.02, 1.53); the ratio is marginally statistically significantly different from 1.0". **(b)** The bootstrap distribution is right skewed, with moderate bias, hence a BCa or tilting interval would be preferred, and a t interval would be inaccurate. The bootstrap percentile interval is (1.031, 1.555), which is a bit different than the BCa interval. The most important difference is that it is about 1.5 times as far on the left side from the null hypothesis value of 1.0, so it would give an impression of stronger statistical significance.

```
boot56 = bootstrap2(Table14.6$retinol, mean,
  treatment = Table14.6$group, ratio=T, seed=0)
plot(boot56)
qqnorm(boot56)
boot56
limits.bca(boot56)
limits.percentile(boot56)
```

bootstrap : Table14.6$retinol : mean : uninfected / infected

bootstrap : Table14.6$retinol : mean : uninfected / infected

14.59. (a) Some of the ratios were infinite, because the permutation test produced a standard deviation of 0 in the denominator. The mean and SE of the permutation distribution are undefined, but we can still obtain the *P*-value of 0.366. This *P*-value indicates that there is not strong evidence that the variability in the repair times for ILEC and CLEC customers differ. **(b)** These *P*-values are very different, indicating that the F test is inaccurate. The *F* test depends on normality; here the distributions are very nonnormal.

```
perm59 = permutationTest2(Exercise14.49, stdev(Time), treatment=Group,
                          ratio = T, seed=0)
perm59
plot(perm59)
table(Exercise14.49$Group)  # 10 CLEC, 95 ILEC
var59 = groupVars(Exercise14.49$Time, Exercise14.49$Group) # 3.73, 3.24
(1 - pf( var59[1] / var59[2], 9, 94 )) * 2
```

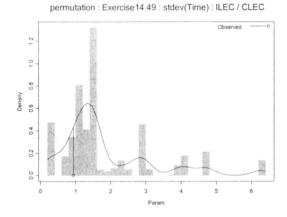

14.60. The permutation distribution is roughly normal except for discreteness, with about 7 equally spaced values. The two-sided *P*-value is 0.546; we conclude that there is not significant evidence that the population proportions differ.

```
# From the graphical interface we can enter the numbers in the table.
# Here we have to expand them into a dataset of 31 observations.
# We'll let 1 = success, 0 = fail, so the proportion of successes
# is the same as the mean.
Exercise14.60 = data.frame(
  Group = rep(c("Calcium","Placebo"), c(10,11)),
  Result = rep(c(1,0,1,0), c(6,4,4,7)))
groupMeans(Exercise14.60$Result, Exercise14.60$Group) # check of data
perm60 = permutationTestMeans(Exercise14.60, treatment=Group, seed=0)
plot(perm60)
perm60
```

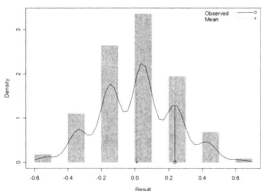

14.61. (a) The plus four interval is (–0.186, 0.583). **(b)** The bootstrap *z* interval is (–0.17, 0.64), the percentile interval is (–0.15, 0.63), the BCa interval is (–0.16, 0.62), and tilting interval is (–0.21, 0.62). The tilting interval reaches farther to the left than do the other bootstrap intervals; the left endpoint of the plus four interval falls between that of the tilting and the other bootstrap intervals. The tilting interval is wider than the plus four interval. As a side note, the tilting interval is preferred here, because it handles discrete or semi-discrete bootstrap distributions for proportions better than do the percentile or BCa intervals. The latter two could give confidence interval endpoints only at one of the discrete values in the bootstrap distribution, while the tilting interval can give endpoints that fall between those values.

```
p1 = (6+1)/(10+2)
p2 = (4+1)/(11+2)
p1 - p2 + c(-1,1) * qnorm(.975) * sqrt(p1*(1-p1)/(10+2) + p2*(1-
p2)/(11+2))
boot61 = bootstrap2(Exercise14.60$Result, mean,
  treatment=Exercise14.60$Group, seed=0)
plot(boot61)  # Unusual plot -- high-low pattern
# Histograms are sensitive              bin edges are.
plot(boot61, nclass=10)  #
plot(boot61, nclass=40)  #
qqnorm(boot61)# note the bunching & gaps, explains the high-low pattern
boot61
limits.t(boot61, z=T)  # Do a z rather than t interval
limits.percentile(boot61)
limits.bca(boot61)
limits.tilt(boot61)
```

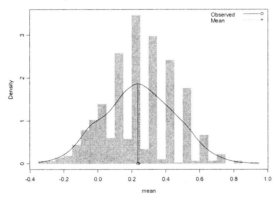

bootstrap : Exercise14.60$Result : mean : Calcium - Placebo

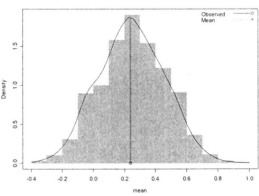

bootstrap : Exercise14.60$Result : mean : Calcium - Placebo

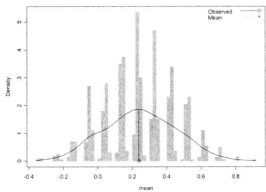

bootstrap : Exercise14.60$Result : mean : Calcium - Placebo

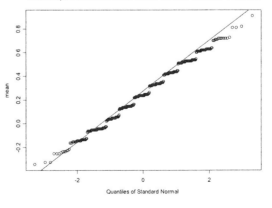

bootstrap : Exercise14.60$Result : mean : Calcium - Placebo

14.62. The one-sided *P*-value is 0.065. The difference is not statistically significant (though it is borderline).

```
Table14.7 # variables:  group groupid begin end decrease
perm62 = permutationTestMeans(Table14.7$decrease,
  treatment = Table14.7$group, alternative="greater", seed=0)
plot(perm62)
perm62
```

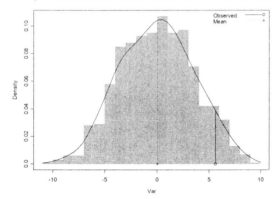

14.63. **(a)** H_0 is that $\sigma_1 = \sigma_2$; H_a is $\sigma_1 \neq \sigma_2$, where σ_1 and σ_2 are the standard deviations of the two populations. **(b)** The *P*-value is 0.212; there is not significant evidence that the population standard deviations differ. **(c)** The *P*-value from the *F* test is 0.236. The data are approximately normal, so the *F* test is reasonably accurate.

```
perm63 = permutationTest2(Table14.7$decrease, var, ratio=T,
  treatment = Table14.7$group, seed=0)
plot(perm63)
perm63
```

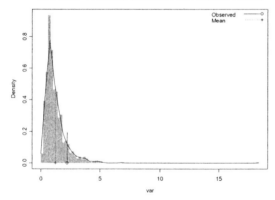

14.64. A permutation test comparing the means gives a *P*-value of 0.80; a permutation test comparing the standard deviations gives a *P*-value of 0.67. In both cases there is not statistically significant evidence of a difference between the operators. The differences could easily arise by chance — even larger differences would occur by chance more than half the time.

```
perm64a = permutationTestMeans(Exercise14.64$op1,
  data2=Exercise14.64$op2, paired=T, seed=0)
plot(perm64a)
perm64a
perm64b = permutationTest2(Exercise14.64$op1,
  data2=Exercise14.64$op2, stdev, paired=T, seed=0)
plot(perm64b)
perm64b
```

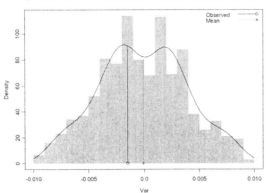

permutation : mean : Exercise14.64$op1 - Exercise14.64$op2

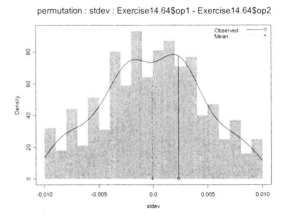

permutation : stdev : Exercise14.64$op1 - Exercise14.64$op2

14.65. The bootstrap t interval is (209, 279), percentile interval is (212, 280), BCa interval is (212, 281), and tilting interval is (213, 280). The right endpoints are similar, but the left endpoint for the bootstrap t is different from the other intervals. The bootstrap t ignores the skewness in the bootstrap distribution; here it appears that any of the other intervals (including the percentile interval) would be preferable. The percentile and t intervals would be adequate if high accuracy is not needed.

```
# boot10 = bootstrap(Table14.1, mean(Price02, trim=.25), seed=0)
limits.t(boot10)
limits.percentile(boot10)
limits.bca(boot10)
limits.tilt(boot10)
qqnorm(boot10)
plotWithIntervals(boot10) # defined in Exercise 14.32
```

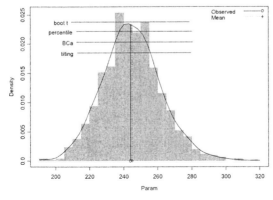

bootstrap : Table14.1 : mean(Price02, tri...

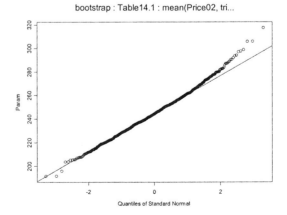

bootstrap : Table14.1 : mean(Price02, tri...

14.66. (a) The distribution is approximately normal, aside from being discrete. **(b)** The sample mean is 3.62; its SE is 0.52. **(c)** The bootstrap SE is 0.51; this is comparable to the formula SE, though slightly smaller.

```
hist(Exercise14.66$change)
qqnorm(Exercise14.66$change)
mean(Exercise14.66$change)
stdev(Exercise14.66$change) / sqrt(length(Exercise14.66$change))
boot66 = bootstrap(Exercise14.66$change, mean, seed=0)
boot66
plot(boot66)
qqnorm(boot66)
```

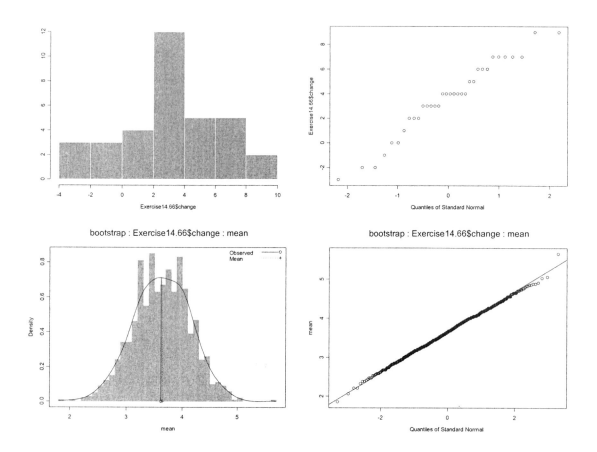

14.67. In this problem, the answers will depend strongly on the random sample drawn. **(a)** For a uniform distribution on 0 to 1, the population median is 0.5. The shape of the bootstrap distribution will depend on the sample drawn. **(b)** The bootstrap SE is 0.054. A 95% bootstrap t interval is (0.45, 0.67). (Both depend heavily on the sample drawn.) **(c)** The intervals are (0.43, 0.63) and (0.45, 0.63). (Both depend heavily on the sample drawn.) The t interval is not reliable here. Students will probably say so, and give an explanation that the bootstrap distribution does not appear normal. The actual reason is that the bootstrap SE is unreliable, depending strongly on the sizes of the gaps between the observations near the middle. As a side note, even though the bootstrap distribution shapes and spreads are unreliable estimates for sample medians, the bootstrap percentile, BCa, and tilting intervals are not bad. They give answers similar to the exact rank-based confidence intervals obtained by inverting hypothesis tests. One variation of tilting intervals matches the exact intervals.

```
x67 = runif(50)
median(x67)
boot67 = bootstrap(x67, median, seed=0)
plot(boot67)
qqnorm(boot67)
boot67
limits.t(boot67)
limits.bca(boot67)
limits.tilt(boot67)
```

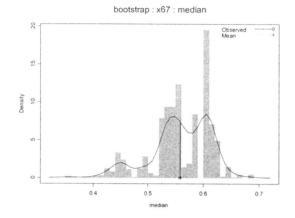

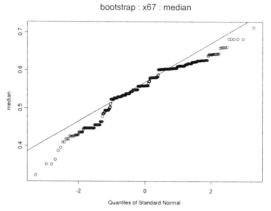

14.68. (a) The difference appears quite large; it should be significant.

```
      :  1  :  9
      :  2  :  01
   3  :  2  :  2233
   5  :  2  :  4
   6  :  2  :
 899  :  2  :
  01  :  3  :
  22  :  3  :
   5  :  3  :
```

(b) The *P*-value is about 0.00056 (based on 100,000 resamples). For 1000 resamples, the answer will usually be either 0.002 or 0.004 (round up, then double). **(c)** We conclude that there is significant evidence that the mean ages differ. Note: with enough resamples we see that the permutation test *P*-value is consistent with the answer from a *t* test, but students doing only 1000 resamples will get a larger answer. They may then answer that the *t* test *P*-value is too small.

```
Exercise14.68 # variables Age and Sex (male or female)
stem(Exercise14.68$Age[ Exercise14.68$Sex == "male" ],
    scale = -1, nl=2)
stem(Exercise14.68$Age[ Exercise14.68$Sex == "female" ],
    scale = -1, nl=2)
# do back-to-back stemplot by hand
perm68 = permutationTestMeans(Exercise14.68, treatment=Sex, seed=0)
plot(perm68)
perm68
permutationTestMeans(Exercise14.68, treatment=Sex, B=99999, seed=0)
```

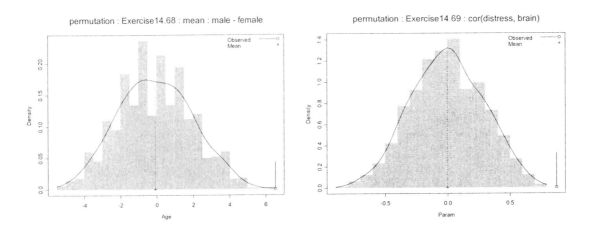

14.69. The one-sided permutation test using 1000 samples gives a *P*-value of 0.001, the smallest possible value. We conclude there is a significant positive relationship.

```
plot(Exercise14.69$distress, Exercise14.69$brain)
perm69 = permutationTest(Exercise14.69,
  cor(distress, brain), resampleColumns = "brain",
  alternative = "greater", seed=0)
plot(perm69)
perm69
```

14.70. (a) The permutation distribution is centered about 0.0, because for a hypothesis test we resample in a way that is consistent with the null hypothesis of no correlation. In contrast, the bootstrap is centered approximately at the observed correlation of 0.878. The right tail is bounded above by 1.0, whereas the left tail can be much longer. **(b)** The bootstrap BCa confidence interval is (0.652, 0.955); the percentile interval is (0.680, 0.961). Neither is even close to including the value of 0; we conclude that there is a significant positive relationship.

```
boot70 = bootstrap(Exercise14.69, cor(distress, brain), seed=0)
plot(boot70)
qqnorm(boot70)
limits.t(boot70)
limits.percentile(boot70)
limits.bca(boot70)
limits.tilt(boot70)
```

14.71. (a) The 2000 data is strongly right-skewed with two outliers. This violates the guideline for using the *t* procedure given in Chapter 7, namely for a sample size of at least 15, that *t* procedures can be used except in the presence of outliers or strong skewness. The 2001 data is approximately normal. **(b)** The *P*-value for the permutation test for the difference in means is 0.292. We conclude that there is not strong evidence that the mean selling prices are different for all Seattle real estate in 2000 and in 2001.

```
Exercise14.71 # variable Price00
par(mfrow=c(2,2))  # do plots on a 2x2 grid
hist(Table14.5$Price01, xlim=c(0,2000))
qqnorm(Table14.5$Price01)
hist(Exercise14.71$Price00, xlim=c(0,2000))
qqnorm(Exercise14.71$Price00)
par(mfrow=c(1,1))  # back to normal
perm71 = permutationTestMeans(Table14.5$Price01,
  data2 = Exercise14.71$Price00, seed=0)
plot(perm71)
perm71
```

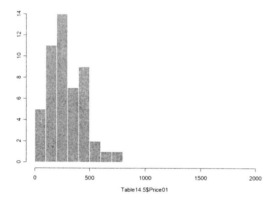
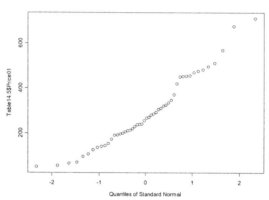
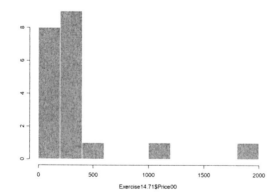
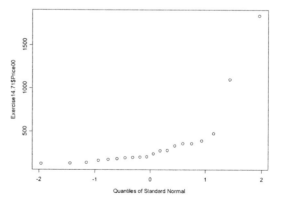

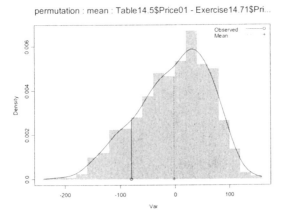

permutation : mean : Table14.5$Price01 - Exercise14.71$Pri...

14.72. (a) The formula t interval is (98.1, 110.1). **(b)** The BCa interval is (100.1, 110.8); the tilting interval is (99.6, 110.2). **(c)** The bootstrap distribution is approximately normal but is quite skewed for a bootstrap distribution. **(d)** All intervals indicate that the value 105 is well within the range of the interval. If the results were more borderline we should use a more accurate interval, but here a t interval is fine.

```
t.test(Exercise14.72$pCi)
boot72 = bootstrap(Exercise14.72$pCi, mean, seed=0)
limits.bca(boot72)
limits.tilt(boot72)
plot(boot72)
qqnorm(boot72)
plotWithIntervals(boot72)
```

bootstrap : Exercise14.72$pCi : mean

bootstrap : Exercise14.72$pCi : mean

14.73. The study described in Exercise 14.72 is a one-sample problem. We have no methods for carrying out a permutation test in such one-sample problems (there is no obvious way to permute the data that is consistent with the null hypothesis).

14.74. (a) $s = 1.32$. **(b)** The bootstrap SE for s is 0.036. **(c)** The bootstrap t interval is (1.25, 1.40). **(d)** The BCa interval is (1.26, 1.41); the tilting interval is (1.26, 1.41). The bootstrap t interval is a bit low on both ends.

```
stdev(Exercise14.74$Return)
boot74 = bootstrap(Exercise14.74$Return, stdev, seed=0)
```

```
boot74
plot(boot74)
qqnorm(boot74)
limits.t(boot74)
limits.bca(boot74)
limits.tilt(boot74)
```

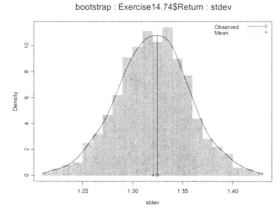

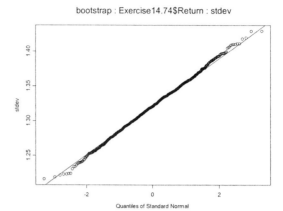

14.75. (a) We are interested in whether the presentation causes an improvement in glove use. We must use a matched pairs method, because the same nurses were recorded both times. **(b)** The *P*-value is 0.002. This provides significant evidence that the presentation was helpful.

```
Exercise14.75 # variables Before and After
perm75 = permutationTestMeans(Exercise14.75$Before,
                    data2 = Exercise14.75$After, paired=T,
                    alternative = "less", seed=0)
plot(perm75)
perm75
```

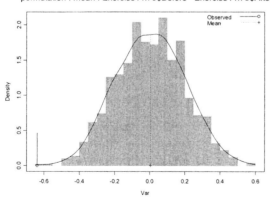

14.76. A 95% bootstrap *t* confidence interval for the mean change (after–before) is (0.41, 0.87). Zero is outside this interval, so the result is significant at the 0.05 level. We conclude that there is strong evidence that the mean change is different from 0, that is, positive. The other bootstrap intervals differ somewhat, but the differences are not nearly enough to change this conclusion.

```
change = Exercise14.75$After - Exercise14.75$Before
boot76 = bootstrap(change, mean, seed=0)
plot(boot76)
```

```
qqnorm(boot76)
limits.t(boot76)
limits.percentile(boot76)
limits.bca(boot76)
limits.tilt(boot76)
```

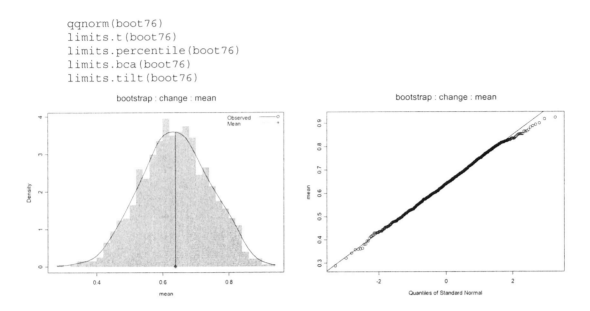

14.77. (a) The bootstrap distribution is very normal with no appreciable bias, so a bootstrap *t* interval is adequate; the interval is (0.188, 0.200). A bootstrap percentile interval is nearly identical. **(b)** The *P*-value is 0.001. The plot of the permutation distribution is even more striking, suggesting how exceedingly rare it would be to observe a difference this large by chance. **(c)** The bootstrap distribution for the difference is very normal with no appreciable bias. The bootstrap *t* interval for the difference in proportions is (0.045, 0.069); the bootstrap percentile interval is nearly identical.

```
# From the graphical interface we can enter the numbers in the table.
# Here we have to expand them into a dataset of many observations.
# We'll let 1 = binge drinker, 0 = other, so the proportion of binge
# drinkers is the same as the mean.
Exercise14.77 = data.frame(
  Gender = rep(c("Men","Women"), c(7180,9916)),
  Binge = rep(c(1,0,1,0), c(1630,7180-1630,1684,9916-1684)))
boot77a = bootstrap(Exercise14.77$Binge, mean, seed=0)
plot(boot77a)
qqnorm(boot77a)
limits.t(boot77a)
limits.percentile(boot77a)
perm77 = permutationTestMeans(Exercise14.77, treatment=Gender,
  alternative = "greater", seed=0)
plot(perm77)
perm77
boot77b = bootstrap2(Exercise14.77, mean(Binge), treatment=Gender,
seed=0)
plot(boot77b)
qqnorm(boot77b)
limits.t(boot77b)
limits.percentile(boot77b)
```

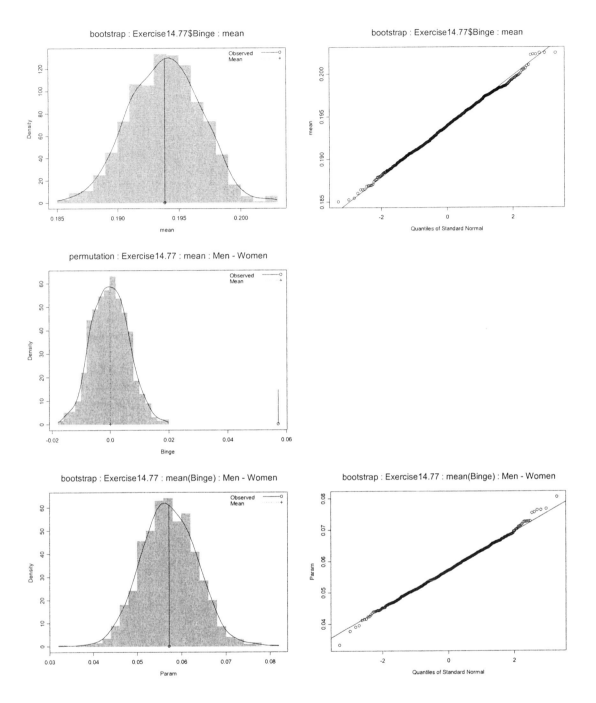

14.78. (a) The histograms do not give the impression of normality. However, the normal quantile plots suggest that the underlying distributions could well be normal; there are no outliers or systematic deviations from normality. The mean word counts are 140 and 121.4 for the High and Medium education levels, respectively. **(b)** The bootstrap SEs are 17.0 and 14.7 for the High and Medium groups, respectively. **(c)** The bootstrap distributions appear very close to normal; they are centered at the respective sample means, with about the same amount of spread. **(d)** The percentile intervals are (106.4, 173.7) and (93.3, 146.6), and the tilting intervals are (106.8, 171.1) and (94.6, 150.9). Using either confidence interval method, the intervals for the two groups overlap. This suggests that there may not be a statistically significant difference between the two groups. However, we should do a confidence interval for the difference to answer that question. **(e)** The 95% bootstrap percentile confidence interval for the difference is (–26.3, 62.4). This interval includes zero. The observed data do not provide strong evidence of a difference in mean word counts.

```
Exercise14.78 # variables WordCount and Education (High, Medium)
histogram(~WordCount | Education, data=Exercise14.78)
qqmath(~WordCount | Education, data=Exercise14.78)
groupMeans(Exercise14.78$WordCount, group=Exercise14.78$Education)
x78 = split(Exercise14.78$WordCount, Exercise14.78$Education)
boot78a = bootstrap(x78$High, mean, seed=0)
boot78b = bootstrap(x78$Medium, mean, seed=0)
boot78a
boot78b
par(mfrow=c(2,2)) # 2x2 grid for plots
plot(boot78a);qqnorm(boot78a)
plot(boot78b);qqnorm(boot78b)
par(mfrow=c(1,1)) # back to normal plots
limits.percentile(boot78a)
limits.tilt(boot78a)
limits.percentile(boot78b)
limits.tilt(boot78b)
boot78c = bootstrap2(Exercise14.78$WordCount, mean,
                    treatment = Exercise14.78$Education, seed=0)
plot(boot78c)
qqnorm(boot78c)
limits.percentile(boot78c)
```

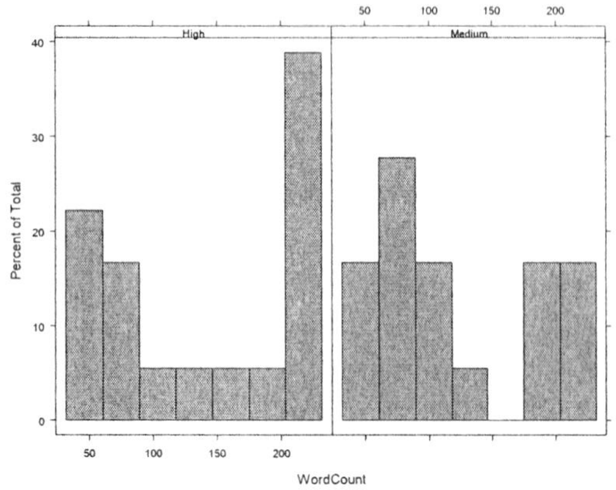

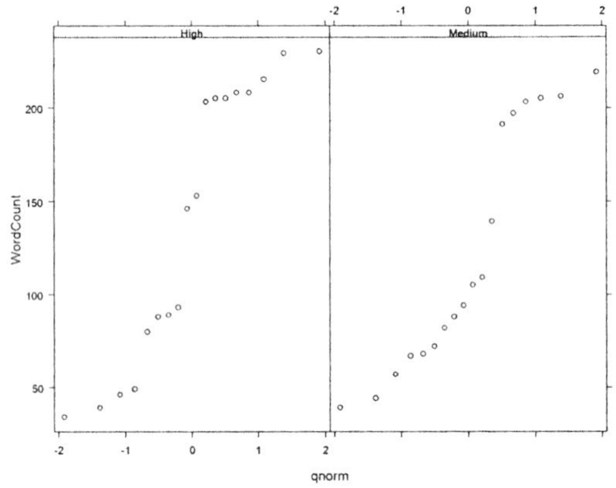

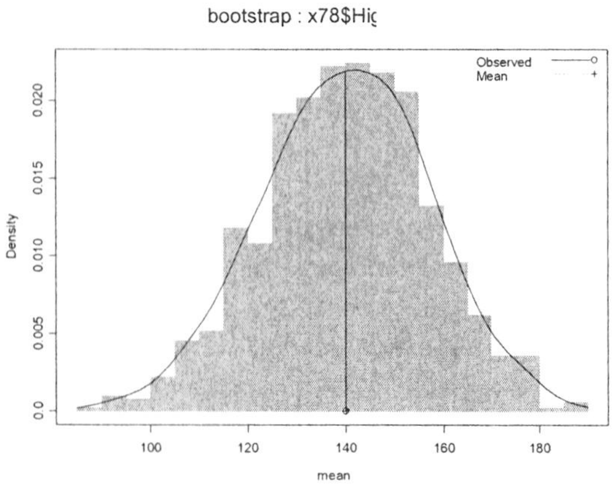

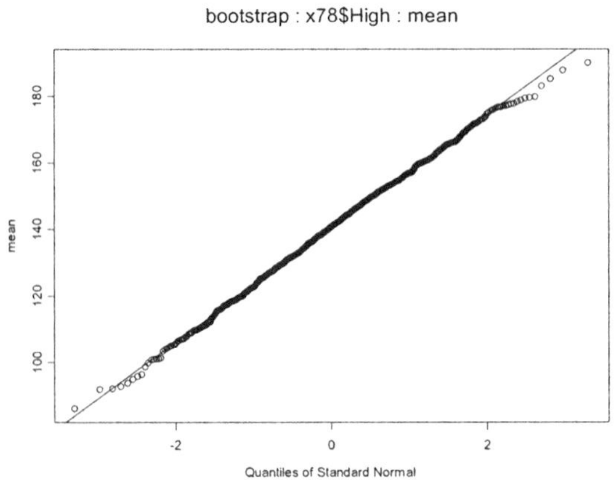

bootstrap : x78$Hig

bootstrap : x78$High : mean

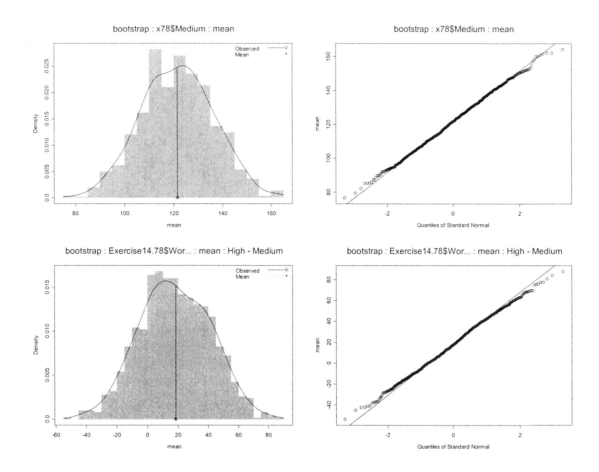

14.79. We test the hypotheses H_0: $\mu_1 = \mu_2$ vs. H_a: $\mu_1 > \mu_2$. The *P*-value is 0.212. Thus, there is not strong evidence that the mean word count is higher for ads placed in magazines aimed at people with high education levels, as opposed to ads placed in magazines aimed at people with medium education levels. The 95% confidence interval in Exercise 14.78 for the difference in means contained 0. This suggests that there is not strong evidence of a difference in mean word counts. Here we conclude that there is not strong evidence that the mean word count is higher for ads placed in magazines aimed at people with high education levels as opposed to ads placed in magazines aimed at people with medium education levels.

```
perm79 = permutationTestMeans(Exercise14.78, treatment = Education,
                        alternative = "greater", seed=0)
plot(perm79)
perm79
```

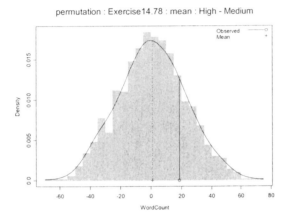

permutation : Exercise14.78 : mean : High - Medium

14.80. (a) Roughly normal. **(b)** The average number of burglaries was 64.3 before and 60.6 after the program began. This is a one-sided test, because we wish to test whether or not the program made an improvement. The *P*-value for the two-sample *t* test is 0.22. **(c)** The *P*-value for the permutation test is 0.22. This is the same (after rounding) as for the formula *t* test. **(d)** The *P*-value is 0.788. This is testing whether the data provide strong evidence that burglaries have increased. That is the opposite of our goal, to determine whether the program has reduced burglaries. The *P*-value is more than 50%, because the actual change was negative rather than positive; there is greater than a 50% chance that random chance would yield an increase greater than –3.7.

```
Exercise14.80 # variables Burglaries, When (Before and After)
groupMeans(Exercise14.80$Burglaries, Exercise14.80$When)
histogram(~Burglaries | When, data=Exercise14.80)
qqmath(~Burglaries | When, data=Exercise14.80)
x80 = split(Exercise14.80$Burglaries, Exercise14.80$When)
t.test(x80$Before, x80$After, alternative="greater")
perm80a = permutationTestMeans(Exercise14.80, treatment = When,
                            alternative = "greater", seed=0)
perm80a
plot(perm80a)
qqnorm(perm80a)
perm80b = permutationTestMeans(Exercise14.80, treatment = When,
                            alternative = "less", seed=0)
perm80b
```

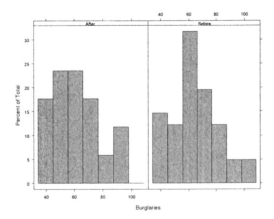

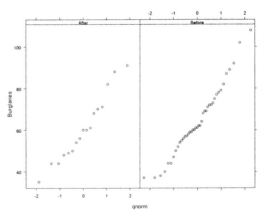

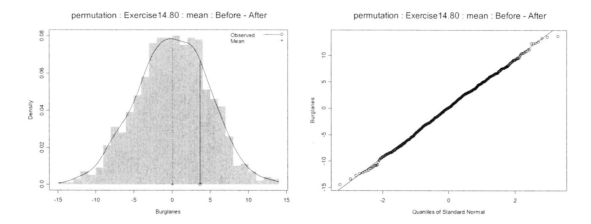

permutation : Exercise14.80 : mean : Before - After   permutation : Exercise14.80 : mean : Before - After

14.81. **(a)** The bootstrap distribution appears to be approximately normal. **(b)** The bootstrap SE is 4.6. A 95% bootstrap t confidence interval using the conservative method for the degrees of freedom is $(-13.4, 6.1)$. Using df $= n_1 + n_2 - 2$ gives a narrower interval $(-12.9, 5.6)$. **(c)** A 95% bootstrap percentile interval is $(-12.5, 5.6)$. This agrees closely with the second interval found in (b), so we conclude that the intervals are reasonably accurate. These intervals include 0 so we conclude that there is not strong evidence (at the 0.05 level) of a difference in the mean monthly burglary counts. The tests in the previous exercise were one-sided tests and showed no strong evidence of a decrease in mean monthly burglaries, so the two sets of conclusions are consistent.

```
boot81 = bootstrap2(Exercise14.80$Burglaries, mean,
                treatment=Exercise14.80$When, seed=0)
plot(boot81)
qqnorm(boot81)
boot81
limits.t(boot81, df = "smaller")
limits.t(boot81, df = "pooled")
limits.t(boot81) # estimate the degrees of freedom
t.test(x80$Before, x80$After)
limits.percentile(boot81)
```

bootstrap : Exercise14.80$Bur... : mean : Before - After   bootstrap : Exercise14.80$Bur... : mean : Before - After

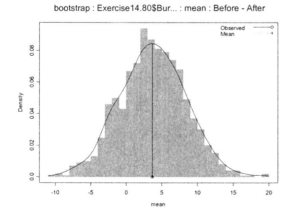
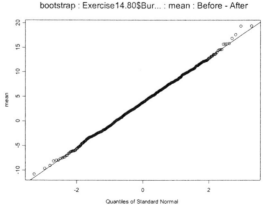

Chapter 15 Solutions

15.1. (a) Normal quantile plots are not shown. The score 0.00 for child 8 seems to be a low outlier (although with only five observations, such judgments are questionable). **(b)** For testing H_0: $\mu_1 = \mu_2$ vs. H_a: $\mu_1 > \mu_2$, we have $\bar{x}_1 = 0.676$, $s_1 \doteq 0.1189$, $\bar{x}_2 = 0.406$, and $s_2 \doteq 0.2675$. Then $t = 2.062$, which gives $P = 0.0447$ (df = 5.5). We have some evidence that high-progress readers have higher mean scores. **(c)** We test

H_0: Scores for both groups are identically distributed   vs.

H_a: High-progress children systematically score higher

for which we find $W = 36$ and $P \doteq 0.0473$ or 0.0463—significant evidence (at $\alpha = 0.05$) against the hypothesis of identical distributions. This is equivalent to the conclusion reached in (b).

   Note: Minitab refers to the medians as ETA1 and ETA2 ("eta" is the Greek letter η). Minitab also reports an estimate of 0.21 for the difference $\eta_1 - \eta_2$; note that this is not the same as the difference between the two sample medians ($0.7 - 0.4 = 0.3$). This estimate, called the Hodges-Lehmann estimate, is not discussed in the text, and has been removed from the Minitab outputs accompanying other solutions for this chapter. Briefly, this estimate is found by taking every response from the first group and subtracting every response from the second group, yielding (in this case) a total of 25 differences. The median of this set of differences is the Hodges-Lehmann estimate.

Minitab output

```
Mann-Whitney Confidence Interval and Test

HiProg1    N =   5     Median =      0.7000
LoProg1    N =   5     Median =      0.4000
Point estimate for ETA1-ETA2 is      0.2100
96.3 Percent C.I. for ETA1-ETA2 is (-0.0199,0.7001)
W = 36.0
Test of ETA1 = ETA2  vs.  ETA1 > ETA2 is significant at 0.0473
The test is significant at 0.0463 (adjusted for ties)
```

15.2. (a) Normal quantile plots are not shown. The score 0.54 for child 3 seems to be a low outlier. **(b)** For testing H_0: $\mu_1 = \mu_2$ vs. H_a: $\mu_1 > \mu_2$, we have $\bar{x}_1 = 0.768$, $s_1 \doteq 0.1333$, $\bar{x}_2 = 0.516$, $s_2 \doteq 0.2001$. Then $t = 2.344$, which gives $P = 0.0259$ (df = 6.97). We have fairly strong evidence that high-progress readers have higher mean scores. **(c)** We test

H_0: Scores for both groups are identically distributed   vs.

H_a: High-progress children systematically score higher

for which we find $W = 38$ and $P \doteq 0.0184$. This is evidence against H_0, slightly stronger than that found in (b).

Minitab output

```
Mann-Whitney Confidence Interval and Test

HiProg2    N =   5     Median =      0.8000
LoProg2    N =   5     Median =      0.4900
W = 38.0
Test of ETA1 = ETA2  vs.  ETA1 > ETA2 is significant at 0.0184
```

15.3. (a) See table. **(b)** For Story 2, $W = 8 + 9 + 4 + 7 + 10 = 38$. Under H_0,

$$\mu_W = \frac{(5)(11)}{2} = 27.5$$

$$\sigma_W = \sqrt{\frac{(5)(5)(11)}{12}} \doteq 4.787$$

(c) $z = \frac{38-27.5}{4.787} \doteq 2.19$; with the continuity correction, we compute $\frac{37.5-27.5}{4.787} \doteq 2.09$, which gives $P = P(Z > 2.09) = 0.0183$. **(d)** See the table.

		Story 1		Story 2	
Child	Progress	Score	Rank	Score	Rank
1	high	0.55	4.5	0.80	8
2	high	0.57	6	0.82	9
3	high	0.72	8.5	0.54	4
4	high	0.70	7	0.79	7
5	high	0.84	10	0.89	10
6	low	0.40	3	0.77	6
7	low	0.72	8.5	0.49	3
8	low	0.00	1	0.66	5
9	low	0.36	2	0.28	1
10	low	0.55	4.5	0.38	2

15.4. (a) We find $W = 26$ and $P \doteq 0.0152$. We have strong evidence against the hypothesis of identical distributions; we conclude that the weed-free yield is higher. **(b)** For testing H_0: $\mu_0 = \mu_9$ vs. H_a: $\mu_0 > \mu_9$, we find $\bar{x}_0 = 170.2$, $s_0 \doteq 5.4216$, $\bar{x}_9 = 157.575$, $s_9 \doteq 10.1181$, and $t = 2.20$, which gives $P = 0.0423$ (df = 4.6). We have fairly strong evidence that the mean yield is higher with no weeds—but the evidence is not quite as strong as in (a). **(c)** Both tests still reach the same conclusion, so there is no "practically important impact" on our conclusions. The Wilcoxon evidence is slightly weaker: $W = 22$, $P \doteq 0.0259$. The t-test evidence is slightly stronger: $t = 2.79$, df = 3, $P = 0.0341$. The new statistics for the 9-weeds-per-meter group are $\bar{x}_9 = 162.633$ and $s_9 \doteq 0.2082$; these are substantial changes for each value.

Minitab output

```
– – – – – – – – – – – – – – – – – All points  – – – – – – – – – – – – – – – –
Weed0       N =   4     Median =       169.45
Weed9       N =   4     Median =       162.55
W = 26.0
Test of ETA1 = ETA2  vs.  ETA1 > ETA2 is significant at 0.0152
– – – – – – – – – – – – – –  With outlier removed  – – – – – – – – – – – – – –
C2          N =   4     Median =       169.45
C4          N =   3     Median =       162.70
W = 22.0
Test of ETA1 = ETA2  vs.  ETA1 > ETA2 is significant at 0.0259
```

15.5. (a) The distributions do not appear to have the same shape; in particular, the 16-week distribution is much more spread out. **(b)** The Wilcoxon rank-sum test gives $W = 33$ and $P \doteq 0.1481$ (0.1467, adjusted for ties). We do not have enough evidence to conclude that burial lowers breaking strength.

2 weeks		16 weeks
	9	8
	10	
8	11	00
9660	12	4
	13	
	14	0

Minitab output

```
2weeks      N =   5     Median =       126.00
16weeks     N =   5     Median =       110.00
W = 33.0
Test of ETA1 = ETA2  vs.  ETA1 > ETA2 is significant at 0.1481
The test is significant at 0.1467 (adjusted for ties)
```

15.6. (a) The outline is shown below. **(b)** We consider score improvements (posttest minus pretest). The means, medians, and standard deviations are:

Treatment: $\bar{x} = 11.4$ $M = 11.5$ $s \doteq 3.1693$
Control: $\bar{x} = 8.25$ $M = 7.5$ $s \doteq 3.6936$

Treatment		Control
	0	455
76	0	7
	0	8
110	1	1
332	1	2
5	1	4
6	1	

A back-to-back stemplot is one way to compare the distributions graphically. Both of these comparisons support the idea that the positive subliminal message resulted in higher test scores. **(c)** We have $W = 114$, for which $P = 0.0501$ (or 0.0494, adjusted for ties). This is just about significant at $\alpha = 0.05$, and at least warrants further study.

Minitab output

```
Trtmt      N =   10      Median =      11.500
Ctrl       N =    8      Median =       7.500
W = 114.0
Test of ETA1 = ETA2  vs.  ETA1 > ETA2 is significant at 0.0501
The test is significant at 0.0494 (adjusted for ties)
```

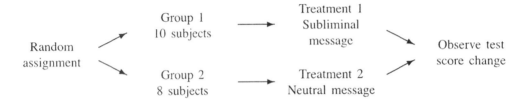

15.7. (a) At right. Unlogged plots appear to have a greater number of species. **(b)** H_0: There is no difference in the number of species on logged and unlogged plots vs. H_a: Unlogged plots have a greater variety of species. The Wilcoxon test gives $W = 159$ and $P \doteq 0.0298$ (0.0290, adjusted for ties). We conclude that the observed difference is significant; unlogged plots really do have a greater number of species.

Unlogged		Logged
	0	4
	0	
	0	
333	1	0
55	1	2
	1	455
	1	7
998	1	88
10	2	
22	2	

Minitab output

```
Unlogged   N =   12      Median =      18.500
Logged     N =    9      Median =      15.000
W = 159.0
Test of ETA1 = ETA2  vs.  ETA1 > ETA2 is significant at 0.0298
The test is significant at 0.0290 (adjusted for ties)
```

15.8. For the Wilcoxon test, we have $W = 579$, for which $P = 0.0064$ (0.0063, adjusted for ties). The evidence is slightly stronger with the Wilcoxon test than for the t and permutation tests.

Minitab output

```
Trtmt      N =   21      Median =      53.00
Ctrl       N =   23      Median =      42.00
W = 579.0
Test of ETA1 = ETA2  vs.  ETA1 > ETA2 is significant at 0.0064
The test is significant at 0.0063 (adjusted for ties)
```

15.9. A table of counts and percents suggests that women do give higher ratings. One could do a chi-square test (which yields $X^2 = 21.940$ and P tiny), but this is not advisable because there are so many small counts. The Wilcoxon test is better; it gives $W = 32{,}267.5$ and $P = 0.0003$ (or $P = 0.0001$ adjusted for ties)—strong evidence that women really do rate restaurant food as less safe than men do.

Rating	Women Count	Women %	Men Count	Men %
1	48	24.49	52	48.60
2	123	62.76	45	42.06
3	19	9.69	8	7.48
4	5	2.55	0	0
5	1	0.51	2	1.87

Minitab output

```
women      N = 196    Median =        2.0000
men        N = 107    Median =        2.0000
W = 32267.5
Test of ETA1 = ETA2  vs.  ETA1 > ETA2 is significant at 0.0003
The test is significant at 0.0001 (adjusted for ties)
```

15.10. We do not have independent samples from two populations; rather, we have dependent samples (each person answered both questions).

15.11. (a) We find $X^2 = 3.955$ with df $= (5 - 1)(2 - 1) = 4$, giving $P = 0.413$. There is little evidence to make us believe that there is a relationship between city and income. (b) Minitab reports $W = 56{,}370$, with $P \doteq 0.5$; again, there is no evidence that incomes are systematically higher in one city.

Minitab output

```
City1      N = 241    Median =        2.0000
City2      N = 218    Median =        2.0000
W = 56370.0
Test of ETA1 = ETA2  vs.  ETA1 ~= ETA2 is significant at 0.5080
The test is significant at 0.4949 (adjusted for ties)
```

15.12. (a) The differences (treatment minus control) were 0.01622, 0.01102, and 0.01607. The mean difference was $\bar{x} \doteq 0.01444$, and $s \doteq 0.002960$. The fact that all are positive supports the idea that there was more growth in the treated plots. (b) For testing H_0: $\mu = 0$ vs. H_a: $\mu > 0$, with μ the mean (treatment minus control) difference, we have $t = \frac{\bar{x}}{s/\sqrt{3}} \doteq 8.45$, df $= 2$, $P = 0.0069$. We conclude that growth was greater in treated plots. (c) The Wilcoxon statistic is $W^+ = 6$, for which $P = 0.091$. We would not reject H_0 (which states that there is no difference among pairs). (d) A low-power test has a low probability of rejecting H_0 when it is false.

Minitab output

```
Wilcoxon Signed Rank Test

TEST OF MEDIAN = 0.000000 VERSUS MEDIAN G.T. 0.000000

              N FOR   WILCOXON            ESTIMATED
          N   TEST    STATISTIC  P-VALUE    MEDIAN
Diff      3    3          6.0      0.091    0.01485
```

Note: *With only three pairs, the Wilcoxon signed rank test can never give a P-value smaller than 0.091. This is one difference between some nonparametric tests and parametric tests like the t test: With the t test, the power improves when we consider alternatives that are* *farther from the null hypothesis; for example, if H_0 says $\mu = 0$, we have higher power for the alternative $\mu = 10$ than for $\mu = 5$. With the Wilcoxon signed rank test, all alternatives look the same; the values of W^+ and P would be the same if the three differences had been 100, 200, and 300.*

Also, note that the "estimated median" in the Minitab output (0.01485) is not the same as the median of the three differences (0.01607). The process of computing this point estimate is not discussed in the text, but we will illustrate it for this simple case: The Wilcoxon estimated median is the median of the set of Walsh averages of the differences. This set consists of every possible pairwise average $(x_i + x_j)/2$ for $i \le j$; note that this includes $i = j$, in which case the average is x_i. In general, there are $n(n + 1)/2$ such averages, so with $n = 3$ differences, we have 6 Walsh averages: the three differences (0.01622, 0.01102, and 0.01607), and the averages of each pair of distinct differences (0.013545, 0.01362, and 0.016145). The median of

$$0.01102, \quad 0.013545, \quad 0.01362, \quad 0.01607, \quad 0.016145, \quad 0.01622$$

is 0.014845.

15.13. We examine the heart-rate increase (final minus resting) from low-rate exercise; our hypotheses are H_0: median $= 0$ vs. H_a: median > 0. The statistic is $W^+ = 10$ (the first four differences are positive, and the fifth is 0, so we drop it). We compute

$$P = P(W^+ \ge 9.5) = P\left(\frac{W^+ - 5}{2.739} \ge \frac{9.5 - 5}{2.739}\right) \doteq P(Z \ge 1.64) = 0.0505.$$ This is right on the borderline of significance: It is fairly strong evidence that heart rate increases, but (barely) not significant at 5%. (See the note in the solution to the previous exercise for an explanation of the estimated median reported by Minitab.)

Minitab output

```
TEST OF MEDIAN = 0.000000 VERSUS MEDIAN G.T. 0.000000

                 N FOR    WILCOXON              ESTIMATED
           N     TEST     STATISTIC  P-VALUE     MEDIAN
LowDiff    5      4          10.0     0.050       7.500
```

15.14. **(a)** For this exercise, we must first find the Final − Resting differences for both exercise rates (Low: 15, 9, 6, 9, 0; Medium: 21, 24, 15, 15, 18), then compute the differences of these differences (6, 15, 9, 6, 18). To this last list of differences, we apply the Wilcoxon signed rank test. The hypotheses are H_0: median $= 0$ vs. H_a: median > 0. (The rank sum test is not appropriate because we do not have two independent samples.) **(b)** The statistic is $W^+ = 15$ (all five differences were positive), and the reported P-value is 0.030—fairly strong evidence that medium-rate exercise increases are greater than low-rate exercise increases. (See the note in the solution to Exercise 15.12 for an explanation of the estimated median reported by Minitab.)

Minitab output

```
TEST OF MEDIAN = 0.000000 VERSUS MEDIAN G.T. 0.000000

                 N FOR    WILCOXON              ESTIMATED
           N     TEST     STATISTIC  P-VALUE     MEDIAN
LowMed     5      5          15.0     0.030       10.50
```

15.15. For testing H_0: median $= 0$ vs. H_a: median > 0, the Wilcoxon statistic is $W^+ = 119$ (14 of the 15 differences were positive, and the one negative difference was the smallest in absolute value), and $P < 0.0005$—very strong evidence that there are more aggressive incidents during moon days. This agrees with the results of the t and permutation tests. (See the note in the solution to Exercise 15.12 for an explanation of the estimated median reported by Minitab.)

Minitab output

```
TEST OF MEDIAN = 0.000000 VERSUS MEDIAN G.T. 0.000000

              N FOR   WILCOXON            ESTIMATED
          N   TEST   STATISTIC  P-VALUE    MEDIAN
diff      15    15     119.0     0.000      2.570
```

15.16. There are 17 nonzero differences; only one is negative (the boldface 6 in the list below).

Diff:	1	1	2	2	2	3	3	3	3	3	3	**6**	6	6	6	6	6
Rank:	1	2	3	4	5	6	7	8	9	10	11	12	13	14	15	16	17
Value:	1.5		4					8.5						14.5			

This gives $W^+ = 138.5$. (Note that the only tie we really need to worry about is the last group; all other ties involve only positive differences.)

15.17. For the differences sfair − srest, we find $\bar{x} = 0.5149$ and $M = 0.5$. Applying the Wilcoxon signed rank test to these differences, with the one-sided alternative—"food at fairs is systematically rated higher (less safe) than restaurant food"—we obtain $W^+ = 10{,}850.5$ ($P < 0.0005$), so we conclude that restaurant food is viewed as being safer. However, there were 146 ties; the text cautions us that when there are many ties, the test may be biased in favor of H_a, so we must be cautious about our conclusion. (See the note in the solution to Exercise 15.12 for an explanation of the estimated median reported by Minitab.)

Minitab output

```
TEST OF MEDIAN = 0.000000 VERSUS MEDIAN G.T. 0.000000

              N FOR   WILCOXON            ESTIMATED
          N   TEST   STATISTIC  P-VALUE    MEDIAN
Diffs    303   157    10850.5    0.000     0.5000
```

15.18. Considering the differences (after − before), we test H_0: median $= 0$ vs. H_a: median > 0. The Wilcoxon statistic is $W^+ = 66$ (11 of the 14 differences were positive, and the other 3 were 0), and $P = 0.002$—very strong evidence that glove use increased after the presentation. (See the note in the solution to Exercise 15.12 for an explanation of the estimated median reported by Minitab.)

Minitab output

```
TEST OF MEDIAN = 0.000000 VERSUS MEDIAN G.T. 0.000000

              N FOR   WILCOXON            ESTIMATED
          N   TEST   STATISTIC  P-VALUE    MEDIAN
Diff      14    11      66.0     0.002     0.6665
```

15.19. (a) At right. The distribution is clearly right-skewed but has no
outliers. **(b)** $W^+ = 31$ (only 4 of 12 differences were positive) and
$P = 0.556$—there is no evidence that the median is other than 105.
(See the note in the solution to Exercise 15.12 for an explanation of the
estimated median reported by Minitab.)

```
 9 | 1
 9 | 5679
10 | 134
10 | 5
11 | 1
11 | 9
12 | 2
```

Minitab output

```
TEST OF MEDIAN = 105.0 VERSUS MEDIAN N.E. 105.0

                N FOR    WILCOXON            ESTIMATED
          N     TEST    STATISTIC  P-VALUE    MEDIAN
Radon    12      12        31.0     0.556     103.2
```

15.20. If we compute Haiti content minus factory content (so that a negative
difference means that the amount of vitamin C decreased), we find that the
mean change is -5.33 and the median is -6. (See the note in the solution
to Exercise 15.12 for an explanation of the estimated median reported by
Minitab.) The stemplot is right-skewed. There are five positive differences;
the Wilcoxon statistic is $W^+ = 37$, for which $P < 0.0005$. The differences
are systematically negative, so vitamin C content is lower in Haiti.

```
-1 | 4
-1 | 3322
-1 |
-0 | 9988
-0 | 7776666
-0 | 5444
-0 | 2
-0 | 1
 0 | 1
 0 | 33
 0 | 4
 0 |
 0 | 8
```

Minitab output

```
TEST OF MEDIAN = 0.000000 VERSUS MEDIAN L.T.  0.000000

                 N FOR    WILCOXON            ESTIMATED
           N     TEST    STATISTIC  P-VALUE    MEDIAN
Change    27      27        37.0     0.000     -5.500
```

15.21. (a) The Wilcoxon statistic is $W^+ = 0$ (all of the differences were less than 16), for
which $P = 0$—very strong evidence against H_0. We conclude that the median weight gain
is less than 16 pounds. **(b)** Minitab gives the interval 3.75 to 5.90 kg for the median weight
gain. (For comparison, in the solution to Exercise 7.10, the 95% confidence interval for the
mean μ was about 3.80 to 5.66 kg. See the note in the solution to Exercise 15.12 for an
explanation of the estimated median reported by Minitab.)

Minitab output

```
TEST OF MEDIAN = 16.00 VERSUS MEDIAN N.E. 16.00

                N FOR    WILCOXON            ESTIMATED
          N     TEST    STATISTIC  P-VALUE    MEDIAN
Diff     16      16         0.0     0.000      4.800
- - - - - - - - - - - - -  Confidence interval  - - - - - - - - - - - - -
Wilcoxon Signed Rank Confidence Interval

                ESTIMATED    ACHIEVED
          N      MEDIAN    CONFIDENCE   CONFIDENCE INTERVAL
Diff     16       4.80        94.8    (   3.75,    5.90)
```

15.22. (a) The Kruskal-Wallis test (Minitab output below) gives $H = 8.73$, df $= 4$, and
$P = 0.069$—not significant at $\alpha = 0.05$. Note, however, that the rankings clearly suggest
that vitamin C content decreases over time; the samples are simply too small to achieve
significance even with such seemingly strong evidence. (See also a related comment in
the solution to Exercise 15.12.) **(b)** The more accurate P-value is more in line with the

apparent strength of the evidence, and does change our conclusion. With it, we reject H_0 and conclude that the distribution changes over time.

Minitab output

```
Kruskal-Wallis Test

LEVEL     NOBS    MEDIAN   AVE. RANK   Z VALUE
    0        2    48.705        9.5      2.09
    1        2    41.955        7.5      1.04
    3        2    21.795        5.5      0.00
    5        2    12.415        3.5     -1.04
    7        2     8.320        1.5     -2.09
OVERALL     10                  5.5

H = 8.73   d.f. = 4   p = 0.069
```

15.23. (a) Diagram below. **(b)** The stemplots (right) suggest greater density for high-jump rats, but a greater spread for the control group. **(c)** $H = 10.66$ with $P = 0.005$. We conclude that bone density differs among the groups. ANOVA tests H_0: all means are equal, assuming normal distributions with the same standard deviation. For Kruskal-Wallis, the null hypothesis is that the distributions are the same (but not necessarily normal). **(d)** There is strong evidence that the three groups have different bone densities; specifically, the high-jump group has the highest average rank (and the highest density), the low-jump group is in the middle, and the control group is lowest.

Control		Low jump		High jump	
55	4	55		55	
56	9	56		56	
57		57		57	
58		58	8	58	
59	33	59	469	59	
60	03	60	57	60	
61	14	61		61	
62	1	62		62	2266
63		63	1258	63	1
64		64		64	33
65	3	65		65	00
66		66		66	
67		67		67	4

Minitab output

```
LEVEL     NOBS    MEDIAN   AVE. RANK   Z VALUE
Ctrl       10     601.5        10.2     -2.33
Low        10     606.0        13.6     -0.81
High       10     637.0        22.6      3.15
OVERALL     30                 15.5

H = 10.66   d.f. = 2   p = 0.005
H = 10.68   d.f. = 2   p = 0.005 (adjusted for ties)
```

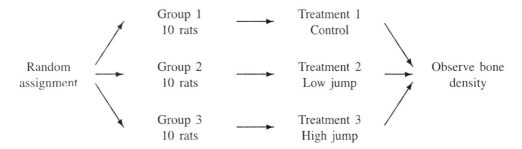

15.24. (a) For ANOVA, H_0: $\mu_1 = \mu_2 = \mu_3 = \mu_4$ vs. H_a: Not all μ_i are equal. For Kruskal-Wallis, H_0 says that the distribution of the trapped insect count is the same for all board colors; the alternative is that the count is systematically higher for some colors. (b) In the order given, the medians are 46.5, 15.5, 34.5, and 15 insects; it appears that yellow is most effective, green is in the middle, and white and blue are least effective. The Kruskal-Wallis test statistic is $H = 16.95$, with df $= 3$; the P-value is 0.001, so we have strong evidence that color affects the insect count (that is, the difference we observed is statistically significant).

Minitab output

```
LEVEL      NOBS    MEDIAN   AVE. RANK    Z VALUE
Lemon        6     46.50       21.2       3.47
White        6     15.50        7.3      -2.07
Green        6     34.50       14.8       0.93
Blue         6     15.00        6.7      -2.33
OVERALL     24                 12.5

H = 16.95  d.f. = 3   p = 0.001
H = 16.98  d.f. = 3   p = 0.001 (adjusted for ties)
```

15.25. (a) $I = 4$, $n_i = 6$, $N = 24$. (b) The table below lists color, insect count, and rank. There are only three ties (and the second could be ignored, as both of those counts are for white boards). The R_i (rank sums) are

$$
\begin{aligned}
\text{Yellow} &\quad 17 + 20 + 21 + 22 + 23 + 24 &&= 127 \\
\text{White} &\quad 3 + 4 + 5.5 + 9.5 + 9.5 + 12.5 &&= 44 \\
\text{Green} &\quad 7 + 14 + 15 + 16 + 18 + 19 &&= 89 \\
\text{Blue} &\quad 1 + 2 + 5.5 + 8 + 11 + 12.5 &&= 40
\end{aligned}
$$

(c) $H = \dfrac{12}{24(25)}\left(\dfrac{127^2 + 44^2 + 89^2 + 40^2}{6}\right) - 3(25) = 91.95\overline{3} - 75 = 16.95\overline{3}$.

Under H_0, this has approximately the chi-squared distribution with df $= I - 1 = 3$; comparing to this distribution tells us that $0.0005 < P < 0.001$.

B	B	W	W	W	B	G	B	W	W	B	W	B	G	G	G	Y	G	G	Y	Y	Y	Y	Y
7	11	12	13	14	14	15	16	17	17	20	21	21	25	32	37	38	39	41	45	46	47	48	59
1	2	3	4	5	6	7	8	9	10	11	12	13	14	15	16	17	18	19	20	21	22	23	24

5.5   9.5   12.5

15.26. (a) The standard deviations are (in order) 4.6043, 6.5422, 9.0443, and 16.0873 pounds. (b) The four medians are 126, 126, 131, and 110 pounds. The Kruskal-Wallis hypotheses are H_0: all medians are equal vs. H_a: at least one median is different. (Recall that the hypotheses can be stated in terms of the distributions, or in terms of the medians.) (c) With $H = 5.35$, df $= 3$, and $P \doteq 0.149$, we do not have enough evidence to conclude that breaking strength differs for varying lengths of burial.

Minitab output

LEVEL	NOBS	MEDIAN	AVE. RANK	Z VALUE
2	5	126.0	9.7	-0.35
4	5	126.0	10.2	-0.13
8	5	131.0	15.3	2.09
16	5	110.0	6.8	-1.61
OVERALL	20		10.5	

```
H = 5.35  d.f. = 3  p = 0.149
H = 5.38  d.f. = 3  p = 0.147 (adjusted for ties)
```

15.27. For the Kruskal-Wallis test, we need two or more independent samples. Because these data come from different questions being asked of the same people, the responses are not independent. (We have several variables measured from a single group, rather than a single variable measured for several different groups.)

15.28. (a) The stemplots (right) appear to suggest that logging reduces the number of species per plot and that recovery is slow (the 1-year-after and 8-years-after stemplots are similar). The logged stemplots have some outliers and appear to have more spread than the unlogged stemplot. The medians are 18.5, 12.5, and 15. (b) For testing H_0: all medians are equal vs. H_a: at least one median is different, we have $H = 9.31$, df $= 2$, and $P = 0.010$ (or 0.009, adjusted for ties). This is good evidence of a difference among the groups.

Unlogged		1 year ago		8 years ago	
0		0	2	0	
0		0		0	4
0		0	7	0	
0		0	8	0	
1		1	11	1	0
1	333	1	23	1	2
1	55	1	4555	1	455
1		1		1	7
1	899	1	8	1	88
2	01	2		2	
2	22	2		2	

Minitab output

LEVEL	NOBS	MEDIAN	AVE. RANK	Z VALUE
1	12	18.50	23.4	2.88
2	12	12.50	11.5	-2.47
3	9	15.00	15.8	-0.44
OVERALL	33		17.0	

```
H = 9.31  d.f. = 2  p = 0.010
H = 9.44  d.f. = 2  p = 0.009 (adjusted for ties)
```

15.29. (a) Yes, the data support this statement: $\frac{68}{211} \doteq 32.2\%$ of high-SES subjects have never smoked, compared to 17.3% and 23.7% of middle- and low-SES subjects (respectively). Also, only $\frac{51}{211} \doteq 24.2\%$ of high-SES subjects are current smokers, versus 42.3% and 46.2% of those in the middle- and low-SES groups. **(b)** $X^2 = 18.510$ with df = 4; this has $P = 0.001$ (Minitab output on the right). There is a significant relationship. **(c)** $H = 12.72$ with df = 2, so $P = 0.002$—or, after adjusting for ties,

Minitab output

	Never	Former	Curr	Total
High	68	92	51	211
	58.68	83.57	68.75	
Mid	9	21	22	52
	14.46	20.60	16.94	
Low	22	28	43	93
	25.86	36.83	30.30	
Total	99	141	116	356

```
ChiSq =  1.481 +  0.850 +  4.584 +
         2.062 +  0.008 +  1.509 +
         0.577 +  2.119 +  5.320 = 18.510
df = 4,  p = 0.001
```

$H = 14.43$ and $P = 0.001$ (Minitab output below). The observed differences are significant; some SES groups smoke systematically more.

Minitab output

LEVEL	NOBS	MEDIAN	AVE. RANK	Z VALUE
High	211	2.000	162.4	-3.56
Mid	52	2.000	203.6	1.90
Low	93	2.000	201.0	2.46
OVERALL	356		178.5	

```
H = 12.72  d.f. = 2  p = 0.002
H = 14.43  d.f. = 2  p = 0.001 (adjusted for ties)
```

15.30. (a) On the right is a histogram of service times for Verizon customers. With only 10 CLEC service calls, it is hardly necessary to make such a graph for them; we can simply observe that 7 of those 10 calls took 5 hours, which is quite different from the distribution for Verizon customers. The means and medians tell the same story: For Verizon customers, $\bar{x}_V \doteq 1.7263$ hr and $M_V = 1$ hr, while for CLEC customers, $\bar{x}_C = 3.8$ hr and $M_C = 5$ hr. **(b)** The

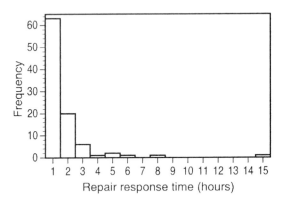

distributions are sharply skewed, and the sample sizes are quite different; the *t* test is not reliable in situations like this. The Wilcoxon rank-sum test gives $W = 4778.5$, which is highly significant ($P = 0.0026$ or 0.0006). We have strong evidence that response times for Verizon customers are shorter. It is also possible to apply the Kruskal-Wallis test (with two groups). While the *P*-values are slightly different ($P = 0.005$, or 0.001 adjusted for ties), the conclusion is the same: We have strong evidence of a difference in response times.

Minitab output

```
— — — — — — — — — — — — Wilcoxon rank-sum test   — — — — — — — — — — — —
Mann-Whitney Confidence Interval and Test

Verizon    N =  95    Median =        1.000
CLEC       N =  10    Median =        5.000
W = 4778.5
Test of ETA1 = ETA2  vs.  ETA1 < ETA2 is significant at 0.0026
The test is significant at 0.0006 (adjusted for ties)
— — — — — — — — — — — — — Kruskal-Wallis test   — — — — — — — — — — — — — —
LEVEL    NOBS    MEDIAN   AVE. RANK    Z VALUE
    1      95     1.000       50.3       -2.80
    2      10     5.000       78.7        2.80
OVERALL   105                53.0

H =  7.84   d.f. = 1   p = 0.005
H = 10.54   d.f. = 1   p = 0.001 (adjusted for ties)
```

15.31. See also the solution to Exercise 7.140. **(a)** The distribution of prices for three-bedroom houses is clearly right-skewed, with high outliers. **(b)** For testing H_0: $\mu_3 = \mu_4$ vs. H_a: $\mu_3 \neq \mu_4$, we have $t \doteq -3.08$ with either df $= 12.1$ ($P = 0.0095$) or df $= 8$ ($P = 0.0151$). We conclude that the mean prices are different (specifically, that 4BR houses are more expensive). Summary statistics are below. **(c)** We test H_0: medians are equal vs. H_a: medians are different, for which $W = 447$ and $P \doteq 0.0028$—significant evidence that prices differ. This is equivalent to the conclusion reached in (b).

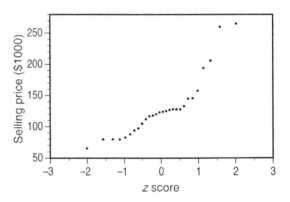

Minitab output

```
Mann-Whitney Confidence Interval and Test

BR3        N =  28    Median =        123450
BR4        N =   9    Median =        176900
W = 447.0
Test of ETA1 = ETA2  vs.  ETA1 ~= ETA2 is significant at 0.0028
The test is significant at 0.0028 (adjusted for ties)
```

	n	$\bar{x}$	s	Min	Q_1	M	Q_3	Max
3BR	28	$129,546	$49,336	$65,500	$95,750	$123,450	$138,950	$265,000
4BR	9	$194,944	$57,204	$121,900	$148,450	$176,900	$240,000	$294,000

15.32. (a) Means and standard deviations are in the table below; medians are in the Minitab output.

	$\bar{x}$	s
Fall	1081.25	231.46
Winter	209	136.57
Spring	1648.75	1071.24
Summer	2138.5	906.43

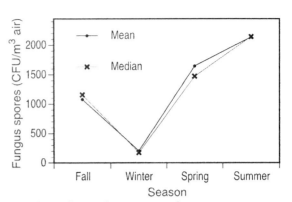

Graphical displays may vary; one approach is the plot on the right, which shows how means and medians change over the seasons. **(b)** Using the Kruskal-Wallis test, we find $H = 9.95$, df $= 3$, $P = 0.019$—significant evidence at $\alpha = 0.05$ that spore count varies over the seasons.

Minitab output

```
Kruskal-Wallis Test

LEVEL     NOBS     MEDIAN   AVE. RANK    Z VALUE
   Fall      4     1159.5        8.8       0.12
 Winter      4      177.5        2.5      -2.91
 Spring      4     1473.5       10.0       0.73
 Summer      4     2144.5       12.8       2.06
OVERALL     16                   8.5

H = 9.95  d.f. = 3  p = 0.019
```

15.33. See also the solutions to Exercises 1.59 and 12.27; the latter exercise requests the same analysis for ANOVA. Medians are given in the Minitab output, and in the plot on the right. The means and standard deviations (all in millimeters) are:

Variety	n	$\bar{x}$	s
bihai	16	47.5975	1.2129
red	23	39.7113	1.7988
yellow	15	36.1800	0.9753

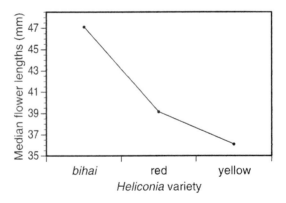

We reject H_0 and conclude that at least one species has different lengths ($H = 45.35$, df $= 2$, $P < 0.0005$).

Minitab output

```
Kruskal-Wallis Test

LEVEL     NOBS     MEDIAN   AVE. RANK    Z VALUE
    1       16      47.12       46.5       5.76
    2       23      39.16       26.7      -0.32
    3       15      36.11        8.5      -5.51
OVERALL     54                  27.5

H = 45.35  d.f. = 2  p = 0.000
H = 45.36  d.f. = 2  p = 0.000 (adjusted for ties)
```

15.34. (a) The mean and median suggest that iron content is least for aluminum pots, and greatest for iron pots. ANOVA requires normal data with equal standard deviations; the former is difficult to assess with such small samples, and for the latter, the largest-to-smallest ratio is 1.99—just within our guidelines for pooling. (b) The Kruskal-Wallis test gives $H = 8.00$, df $= 2$, $P = 0.019$. We conclude that vegetable iron content differs by pot type.

	n	M	$\bar{x}$	s
Aluminum	4	1.185	1.2325	0.2313
Clay	4	1.615	1.46	0.4601
Iron	4	2.79	2.79	0.2399

Minitab output

```
LEVEL    NOBS    MEDIAN  AVE. RANK   Z VALUE
 Alum      4     1.185      3.5      -2.04
 Clay      4     1.615      5.5      -0.68
 Iron      4     2.860     10.5       2.72
OVERALL   12                6.5

H = 8.00   d.f. = 2   p = 0.019
```

15.35. Use the Wilcoxon rank sum test with a two-sided alternative. For meat, $W = 15$ and $P = 0.4705$, and for legumes, $W = 10.5$ and $P = 0.0433$ (or 0.0421). There is no evidence of a difference in iron content for meat, but for legumes the evidence is significant at $\alpha = 0.05$.

Minitab output

```
— — — — — — — — — — — — — — — —  Meat  — — — — — — — — — — — — — — —
Alum      N =  4     Median =      2.050
Clay      N =  4     Median =      2.375
W = 15.0
Test of ETA1 = ETA2  vs.  ETA1 ~= ETA2 is significant at 0.4705
Cannot reject at alpha = 0.05
— — — — — — — — — — — — — — —  Legumes  — — — — — — — — — — — — — — —
Alum      N =  4     Median =      2.3700
Clay      N =  4     Median =      2.4550
W = 10.5
Test of ETA1 = ETA2  vs.  ETA1 ~= ETA2 is significant at 0.0433
The test is significant at 0.0421 (adjusted for ties)
```

15.36. Using a Kruskal-Wallis test, we find $H = 9.85$, df $= 2$, and $P = 0.007$. We conclude that there is a difference in iron content for foods cooked in iron pots.

Minitab output

```
LEVEL    NOBS    MEDIAN  AVE. RANK   Z VALUE
 Meat      4     4.695     10.5       2.72
  Leg      4     3.705      6.5       0.00
  Veg      4     2.860      2.5      -2.72
OVERALL   12                6.5

H = 9.85   d.f. = 2   p = 0.007
```

15.37. (a) The three pairwise comparisons are *bihai*-red, *bihai*-yellow, and red-yellow. **(b)** The test statistics and *P*-values are given in the Minitab output below; all *P*-values are reported as 0 to four decimal places. **(c)** All three comparisons are significant at the overall 0.05 level (and would even be significant at the overall 0.01 level).

Minitab output

```
– – – – – – – – – – – – – – –    bihai – red    – – – – – – – – – – – – – – –
bihai      N =  16     Median =      47.120
red        N =  23     Median =      39.160
W = 504.0
Test of ETA1 = ETA2  vs.  ETA1 ~= ETA2 is significant at 0.0000
The test is significant at 0.0000 (adjusted for ties)
– – – – – – – – – – – – – – –    bihai – yellow    – – – – – – – – – – – – – –
bihai      N =  16     Median =      47.120
yellow     N =  15     Median =      36.110
W = 376.0
Test of ETA1 = ETA2  vs.  ETA1 ~= ETA2 is significant at 0.0000
The test is significant at 0.0000 (adjusted for ties)
– – – – – – – – – – – – – – –    red – yellow    – – – – – – – – – – – – – – –
red        N =  23     Median =      39.160
yellow     N =  15     Median =      36.110
W = 614.0
Test of ETA1 = ETA2  vs.  ETA1 ~= ETA2 is significant at 0.0000
The test is significant at 0.0000 (adjusted for ties)
```

15.38. In order to be significant at the overall 0.05 level, an individual *P*-value must be less than $0.05/6 = 0.008\overline{3}$. None of the differences are significant at this level, in spite of the fact that winter differs from the other three seasons as much as possible (that is, all four of the winter CFUs are less than every other measurement); the *P*-values for those three comparisons are as small as possible for this test with these sample sizes.

Minitab output

```
– – – – – – – – – – – – – –    The four medians    – – – – – – – – – – – – – –
Fall       N =   4     Median =      1159.5
Winter     N =   4     Median =       177.5
Spring     N =   4     Median =      1473.5
Summer     N =   4     Median =      2144.5
– – – – – – – – – – – – – –    Fall – winter    – – – – – – – – – – – – – – – –
W = 26.0
Test of ETA1 = ETA2  vs.  ETA1 ~= ETA2 is significant at 0.0304
– – – – – – – – – – – – – –    Fall – spring    – – – – – – – – – – – – – – – –
W = 17.0
Test of ETA1 = ETA2  vs.  ETA1 ~= ETA2 is significant at 0.8852
– – – – – – – – – – – – – –    Fall – summer    – – – – – – – – – – – – – – – –
W = 12.0
Test of ETA1 = ETA2  vs.  ETA1 ~= ETA2 is significant at 0.1124
– – – – – – – – – – – – – –    Winter – spring    – – – – – – – – – – – – – – –
W = 10.0
Test of ETA1 = ETA2  vs.  ETA1 ~= ETA2 is significant at 0.0304
– – – – – – – – – – – – – –    Winter – summer    – – – – – – – – – – – – – – –
W = 10.0
Test of ETA1 = ETA2  vs.  ETA1 ~= ETA2 is significant at 0.0304
– – – – – – – – – – – – – –    Spring – summer    – – – – – – – – – – – – – – –
W = 15.0
Test of ETA1 = ETA2  vs.  ETA1 ~= ETA2 is significant at 0.4705
```

Chapter 16 Solutions

16.1. (a) H_0 should refer to β_1 (the population slope) rather than b_1 (the estimated slope).
(b) The logistic regression model has no error term. (c) The appropriate test would be a chi-square test with df $= 5$.

16.2. (a) $\hat{p}_1 = \frac{108}{142} \doteq 0.7606$ for exclusive-territory firms. (b) $\hat{p}_2 = \frac{15}{28} \doteq 0.5357$ for other firms.
(c) $\text{ODDS}_1 = \frac{\hat{p}_1}{1-\hat{p}_1} \doteq 3.1765$ and $\text{ODDS}_2 = \frac{\hat{p}_2}{1-\hat{p}_2} \doteq 1.1538$. (d) $\log(\text{ODDS}_1) \doteq 1.1558$ and
$\log(\text{ODDS}_2) \doteq 0.1431$. (Be sure to use the *natural* logarithm for this computation.)

16.3. (a) $\hat{p}_w = \frac{63}{296} \doteq 0.2128$ for women and $\hat{p}_m = \frac{27}{251} \doteq 0.1076$ for men.
(b) $\text{ODDS}_w = \frac{\hat{p}_w}{1-\hat{p}_w} \doteq 0.2704$ and $\text{ODDS}_m = \frac{\hat{p}_m}{1-\hat{p}_m} \doteq 0.1205$.
(c) $\log(\text{ODDS}_w) \doteq -1.3079$ and $\log(\text{ODDS}_m) \doteq -2.1158$.

16.4. (a) $b_0 = \log(\text{ODDS}_2) \doteq 0.1431$ and $b_1 = \log(\text{ODDS}_1) - \log(\text{ODDS}_2) \doteq 1.0127$.
(b) The fitted model is $\log(\text{ODDS}) = 0.1431 + 1.0127x$. (c) The odds ratio is
$\text{ODDS}_1/\text{ODDS}_2 = e^{b_1} \doteq 2.7529$.

Minitab output

Predictor	Coef	SE Coef	Z	P	Ratio	Lower	Upper
Constant	0.143101	0.378932	0.38	0.706			
Exclusive							
Yes	1.01267	0.426920	2.37	0.018	2.75	1.19	6.36

16.5. (a) $b_0 = \log(\text{ODDS}_m) \doteq -2.1158$ and $b_1 = \log(\text{ODDS}_w) - \log(\text{ODDS}_m) \doteq 0.8079$.
(b) The fitted model is $\log(\text{ODDS}) = -2.1158 + 0.8079x$. (c) The odds ratio is
$\text{ODDS}_w/\text{ODDS}_m = e^{b_1} \doteq 2.2432$.

Minitab output

Predictor	Coef	SE Coef	Z	P	Odds Ratio	95% CI Lower	Upper
Constant	-2.11581	0.203719	-10.39	0.000			
gender							
w	0.807905	0.248327	3.25	0.001	2.24	1.38	3.65

16.6. Recall that, by properties of exponents, $\dfrac{e^a}{e^b} = e^{a-b}$. Therefore

$$\frac{\text{ODDS}_{x+1}}{\text{ODDS}_x} = \frac{e^{-13.71} \times e^{2.25(x+1)}}{e^{-13.71} \times e^{2.25x}} = e^{2.25(x+1)-2.25x} = e^{2.25}.$$

16.7. With $b_1 \doteq 3.1088$ and $\text{SE}_{b_1} \doteq 0.3879$, the 99% confidence interval is
$b_1 \pm 2.576\text{SE}_{b_1} \doteq b_1 \pm 0.9992$, or 2.1096 to 4.1080.

16.8. To find the confidence interval for the odds ratio, we first make a confidence interval for
the slope b_1 and then transform (exponentiate) it: $b_1 \pm z^*\text{SE}_{b_1} = 3.1088 \pm (1.96)(0.3879) \doteq$
2.3485 to 3.8691, so the odds ratio interval is $e^{2.3485} \doteq 10.470$ to $e^{3.8691} \doteq 47.898$. Up to
rounding error, this agrees with the software output.

16.9. (a) $z = \frac{3.1088}{0.3879} \doteq 8.01$. **(b)** $z^2 \doteq 64.23$, which agrees with the value of X^2 given by SPSS and SAS. **(c)** The sketches are below. For both the normal and chi-square distribution, the test statistics are quite extreme, consistent with the reported P-value.

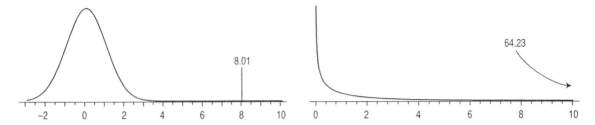

16.10. (a) For each explanatory variable, we test H_0: $\beta_i = 0$ vs. H_a: $\beta_i \neq 0$. **(b)** Under the null hypotheses, the z statistic has a standard normal distribution. Therefore, we reject H_0 at the 5% level if $|z| > 1.96$. We do not reject H_0 for "Men's magazines," but have very strong evidence that all other coefficients (as well as the constant) are not zero. **(c)** The probability that the model's clothing is sexual is higher for magazines targeted at young adults (as the problem states), when the model is female, and for magazines aimed at men, or at men and women. **(d)** The fitted model is $\log(\mathrm{ODDS}) = -2.32 + 0.50x_1 + 1.31x_2 - 0.05x_3 + 0.45x_4$.

16.11. (a) For men's magazines, the odds ratio confidence interval includes 1. This indicates that this explanatory variable has no effect on the probability that a model's clothing is not sexual, which is consistent with our failure to reject H_0 for men's magazines in the previous exercise. For all other explanatory variables, the odds ratio does not include 1, equivalent to the significant evidence against H_0 for those variables. **(b)** The odds that the model's clothing is not sexual are 1.27 to 2.16 times higher for magazines targeted at mature adults, 2.74 to 5.01 times higher when the model is male, and 1.11 to 2.23 times higher for magazines aimed at women. (These statements can also be made in terms of the odds that the model's clothing *is* sexual; for example, those odds are 1.27 to 2.16 times higher for magazines targeted at *young* adults, and so forth.) **(c)** The summary might note that it is easier to interpret the odds ratio rather than the regression coefficients, because of the difficulty of thinking in terms of a log-odds scale.

16.12. (a) $\hat{p}_1 = \frac{487}{811} \doteq 0.6005$. **(b)** $\mathrm{ODDS}_1 = \frac{\hat{p}_1}{1 - \hat{p}_1} \doteq 1.5031$. **(c)** $\hat{p}_2 = \frac{324}{811} \doteq 0.3995$.
(d) $\mathrm{ODDS}_2 = \frac{\hat{p}_2}{1 - \hat{p}_2} \doteq 0.6653$. **(e)** The probabilities in (a) and (c) are *complements* (their sum is 1), and the odds in (b) and (d) are *reciprocals* (their product is 1).

16.13. (a) $\hat{p}_{\mathrm{hi}} = \frac{73}{91} \doteq 0.8022$, and $\mathrm{ODDS}_{\mathrm{hi}} = \frac{\hat{p}_{\mathrm{hi}}}{1 - \hat{p}_{\mathrm{hi}}} = 4.0\overline{5}$. **(b)** $\hat{p}_{\mathrm{non}} = \frac{75}{109} \doteq 0.6881$ and
$\mathrm{ODDS}_{\mathrm{non}} = \frac{\hat{p}_{\mathrm{non}}}{1 - \hat{p}_{\mathrm{non}}} \doteq 2.2059$. **(c)** The odds ratio is $\mathrm{ODDS}_{\mathrm{hi}}/\mathrm{ODDS}_{\mathrm{non}} \doteq 1.8385$. The odds of a high-tech company offering stock options are about 1.84 times those for a non-high-tech firm.

16.14. (a) $\log(\mathrm{ODDS}_{\mathrm{hi}}) \doteq 1.4001$ and $\log(\mathrm{ODDS}_{\mathrm{non}}) \doteq 0.7911$. **(b)** In the model, $\log(\mathrm{ODDS}_{\mathrm{non}}) = \beta_0$ and $\log(\mathrm{ODDS}_{\mathrm{hi}}) = \beta_0 + \beta_1$, so we find the estimates of β_0 and β_1 from the observed log-odds: $b_0 = \log(\mathrm{ODDS}_{\mathrm{non}}) \doteq 0.7911$ and $b_1 = \log(\mathrm{ODDS}_{\mathrm{hi}}) - \log(\mathrm{ODDS}_{\mathrm{non}}) \doteq 0.6090$. **(c)** $e^{b_1} \doteq e^{0.6090} \doteq 1.8385$, as we found in 16.13(c).

16.15. (a) With $b_1 \doteq 0.6090$ and $SE_{b_1} \doteq 0.3347$, the 95% confidence interval is $b_1 \pm 1.96 SE_{b_1} \doteq b_1 \pm 0.6560$, or -0.0470 to 1.2650. (b) Exponentiating the confidence limits gives the interval 0.9540 to 3.5430. (c) Because the confidence interval for β_1 contains 0, or equivalently because 1 is in the interval for the odds ratio, we could not reject H_0: $\beta_1 = 0$ at the 5% level. There does not appear to be a significant difference between the odds of stock options for high-tech and other firms.

   Note: *Software reports $z = 1.820$ and a P-value of 0.0688, which are nearly identical to the results for a two-proportion z test with the same counts ($z = -1.832$ and $P = 0.0669$)—see the solutions to Exercises 8.43 and 8.44. For large samples, these two tests should give similar results.*

Minitab output

Predictor	Coef	SE Coef	Z	P	Odds Ratio	95% CI Lower	Upper
Constant	0.791128	0.206749	3.83	0.000			
HT							
Yes	0.608960	0.334663	1.82	0.069	1.84	0.95	3.54

16.16. All proportions, odds, odds ratios, and parameter estimates (b_0 and b_1) are unchanged. Because the standard error is smaller, the 95% confidence interval is narrower: $b_1 \pm 1.96 SE_{b_1} \doteq b_1 \pm 0.4637$, or 0.1452 to 1.0727. The odds-ratio interval is therefore 1.1563 to 2.9233. Because 0 is not in the confidence interval for β_1 and 1 is not in the odds-ratio interval, we have significant evidence of a difference in the odds between the two types of companies.

   Note: *For testing H_0: $\beta_1 = 0$, software reports $z = 2.573$ and $P = 0.0101$. For comparison, the test of $p_1 = p_2$ yields $z = 2.591$ and $P = 0.0096$.*

Minitab output

Predictor	Coef	SE Coef	Z	P	Odds Ratio	95% CI Lower	Upper
Constant	0.791128	0.146194	5.41	0.000			
HT							
Yes	0.608960	0.236642	2.57	0.010	1.84	1.16	2.92

16.17. (a) For the high blood pressure group, $\hat{p}_{hi} = \frac{55}{3338} \doteq 0.01648$, giving $ODDS_{hi} = \frac{\hat{p}_{hi}}{1-\hat{p}_{hi}} \doteq 0.01675$, or about 1 to 60. (If students give odds in the form "a to b," their choices of a and b might be different.) (b) For the low blood pressure group, $\hat{p}_{lo} = \frac{21}{2676} \doteq 0.00785$, giving $ODDS_{lo} = \frac{\hat{p}_{lo}}{1-\hat{p}_{lo}} \doteq 0.00791$, or about 1 to 126 (or 125). (c) The odds ratio is $ODDS_{hi}/ODDS_{lo} \doteq 2.1181$. Odds of death from cardiovascular disease are about 2.1 times greater in the high blood pressure group.

16.18. (a) For female references, $\hat{p}_w = \frac{48}{60} = 0.8$, giving $ODDS_w = \frac{\hat{p}_w}{1-\hat{p}_w} = 4$ ("4 to 1").
   (b) For male references, $\hat{p}_m = \frac{52}{132} = 0.\overline{39}$, giving $ODDS_m = \frac{\hat{p}_m}{1-\hat{p}_m} = 0.65$ ("13 to 20").
   (c) The odds ratio is $ODDS_w/ODDS_m \doteq 6.1538$. (The odds of a juvenile reference are more than six times greater for females.)

16.19. (a) The interval is $b_1 \pm 1.96 SE_{b_1}$, or 0.2452 to 1.2558. (b) $X^2 = \left(\frac{0.7505}{0.2578}\right)^2 \doteq 8.47$. This gives a P-value between 0.0025 and 0.005. (c) We have strong evidence that there is a real (significant) difference in risk between the two groups.

16.20. (a) The interval is $b_1 \pm 1.96\mathrm{SE}_{b_1}$, or 1.0946 to 2.5396. (b) $X^2 = \left(\frac{1.8171}{0.3686}\right)^2 \doteq 24.3$. This gives $P < 0.0005$. (c) We have strong evidence that there is a real (significant) difference in juvenile references between male and female references.

16.21. (a) The estimated odds ratio is $e^{b_1} \doteq 2.1181$ (as we found in Exercise 16.17). Exponentiating the interval for β_1 in Exercise 16.19(a) gives odds-ratio intervals from about 1.28 to 3.51. (b) We are 95% confident that the odds of death from cardiovascular disease are about 1.3 to 3.5 times greater in the high blood pressure group.

Minitab output

Predictor	Coef	SE Coef	Z	P	Odds Ratio	95% CI Lower	Upper
Constant	-4.83968	0.219078	-22.09	0.000			
BP							
hi	0.750498	0.257840	2.91	0.004	2.12	1.28	3.51

16.22. (a) The estimated odds ratio is $e^{b_1} \doteq 6.1538$ (as we found in Exercise 16.18). Exponentiating the interval for β_1 in Exercise 16.20(a) gives odds-ratio intervals from about 2.99 to 12.67. (b) We are 95% confident that the odds of a juvenile reference are about 3 to 13 times greater among females.

Minitab output

Predictor	Coef	SE Coef	Z	P	Odds Ratio	95% CI Lower	Upper
Constant	-0.430783	0.178131	-2.42	0.016			
gender							
Female	1.81708	0.368641	4.93	0.000	6.15	2.99	12.67

16.23. (a) The model is $\log\left(\frac{p_i}{1-p_i}\right) = \beta_0 + \beta_1 x_i$, where $x_i = 1$ if the ith person is over 40, and 0 if he/she is under 40. (b) p_i is the probability that the ith person is terminated; this model assumes that the probability of termination depends on age (over/under 40). In this case, that seems to have been the case, but we might expect that other factors were taken into consideration. (c) The estimated odds ratio is $e^{b_1} \doteq 3.859$. (Of course, we can also get this from $\frac{41/765}{7/504}$.) We can also find, for example, a 95% confidence interval for b_1: $b_1 \pm 1.96\mathrm{SE}_{b_1} = 0.5409$ to 2.1599. Exponentiating this translates to a 95% confidence interval for the odds: 1.7176 to 8.6701. The odds of being terminated are 1.7 to 8.7 times greater for those over 40. (d) Use a multiple logistic regression model, for example, $\log\left(\frac{p_i}{1-p_i}\right) = \beta_0 + \beta_1 x_{1,i} + \beta_2 x_{2,i}$.

16.24. Before the change, the odds of a repair order being returned within five days were $\mathrm{ODDS}_{\text{before}} = \frac{32}{168} \doteq 0.1905$. After the change, the odds rose to $\mathrm{ODDS}_{\text{after}} = \frac{180}{2} = 9$. Using a logistic regression model $\log\left(\frac{p}{1-p}\right) = \beta_0 + \beta_1 x$, with $x = 0$ for before and $x = 1$ for after, we estimate $b_0 = \log(\mathrm{ODDS}_{\text{before}}) \doteq -1.6582$, and $b_1 = \log(\mathrm{ODDS}_{\text{after}}) - \log(\mathrm{ODDS}_{\text{before}}) \doteq 3.8555$. The odds ratio is $e^{b_1} \doteq 47.25$; the change increased the odds by a factor of about 47. (Of course, this ratio can be found without fitting the logistic regression model.)

16.25. There were a total of $1132 + 852 = 1984$ people in the sample, of which $643 + 349 = 992$ had completed college and the rest (also 992) had not. Among college graduates, 643 use the Internet for travel arrangements, so $\hat{p}_c = \frac{643}{992} \doteq 0.6482$ and $ODDS_c = \frac{643}{349} \doteq 1.8424$. Among those who have not completed college, $1132 - 643 = 489$ use the Internet, so $\hat{p}_n = \frac{489}{992} \doteq 0.4929$ and $ODDS_n = \frac{489}{503} \doteq 0.9722$. With the model $\log\left(\frac{p}{1-p}\right) = \beta_0 + \beta_1 x$, where $x = 1$ for college graduates, we estimate $b_0 = \log(ODDS_n) \doteq -0.0282$, and $b_1 = \log(ODDS_c) - \log(ODDS_n) \doteq 0.6393$. (We can also find b_1 as the logarithm of the odds ratio $ODDS_c/ODDS_n \doteq 1.8952$.) The odds of a college graduate using the Internet for travel arrangements are about 1.90 times higher than those for a noncollege graduate.

Note: *Exercise 8.59 uses the same data but asks about proportions of college graduates among each group (users and nonusers), rather than proportions of users among graduates and nongraduates.*

16.26. A total of $493 + 378 + 477 + 200 = 1548$ people responded to the income question, of which $493 + 477 = 970$ had incomes below \$50,000 and the rest (578) had incomes over \$50,000. In the high-income group, 378 use the Internet for travel arrangements, so $\hat{p}_{hi} = \frac{378}{578} \doteq 0.6540$ and $ODDS_{hi} = \frac{378}{200} = 1.89$. In the low-income group, 493 use the Internet, so $\hat{p}_{lo} = \frac{493}{970} \doteq 0.5082$ and $ODDS_{lo} = \frac{493}{477} \doteq 1.0335$. With the model $\log\left(\frac{p}{1-p}\right) = \beta_0 + \beta_1 x$, where $x = 1$ for income over \$50,000, we estimate $b_0 = \log(ODDS_{lo}) \doteq 0.0330$, and $b_1 = \log(ODDS_{hi}) - \log(ODDS_{lo}) \doteq 0.6036$. (We can also find b_1 as the logarithm of the odds ratio $ODDS_{hi}/ODDS_{lo} \doteq 1.8287$.) For someone with income over \$50,000, the odds of using the Internet for travel arrangements are about 1.83 times higher than those for someone in the lower-income group.

Note: *Exercise 8.60 uses the same data, but asks about income proportions in each group (users and nonusers), rather than proportions of users in each income group.*

16.27. For women, the proportion, odds, and log-odds for testing positive are $\hat{p}_f = \frac{27}{191} \doteq 0.1414$, $ODDS_f = \frac{\hat{p}_f}{1-\hat{p}_f} \doteq 0.1646$, and $\log(ODDS_f) \doteq -1.8040$. For men, these numbers are $\hat{p}_m = \frac{515}{1520} \doteq 0.3388$, $ODDS_m = \frac{\hat{p}_m}{1-\hat{p}_m} \doteq 0.5124$, and $\log(ODDS_m) \doteq -0.6686$. The fitted logistic regression model depends on whether we use $x = 1$ to indicate male or female (the exercise does not specify which to use). If $x = 1$ for males, we have

$\log(ODDS) = -1.8040 + 1.1355x$ and odds ratio 3.1126.

If $x = 1$ for females, we have

$\log(ODDS) = -0.6686 - 1.1355x$ and odds ratio 0.3213.

The odds of testing positive for alcohol are about three times higher for men than for women. (Or, those odds are about one-third as high for women as for men.)

Minitab output

```
- - - - - - - - - - - - - - - -  Male = 1   - - - - - - - - - - - - - - - - -
                                                Odds      95% CI
Predictor      Coef     SE Coef        Z      P  Ratio  Lower  Upper
Constant    -1.80403   0.207682    -8.69  0.000
Male         1.13545   0.214636     5.29  0.000   3.11   2.04   4.74
- - - - - - - - - - - - - - - -  Female = 1   - - - - - - - - - - - - - - - -
                                                Odds      95% CI
Predictor      Coef     SE Coef        Z      P  Ratio  Lower  Upper
Constant    -0.668576  0.0541920  -12.34  0.000
Female      -1.13545   0.214636    -5.29  0.000   0.32   0.21   0.49
```

16.28. For the model $\log\left(\frac{p}{1-p}\right) = \beta_0 + \beta_1 x$, we obtain the fitted model $\log(\text{ODDS}) = b_0 + b_1 x = -7.2789 + 0.9399x$. (Here p is the probability that the cheese is acceptable, and x is the value of H2S.) We have $b_1 = 0.9399$ and $\text{SE}_{b_1} = 0.3443$, so we estimate that the odds ratio increases by a factor of $e^{b_1} \doteq 2.56$ for every unit increase in H2S. For testing $\beta_1 = 0$, we find $X^2 = 7.45$ ($P = 0.0063$), so we conclude that $\beta_1 \neq 0$. We are 95% confident that β_1 is in the interval $b_1 \pm 1.96\text{SE}_{b_1} = 0.2651$ to 1.6147; exponentiating this tells us that the odds ratio increases by a factor between 1.3035 and 5.0265 (with 95% confidence) for each unit increase in H2S.

Minitab output

Predictor	Coef	SE Coef	Z	P	Odds Ratio	95% CI Lower	Upper
Constant	-7.27894	2.52165	-2.89	0.004			
h2s	0.939916	0.344331	2.73	0.006	2.56	1.30	5.03

GLMStat output

	estimate	se(est)	z ratio	Prob>|z|
1 Constant	-7.279	2.519	-2.889	0.0039
2 h2s	0.9399	0.3443	2.730	0.0063

	odds ratio	lower 95% ci	upper 95% ci
1 Constant	6.899e-4	4.945e-6	9.625e-2
2 h2s	2.560	1.304	5.024

16.29. For the model $\log\left(\frac{p}{1-p}\right) = \beta_0 + \beta_1 x$, we obtain the fitted model $\log(\text{ODDS}) = b_0 + b_1 x = -10.7799 + 6.3319x$. (Here p is the probability that the cheese is acceptable, and x is the value of Lactic.) We have $b_1 = 6.3319$ and $\text{SE}_{b_1} = 2.4532$, so we estimate that the odds ratio increases by a factor of $e^{b_1} \doteq 562.22$ for every unit increase in Lactic. For testing $\beta_1 = 0$, we find $X^2 = 6.66$ ($P = 0.0098$), so we conclude that $\beta_1 \neq 0$. We are 95% confident that β_1 is in the interval $b_1 \pm 1.96\text{SE}_{b_1} = 1.5236$ to 11.1402; exponentiating this tells us that the odds ratio increases by a factor between 4.5889 and about $68,884$ (with 95% confidence) for each unit increase in Lactic.

Minitab output

Predictor	Coef	SE Coef	Z	P	Odds Ratio	95% CI Lower	Upper
Constant	-10.7799	3.97542	-2.71	0.007			
lactic	6.33193	2.45317	2.58	0.010	562.24	4.59	68880.95

GLMStat output

	estimate	se(est)	z ratio	Prob>|z|
1 Constant	-10.78	3.973	-2.713	0.0067
2 lactic	6.332	2.452	2.583	0.0098

	odds ratio	lower 95% ci	upper 95% ci
1 Constant	2.081e-5	8.644e-9	5.012e-2
2 lactic	562.2	4.603	6.867e+4

16.30. The seven models are summarized below. The P-value in the right column is for the null hypothesis that all slopes equal 0 (that is, the significance of the regression); all are significant.

For the models with two predictors, all have only one coefficient significantly different from 0 (in the last case, arguably neither coefficient is nonzero). The standard errors are given in parentheses below each coefficient: the six respective *P*-values are 0.4276, 0.0238; 0.3094, 0.0355; 0.0567, 0.1449.

In summary, we might conclude that H2S has the greatest effect: It had the smallest *P*-value among the three single-predictor models, and in the three multiple logistic regression models in which it was used, it had the minimum *P*-value. (It was the closest to being significant in the last two models in the table below.)

Note: *In Exercises 11.43 through 11.51, in considering multiple regression models to predict taste from Acetic, H2S, and Lactic, the H2S/Lactic model was chosen as the best. In every model that included H2S, its t statistic was the largest.*

Fitted Model	*P*
$\log(\text{ODDS}) = -13.71 + 2.249$ Acetic	0.0285
$\log(\text{ODDS}) = -7.279 \qquad\qquad\qquad + 0.9399$ H2S	0.0063
$\log(\text{ODDS}) = -10.78 \qquad\qquad\qquad\qquad\qquad + 6.332$ Lactic	0.0098
$\log(\text{ODDS}) = -12.85 + 1.096$ Acetic $+ 0.8303$ H2S (1.382) (0.3673)	0.0008
$\log(\text{ODDS}) = -16.56 + 1.309$ Acetic $\qquad\qquad + 5.257$ Lactic (1.288) (2.500)	0.0016
$\log(\text{ODDS}) = -11.72 \qquad\qquad + 0.7346$ H2S $+ 3.777$ Lactic (0.3866) (2.596)	0.0003
$\log(\text{ODDS}) = -14.26 + 0.584$ Acetic $+ 0.6849$ H2S $+ 3.468$ Lactic	0.0010

16.31. Portions of SAS and GLMStat output are given below. **(a)** The X^2 statistic for testing this hypothesis is 33.65 (df = 3), which has $P = 0.0001$. We conclude that at least one coefficient is not 0. **(b)** The fitted model is log(ODDS) = $-6.053 + 0.3710$ HSM $+ 0.2489$ HSS $+ 0.03605$ HSE. The standard errors of the three coefficients are 0.1302, 0.1275, and 0.1253, giving respective 95% confidence intervals 0.1158 to 0.6262, -0.0010 to 0.4988, and -0.2095 to 0.2816. **(c)** Only the coefficient of HSM is significantly different from 0, though HSS may also be useful.

Note: *In the multiple regression case study of Chapter 11, HSM was also the only significant explanatory variable among high school grades, and HSS was not even close to significant. See Figure 11.4 on page 694 of the text.*

SAS output

```
                            Intercept
                Intercept      and
Criterion        Only       Covariates   Chi-Square for Covariates
-2 LOG L        295.340      261.691        33.648 with 3 DF (p=0.0001)
```

Analysis of Maximum Likelihood Estimates

Variable	DF	Parameter Estimate	Standard Error	Wald Chi-Square	Pr > Chi-Square	Standardized Estimate
INTERCPT	1	-6.0528	1.1562	27.4050	0.0001	.
HSM	1	0.3710	0.1302	8.1155	0.0044	0.335169
HSS	1	0.2489	0.1275	3.8100	0.0509	0.233265
HSE	1	0.0361	0.1253	0.0828	0.7736	0.029971

GLMStat output

		estimate	se(est)	z ratio	Prob>|z|
1	Constant	-6.053	1.156	-5.236	<0.0001
2	HSM	0.3710	0.1302	2.849	0.0044
3	HSS	0.2489	0.1275	1.952	0.0509
4	HSE	3.605e-2	0.1253	0.2877	0.7736

16.32. Portions of SAS and GLMStat output are given below. **(a)** The X^2 statistic for testing this hypothesis is 14.2 (df = 2), which has $P = 0.0008$. We conclude that at least one coefficient is not 0. **(b)** The model is log(ODDS) $= -4.543 + 0.003690$ SATM $+ 0.003527$ SATV. The standard errors of the two coefficients are 0.001913 and 0.001751, giving respective 95% confidence intervals -0.000059 to 0.007439, and 0.000095 to 0.006959. (The first coefficient has a P-value of 0.0537, and the second has $P = 0.0440$.) **(c)** We (barely) cannot reject $\beta_{\text{SATM}} = 0$—though because 0 is just in the confidence interval, we are reluctant to discard SATM. Meanwhile, we conclude that $\beta_{\text{SATV}} \neq 0$.

Note: *By contrast, with multiple regression of GPA on SAT scores, we found SATM useful but not SATV. See Figure 11.7 on page 698 of the text.*

SAS output

Criterion	Intercept Only	Intercept and Covariates	Chi-Square for Covariates
-2 LOG L	295.340	281.119	14.220 with 2 DF (p=0.0008)

Analysis of Maximum Likelihood Estimates

Variable	DF	Parameter Estimate	Standard Error	Wald Chi-Square	Pr > Chi-Square	Standardized Estimate
INTERCPT	1	-4.5429	1.1618	15.2909	0.0001	.
SATM	1	0.00369	0.00191	3.7183	0.0538	0.175778
SATV	1	0.00353	0.00175	4.0535	0.0441	0.180087

GLMStat output

		estimate	se(est)	z ratio	Prob>|z|
1	Constant	-4.543	1.161	-3.915	<0.0001
2	SATM	3.690e-3	1.913e-3	1.929	0.0537
3	SATV	3.527e-3	1.751e-3	2.014	0.0440

16.33. The coefficients and standard errors for the fitted model are below. Note that the tests requested in (a) and (b) are not available with all software packages. **(a)** The X^2 statistic for testing this hypothesis is given by SAS (below) as 19.2256 (df = 3); because $P = 0.0002$, we reject H_0 and conclude that high school grades add a significant amount to the model with SAT scores. **(b)** The X^2 statistic for testing this hypothesis is 3.4635 (df = 2); because $P = 0.1770$, we cannot reject H_0; SAT scores do not add significantly to the model with high school grades. **(c)** For modeling the odds of HIGPA, high school grades (specifically HSM, and to a lesser extent HSS) are useful, while SAT scores are not.

SAS output

Analysis of Maximum Likelihood Estimates

Variable	DF	Parameter Estimate	Standard Error	Wald Chi-Square	Pr > Chi-Square	Standardized Estimate
INTERCPT	1	-7.3732	1.4768	24.9257	0.0001	.
HSM	1	0.3427	0.1419	5.8344	0.0157	0.309668
HSS	1	0.2249	0.1286	3.0548	0.0805	0.210704
HSE	1	0.0190	0.1289	0.0217	0.8829	0.015784
SATM	1	0.000717	0.00220	0.1059	0.7448	0.034134
SATV	1	0.00289	0.00191	2.2796	0.1311	0.147566

Linear Hypotheses Testing

Label	Wald Chi-Square	DF	Pr > Chi-Square
HS	19.2256	3	0.0002
SAT	3.4635	2	0.1770

GLMStat output

	estimate	se(est)	z ratio	Prob>|z|
1 Constant	-7.373	1.477	-4.994	<0.0001
2 SATM	7.166e-4	2.201e-3	0.3255	0.7448
3 SATV	2.890e-3	1.914e-3	1.510	0.1311
4 HSM	0.3427	0.1419	2.416	0.0157
5 HSS	0.2249	0.1286	1.748	0.0805
6 HSE	1.899e-2	0.1289	0.1473	0.8829

16.34. (a) The fitted model is $\log(\text{ODDS}) = -0.6124 + 0.0609\,\text{Gender}$; the coefficient of gender is not significantly different from 0 ($z = 0.21$, $P = 0.8331$). **(b)** Now $\log(\text{ODDS}) = -5.214 + 0.3028\,\text{Gender} + 0.004191\,\text{SATM} + 0.003447\,\text{SATV}$. In this model, gender is still not significant ($P = 0.3296$). **(c)** Gender is not useful for modeling the odds of HIGPA.

GLMStat output

			Gender only		
	estimate	se(est)	z ratio	Prob>|z|	
1 Constant	-0.6124	0.4156	-1.474	0.1406	
2 Gender	6.087e-2	0.2889	0.2107	0.8331	
		Gender and SAT scores			
	estimate	se(est)	z ratio	Prob>|z|	
1 Constant	-5.214	1.362	-3.828	0.0001	
2 Gender	0.3028	0.3105	0.9750	0.3296	
3 SATM	4.191e-3	1.987e-3	2.109	0.0349	
4 SATV	3.447e-3	1.760e-3	1.958	0.0502	

16.35. The models reported below are for the odds of *death*, as requested in the instructions. If a student models odds of survival, or codes the indicator variables for hospital and condition differently, his or her answers will be slightly different from these (but the conclusions should be the same). **(a)** The fitted model is $\log(\text{ODDS}) = -3.892 + 0.4157\,\text{Hospital}$, using 1 for Hospital A and 0 for Hospital B. With $b_1 \doteq -0.4157$ and $\text{SE}_{b_1} \doteq 0.2831$, we find that $z = -1.47$ or $X^2 = 2.16$ ($P = 0.1420$), so we do not have evidence to suggest that β_1 is not 0. A 95% confidence interval for β_1 is -0.1392 to 0.9706 (this interval includes 0). We estimate the odds ratio to be $e^{b_1} \doteq 1.515$, with confidence interval 0.87 to 2.64 (this includes 1, since β_1 might be 0). **(b)** The fitted model is $\log(\text{ODDS}) = -3.109 - 0.1320 \text{ Hospital} - 1.266 \text{ Condition}$; as before, use 1 for Hospital A and 0 for Hospital B, and 1 for good condition, and 0 for poor. Now we estimate the odds ratio to be $e^{b_1} \doteq 0.8764$, with confidence interval 0.48 to 1.60. **(c)** In neither case is the effect of Hospital significant. However, we can see the effect of Simpson's paradox in the coefficient of Hospital, or equivalently in the odds ratio. In the model with Hospital alone, this coefficient was positive and the odds ratio was greater than 1, meaning that Hospital A patients have higher odds of death. When condition is added to the model, this coefficient is negative and the odds ratio is less than 1, meaning that Hospital A patients have lower odds of death.

GLMStat output

```
– – – – – – – – – – – – – –   Hospital only   – – – – – – – – – – – – – – –
              estimate    se(est)    z ratio    Prob>|z|
1 Constant    -3.892      0.2525     -15.41      <0.0001
2 Hosp         0.4157     0.2831     -1.469      0.1420

              odds ratio  lower 95% ci  upper 95% ci
1 Constant    2.041e-2    1.244e-2      3.348e-2
2 Hosp        1.515       0.8701        2.639
– – – – – – – – – – – – –   Hospital and condition   – – – – – – – – – – – – –
              estimate    se(est)    z ratio    Prob>|z|
1 Constant    -3.109      0.2959     -10.51      <0.0001
2 Hosp        -0.1320     0.3078     -0.4288     0.6681
3 Cond        -1.266      0.3218     -3.935      <0.0001

              odds ratio  lower 95% ci  upper 95% ci
1 Constant    4.463e-2    2.499e-2      7.971e-2
2 Hosp        0.8764      0.4794        1.602
3 Cond        0.2820      0.1501        0.5298
```

Chapter 17 Solutions

17.4. These DRGs account for a total of 80.5% of all losses. Certainly the first two (209 and 116) should be among those that are studied first; some students may also include 107, 462, and so on.

For 17.4. *For 17.5.*

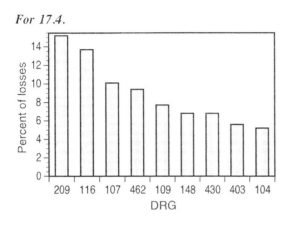
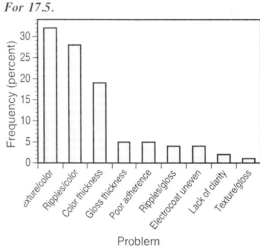

17.5. The most common problems are related to the application of the color coat; that should be the focus of our initial efforts.

17.6. Possible examples of special causes might include: Wind speed and direction, traffic, temperature, Jeannine's health, or mechanical problems with the bicycle (a flat tire or a broken brake cable).

17.8. Common causes of variation might include time spent showering, getting dressed, or preparing and eating breakfast. Examples of special causes might include forgetting to set the alarm, encountering (or being in) a traffic accident, waiting for a train, or getting an unexpected phone call before leaving.

17.9. Possible causes could include: alarm not set, had to wait for a train (or traffic), flat tire, spent too much time eating breakfast, and so forth.

17.10. The center line is at $\mu = 75°$ F; the control limits should be at $\mu \pm 3\sigma/\sqrt{4}$, which means 74.25° F and 75.75° F.

17.11. (a) Center: 11.5; control limits: $\mu \pm 3\sigma/\sqrt{4} = 11.5 \pm 0.3 = 11.2$ and 11.8. **(b)** Graphs at right and below. Points outside control limits are marked with an "X." **(c)** Set B is from the in-control process. The process mean shifted suddenly for Set A; it appears to have changed on about the 11th or 12th sample. The mean drifted gradually for the process in Set C.

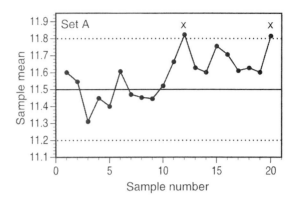

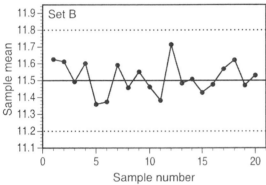

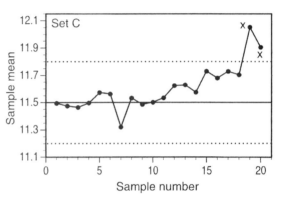

17.12. For $n = 4$, $c_4 = 0.9213$, so the center line is $(0.9213)(0.5) = 0.46065°$ F. B_5 is not given, so the lower control limit is $0°$ F, and $B_6 = 2.088$, so the upper control limit is $1.044°$ F.

17.13. (a) For the $\bar{x}$ chart, the center line is 11.5 and the control limits are 11.2 and 11.8 (as in Exercise 17.11). For $n = 4$, $c_4 = 0.9213$ and $B_6 = 2.088$, so the center line for the s chart is $(0.9213)(0.2) = 0.18426$, and the control limits are 0 and 0.4176. **(b)** The s chart is certainly out of control at sample 11; the increase might have happened slightly before that point. The s chart is consistently above the center line (and often above the UCL) after that; the $\bar{x}$ chart is noticeably out of control shortly after that sample. **(c)** A change in the mean does not affect the s chart; the effect on the $\bar{x}$ chart is masked by the change in σ: Because of the increased variability, the sample means are sometimes below the center line even after the process mean shifts.

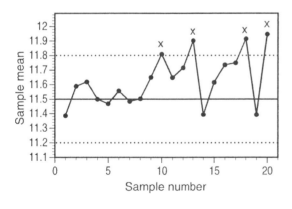

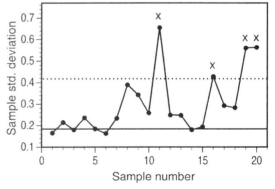

17.14. (a) Common causes might include processing time, normal workload fluctuation, or postal delivery time. **(b)** s-type special causes might include a new employee working in the personnel department. **(c)** Special causes affecting $\bar{x}$ might include a sudden large influx of applications, or perhaps introducing a new filing system for applications.

17.15. For the s chart with $n = 5$, we have $c_4 = 0.94$, $B_5 = 0$, and $B_6 = 1.964$, so the center line is 0.001128 and the control limits are 0 and 0.0023568. For the $\bar{x}$ chart, the center line is $\mu = 0.8750$ inch, and the control limits are $\mu \pm 3\sigma/\sqrt{5} \doteq 0.8750 \pm 0.0016 = 0.8734$ and 0.8766 inches.

17.16. (a) For $n = 5$, we have $c_4 = 0.94$, $B_5 = 0$, and $B_6 = 1.964$, so the center line is 0.11938 and the control limits are 0 and 0.249428. **(b)** The center line is $\mu = 4.22$, and the control limits are $\mu \pm 3\sigma/\sqrt{5} \doteq 4.00496$ to 4.3904.

17.17. The first two means and standard deviations are $\bar{x}_1 = 48$, $s_1 = 8.9$, $\bar{x}_2 = 46$, and $s_2 = 13.0$. For the $\bar{x}$ chart, the center line is 43 and the control limits are 25.91 and 60.09. For $n = 5$, $c_4 = 0.9400$ and $B_6 = 1.964$, so the center line for the s chart is $(0.9400)(12.74) = 11.9756$, and the control limits are 0 and 25.02. The control charts (below) show that sample 5 was above the UCL on the s chart, but it appears to have been special cause variation, as there is no indication that the samples that followed it were out of control.

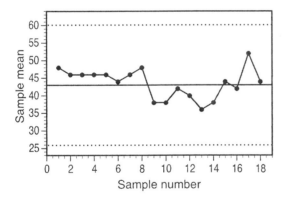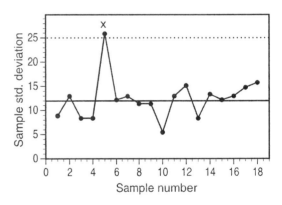

17.18. The new type of yarn would appear on the $\bar{x}$ chart because it would cause a shift in the mean pH. (It might also affect the process variability, and therefore show up on the s chart.) Additional water in the kettle would change the pH for that kettle, which would change the mean pH and also change the process variability, so we would expect that special cause to show up on both the $\bar{x}$ and s charts.

17.19. If $\mu = 693$ and $\sigma = 12$, then $\bar{x}$ is approximately normal with mean 693 and standard deviation $\sigma/\sqrt{4} = 6$, so $\bar{x}$ will fall outside the control limits with probability $1 - P(687 < \bar{x} < 713) = 1 - P(-1 < Z < 3.33) = 0.1591$.

17.20. $c = 3.090$. (Looking at Table A, there appear to be three possible answers—3.08, 3.09, or 3.10. Software gives the answer 3.090232....)

17.21. The usual 3σ limits are $\mu \pm 3\sigma/\sqrt{n}$ for an $\bar{x}$ chart and $(c_4 \pm 3c_5)\sigma$ for an s chart. For 2σ limits, simply replace "3" with "2." **(a)** $\mu \pm 2\sigma/\sqrt{n}$. **(b)** $(c_4 \pm 2c_5)\sigma$.

17.22. (a) Either (ii) or (iii), depending on whether the deterioration happens quickly or gradually. We would not necessarily expect that this deterioration would result in a change in variability (s or R). **(b)** (i) s or R chart: A change in precision suggests altered variability (s or R), but not necessarily a change in center ($\bar{x}$). **(c)** (i) s or R chart: Assuming there are other (fluent) customer service representatives answering the phones, this new person would have unusually long times, which should most quickly show up as an increase in variability. **(d)** (iii) A run on the $\bar{x}$ chart: "The runs signal responds to a gradual shift more quickly than the one-point-out signal."

17.23. One possible $\bar{x}$ chart is shown, created with the (arbitrary) assumption that the experienced clerk processes invoices in an average of 2 minutes, while the new hire takes an average of 4 minutes. (The control limits were set arbitrarily as well.)

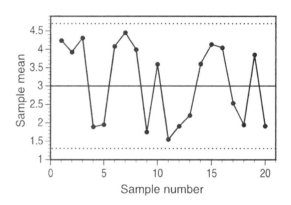

17.24. We estimate $\hat{\sigma}$ to be $\bar{s}/0.9213 \doteq 0.9986$, so the $\bar{x}$ chart has center line $\bar{\bar{x}} = 48.7$ and control limits $\bar{\bar{x}} \pm 3\hat{\sigma}/\sqrt{4} = 47.2$ to 50.2. The s chart has center line $\bar{s} = 0.92$ and control limits 0 and $2.088\hat{\sigma} = 2.085$.

17.25. (a) Average the 20 sample means and standard deviations, and estimate μ to be $\hat{\mu} = \bar{\bar{x}} = 275.07$ and σ to be $\hat{\sigma} = \bar{s}/c_4 = 34.55/0.9213 \doteq 37.50$. **(b)** In the s chart shown in Figure 17.7, most of the points fall below the center line.

17.26. For the 15 samples, we have $\bar{s} = \$799.1$ and $\bar{\bar{x}} = \$6442.4$. **(a)** $\hat{\sigma} = \bar{s}/c_4 = 799.1/0.9650 = 828.1$; the center line is $\bar{s}$, and the control limits are $B_5\hat{\sigma} = (0.179)(\$828.1) = \$148.2$ and $B_6\hat{\sigma} = (1.751)(\$828.1) = \$1450.0$. **(b)** For the $\bar{x}$ chart, the center line is $\bar{\bar{x}} = \$6442.4$ and the control limits are $\bar{\bar{x}} \pm 3\hat{\sigma}/\sqrt{8} = \$5564.1$ to $\$7320.7$. The control chart shows that the process is in control.

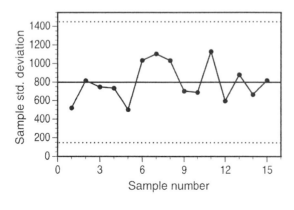
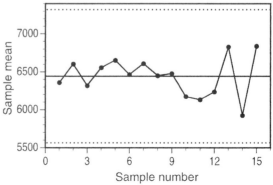

17.27. If the manufacturer practices SPC, that provides some assurance that the monitors are roughly uniform in quality—as the text says, "We know what to expect in the finished product." So, assuming that uniform quality is sufficiently high, the purchaser does not need to inspect the monitors as they arrive because SPC has already achieved the goal of that inspection: to avoid buying many faulty monitors. (Of course, a few unacceptable monitors may be produced and sold even when SPC is practiced—but inspection would not catch all such monitors anyway.)

17.28. The standard deviation of all 120 measurements is $s \doteq \$811.53$, and the mean is $\bar{x} \doteq \$6442.4$ (the same as $\bar{\bar{x}}$—as it must be, provided all the individual samples were the same size). The natural tolerances are $\bar{x} \pm 3s = \$4007.8$ to $\$8877.0$.

17.29. A histogram (right) or stemplot shows that the number of losses between \$6000 and \$6500 is noticeably higher than we might expect from a Normal distribution, but otherwise the shape of the graph suggests that the natural tolerances should be fairly trustworthy.

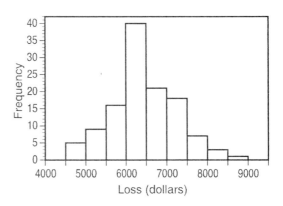

    Note: *In fact, the smallest and largest losses were \$4727 and \$8794; these are both within the tolerances, but note that the minimum is quite a bit more than the lower limit of the tolerances (\$4008). The large number of losses between \$6000 and \$6500 makes the mean slightly lower, and therefore lowers both of the tolerance limits.*

17.30. **(a)** About 99.9% meet the old specifications: If X is the mesh tension on a randomly chosen monitor, then

$$P(100 < X < 400) = P\left(\frac{100-275}{38.4} < Z < \frac{400-275}{38.4}\right) = P(-4.56 < Z < 3.26) \doteq 0.9994.$$

(b) About 97.4% meet the new specifications:

$$P(150 < X < 350) = P\left(\frac{150-275}{38.4} < Z < \frac{350-275}{38.4}\right) = P(-3.26 < Z < 1.95) \doteq 0.9738.$$

17.31. If we shift the process mean to 250 mV, about 99% will meet the new specifications:

$$P(150 < X < 350) = P\left(\frac{150-250}{38.4} < Z < \frac{350-250}{38.4}\right) = P(-2.60 < Z < 2.60) \doteq 0.9906.$$

17.32. **(a)** The means (1.2605 and 1.2645) agree exactly with those given; the standard deviations are the same up to rounding. **(b)** The s chart tracks process spread. For the 30 samples, we have $\bar{s} = 0.0028048$, so $\hat{\sigma} = \bar{s}/c_4 = \bar{s}/0.7979 \doteq 0.003515$; the center line is $\bar{s}$, and the control limits are $B_5\hat{\sigma} = 0$ and $B_6\hat{\sigma} = 2.606\hat{\sigma} \doteq 0.009161$. Short-term variation seems to be in control. **(c)** For the $\bar{x}$ chart, which monitors the process center, the center line is $\bar{\bar{x}} = 1.26185$ and the control limits are $\bar{\bar{x}} \pm 3\hat{\sigma}/\sqrt{2} \doteq 1.2544$ to 1.2693. The control chart shows that the process is in control.

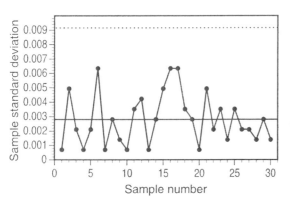
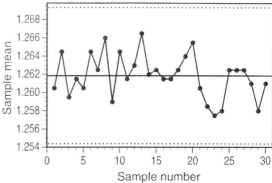

17.33. The mean of the 17 in-control samples is $\bar{\bar{x}} = 43.4118$, and the standard deviation is 11.5833, so the natural tolerances are $\bar{\bar{x}} \pm 3s = 8.66$ to 78.16.

17.34. There were no out-of-control points, so we estimate the mean of the process using $\hat{\mu} = \bar{\bar{x}} = 1.26185$. The estimated standard deviation is computed from the 60 individual data points; this gives $s \doteq 0.003328$. The natural tolerances are $\bar{\bar{x}} \pm 3s = 1.2519$ to 1.2718.

17.35. Only about 44% of meters meet the specifications: Using the mean (43.4118) and standard deviation (11.5833) found in the solution to 17.33,

$$P(44 < X < 64) = P\left(\frac{44-43.4118}{11.5833} < Z < \frac{64-43.4118}{11.5833}\right) = P(0.05 < Z < 1.78) \doteq 0.4426.$$

17.36. There is no clear deviation from normality apart from granularity due to the limited accuracy of the recorded measurements.

For 17.36.   *For 17.37.*

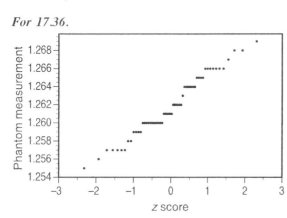
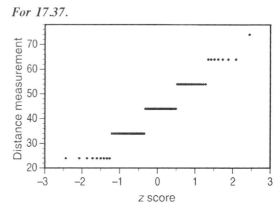

17.37. The limited precision of the measurements shows up in the granularity (stair-step appearance) of the graph. Aside from this, there is no particular departure from normality.

17.38. (a) For the 21 samples, we have $\bar{s} \doteq 0.2786$, so $\hat{\sigma} = \bar{s}/c_4 = 0.2786/0.9213 \doteq 0.3024$; the center line is $\bar{s}$, and the control limits are $B_5\hat{\sigma} = 0$ and $B_6\hat{\sigma} = (2.088)(0.3024) \doteq 0.6313$. Short-term variation seems to be in control. **(b)** For the $\bar{x}$ chart, the center line is 0 and the control limits are $\pm 3\hat{\sigma}/\sqrt{4} = \pm 0.4536$. The $\bar{x}$ chart suggests that the process mean has drifted. (Only the first four out-of-control points are marked.) One possible cause for the increase in the mean is that the cutting blade is getting dull.

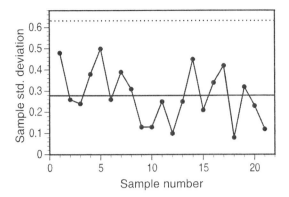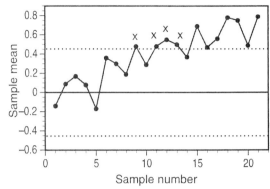

17.39. (a) (ii) A sudden change in the $\bar{x}$ chart: This would immediately increase the amount of time required to complete the checks. **(b)** (i) A sudden change (decrease) in s or R, because the new measurement system will remove (or decrease) the variability introduced by human error. **(c)** (iii) A gradual drift in the $\bar{x}$ chart (presumably a drift up, if the variable being tracked is the length of time to complete a set of invoices).

17.41. The process is no longer the same as it was during the downward trend (from the 1950s into the 1980s). In particular, including those years in the data used to establish the control limits results in a mean that is too high to use for current winning times, and a standard deviation that includes variation attributable to the "special cause" of the changing conditioning and professional status of the best runners. Such special cause variation should not be included in a control chart.

17.42. The centerline is 162 pounds and the control limits are $162 \pm 2.6 = 159.4$ and 164.6 pounds. The first five points, and the eighth, are above the upper control limit; the first nine points are a "run of nine" above the centerline. However, the overall impression is that Joe's weight returns to being "in control"; it decreases fairly steadily, and the last eight points are between the control limits.

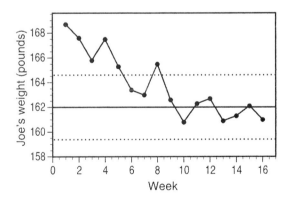

17.43. LSL and USL are specification limits on the individual observations. This means that they do not apply to averages, and that they are *specified* as desired output levels, rather than being *computed* based on observation of the process. LCL and UCL are control limits for the averages of samples drawn from the process. They may be determined from past data, or independently specified, but the main distinction is that the purpose of control limits is to detect whether the process is functioning "as usual," while specification limits are used to determine what percentage of the outputs meet certain specifications (are acceptable for use).

17.44. In each graph below, the tick marks are 3σ apart: because $C_p = 3$, the specification limits are six ticks apart in each case. The first two graphs could be flipped (that is, the curve could be at the left end rather than the right end.) **(a)** $C_{pk} = 1$ means that the nearer specification limit is exactly on one "end" of the normal curve, 3σ above (or below) the mean. **(b)** $C_{pk} = 2$ means that the nearer specification limit is 6σ above (or below) the mean. **(c)** Because $C_{pk} = 3$, the mean is halfway between the specification limits.

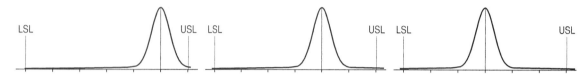

17.45. (a) $\hat{C}_p = \dfrac{400 - 100}{6 \times 38.38} \doteq 1.3027$ and $\hat{C}_{pk} = \dfrac{400 - 275.065}{3 \times 38.38} \doteq 1.0851$.
 (b) $\hat{C}_p = \dfrac{350 - 150}{6 \times 38.38} \doteq 0.8685$ and $\hat{C}_{pk} = \dfrac{350 - 275.065}{3 \times 38.38} \doteq 0.6508$.

17.46. (a) With the original specifications, $\hat{C}_p \doteq 1.3027$ (unchanged from the previous exercise, because $\hat{C}_p$ does not depend on μ) and $\hat{C}_{pk} = \dfrac{400 - 250}{3 \times 38.38} \doteq 1.3028$. **(b)** Once again, $\hat{C}_p \doteq 0.8685$ is unchanged. $\hat{C}_{pk} = \dfrac{350 - 250}{3 \times 38.38} \doteq 0.8685$.

17.47. (a) $C_{pk} = \dfrac{0.75 - 0.25}{3\sigma} \doteq 0.5767$. 50% of the output meets the specifications. **(b)** LSL and USL are 0.865 standard deviations above and below to mean, so the proportion meeting specifications is $P(-0.865 < Z < 0.865) \doteq 0.6130$. **(c)** The relationship between C_{pk} and the proportion of the output meeting specifications depends on the shape of the distribution.

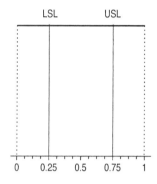

17.48. In the solution to Exercise 17.25, we found $\hat{\sigma} = s/c_4 \doteq 37.50$; from this, we compute $\hat{C}_{pk} = \dfrac{350 - 250}{3 \times 37.50} \doteq 0.8889$, which is larger than the previous value (0.8685).

17.49. See also the solution to Exercise 17.33. **(a)** Use the mean and standard deviation of the 85 remaining observations: $\hat{\mu} = \bar{x} = 43.4118$ and $\hat{\sigma} = s = 11.5833$. **(b)** $\hat{C}_p = \dfrac{20}{6\hat{\sigma}} \doteq 0.2878$ and $\hat{C}_{pk} = 0$ (because $\hat{\mu}$ is outside the specification limits). This process has very poor capability: The mean is too low, and the spread too great. Only about 46% of the process output meets specifications.

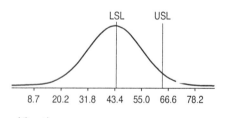

17.50. See also the solution to Exercise 17.28. **(a)** About 97.1%: For the 120 observations in Table 17.6, we find $\hat{\mu} = \bar{x} \doteq \$6442.4$ and $\hat{\sigma} = s \doteq \$811.53$. Therefore, we estimate $P(\$4000 < X < \$8000) = P(-3.01 < Z < 1.92) = 0.9726 - 0.0013 = 0.9713$. **(b)** $C_p = \dfrac{4000}{6\hat{\sigma}} \doteq 0.8215$. **(c)** $C_{pk} = \dfrac{8000 - \bar{x}}{3\hat{\sigma}} \doteq 0.6398$.

17.51. (a) About 97.4%: We estimate $P(14.5 < X < 15.5) = P(-2.19 < Z < 2.28) = 0.9887 - 0.0143 = 0.9744$. **(b)** $C_{pk} = \frac{14.99-14.5}{3s} \doteq 0.7295$.

17.52. (a) The number of nonconforming clips produced by an operator is (for the most part) a result of random variation within the system; no incentive can cause the operator to do better than the system allows. Part (c) offers a slightly different viewpoint. **(b)** Assuming the new machine has less variability (smaller σ), this should improve the process capability. **(c)** If some of the nonconforming clips are due to operator error, further training may have the effect of reducing σ and increasing C_{pk}. **(d)** This is unlikely to have any beneficial effect; it would result in more frequent adjustments, but these would often be unnecessary, and so might degrade capability. Control limits are for correcting special-cause variation, not common-cause variation. **(e)** Better raw material should (presumably) result in better product, so this should improve the capability.

17.53. This graph shows a process with normal output and $C_p = 2$. The tick marks are σ units apart; this is called "six-sigma quality" because the specification limits are (at least) six standard deviations above and below the mean.

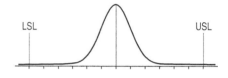

17.54. (a) The graph on the right shows the mean shifted toward the USL; it could also be shifted toward the LSL. As in the graph in the previous problem, tick marks are σ units apart. **(b)** $C_{pk} = \frac{4.5\sigma}{3\sigma} = 1.5$.

Six-sigma quality does *not* mean that $C_{pk} \geq 2$; the latter is a stronger requirement. **(c)** The desired probability is $1 - P(-7.5 < Z < 4.5)$, for which software gives 3.4×10^{-6}, or about 3.4 out-of-spec parts per million.

17.55. Students will have varying justifications for the sampling choice. Choosing six calls per shift gives an idea of the variability and mean for the shift as a whole. If we took six consecutive calls (at a randomly chosen time), we might see additional variability in $\bar{x}$, because sometimes those six calls might be observed at particularly busy times (when a customer has to wait for a long time until a representative is available, or when a representative is using the restroom).

17.56. (a) For $n = 6$, we have $c_4 = 0.9515$, $B_5 = 0.029$, and $B_6 = 1.874$. With $\bar{s} = 29.985$ seconds, we compute $\hat{\sigma} = \bar{s}/c_4 \doteq 31.5134$ seconds, so the initial s chart has centerline $\bar{s}$ and control limits $B_5\hat{\sigma} \doteq 0.9139$ and $B_6\hat{\sigma} \doteq 59.0561$ seconds. There are four out-of-control points, from samples 28, 39, 42, and 46. **(b)** With the remaining 46 samples, $\bar{s} = 24.3015$, so $\hat{\sigma} = \bar{s}/c_4 = 25.54$ seconds, and the control limits are $B_5\hat{\sigma} = 0.741$ and $B_6\hat{\sigma} = 47.86$ seconds. There are no more out-of-control points. (The second s chart is not shown.) **(c)** We have center line $\bar{\bar{x}} = 29.2087$ seconds, and control limits $\bar{\bar{x}} \pm 3\hat{\sigma}/\sqrt{6} = -2.072$ and 60.489 seconds. (The lower control limit should be ignored or changed to 0.) The $\bar{x}$ chart has no out-of-control points.

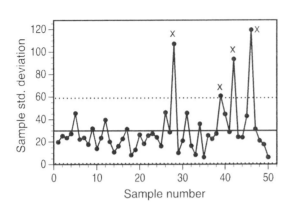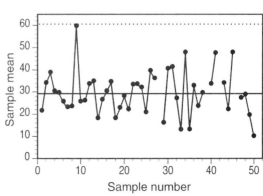

17.57. The outliers are 276 seconds (sample 28), 244 seconds (sample 42), and 333 seconds (sample 46). After dropping those outliers, the standard deviations drop to 9.284, 6.708, and 31.011 seconds. (Sample #39, the other out-of-control point, has two moderately large times, 144 and 109 seconds; if they are removed, s drops to 3.416.)

17.58. For those 10 days, there were 961 absences, and $10 \cdot 987 = 9870$ person-days available for work, so $\bar{p} = \dfrac{961}{9870} \doteq 0.09737$, and

$$\text{CL} = \bar{p} = 0.09737, \text{ control limits: } \bar{p} \pm 3\sqrt{\frac{\bar{p}(1 - \bar{p})}{987}} = 0.06906 \text{ and } 0.12567.$$

17.59. (a) For those 10 months, there were 960 overdue invoices out of 28,750 total invoices (opportunities), so $\bar{p} = \dfrac{960}{28750} \doteq 0.03339$. **(b)** The center line and control limits are

$$\text{CL} = \bar{p} = 0.03339, \text{ control limits: } \bar{p} \pm 3\sqrt{\frac{\bar{p}(1 - \bar{p})}{2875}} = 0.02334 \text{ and } 0.04344.$$

17.60. One complaint per 200 passengers means that the center line is $\bar{p} = 0.005$ (one-half of 1%), and the control limits are $\bar{p} \pm 3\sqrt{\dfrac{\bar{p}(1 - \bar{p})}{1000}} = 0.005 \pm 0.0067$. As the problem says, we take LCL $= 0$, and the UCL is 0.0117.

17.61. The center line is $\bar{p} = \frac{208}{34,700} \doteq 0.005994$, and the control limits are

$\bar{p} \pm 3\sqrt{\dfrac{\bar{p}(1 - \bar{p})}{1070}} = 0.005994 \pm 0.007079$. Take the lower limit to be 0; the upper limit is 0.01307.

17.62. The initial center line and control limits are

$$\text{CL} = p = 0.01, \text{ control limits: } p \pm 3\sqrt{\frac{p(1 - p)}{75,000}} = 0.008910 \text{ and } 0.011090.$$

On a day when only 50,000 prescriptions are filled, the center line is unchanged, while the control limits change to

$$p \pm 3\sqrt{\frac{p(1 - p)}{50,000}} = 0.008665 \text{ and } 0.011335.$$

17.63. (a) The student counts sum to 9218, while the absentee total is 3277, so $\bar{p} = \frac{3277}{9218} = 0.3555$ and $\bar{n} = 921.8$. **(b)** The center line is $\bar{p} = 0.3555$, and the control limits are

$$\bar{p} \pm 3\sqrt{\frac{\bar{p}(1-\bar{p})}{921.8}} = 0.3082 \text{ and } 0.4028.$$

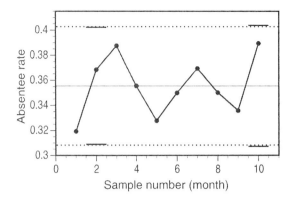

The p chart suggests that absentee rates are in control. **(c)** For October, the limits are 0.3088 and 0.4022; for June, they are 0.3072 and 0.4038. These limits appear as solid lines on the p chart, but they are not substantially different from the control limits found in (b). Unless n varies *a lot* from sample to sample, it is sufficient to use $\bar{n}$.

17.64. (a) $\bar{p} = \frac{3.5}{1,000,000} = 0.0000035$. At 5000 pieces per day, we expect 0.0175 defects per day; in a 24-day month, we would expect 0.42 defects. **(b)** The center line is 0.0000035; assuming that every day we examine all 5000 pieces, the LCL is negative (so we use 0), and the UCL is 0.0000083. **(c)** Note that most of the time, we will find 0 defects, so that $\hat{p} = 0$. If we should ever find even one defect, we would have $\hat{p} = 0.0002$, and the process would be out of control. On top of this, it takes an absurd amount of testing in order to catch the rare defect.

17.65. (a) $\bar{p} = \frac{8000}{1,000,000} = 0.008$. We expect about $4 = (500)(0.008)$ defective orders per month. **(b)** The center line and control limits are

$$\text{CL} = \bar{p} = 0.008, \text{ control limits: } \bar{p} \pm 3\sqrt{\frac{\bar{p}(1-\bar{p})}{500}} = -0.00395 \text{ and } 0.01995.$$

(We take the lower control limit to be 0.) It takes at least ten bad orders in a month to be out of control because $(500)(0.01995) = 9.975$.

17.66. Control charts focus on ensuring that the *process* is consistent, not that the *product* is good. An in-control process may consistently produce some percentage of low-quality products. Keeping a process in control allows one to detect shifts in the distribution of the output (which may have been caused by some correctable error); it does not help in fixing problems that are inherent to the process.

17.67. (a) The percents do not add to 100% because one customer might have several complaints; that is, he or she could be counted in several categories. **(b)** Clearly, top priority should be given to the process of creating, correcting, and adjusting invoices, as the three most common complaints involved invoices.

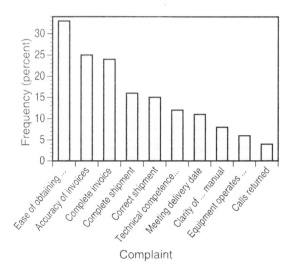

17.68. (a) Use $\bar{x}$ and s charts to track the time required. **(b)** Use a p chart to track the acceptance percentage. **(c)** Use a p chart to track the proportion of employees participating.

17.69. (a) Depending on how one interprets "availability," either $\bar{x}$ and s charts, or a p chart is appropriate. **(b)** Use $\bar{x}$ and s (or R) charts to control response time. **(c)** Use a p chart for undocumented programming changes.

17.70. This situation calls for a p chart with center line $\bar{p} = \frac{5}{1000} = 0.005$ and control limits $\bar{p} \pm 3\sqrt{\dfrac{\bar{p}(1-\bar{p})}{300}} = 0.005 \pm 0.0122$. We take LCL $= 0$, and the UCL is 0.0172. (In order to exceed this UCL, we would need to have 6 rejected lots out of 300.)

17.71. We find that $\bar{s} = 7.65$, so with $c_4 = 0.8862$ and $B_6 = 2.276$, we compute $\hat{\sigma} = 8.63$ and UCL $= 19.65$. One point (from sample #1) is out of control. (And, if that cause were determined and the point removed, a new chart would have s for sample #10 out of control.) The second (lower) UCL line on the control chart is the final UCL, after removing both of those samples (per the instructions in Exercise 17.72).

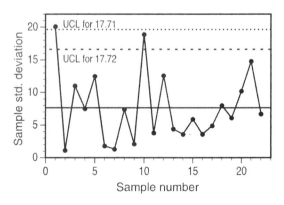

17.72. Without samples 1 and 10, $\bar{s} = 6.465$, $\hat{\sigma} = \bar{s}/c_4 \doteq 7.295$, and the new UCL is $2.276\hat{\sigma} = 16.60$; this line is shown on the control chart in the solution to the previous problem. Meanwhile, $\bar{\bar{x}} = 834.5$, and the control limits are $\bar{\bar{x}} \pm 3\hat{\sigma}/\sqrt{3} = 821.86$ to 847.14. The $\bar{x}$ chart gives no indication of trouble—the process seems to be in control.

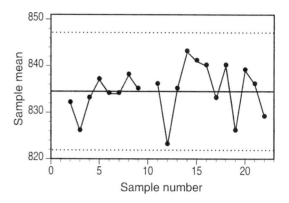

17.73. (a) As was found in the previous exercise, $\hat{\sigma} = \bar{s}/c_4 \doteq 7.295$. Therefore, $C_p = \frac{50}{6\hat{\sigma}} \doteq 1.1423$. This is a fairly small value of C_p; the specification limits are just barely wider than the $6\hat{\sigma}$ width of the process distribution, so if the mean wanders too far from 830, the capability will drop. **(b)** If we adjust the mean to be close to $830 \text{ mm} \times 10^{-4}$ (the center of the specification limits), we will maximize C_{pk}. C_{pk} is more useful when the mean is not in the center of the specification limits. **(c)** The value of $\hat{\sigma}$ used for determining C_p was estimated from the values of s from our control samples. These are for estimating short-term variation (within those samples) rather than the overall process variation. To get a better estimate of the latter, we should instead compute the standard deviation s of the *individual* measurements used to obtain the means and standard deviations given in Table 17.11 (specifically, the 60 measurements remaining after dropping samples 1 and 10). These numbers are not available. (See "How to cheat on C_{pk}" on page 17–47 of Chapter 17.)

17.74. About 99.94%: With $\hat{\sigma} \doteq 7.295$ and mean 830, we compute $P(805 < X < 855) = P(-3.43 < Z < 3.43) = 0.9994$.

17.75. (a) Use a p chart, with center line $\bar{p} = \frac{15}{5000} = 0.003$ and control limits $\bar{p} \pm 3\sqrt{\frac{\bar{p}(1-\bar{p})}{100}}$, or 0 to 0.0194. **(b)** There is little useful information to be gained from keeping a p chart: If the proportion remains at 0.003, about 74% of samples will yield a proportion of 0, and about 22% of proportions will be 0.01. To call the process out of control, we would need to see two or more unsatisfactory films in a sample of 100.

17.76. Assuming $\bar{x}$ is (approximately) normally distributed, the probability that it would fall within the 1σ level is about 0.68, so the probability that it does this 15 times is about $0.68^{15} \doteq 0.0031$.